Operations Management
MGMT 346

13e by William J. Stevenson

Minnesota State University - Mankato

Chapters Selected by

Buddhadev Roychoudhury

create.mheducation.com

ISBN-13: 9781307071597

ISBN-10: 1307071597

Contents

1. Introduction to Operations Management   2
2. Competitiveness, Strategy, and Productivity   40
3. Process Selection and Facility Layout   74
4. Management of Quality   128
5. Quality Control   172
6. Aggregate Planning and Master Scheduling   218
7. MRP and ERP   256
8. Inventory Management   306
9. JIT and Lean Operations   364
10. Supply Chain Management   400
11. Scheduling   438
A. Appendix: Tables   478
B. Subject Index   483
Credits   497

Contents

1 Introduction to Operations Management

LEARNING OBJECTIVES

After completing this chapter, you should be able to:

LO1.1   Define the terms *operations management* and *supply chain*.

LO1.2   Identify similarities and differences between production and service operations.

LO1.3   Explain the importance of learning about operations management.

LO1.4   Identify the three major functional areas of organizations and describe how they interrelate.

LO1.5   Summarize the two major aspects of process management.

LO1.6   Describe the operations function and the nature of the operations manager's job.

LO1.7   Explain the key aspects of operations management decision making.

LO1.8   Briefly describe the historical evolution of operations management.

LO1.9   Describe current issues in business that impact operations management.

LO1.10   Explain the need to manage the supply chain.

CHAPTER OUTLINE

1.1   Introduction *4*

1.2   Production of Goods versus Providing Services *8*

1.3   Why Learn about Operations Management? *10*

1.4   Career Opportunities and Professional Societies *12*

1.5   Process Management *13*
    Managing a Process to Meet Demand *13*
    Process Variation *14*

1.6   The Scope of Operations Management *14*
    Managing the Supply Chain to Achieve Schedule, Cost, and Quality Goals *15*

1.7   Operations Management and Decision Making *18*
    Models *18*
    Quantitative Approaches *19*
    Performance Metrics *19*
    Analysis of Trade-Offs *19*
    Degree of Customization *20*
    A Systems Approach *20*
    Establishing Priorities *20*

1.8   The Historical Evolution of Operations Management *21*
    The Industrial Revolution *21*
    Scientific Management *21*
    The Human Relations Movement *24*
    Decision Models and Management Science *24*

The Influence of Japanese Manufacturers *24*

1.9   Operations Today *24*

1.10   Key Issues for Today's Business Operations *27*
    Environmental Concerns *27*
    Ethical Conduct *29*
    The Need to Manage the Supply Chain *30*
    Elements of Supply Chain Management *32*

Operations Tour: Wegmans Food Markets *33*

Case: Hazel *38*

Problem Solving Guide *39*

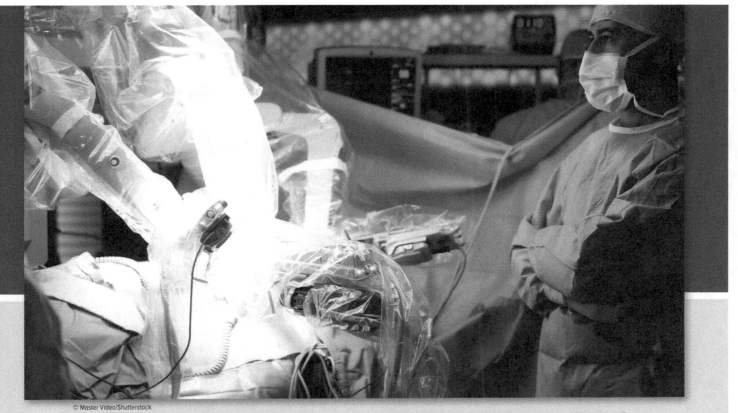

© Master Video/Shutterstock

Recalls of automobiles, foods, toys, and other products; major oil spills; and even dysfunctional state and federal legislatures are all examples of operations failures. They underscore the need for effective operations management. Examples of operations successes include the many electronic devices we all use, medical breakthroughs in diagnosing and treating ailments, and high-quality goods and services that are widely available.

Operations is what businesses do. Operations are processes that either provide services or create goods. Operations take place in businesses such as restaurants, retail stores, supermarkets, factories, hospitals, and colleges and universities. In fact, they take place in every business organization. Moreover, operations are the core of what a business organization does.

As you read this book, you will learn about managing those operations. The subject matter is relevant for you regardless of your major. Productivity, quality, e-business, competition, and customer satisfaction are important for every aspect of a business organization. This first chapter presents an introduction and overview of operations management. Among the issues it addresses are: What is operations management? Why is it important? What do operations management professionals do?

The chapter also provides a description of the historical evolution of operations management and a discussion of the trends and issues that impact operations management.

You will learn about (1) the economic balance that every business organization seeks to achieve; (2) the condition that generally exists that makes achieving the economic balance challenging; (3) the line function that is the core of every business organization; (4) key steps in the history and evolution of operations management; (5) the differences and similarities between producing products and delivering services; (6) what a supply chain is, and why it is essential to manage it; and (7) the key issues for today's business operations.

4   **Chapter One**   Introduction to Operations Management

1.1 INTRODUCTION

Goods Physical items produced by business organizations.

Services Activities that provide some combination of time, location, form, and psychological value.

Operations is that part of a business organization that is responsible for producing goods and/or services. **Goods** are physical items that include raw materials, parts, subassemblies such as motherboards that go into computers, and final products such as cell phones and automobiles. **Services** are activities that provide some combination of time, location, form, or psychological value. Examples of goods and services are found all around you. Every book you read, every video you watch, every e-mail or text message you send, every telephone conversation you have, and every medical treatment you receive involves the operations function of one or more organizations. So does everything you wear, eat, travel in, sit on, and access the Internet with. The operations function in business can also be viewed from a more far-reaching perspective: The collective success or failure of companies' operations functions has an impact on the ability of a nation to compete with other nations, and on the nation's economy.

The ideal situation for a business organization is to achieve an economic match of supply and demand. Having excess supply or excess capacity is wasteful and costly; having too little means lost opportunity and possible customer dissatisfaction. The key functions on the supply side are operations and supply chains, and sales and marketing on the demand side.

While the operations function is responsible for producing products and/or delivering services, it needs the support and input from other areas of the organization. Business organizations have three basic functional areas, as depicted in Figure 1.1: finance, marketing, and operations. It doesn't matter whether the business is a retail store, a hospital, a manufacturing firm, a car wash, or some other type of business; all business organizations have these three basic functions.

Finance is responsible for securing financial resources at favorable prices and allocating those resources throughout the organization, as well as budgeting, analyzing investment proposals, and providing funds for operations. Marketing is responsible for assessing consumer wants and needs, and selling and promoting the organization's goods or services. Operations is responsible for producing the goods or providing the services offered by the organization. To put this into perspective, if a business organization were a car, operations would be its engine. And just as the engine is the core of what a car does, in a business organization, operations is the core of what the organization does. Operations management is responsible for managing that core. Hence **operations management** is the management of systems or processes that create goods and/or provide services.

Operations management The management of systems or processes that create goods and/or provide services.

Supply chain A sequence of organizations—their facilities, functions, and activities—that are involved in producing and delivering a product or service

Operations and supply chains are intrinsically linked, and no business organization could exist without both. A **supply chain** is the sequence of organizations—their facilities, functions, and activities—that are involved in producing and delivering a product or service. The sequence begins with basic suppliers of raw materials and extends all the way to the final customer. See Figure 1.2. Facilities might include warehouses, factories, processing centers, offices, distribution centers, and retail outlets. Functions and activities include forecasting, purchasing, inventory management, information management, quality assurance, scheduling, production, distribution, delivery, and customer service.

One way to think of a supply chain is that it is like a chain, as its name implies. That is shown in Figure 1.2. The links of the chain would represent various production and/or service

FIGURE 1.1
The three basic functions of business organizations

Suppliers' suppliers
Direct suppliers
Producer
Distributor
Final customers

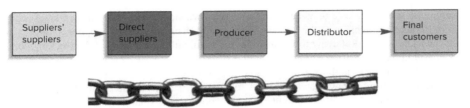

FIGURE 1.2
A simple product supply chain

FIGURE 1.3A
A supply chain for bread

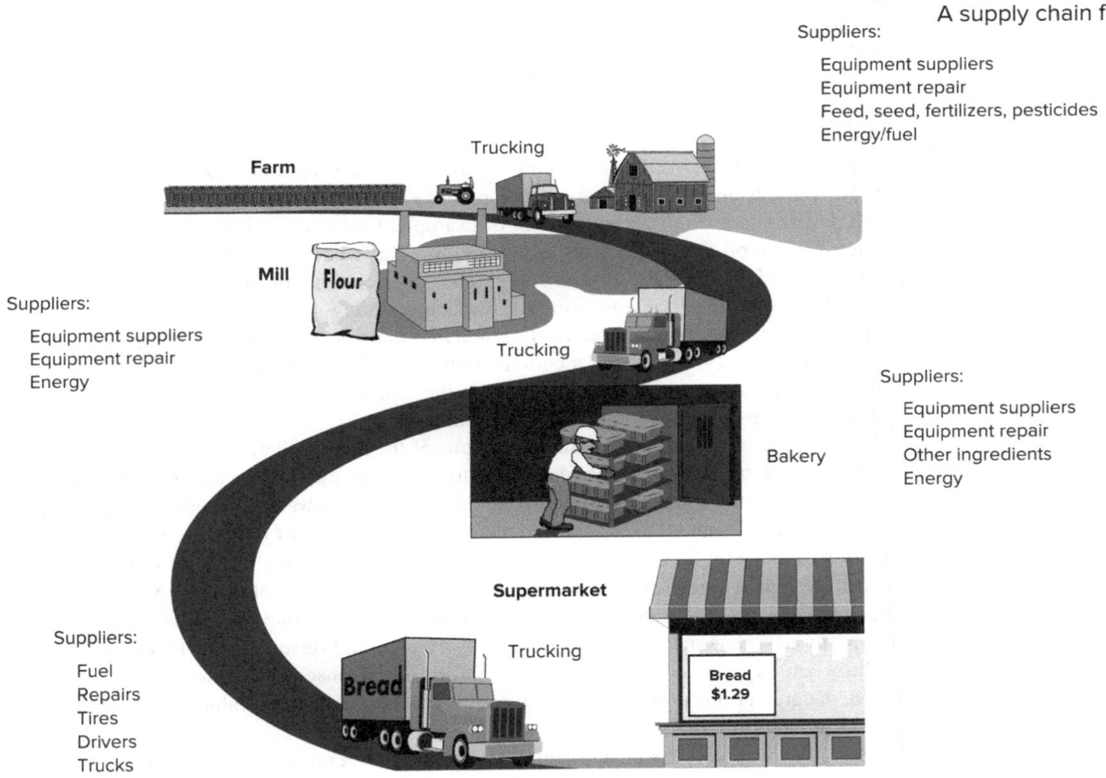

Suppliers:
Equipment suppliers
Equipment repair
Feed, seed, fertilizers, pesticides
Energy/fuel
Farm
Trucking
Mill
Flour
Suppliers:
Equipment suppliers
Equipment repair
Energy
Trucking
Suppliers:
Equipment suppliers
Equipment repair
Other ingredients
Energy
Bakery
Supermarket
Trucking
Bread
Bread
$1.29
Suppliers:
Fuel
Repairs
Tires
Drivers
Trucks

FIGURE 1.3B

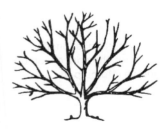

operations such as factories, storage facilities, activities, and modes of transportation (trains, railroads, ships, planes, cars, and people). The chain illustrates both the *sequential* nature of a supply chain and the interconnectedness of the elements of the supply chain. Each link is a customer of the previous link and a supplier to the following link. It also helps to understand that if any one of the links fails for any reason (quality or delivery issues, weather problems, or some other problem [there are numerous possibilities]), that can interrupt the flow in the supply chain for the following portion of the chain.

Figure 1.3a provides another illustration of a supply chain: a chain that extends from wheat growing on a farm and ends with a customer buying a loaf of bread in a supermarket. The value of the product increases as it moves through the supply chain.

Another way to think of a supply chain is as a tree with many branches, as shown in Figure 1.3b. The main branches of the tree represent key suppliers and transporters (e.g., trucking companies). That view is helpful in grasping the size and complexity that often exists in supply chains. Notice that the main branches of the tree have side branches (their own key suppliers), and those side branches also have their own side branches (their own key suppliers). In fact, an extension of the tree view of a supply chain is that each supplier (branch) has its own supply tree. Referring to Figure 1.3a, the farm, mill, and bakery of the trucking companies would have their own "tree" of suppliers.

Supply chains are both external and internal to the organization. The external parts of a supply chain provide raw materials, parts, equipment, supplies, and/or other inputs to the organization, and they deliver outputs that are goods to the organization's customers. The internal parts of a supply chain are part of the operations function itself, supplying operations with parts and materials, performing work on products, and/or performing services.

The creation of goods or services involves transforming or converting inputs into outputs. Various inputs such as capital, labor, and information are used to create goods or services using one or more *transformation processes* (e.g., storing, transporting, repairing). To ensure that the desired outputs are obtained, an organization takes measurements at various points in the transformation process (*feedback*) and then compares them with previously established standards to determine whether corrective action is needed (*control*). Figure 1.4 depicts the conversion system.

Table 1.1 provides some examples of inputs, transformation processes, and outputs. Although goods and services are listed separately in Table 1.1, it is important to note that goods and services often occur jointly. For example, having the oil changed in your car is a service, but the oil that is delivered is a good. Similarly, house painting is a service, but the paint is a good. The goods–service combination is a continuum. It can range from primarily goods, with little service, to primarily service, with few goods. Figure 1.5 illustrates this continuum. Because there are relatively few pure goods or pure services, companies usually sell *product packages,* which are a combination of goods and services. There are elements of both goods production and service delivery in these product packages. This makes managing operations more interesting, and also more challenging.

Table 1.2 provides some specific illustrations of the transformation process.

The essence of the operations function is to *add value* during the transformation process: **Value-added** is the term used to describe the difference between the cost of inputs and the value or price of outputs. In nonprofit organizations, the value of outputs (e.g., highway construction, police and fire protection) is their value to society; the greater the value-added, the greater the effectiveness of these operations. In for-profit organizations, the value of outputs is measured by the prices that customers are willing to pay for those goods or services. Firms use the money generated by value-added for research and development, investment in new facilities and equipment, worker salaries, and *profits.* Consequently, the greater the value-added, the greater the amount of funds available for these purposes. Value can also be psychological, as in *branding.*

Many factors affect the design and management of operations systems. Among them are the degree of involvement of customers in the process and the degree to which technology

> **Value-added** The difference between the cost of inputs and the value or price of outputs.

FIGURE 1.4
The operations function involves the conversion of inputs into outputs

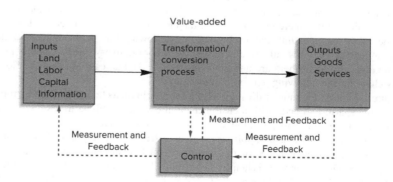

Inputs	Transformation	Outputs
Land	Processes	High goods percentage
Human	Cutting, drilling	Houses
Physical labor	Transporting	Automobiles
Intellectual labor	Teaching	Clothing
Capital	Farming	Computers
Raw materials	Mixing	Machines
Water	Packing	Televisions
Metals	Copying	Food products
Wood	Analyzing	Textbooks
Equipment	Developing	DVD players
Machines	Searching	High service percentage
Computers	Researching	Health care
Trucks	Repairing	Entertainment
Tools	Innovating	Car repair
Facilities	Debugging	Legal
Hospitals	Selling	Banking
Factories	Emailing	Communication
Retail stores		
Energy		
Other		
Information		
Time		
Legal constraints		
Government regulations		

TABLE 1.1
Examples of inputs, transformation, and outputs

is used to produce and/or deliver a product or service. The greater the degree of customer involvement, the more challenging it can be to design and manage the operation. Technology choices can have a major impact on productivity, costs, flexibility, and quality and customer satisfaction.

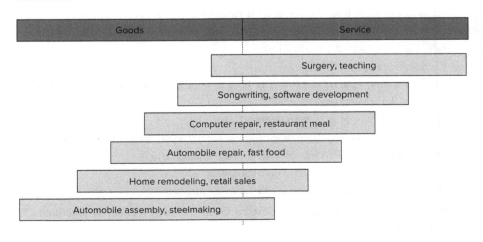

FIGURE 1.5
The goods–service continuum

TABLE 1.2
Illustrations of the transformation process

	Inputs	Processing	Output
Food Processor	Raw vegetables	Cleaning	Canned vegetables
	Metal sheets	Making cans	
	Water	Cutting	
	Energy	Cooking	
	Labor	Packing	
	Building	Labeling	
	Equipment		
Hospital	Doctors, nurses	Examination	Treated patients
	Hospital	Surgery	
	Medical supplies	Monitoring	
	Equipment	Medication	
	Laboratories	Therapy	

1.2 PRODUCTION OF GOODS VERSUS PROVIDING SERVICES

LO1.2 Identify the similarities and differences between production and service operations.

Although goods and services often go hand in hand, there are some very basic differences between the two, differences that impact the management of the goods portion versus management of the service portion. There are also many similarities between the two.

Production of goods results in a *tangible output,* such as an automobile, eyeglasses, a golf ball, a refrigerator—anything that we can see or touch. It may take place in a factory, but it can occur elsewhere. For example, farming and restaurants produce *nonmanufactured* goods. Delivery of service, on the other hand, generally implies an *act.* A physician's examination, TV and auto repair, lawn care, and the projection of a film in a theater are examples of services. The majority of service jobs fall into these categories:

Professional services (e.g., financial, health care, legal)

Mass services (e.g., utilities, Internet, communications)

Service shops (e.g., tailoring, appliance repair, car wash, auto repair/maintenance)

Personal care (e.g., beauty salon, spa, barbershop)

Government (e.g., Medicare, mail, social services, police, fire)

Education (e.g., schools, universities)

Food service (e.g., catering)

Services within organizations (e.g., payroll, accounting, maintenance, IT, HR, janitorial)

Retailing and wholesaling

Shipping and delivery (e.g., truck, railroad, boat, air)

Residential services (e.g., lawn care, painting, general repair, remodeling, interior design)

Transportation (e.g., mass transit, taxi, airlines, ambulance)

Travel and hospitality (e.g., travel bureaus, hotels, resorts)

Miscellaneous services (e.g., copy service, temporary help)

Manufacturing and service are often different in terms of *what* is done but quite similar in terms of *how* it is done.

Chapter One Introduction to Operations Management

9

Consider these points of comparison:

Degree of customer contact. Many services involve a high degree of customer contact, although services such as Internet providers, utilities, and mail service do not. When there is a high degree of contact, the interaction between server and customer becomes a "moment of truth" that will be judged by the customer every time the service occurs.

Labor content of jobs. Services often have a higher degree of labor content than manufacturing jobs do, although automated services are an exception.

Uniformity of inputs. Service operations are often subject to a higher degree of variability of inputs. Each client, patient, customer, repair job, and so on presents a somewhat unique situation that requires assessment and flexibility. Conversely, manufacturing operations often have a greater ability to control the variability of inputs, which leads to more-uniform job requirements.

Measurement of productivity. Measurement of productivity can be more difficult for service jobs due largely to the high variations of inputs. Thus, one doctor might have a higher level of routine cases to deal with, while another might have more difficult cases. Unless a careful analysis is conducted, it may appear that the doctor with the difficult cases has a much lower productivity than the one with the routine cases.

© dolgachov/123RF

Quality assurance. Quality assurance is usually more challenging for services due to the higher variation in input, and because delivery and consumption occur at the same time. Unlike manufacturing, which typically occurs away from the customer and allows mistakes that are identified to be corrected, services have less opportunity to avoid exposing the customer to mistakes.

Inventory. Many services tend to involve less use of inventory than manufacturing operations, so the costs of having inventory on hand are lower than they are for manufacturing. However, unlike manufactured goods, services cannot be stored. Instead, they must be provided "on demand."

Wages. Manufacturing jobs are often well paid, and have less wage variation than service jobs, which can range from highly paid professional services to minimum-wage workers.

Ability to patent. Product designs are often easier to patent than service designs, and some services cannot be patented, making them easier for competitors to copy.

There are also many *similarities* between managing the production of products and managing services. In fact, most of the topics in this book pertain to both. When there are important service considerations, these are highlighted in separate sections. Here are some of the primary factors for both:

a. Forecasting and capacity planning to match supply and demand

b. Process management

c. Managing variations

d. Monitoring and controlling costs and productivity

e. Supply chain management

f. Location planning, inventory management, quality control, and scheduling

Note that many service activities are essential in goods-producing companies. These include training, human resource management, customer service, equipment repair, procurement, and administrative services.

Table 1.3 provides an overview of the differences between production of goods and service operations. Remember, though, that most systems involve a blend of goods and services.

TABLE 1.3
Typical differences between production of goods and provision of services

Characteristic	Goods	Services
Output	Tangible	Intangible
Customer contact	Low	High
Labor content	Low	High
Uniformity of input	High	Low
Measurement of productivity	Easy	Difficult
Opportunity to correct problems before delivery	High	Low
Inventory	Much	Little
Wages	Narrow range	Wide range
Patentable	Usually	Not usually

1.3 WHY LEARN ABOUT OPERATIONS MANAGEMENT?

LO1.3 Explain the importance of learning about operations management.

Whether operations management is your major or not, the skill set you gain studying operations management will serve you well in your career.

There are many career-related reasons for wanting to learn about operations management, whether you plan to work in the field of operations or not. This is because every aspect of business affects or is affected by operations. Operations and sales are the two line functions in a business organization. All other functions—accounting, finance, marketing, IT, and so on—support the two line functions. Among the service jobs that are closely related to operations are financial services (e.g., stock market analyst, broker, investment banker, and loan officer), marketing services (e.g., market analyst, marketing researcher, advertising manager, and product manager), accounting services (e.g., corporate accountant, public accountant, and budget analyst), and information services (e.g., corporate intelligence, library services, management information systems design services).

A common complaint from employers is that college graduates come to them very focused, when employers would prefer them to have more of a general knowledge of how business organizations operate. This book provides some of the breadth that employers are looking for in their new hires. Apart from the career-related reasons is a not so obvious one: Through learning about operations and supply chains, you will have a much better understanding of the world you live in, the global dependencies of companies and nations, some of the reasons that companies succeed or fail, and the importance of working with others.

Working together successfully means that all members of the organization understand not only their own role, but they also understand the roles of others. In practice, there is significant interfacing and *collaboration* among the various functional areas, involving *exchange of information* and *cooperative decision making*. For example, although the three primary functions in business organizations perform different activities, many of their decisions impact the other areas of the organization. Consequently, these functions have numerous interactions, as depicted by the overlapping circles shown in Figure 1.6.

Finance and operations management personnel cooperate by exchanging information and expertise in such activities as the following:

1. **Budgeting.** Budgets must be periodically prepared to plan financial requirements. Budgets must sometimes be adjusted, and performance relative to a budget must be evaluated.

2. **Economic analysis of investment proposals.** Evaluation of alternative investments in plant and equipment requires inputs from both operations and finance people.

3. **Provision of funds.** The necessary funding of operations and the amount and timing of funding can be important and even critical when funds are tight. Careful planning can help avoid cash-flow problems.

Marketing's focus is on selling and/or promoting the goods or services of an organization. Marketing is also responsible for assessing customer wants and needs, and for communicating

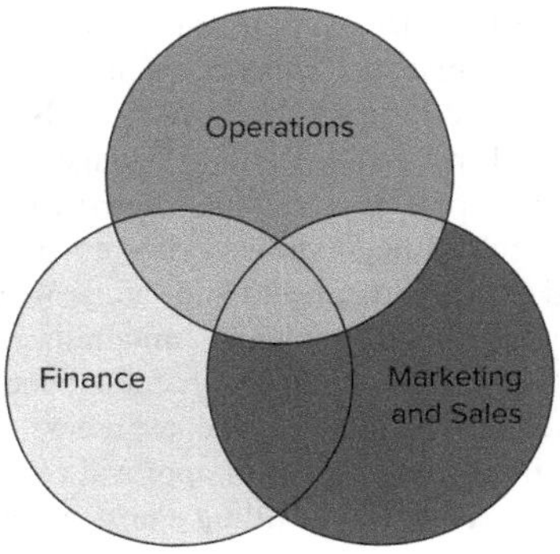

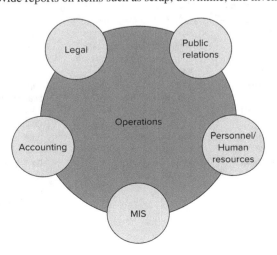

FIGURE 1.6
The three major functions of business organizations overlap

those to operations people (short term) and to design people (long term). That is, operations needs information about demand over the short to intermediate term so that it can plan accordingly (e.g., purchase materials or schedule work), while design people need information that relates to improving current products and services and designing new ones. Marketing, design, and production must work closely together to successfully implement design changes and to develop and produce new products. Marketing can provide valuable insight on what competitors are doing. Marketing also can supply information on consumer preferences so that design will know the kinds of products and features needed; operations can supply information about capacities and judge the *manufacturability* of designs. Operations will also have advance warning if new equipment or skills will be needed for new products or services. Finance people should be included in these exchanges in order to provide information on what funds might be available (short term) and to learn what funds might be needed for new products or services (intermediate to long term). One important piece of information marketing needs from operations is the manufacturing or service **lead time** in order to give customers realistic estimates of how long it will take to fill their orders.

Thus, marketing, operations, and finance must interface on product and process design, forecasting, setting realistic schedules, quality and quantity decisions, and keeping each other informed on the other's strengths and weaknesses.

People in every area of business need to appreciate the importance of managing and coordinating operations decisions that affect the supply chain and the matching of supply and demand, and how those decisions impact other functions in an organization.

Operations also interacts with other functional areas of the organization, including legal, management information systems (MIS), accounting, personnel/human resources, and public relations, as depicted in Figure 1.7.

The *legal* department must be consulted on contracts with employees, customers, suppliers, and transporters, as well as on liability and environmental issues.

Accounting supplies information to management on costs of labor, materials, and overhead, and may provide reports on items such as scrap, downtime, and inventories.

LO1.4 Identify the three major functional areas of organizations and describe how they interrelate.

Lead time The time between ordering a good or service and receiving it.

FIGURE 1.7
Operations interfaces with a number of supporting functions

Management information systems (MIS) is concerned with providing management with the information it needs to effectively manage. This occurs mainly through designing systems to capture relevant information and designing reports. MIS is also important for managing the control and decision-making tools used in operations management.

The *personnel* or *human resources* department is concerned with recruitment and training of personnel, labor relations, contract negotiations, wage and salary administration, assisting in manpower projections, and ensuring the health and safety of employees.

Public relations is responsible for building and maintaining a positive public image of the organization. Good public relations provides many potential benefits. An obvious one is in the marketplace. Other potential benefits include public awareness of the organization as a good place to work (labor supply), improved chances of approval of zoning change requests, community acceptance of expansion plans, and instilling a positive attitude among employees.

1.4 CAREER OPPORTUNITIES AND PROFESSIONAL SOCIETIES

There are many career opportunities in the operations management and supply chain fields. Among the numerous job titles are operations manager, production analyst, production manager, inventory manager, purchasing manager, schedule coordinator, distribution manager, supply chain manager, quality analyst, and quality manager. Other titles include office manager, store manager, and service manager.

People who work in the operations field should have a skill set that includes both people skills and knowledge skills. People skills include political awareness; mentoring ability; and collaboration, negotiation, and communication skills. Knowledge skills, necessary for credibility and good decision making, include product and/or service knowledge, process knowledge, industry and global knowledge, financial and accounting skills, and project management skills. See Table 1.4.

If you are thinking of a career in operations management, you can benefit by joining one or more of the professional societies.

APICS, the Association for Operations Management 8430 West Bryn Mawr Avenue, Suite 1000, Chicago, Illinois 60631 www.apics.org

American Society for Quality (ASQ) 230 West Wells Street, Milwaukee, Wisconsin 53203 www.asq.org

Institute for Supply Management (ISM) 2055 East Centennial Circle, Tempe, Arizona 85284 www.ism.ws

TABLE 1.4
Sample operations management job descriptions

Production Supervisor	Supply Chain Manager	Social Media Product Manager
• Manage a production staff of 10–20.	• Have a general knowledge of materials management, information systems, and basic statistics.	• Identify ways to increase consumer engagement.
• Ensure the department meets daily goals through the management of productivity.	• Direct, monitor, evaluate, and motivate employee performance.	• Analyze the key performance indicators and recommend improvements.
• Enforce safety policies.		• Lead cross-functional teams to define product specifications.
• Coordinate work between departments.	• Be knowledgeable about shipping regulations.	• Collaborate with design and technical to create key product improvements.
• Have strong problem-solving skills, and strong written and oral communication skills.	• Manage budgetary accounts	
	• Manage projects.	• Develop requirements for new website enhancements.
		• Monitor the competition to identify need for changes.

Institute for Operations Research and the Management Sciences (INFORMS) 901 Elkridge Landing Road, Linthicum, Maryland 21090-2909 www.informs.org

The Production and Operations Management Society (POMS) College of Engineering, Florida International University, EAS 2460, 10555 West Flagler Street, Miami, Florida 33174 www.poms.org

The Project Management Institute (PMI) 4 Campus Boulevard, Newtown Square, Pennsylvania 19073-3299 www.pmi.org

Council of Supply Chain Management Professionals (CSCMP) 333 East Butterfield Road, Suite 140, Lombard, Illinois 60148 https//cscmp.org

APICS, ASQ, ISM, and other professional societies offer a practitioner certification examination that can enhance your qualifications. Information about job opportunities can be obtained from all of these societies as well as from other sources, such as the Decision Sciences Institute (University Plaza, Atlanta, Georgia 30303) and the Institute of Industrial Engineers (25 Technology Park, Norcross, Georgia 30092).

1.5 PROCESS MANAGEMENT

A key aspect of operations management is process management. A **process** consists of one or more actions that transform inputs into outputs. In essence, the central role of all management is process management.

LO1.5 Summarize the two major aspects of process management.

Process One or more actions that transform inputs into outputs.

Businesses are composed of many interrelated processes. Generally speaking, there are three categories of business processes:

1. **Upper-management processes.** These govern the operation of the entire organization. Examples include organizational governance and organizational strategy.
2. **Operational processes.** These are the core processes that make up the value stream. Examples include purchasing, production and/or service, marketing, and sales.
3. **Supporting processes.** These support the core processes. Examples include accounting, human resources, and IT (information technology).

Business processes, large and small, are composed of a series of supplier–customer relationships, where every business organization, every department, and every individual operation is both a customer of the previous step in the process and a supplier to the next step in the process. Figure 1.8 illustrates this concept.

A major process can consist of many subprocesses, each having its own goals that contribute to the goals of the overall process. Business organizations and supply chains have many such processes and subprocesses, and they benefit greatly when management is using a process perspective. Business process management (BPM) activities include process design, process execution, and process monitoring. Two basic aspects of this for operations and supply chain management are managing processes to meet demand and dealing with process variability.

Managing a Process to Meet Demand

Ideally, the capacity of a process will be such that its output just matches demand. Excess capacity is wasteful and costly; too little capacity means dissatisfied customers and lost revenue. Having the right capacity requires having accurate forecasts of demand, the ability to translate forecasts into capacity requirements, and a process in place capable of meeting

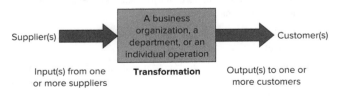

Supplier(s) → A business organization, a department, or an individual operation → Customer(s)

Input(s) from one or more suppliers   **Transformation**   Output(s) to one or more customers

FIGURE 1.8

Business processes form a sequence of suppliers and customers expected demand. Even so, process variation and demand variability can make the achievement of a match between process output and demand difficult. Therefore, to be effective, it is also necessary for managers to be able to deal with variation.

Process Variation

Variation occurs in all business processes. It can be due to variety or variability. For example, random variability is inherent in every process; it is always present. In addition, variation can occur as the result of deliberate management choices to offer customers variety.

There are four basic sources of variation:

1. **The variety of goods or services being offered.** The greater the variety of goods and services, the greater the variation in production or service requirements.
2. **Structural variation in demand.** These variations, which include trends and seasonal variations, are generally predictable. They are particularly important for capacity planning.
3. **Random variation.** This natural variability is present to some extent in all processes, as well as in demand for services and products, and it cannot generally be influenced by managers.
4. **Assignable variation.** These variations are caused by defective inputs, incorrect work methods, out-of-adjustment equipment, and so on. This type of variation can be reduced or eliminated by analysis and corrective action.

Variations can be disruptive to operations and supply chain processes, interfering with optimal functioning. Variations result in additional cost, delays and shortages, poor quality, and inefficient work systems. Poor quality and product shortages or service delays can lead to dissatisfied customers and can damage an organization's reputation and image. It is not surprising, then, that the ability to deal with variability is absolutely necessary for managers.

Throughout this book, you will learn about some of the tools managers use to deal with variation. An important aspect of being able to deal with variation is to use metrics to describe it. Two widely used metrics are the *mean* (average) and the *standard deviation*. The standard deviation quantifies variation around the mean. The mean and standard deviation are used throughout this book in conjunction with variation. So, too, is the normal distribution. Because you will come across many examples of how the normal distribution is used, you may find the overview on working with the normal distribution in the appendix at the end of the book helpful.

1.6 THE SCOPE OF OPERATIONS MANAGEMENT

LO1.6 Describe the operations function and the nature of the operations manager's job.

The scope of operations management ranges across the organization. Operations management people are involved in product and service design, process selection, selection and management of technology, design of work systems, location planning, facilities planning, and quality improvement of the organization's products or services.

The operations function includes many interrelated activities, such as forecasting, capacity planning, scheduling, managing inventories, assuring quality, motivating employees, deciding where to locate facilities, and more.

We can use an airline company to illustrate a service organization's operations system. The system consists of the airplanes, airport facilities, and maintenance facilities, sometimes spread out over a wide territory. The activities include:

Forecasting such things as weather and landing conditions, seat demand for flights, and the growth in air travel.

Capacity planning, essential for the airline to maintain cash flow and make a reasonable profit. (Too few or too many planes, or even the right number of planes but in the wrong places, will hurt profits.)

Scheduling planes, cargo, and flight and ground crews is an operations function for an airline.

Doug Letterman/Creative Commons

Locating facilities according to managers' decisions on which cities to provide service for, where to locate maintenance facilities, and where to locate major and minor hubs.

Facilities and layout, important in achieving effective use of workers and equipment.

Scheduling of planes for flights and for routine maintenance; scheduling of pilots and flight attendants; and scheduling of ground crews, counter staff, and baggage handlers.

Managing inventories of such items as foods and beverages, first-aid equipment, in-flight magazines, pillows and blankets, and life preservers.

Assuring quality, essential in flying and maintenance operations, where the emphasis is on safety, and important in dealing with customers at ticket counters, check-in, telephone and electronic reservations, and curb service, where the emphasis is on efficiency and courtesy.

Motivating and training employees in all phases of operations.

Managing the Supply Chain to Achieve Schedule, Cost, and Quality Goals

Consider a bicycle factory. This might be primarily an *assembly* operation: buying components such as frames, tires, wheels, gears, and other items from suppliers, and then assembling bicycles. The factory also might do some of the *fabrication* work itself, forming frames, making the gears and chains, and it might buy mainly raw materials and a few parts and materials such as paint, nuts and bolts, and tires. Among the key management tasks in either case are scheduling production, deciding which components to make and which to buy, ordering parts and materials, deciding on the style of bicycle to produce and how many, purchasing new equipment to replace old or worn-out equipment, maintaining equipment, motivating workers, and ensuring that quality standards are met.

Obviously, an airline company and a bicycle factory are completely different types of operations. One is primarily a service operation, the other a producer of goods. Nonetheless, these two operations have much in common. Both involve scheduling activities, motivating employees, ordering and managing supplies, selecting and maintaining equipment, satisfying quality

A worker is making the bottom bracket lug for a Trek OCLV carbon road bike at Trek Bicycle Company in Waterloo, Wisconsin, world headquarters for Trek. Trek is a world leader in bicycle products and accessories, with 1,500 employees worldwide. Designers and engineers incorporate the most advanced technology into Trek products, resulting in award-winning bikes and components.

Andy Manis/AP Images

standards, and—above all—satisfying customers. And in both businesses, the success of the business depends on short- and long-term planning.

A primary function of an operations manager is to guide the system by decision making. Certain decisions affect the *design* of the system, and others affect the *operation* of the system.

System design involves decisions that relate to system capacity, the geographic location of facilities, arrangement of departments and placement of equipment within physical structures, product and service planning, and acquisition of equipment. These decisions usually, but not always, require long-term commitments. Moreover, they are typically *strategic* decisions. *System operation* involves management of personnel, inventory planning and control, scheduling, project management, and quality assurance. These are generally *tactical* and *operational* decisions. Feedback on these decisions involves *measurement* and *control*. In many instances, the operations manager is more involved in day-to-day operating decisions than with decisions relating to system design. However, the operations manager has a vital stake in system design because *system design essentially determines many of the parameters of system operation*. For example, costs, space, capacities, and quality are directly affected by design decisions. Even though the operations manager is not responsible for making all design decisions, he or she can provide those decision makers with a wide range of information that will have a bearing on their decisions.

A number of other areas are part of, or support, the operations function. They include purchasing, industrial engineering, distribution, and maintenance.

Purchasing has responsibility for procurement of materials, supplies, and equipment. Close contact with operations is necessary to ensure correct quantities and timing of purchases. The purchasing department is often called on to evaluate vendors for quality, reliability, service, price, and ability to adjust to changing demand. Purchasing is also involved in receiving and inspecting the purchased goods.

Industrial engineering is often concerned with scheduling, performance standards, work methods, quality control, and material handling.

Distribution involves the shipping of goods to warehouses, retail outlets, or final customers.

Maintenance is responsible for general upkeep and repair of equipment, buildings and grounds, heating and air-conditioning; removing toxic wastes; parking; and perhaps security.

READING   WHY MANUFACTURING MATTERS

The U.S. economy is becoming more and more service-based. The percentage of employment in manufacturing continues to decrease while the percentage employed in services continues to increase. However, it would be unwise to assume that manufacturing isn't important to the economy, or that service is more important. Let's see why.

Not only is the percentage of manufacturing jobs decreasing, but the actual number of manufacturing jobs is also decreasing. There are two main reasons for the decline: increases in productivity, which means fewer workers are needed to maintain manufacturing output; and outsourcing, especially to countries that have much lower wages, an attractive option for companies seeking to maintain their competitiveness and boost their bottom lines.

However, when companies outsource part (or in some cases, all) of their manufacturing to lower-cost countries, the loss of jobs results in the loss of service jobs as well. Some are lost in the community in retail businesses patronized by the manufacturing workers. Also included in that figure are factory service workers (e.g., workers who do machine repairs, maintenance, material handling, packaging, and so on). General estimates are that four service jobs are lost for each manufacturing job lost.

As the manufacturing base shrinks, workers who lose their manufacturing jobs are finding it tougher to find another opening in manufacturing. Instead they join the ranks of the unemployed, or take a service job, usually at a lower wage rate than what manufacturing paid.

From a national perspective, not only is work transferred to a foreign country, intellectual knowledge is transferred. Moreover, as time passes, the domestic base of manufacturing skills and know-how is lost.

There are important consequences for taxes as well. Unemployment benefits are costly, and the erosion of federal, state, and local tax bases results in lower tax revenues collected from individuals and from corporations.

Lastly, manufacturing is an important source of innovation. It is responsible for 70 percent of private-sector R&D and 90 percent of U.S. patents (Rana Foroohar, "Go Glocal," *Time,* August 20, 2012, p. 30). Much of the work in getting a product ready for volume production is high-value-added knowledge work that supports future innovation. And innovation generates jobs. "Intel has invested tens of billions of dollars in its factories in Oregon, Arizona, and New Mexico so that they are able to produce the most advanced semiconductors" (Willy Shih and Gary Pisano, "Why Manufacturing Matters for America," Special to CNN, Sept. 21, 2012).

Questions

1. How important is the loss of manufacturing jobs to the nation?
2. Can you suggest some actions the government (federal, state, or local) can take to stem the job loss?
3. What evidence is there of the importance of manufacturing innovation?

The operations manager is the key figure in the system: He or she has the ultimate responsibility for the creation of goods or provision of services.

The kinds of jobs that operations managers oversee vary tremendously from organization to organization largely because of the different products or services involved. Thus, managing a banking operation obviously requires a different kind of expertise than managing a steelmaking operation. However, in a very important respect, the *jobs* are the same: They are both essentially *managerial.* The same thing can be said for the job of any operations manager regardless of the kinds of goods or services being created.

The service sector and the manufacturing sector are both important to the economy. The service sector now accounts for more than 70 percent of jobs in the United States, and it is growing in other countries as well. Moreover, the number of people working in services is increasing, while the number of people working in manufacturing is not. The reason for the decline in manufacturing jobs is twofold: As the operations function in manufacturing companies finds more productive ways of producing goods, the companies are able to maintain or even increase their output using fewer workers. Furthermore, some manufacturing work has been *outsourced* to more productive companies, many in other countries, that are able to produce goods at lower costs. Outsourcing and productivity will be discussed in more detail in this and other chapters.

Many of the concepts presented in this book apply equally to manufacturing and service. Consequently, whether your interest at this time is on manufacturing or on service, these concepts will be important, regardless of whether a manufacturing example or service example is used to illustrate the concept.

The Why Manufacturing Matters reading gives another reason for the importance of manufacturing jobs.

1.7 OPERATIONS MANAGEMENT AND DECISION MAKING

LO1.7 Explain the key aspects of operations management decision making.

The chief role of an operations manager is that of planner and decision maker. In this capacity, the operations manager exerts considerable influence over the degree to which the goals and objectives of the organization are realized. Most decisions involve many possible alternatives that can have quite different impacts on costs or profits. Consequently, it is important to make *informed* decisions.

Operations management professionals make a number of key decisions that affect the entire organization. These include the following:

> *What:* What resources will be needed, and in what amounts?
>
> *When:* When will each resource be needed? When should the work be scheduled? When should materials and other supplies be ordered? When is corrective action needed?
>
> *Where:* Where will the work be done?
>
> *How:* How will the product or service be designed? How will the work be done (organization, methods, equipment)? How will resources be allocated?
>
> *Who:* Who will do the work?

An operations manager's daily concerns include costs (budget), quality, and schedules (time).

Throughout this book, you will encounter the broad range of decisions that operations managers must make, and you will be introduced to the tools necessary to handle those decisions. This section describes general approaches to decision making, including the use of models, quantitative methods, analysis of trade-offs, establishing priorities, ethics, and the systems approach. Models are often a key tool used by all decision makers.

Models

Model An abstraction of reality; a simplified representation of something.

A **model** is an abstraction of reality, a simplified representation of something. For example, a child's toy car is a model of a real automobile. It has many of the same visual features (shape, relative proportions, wheels) that make it suitable for the child's learning and playing. But the toy does not have a real engine, it cannot transport people, and it does not weigh 2,000 pounds.

Other examples of models include automobile test tracks and crash tests; formulas, graphs and charts; balance sheets and income statements; and financial ratios. Common statistical models include descriptive statistics such as the mean, median, mode, range, and standard deviation, as well as random sampling, the normal distribution, and regression equations.

Models are sometimes classified as physical, schematic, or mathematical.

> **Physical models** look like their real-life counterparts. Examples include miniature cars, trucks, airplanes, toy animals and trains, and scale-model buildings. The advantage of these models is their visual correspondence with reality.
>
> **Schematic models** are more abstract than their physical counterparts; that is, they have less resemblance to the physical reality. Examples include graphs and charts, blueprints, pictures, and drawings. The advantage of schematic models is that they are often relatively simple to construct and change. Moreover, they have some degree of visual correspondence.
>
> **Mathematical models** are the most abstract: They do not look at all like their real-life counterparts. Examples include numbers, formulas, and symbols. These models are usually the easiest to manipulate, and they are important forms of inputs for computers and calculators.

The variety of models in use is enormous. Nonetheless, all have certain common features: They are all decision-making aids and simplifications of more complex real-life phenomena. Real life involves an overwhelming amount of detail, much of which is irrelevant for any particular problem. Models omit unimportant details so that attention can be concentrated on the most important aspects of a situation.

Because models play a significant role in operations management decision making, they are heavily integrated into the material of this text. For each model, try to learn (1) its purpose,

(2) how it is used to generate results, (3) how these results are interpreted and used, and (4) what assumptions and limitations apply.

The last point is particularly important because virtually every model has an associated set of assumptions or conditions under which the model is valid. Failure to satisfy all of the assumptions will make the results suspect. Attempts to apply the results to a problem under such circumstances can lead to disastrous consequences.

Managers use models in a variety of ways and for a variety of reasons. Models are beneficial because they

1. Are generally easy to use and less expensive than dealing directly with the actual situation.
2. Require users to organize and sometimes quantify information and, in the process, often indicate areas where additional information is needed.
3. Increase understanding of the problem.
4. Enable managers to analyze what-if questions.
5. Serve as a consistent tool for evaluation and provide a standardized format for analyzing a problem.
6. Enable users to bring the power of mathematics to bear on a problem.

This impressive list of benefits notwithstanding, models have certain limitations of which you should be aware. The following are three of the more important limitations.

1. Quantitative information may be emphasized at the expense of qualitative information.
2. Models may be incorrectly applied and the results misinterpreted. The widespread use of computerized models adds to this risk because highly sophisticated models may be placed in the hands of users who are not sufficiently knowledgeable to appreciate the subtleties of a particular model; thus, they are unable to fully comprehend the circumstances under which the model can be successfully employed.
3. The use of models does not guarantee good decisions.

Quantitative Approaches

Quantitative approaches to problem solving often embody an attempt to obtain mathematically optimal solutions to managerial problems. *Quantitative approaches* to decision making in operations management (and in other functional business areas) have been accepted because of calculators and computers capable of handling the required calculations. Computers have had a major impact on operations management. Moreover, the growing availability of software packages for quantitative techniques has greatly increased management's use of those techniques.

Although quantitative approaches are widely used in operations management decision making, it is important to note that managers typically use a combination of qualitative and quantitative approaches, and many important decisions are based on qualitative approaches.

Performance Metrics

Managers use metrics to manage and control operations. There are many metrics in use, including those related to profits, costs, quality, productivity, flexibility, assets, inventories, schedules, and forecast accuracy. As you read each chapter, note the metrics being used and how they are applied to manage operations.

Analysis of Trade-Offs

Operations personnel frequently encounter decisions that can be described as *trade-off* decisions. For example, in deciding on the amount of inventory to stock, the decision maker must take into account the trade-off between the increased level of customer service that the additional inventory would yield and the increased costs required to stock that inventory.

Decision makers sometimes deal with these decisions by listing the advantages and disadvantages—the pros and cons—of a course of action to better understand the consequences of the decisions they must make. In some instances, decision makers add weights

READING **ANALYTICS**

Analytics uses descriptive and predictive models to obtain insight from data and then uses that insight to recommend action or to guide decision making.

Commercial analytics software is available for the challenges of analyzing very large, dynamic data sets, referred to as big data. Analyzing big data presents opportunities for businesses such as those that operate transactional online systems that generate massive volumes of data. For example, the McKinsey Global Institute estimates that the U.S. health care system could save $300 billion from analyzing big data.[1]

[1]"Big Data: The next frontier for innovation, competition and productivity as reported in Building with Big Data" *The Economist*, May 26, 2011.

to the items on their list that reflect the relative importance of various factors. This can help them "net out" the potential impacts of the trade-offs on their decision.

Degree of Customization

A major influence on the entire organization is the degree of customization of products or services being offered to its customers. Providing highly customized products or services such as home remodeling, plastic surgery, and legal counseling tends to be more labor intensive than providing standardized products such as those you would buy "off the shelf" at a mall store or a supermarket or standardized services such as public utilities and Internet services. Furthermore, production of customized products or provision of customized services is generally more time consuming, requires more highly skilled people, and involves more flexible equipment than what is needed for standardized products or services. Customized processes tend to have a much lower volume of output than standardized processes, and customized output carries a higher price tag. The degree of customization has important implications for process selection and job requirements. The impact goes beyond operations and supply chains. It affects marketing, sales, accounting, finance, and information systems.

A Systems Approach

System A set of interrelated parts that must work together.

A systems viewpoint is almost always beneficial in decision making. Think of it as a "big picture" view. A **system** can be defined as a set of interrelated parts that must work together. In a business organization, the organization can be thought of as a system composed of subsystems (e.g., marketing subsystem, operations subsystem, finance subsystem), which in turn are composed of lower subsystems. The systems approach emphasizes interrelationships among subsystems, but its main theme is that *the whole is greater than the sum of its individual parts*. Hence, from a systems viewpoint, the output and objectives of the organization as a whole take precedence over those of any one subsystem.

A systems approach is essential whenever something is being designed, redesigned, implemented, improved, or otherwise changed. It is important to take into account the impact on all parts of the system. For example, if the upcoming model of an automobile will add antilock brakes, a designer must take into account how customers will view the change, instructions for using the brakes, chances for misuse, the cost of producing the new brakes, installation procedures, recycling worn-out brakes, and repair procedures. In addition, workers will need training to make and/or assemble the brakes, production scheduling may change, inventory procedures may have to change, quality standards will have to be established, advertising must be informed of the new features, and parts suppliers must be selected.

Establishing Priorities

In virtually every situation, managers discover that certain issues or items are more important than others. Recognizing this enables the managers to direct their efforts to where they will do the most good.

Pareto phenomenon A few factors account for a high percentage of the occurrence of some event(s).

Typically, a relatively few issues or items are very important, so that dealing with those factors will generally have a disproportionately large impact on the results achieved. This well-known effect is referred to as the **Pareto phenomenon**. This is one of the most important and pervasive concepts in operations management. In fact, this concept can be applied at all levels of management and to every aspect of decision making, both professional and personal.

1.8 THE HISTORICAL EVOLUTION OF OPERATIONS MANAGEMENT

LO1.8 Briefly describe the historical evolution of operations management.

Systems for production have existed since ancient times. For example, the construction of pyramids and Roman aquaducts involved operations management skills. The production of goods for sale, at least in the modern sense, and the modern factory system had their roots in the Industrial Revolution.

The Industrial Revolution

The Industrial Revolution began in the 1770s in England and spread to the rest of Europe and to the United States during the 19th century. Prior to that time, goods were produced in small shops by craftsmen and their apprentices. Under that system, it was common for one person to be responsible for making a product, such as a horse-drawn wagon or a piece of furniture, from start to finish. Only simple tools were available; the machines in use today had not been invented.

Then, a number of innovations in the 18th century changed the face of production forever by substituting machine power for human power. Perhaps the most significant of these was the steam engine, because it provided a source of power to operate machines in factories. Ample supplies of coal and iron ore provided materials for generating power and making machinery. The new machines, made of iron, were much stronger and more durable than the simple wooden machines they replaced.

In the earliest days of manufacturing, goods were produced using **craft production**: highly skilled workers using simple, flexible tools produced goods according to customer specifications.

Craft production System in which highly skilled workers use simple, flexible tools to produce small quantities of customized goods.

Craft production had major shortcomings. Because products were made by skilled craftsmen who custom-fitted parts, production was slow and costly. And when parts failed, the replacements also had to be custom made, which was also slow and costly. Another shortcoming was that production costs did not decrease as volume increased; there were no *economies of scale*, which would have provided a major incentive for companies to expand. Instead, many small companies emerged, each with its own set of standards.

A major change occurred that gave the Industrial Revolution a boost: the development of standard gauging systems. This greatly reduced the need for custom-made goods. Factories began to spring up and grow rapidly, providing jobs for countless people who were attracted in large numbers from rural areas.

Despite the major changes that were taking place, management theory and practice had not progressed much from early days. What was needed was an enlightened and more systematic approach to management.

Scientific Management

The scientific management era brought widespread changes to the management of factories. The movement was spearheaded by the efficiency engineer and inventor Frederick Winslow Taylor, who is often referred to as the father of scientific management. Taylor believed in a "science of management" based on observation, measurement, analysis and improvement of work methods, and economic incentives. He studied work methods in great detail to identify the best method for doing each job. Taylor also believed that management should be responsible for planning, carefully selecting and training workers, finding the best way to perform each job, achieving cooperation between management and workers, and separating management activities from work activities.

Taylor's methods emphasized maximizing output. They were not always popular with workers, who sometimes thought the methods were used to unfairly increase output without a corresponding increase in compensation. Certainly some companies did abuse workers in their quest for efficiency. Eventually, the public outcry reached the halls of Congress, and hearings were held on the matter. Taylor himself was called to testify in 1911, the same year in which his classic book, *The Principles of Scientific Management,* was published. The publicity from those hearings actually helped scientific management principles to achieve wide acceptance in industry.

A number of other pioneers also contributed heavily to this movement, including the following.

Frank Gilbreth was an industrial engineer who is often referred to as the father of motion study. He developed principles of motion economy that could be applied to incredibly small portions of a task.

Henry Gantt recognized the value of nonmonetary rewards to motivate workers, and developed a widely used system for scheduling, called Gantt charts.

Harrington Emerson applied Taylor's ideas to organization structure and encouraged the use of experts to improve organizational efficiency. He testified in a congressional hearing that railroads could save a million dollars a day by applying principles of scientific management.

Henry Ford, the great industrialist, employed scientific management techniques in his factories.

During the early part of the 20th century, automobiles were just coming into vogue in the United States. Ford's Model T was such a success that the company had trouble keeping up with orders for the cars. In an effort to improve the efficiency of operations, Ford adopted the scientific management principles espoused by Frederick Winslow Taylor. He also introduced the *moving assembly line,* which had a tremendous impact on production methods in many industries.

Mass production System in which low-skilled workers use specialized machinery to produce high volumes of standardized goods.

Among Ford's many contributions was the introduction of **mass production** to the automotive industry, a system of production in which large volumes of standardized goods are produced by low-skilled or semiskilled workers using highly specialized, and often costly, equipment. Ford was able to do this by taking advantage of a number of important concepts. Perhaps the key concept that launched mass production was **interchangeable parts**, sometimes attributed to Eli Whitney, an American inventor who applied the concept to assembling muskets in the late 1700s. The basis for interchangeable parts was to standardize parts so that any part in a batch of parts would fit any automobile coming down the assembly line. This meant that parts did not have to be custom fitted, as they were in craft production. The standardized parts could also be used for replacement parts. The result was a tremendous decrease in assembly time and cost. Ford accomplished this by standardizing the gauges used to measure parts during production and by using newly developed processes to produce uniform parts.

Interchangeable parts Parts of a product made to such precision that they do not have to be custom fitted.

Row of "Tin Lizzies," or Model T's, being manufactured on an early Ford assembly line.

© Rykoff Collection/Corbis Documentary/Getty Images

A second concept used by Ford was the **division of labor**, which Adam Smith wrote about in *The Wealth of Nations* (1776). Division of labor means that an operation, such as assembling an automobile, is divided up into a series of many small tasks, and individual workers are assigned to one of those tasks. Unlike craft production, where each worker was responsible for doing many tasks, and thus required skill, with division of labor the tasks were so narrow that virtually no skill was required.

Together, these concepts enabled Ford to tremendously increase the production rate at his factories using readily available inexpensive labor. Both Taylor and Ford were despised by many workers, because they held workers in such low regard, expecting them to perform like robots. This paved the way for the human relations movement.

Division of labor The breaking up of a production process into small tasks, so that each worker performs a small portion of the overall job.

The Human Relations Movement

Whereas the scientific management movement heavily emphasized the technical aspects of work design, the human relations movement emphasized the importance of the human element in job design. Lillian Gilbreth, a psychologist and the wife of Frank Gilbreth, worked with her husband, focusing on the human factor in work. (The Gilbreths were the subject of a classic film, *Cheaper by the Dozen.*) Many of her studies dealt with worker fatigue. In the following decades, there was much emphasis on motivation. Elton Mayo conducted studies at the Hawthorne division of Western Electric. His studies revealed that in addition to the physical and technical aspects of work, worker motivation is critical for improving productivity. Abraham Maslow developed motivational theories, which Frederick Hertzberg refined. Douglas McGregor added Theory X and Theory Y. These theories represented the two ends of the spectrum of how employees view work. Theory X, on the negative end, assumed that workers do not like to work, and have to be controlled—rewarded and punished—to get them to do good work. This attitude was quite common in the automobile industry and in some other industries, until the threat of global competition forced them to rethink that approach. Theory Y, on the other end of the spectrum, assumed that workers enjoy the physical and mental aspects of work and become committed to work. The Theory X approach resulted in an adversarial environment, whereas the Theory Y approach resulted in empowered workers and a more cooperative spirit. William Ouchi added Theory Z, which combined the Japanese approach with such features as lifetime employment, employee problem solving, and consensus building, and the traditional Western approach that features short-term employment, specialists, and individual decision making and responsibility.

Decision Models and Management Science

The factory movement was accompanied by the development of several quantitative techniques. F. W. Harris developed one of the first models in 1915: a mathematical model for inventory order size. In the 1930s, three coworkers at Bell Telephone Labs—H. F. Dodge, H. G. Romig, and W. Shewhart—developed statistical procedures for sampling and quality control. In 1935, L.H.C. Tippett conducted studies that provided the groundwork for statistical sampling theory.

At first, these quantitative models were not widely used in industry. However, the onset of World War II changed that. The war generated tremendous pressures on manufacturing output, and specialists from many disciplines combined efforts to achieve advancements in the military and in manufacturing. After the war, efforts to develop and refine quantitative tools for decision making continued, resulting in decision models for forecasting, inventory management, project management, and other areas of operations management.

During the 1960s and 1970s, management science techniques were highly regarded; in the 1980s, they lost some favor. However, the widespread use of personal computers and user-friendly software in the workplace contributed to a resurgence in the popularity of these techniques.

The Influence of Japanese Manufacturers

A number of Japanese manufacturers developed or refined management practices that increased the productivity of their operations and the quality of their products, due in part to the influence of Americans W. Edwards Deming and Joseph Juran. This made them

TABLE 1.5
Historical summary of operations management

Approximate Date	Contribution/Concept	Originator
1776	Division of labor	Adam Smith
1790	Interchangeable parts	Eli Whitney
1911	Principles of scientific management	Frederick W. Taylor
1911	Motion study, use of industrial psychology	Frank and Lillian Gilbreth
1912	Chart for scheduling activities	Henry Gantt
1913	Moving assembly line	Henry Ford
1915	Mathematical model for inventory ordering	F. W. Harris
1930	Hawthorne studies on worker motivation	Elton Mayo
1935	Statistical procedures for sampling and quality control	H. F. Dodge, H. G. Romig, W. Shewhart, L.H.C. Tippett
1940	Operations research applications in warfare	Operations research groups
1947	Linear programming	George Dantzig
1951	Commercial digital computers	Sperry Univac, IBM
1950s	Automation	Numerous
1960s	Extensive development of quantitative tools	Numerous
1960s	Industrial dynamics	Jay Forrester
1975	Emphasis an manufacturing strategy	W. Skinner
1980s	Emphasis on flexibility, time-based competition, lean production	T. Ohno, S. Shingo, Toyota
1980s	Emphasis on quality	W. Edwards Deming, J. Juran, K. Ishikawa
1990s	Internet, supply chain management	Numerous
2000s	Applications service providers and outsourcing Social media, YouTube, and others.	Numerous Numerous

very competitive, sparking interest in their approaches by companies outside Japan. Their approaches emphasized quality and continual improvement, worker teams and empowerment, and achieving customer satisfaction. The Japanese can be credited with spawning the "quality revolution" that occurred in industrialized countries, and with generating widespread interest in lean production.

The influence of the Japanese on U.S. manufacturing and service companies has been enormous and promises to continue for the foreseeable future. Because of that influence, this book will provide considerable information about Japanese methods and successes.

Table 1.5 provides a chronological summary of some of the key developments in the evolution of operations management.

1.9 OPERATIONS TODAY

LO1.9 Describe current issues in business that impact operations management.

E-business The use of electronic technology to facilitate business transactions.

E-commerce Consumer-to-business transactions.

Advances in information technology and global competition have had a major influence on operations management. While the *Internet* offers great potential for business organizations, the potential as well as the risks must be clearly understood in order to determine if and how to exploit this potential. In many cases, the Internet has altered the way companies compete in the marketplace.

Electronic business, or **e-business**, involves the use of the Internet to transact business. E-business is changing the way business organizations interact with their customers and their suppliers. Most familiar to the general public is **e-commerce**, consumer–business transactions such as buying online or requesting information. However, business-to-business transactions such as e-procurement represent an increasing share of e-business. E-business is receiving increased attention from business owners and managers in developing strategies, planning, and decision making.

The word **technology** has several definitions, depending on the context. Generally, *technology* refers to the application of scientific knowledge to the development and improvement of goods and services. It can involve knowledge, materials, methods, and equipment. The term *high technology* refers to the most advanced and developed machines and methods. Operations management is primarily concerned with three kinds of technology: product and service technology, process technology, and information technology (IT). All three can have a major impact on costs, productivity, and competitiveness.

> ***Product and service technology*** refers to the discovery and development of new products and services. This is done mainly by researchers and engineers, who use the scientific approach to develop new knowledge and translate that into commercial applications.

> ***Process technology*** refers to methods, procedures, and equipment used to produce goods and provide services. They include not only processes within an organization but also supply chain processes.

> ***Information technology (IT)*** refers to the science and use of computers and other electronic equipment to store, process, and send information. Information technology is heavily ingrained in today's business operations. This includes electronic data processing, the use of bar codes to identify and track goods, obtaining point-of-sale information, data transmission, the Internet, e-commerce, e-mail, and more.

Technology The application of scientific knowledge to the development and improvement of products and services and operations processes.

Management of technology is high on the list of major trends, and it promises to be high well into the future. For example, computers have had a tremendous impact on businesses in many ways, including new product and service features, process management, medical diagnosis, production planning and scheduling, data processing, and communication. Advances in materials, methods, and equipment also have had an impact on competition and productivity. Advances in information technology also have had a major impact on businesses. Obviously there have been—and will continue to be—many benefits from technological advances. However, technological advance also places a burden on management. For example, management must keep abreast of changes and quickly assess both their benefits and risks. Predicting advances can be tricky at best, and new technologies often carry a high price tag and usually a high cost to operate or repair. And in the case of computer operating systems, as new systems are introduced, support for older versions is discontinued, making periodic upgrades necessary. Conflicting technologies can exist that make technological choices even more difficult. Technological innovations in both *products* and *processes* will continue to change the way businesses operate, and hence require continuing attention.

The North American Free Trade Agreement (NAFTA) opened borders for trade between the United States and Canada and Mexico. The General Agreement on Tariffs and Trade (GATT) of 1994 reduced tariffs and subsidies in many countries, expanding world trade. The resulting global competition and global markets have had an impact on the strategies and operations of businesses large and small around the world. One effect is the importance business organizations are giving to management of their supply chains.

Globalization and the need for global supply chains have broadened the scope of supply chain management. However, tightened border security in certain instances has slowed some movement of goods and people. Moreover, in some cases, organizations are reassessing their use of offshore outsourcing.

Competitive pressures and changing economic conditions have caused business organizations to put more emphasis on operations strategy, working with fewer resources, revenue management, process analysis and improvement, quality improvement, agility, and lean production.

During the latter part of the 1900s, many companies neglected to include *operations strategy* in their corporate strategy. Some of them paid dearly for that neglect. Now more and more companies are recognizing the importance of operations strategy on the overall success of their business as well as the necessity for relating it to their overall business strategy.

Working with fewer resources due to layoffs, corporate downsizing, and general cost cutting is forcing managers to make trade-off decisions on resource allocation, and to place increased emphasis on cost control and productivity improvement.

READING   AGILITY CREATES A COMPETITIVE EDGE

There is a huge demand in the United States and elsewhere for affordable women's clothing. Low-cost clothing retailers such as Spain's Zara and Sweden's H&M are benefiting from their ability to quickly get mass-produced, trendy new fashions to store shelves while some less-agile competitors like Macy's and Gap struggle to achieve the same results. A key factor for the agile retailers is their nearness to low-cost producers in Romania and Turkey, which greatly shortens transportation time. American retailers often source from China, but increasing wages there and the longer distance lessen their ability to take advantage of quickly introducing new low-cost fashions.

Questions

What possible solutions do you see for competitors such as Macy's and Gap?

Source: Based on Roya Wolverson, "Need for Speed: Glamorizing Cheap Fashion Costs More than You Think," *Time*, August 6, 2012, p. 18.

Six Sigma A process for reducing costs, improving quality, and increasing customer satisfaction.

Revenue management is a method used by some companies to maximize the revenue they receive from fixed operating capacity by influencing demand through price manipulation. Also known as yield management, it has been successfully used in the travel and tourism industries by airlines, cruise lines, hotels, amusement parks, and rental car companies, and in other industries such as trucking and public utilities.

Process analysis and improvement includes cost and time reduction, productivity improvement, process yield improvement, and quality improvement and increasing customer satisfaction. This is sometimes referred to as a **Six Sigma** process.

Given a boost by the "quality revolution" of the 1980s and 1990s, *quality* is now ingrained in business. Some businesses use the term *total quality management (TQM)* to describe their quality efforts. A quality focus emphasizes *customer satisfaction* and often involves *teamwork. Process improvement* can result in improved quality, cost reduction, and *time reduction.* Time relates to costs and to competitive advantage, and businesses seek ways to reduce the time to bring new products and services to the marketplace to gain a competitive edge. If two companies can provide the same product at the same price and quality, but one can deliver it four weeks earlier than the other, the quicker company will invariably get the sale. Time reductions are being achieved in many companies now. Union Carbide was able to cut $400 million of fixed expenses, and Bell Atlantic was able to cut the time needed to hook up long-distance carriers from 15 days to less than 1, at a savings of $82 million.

Agility The ability of an organization to respond quickly to demands or opportunities.

Agility refers to the ability of an organization to respond quickly to demands or opportunities. It is a strategy that involves maintaining a flexible system that can quickly respond to changes in either the volume of demand or changes in product/service offerings. This is particularly important as organizations scramble to remain competitive and cope with increasingly shorter product life cycles and strive to achieve shorter development times for new or improved products and services.

Lean production, a new approach to production, emerged in the 1990s. It incorporates a number of the recent trends listed here, with an emphasis on quality, flexibility, time reduction, and teamwork. This has led to a *flattening* of the organizational structure, with fewer levels of management.

Lean system System that uses minimal amounts of resources to produce a high volume of high-quality goods with some variety.

Lean systems are so named because they use much less of certain resources than typical mass production systems use—space, inventory, and workers—to produce a comparable amount of output. Lean systems use a highly skilled workforce and flexible equipment. In effect, they incorporate advantages of both mass production (high volume, low unit cost) and craft production (variety and flexibility). And quality is higher than in mass production. This approach has now spread to services, including health care, offices, and shipping and delivery.

The skilled workers in lean production systems are more involved in maintaining and improving the system than their mass production counterparts. They are taught to stop an operation if they discover a defect, and to work with other employees to find and correct the cause of the defect so that it won't recur. This results in an increasing level of quality over time and eliminates the need to inspect and rework at the end of the line.

Because lean production systems operate with lower amounts of inventory, additional emphasis is placed on anticipating when problems might occur *before* they arise and avoiding those problems through planning. Even so, problems can still occur at times, and quick resolution is important. Workers participate in both the planning and correction stages.

Compared to workers in traditional systems, much more is expected of workers in lean production systems. They must be able to function in teams, playing active roles in operating and improving the system. Individual creativity is much less important than team success. Responsibilities also are much greater, which can lead to pressure and anxiety not present in traditional systems. Moreover, a flatter organizational structure means career paths are not as steep in lean production organizations. Workers tend to become generalists rather than specialists, another contrast to more traditional organizations.

1.10 KEY ISSUES FOR TODAY'S BUSINESS OPERATIONS

There are a number of issues that are high priorities of many business organizations. Although not every business is faced with these issues, many are. Chief among the issues are the following.

Economic conditions. The lingering recession and slow recovery in various sectors of the economy has made managers cautious about investment and rehiring workers who had been laid off during the recession.

Innovating. Finding new or improved products or services are only two of the many possibilities that can provide value to an organization. Innovations can be made in processes, the use of the Internet, or the supply chain that reduce costs, increase productivity, expand markets, or improve customer service.

Quality problems. The numerous operations failures mentioned at the beginning of the chapter underscore the need to improve the way operations are managed. That relates to product design and testing, oversight of suppliers, risk assessment, and timely response to potential problems.

Risk management. The need for managing risk is underscored by recent events that include financial crises, product recalls, accidents, natural and man-made disasters, and economic ups and downs. Managing risks starts with identifying risks, assessing vulnerability and potential damage (liability costs, reputation, demand), and taking steps to reduce or share risks.

Cyber-security. The need to guard against intrusions from hackers whose goal is to steal personal information of employees and customers is becoming increasingly necessary. Moreover, interconnected systems increase intrusion risks in the form of industrial espionage.

Competing in a global economy. Low labor costs in third-world countries have increased pressure to reduce labor costs. Companies must carefully weigh their options, which include outsourcing some or all of their operations to low-wage areas, reducing costs internally, changing designs, and working to improve productivity.

Three other key areas require more in-depth discussion: environmental concerns, ethical conduct, and managing the supply chain.

Environmental Concerns

Concern about global warming and pollution has had an increasing effect on how businesses operate.

Stricter environmental regulations, particularly in developed nations, are being imposed. Furthermore, business organizations are coming under increasing pressure to reduce their carbon footprint (the amount of carbon dioxide generated by their operations and their supply chains) and to generally operate sustainable processes. **Sustainability** refers to service

Sustainability Using resources in ways that do not harm ecological systems that support human existence.

READING   UNIVERSITIES EMBRACE SUSTAINABILITY

Universities and colleges are increasingly embracing sustainability, linking it to global warming, biodiversity, and global commerce. Some are building sustainability into existing courses, while others are offering new courses, certificate programs, or degree programs. And some, such as Arizona State University and the Rochester Institute of Technology, are offering advanced degree programs.

Some universities are also "practicing what they preach," by applying sustainable practices in their operations. Among them are Dartmouth College, Harvard University, Stanford, Williams College, and the University of British Columbia, which was named by the environmental magazine *Grist* as one of the top 15 universities in the world in reducing greenhouse gas emissions and being energy efficient.

Source: Based on "The Sustainable University: Saving the Planet by Degrees," *Chronicle of Higher Education,* Special Report, October 20, 2006, Stanford News Service, January 2007, and "B.C.'s School of Greener Learning," *Toronto Globe and Mail,* August 25, 2007, p. A6.

Puma's "Clever Little Bag" changes the idea of the shoebox by wrapping footwear in a cardboard structure with 65 percent less cardboard. It uses a bag made of recycled plastic as the outer layer that holds the inner cardboard structure together. Puma expects to cut carbon dioxide emissions by 10,000 tons per year and water, energy, and diesel use by 60 percent by using fewer materials—8,500 fewer tons of paper to be specific—and the new packaging's lighter weight.

© Puma/Getty

and production processes that use resources in ways that do not harm ecological systems that support both current and future human existence. Sustainability measures often go beyond traditional environmental and economic measures to include measures that incorporate social criteria in decision making.

All areas of business will be affected by this. Areas that will be most affected include product and service design, consumer education programs, disaster preparation and response, supply chain waste management, and outsourcing decisions. Note that outsourcing of goods production increases not only transportation costs, but also fuel consumption and carbon released into the atmosphere. Consequently, sustainability thinking may have implications for outsourcing decisions.

Because they all fall within the realm of operations, operations management is central to dealing with these issues. Sometimes referred to as "green initiatives," the possibilities include reducing packaging, materials, water and energy use, and the environmental impact of the supply chain, including buying locally. Other possibilities include reconditioning used equipment (e.g., printers and copiers) for resale, and recycling.

The following reading suggests that even our choice of diet can affect the environment.

READING

DIET AND THE ENVIRONMENT: VEGETARIAN VS. NONVEGETARIAN

It is interesting to examine the environmental impact of dietary choices. There's ample evidence that agricultural practices pollute the soil, air, and water. Factors range from the distance food travels to get to the consumer, to the amount of water and fertilizer used. Of particular concern is the environmental impact of a diet high in animal protein. The Food and Agricultural Organization (FAO) of the United Nations recently reported that livestock production is one of the major causes of global warming and air and water pollution. Using a methodology that considers the entire supply chain, the FAO estimated that livestock accounts for 18 percent of greenhouse gas emissions.

A Vegetarian versus Nonvegetarian Diet and the Environment The eco-friendliness of a meat eater's diet was the subject

of a study conducted by researchers from the Departments of Environmental Health and Nutrition of Loma Linda University in California. They compared the environmental effects of a vegetarian vs. nonvegetarian diet in California in terms of agricultural production inputs, including pesticides and fertilizers, water and energy.

The study indicated that in the combined production of 11 food items the nonvegetarian diet required 2.9 times more water, 2.5 times more primary energy, 13 times more fertilizer, and 1.4 times more pesticides than the vegetarian diet. The greatest differences stemmed from including beef in the diet.

Source: Based on "Finding a Scientific Connection Between Food Choices and the Environment," *Environmental Nutrition Newsletter,* October 2009, p. 3.

Ethical Conduct

The need for ethical conduct in business is becoming increasingly obvious, given numerous examples of questionable actions in recent history. In making decisions, managers must consider how their decisions will affect shareholders, management, employees, customers, the community at large, and the environment. Finding solutions that will be in the best interests of all of these stakeholders is not always easy, but it is a goal that all managers should strive to achieve. Furthermore, even managers with the best intentions will sometimes make mistakes. If mistakes do occur, managers should act responsibly to correct those mistakes as quickly as possible, and to address any negative consequences.

Many organizations have developed *codes of ethics* to guide employees' or members' conduct. **Ethics** is a standard of behavior that guides how one should act in various situations. The Markula Center for Applied Ethics at Santa Clara University identifies five principles for thinking ethically:

Ethics A standard of behavior that guides how one should act in various situations.

- The **Utilitarian Principle:** The good done by an action or inaction should outweigh any harm it causes or might cause. An example is not allowing a person who has had too much to drink to drive.

- The **Rights Principle:** Actions should respect and protect the moral rights of others. An example is not taking advantage of a vulnerable person.

- The **Fairness Principle:** Equals should be held to, or evaluated by, the same standards. An example is equal pay for equal work.

- The **Common Good Principle:** Actions should contribute to the common good of the community. An example is an ordinance on noise abatement.

© Mario Tama/Getty

The Fair Trade Certified™ label guarantees to consumers that strict economic, social, and environmental criteria were met in the production and trade of an agricultural product.

- The **Virtue Principle:** Actions should be consistent with certain ideal virtues. Examples include honesty, compassion, generosity, tolerance, fidelity, integrity, and self-control.

The center expands these principles to create a framework for ethical

Ethical framework A sequence of steps intended to guide thinking and subsequent decision or action.

conduct. An **ethical framework** is a sequence of steps intended to guide thinking and subsequent decisions or actions. Here is the one developed by the Markula Center for Applied Ethics:

1. Recognize an ethical issue by asking if an action could be damaging to a group or an individual. Is there more to it than just what is legal?
2. Make sure the pertinent facts are known, such as who will be impacted, and what options are available.
3. Evaluate the options by referring to the appropriate preceding ethical principle.
4. Identify the "best" option and then further examine it by asking how someone you respect would view it.
5. In retrospect, consider the effect your decision had and what you can learn from it.

More detail is available at the Center's website: http://www.scu.edu/ethics/practicing/decision/framework.html.

Operations managers, like all managers, have the responsibility to make ethical decisions. Ethical issues arise in many aspects of operations management, including:

- Financial statements: accurately representing the organization's financial condition.
- Worker safety: providing adequate training, maintaining equipment in good working condition, maintaining a safe working environment.
- Product safety: providing products that minimize the risk of injury to users or damage to property or the environment.
- Quality: honoring warranties, avoiding hidden defects.
- The environment: not doing things that will harm the environment.
- The community: being a good neighbor.
- Hiring and firing workers: avoiding false pretenses (e.g., promising a long-term job when that is not what is intended).
- Closing facilities: taking into account the impact on a community, and honoring commitments that have been made.
- Workers' rights: respecting workers' rights, dealing with workers' problems quickly and fairly.

The Ethisphere Institute recognizes companies worldwide for their ethical leadership. Here are some samples from their list:

Apparel: Gap
Automotive: Ford Motor Company
Business services: Paychex
Café: Starbucks
Computer hardware: Intel
Computer software: Adobe Systems, Microsoft
Consumer electronics: Texas Instruments, Xerox
E-commerce: eBay
General retail: Costco, Target
Groceries: Safeway, Wegmans, Whole Foods
Health and beauty: L'Oreal
Logistics: UPS

You can see a complete list of recent recipients and the selection criteria at Ethisphere.com.

LO1.10 Explain the need to manage the supply chain.

The Need to Manage the Supply Chain

Supply chain management is being given increasing attention as business organizations face mounting pressure to improve management of their supply chains. In the past, most organizations did little to manage their supply chains. Instead, they tended to concentrate on their own operations and on their immediate suppliers. Moreover, the planning, marketing, production and inventory management functions in organizations in supply chains have often operated independently of each other. As a result, supply chains experienced a range of problems that were seemingly beyond the control of individual organizations. The problems included large oscillations of inventories, inventory stockouts, late deliveries, and quality problems. These and other issues now make it clear that management of supply chains is essential to business success. The other issues include the following:

1. **The need to improve operations.** Efforts on cost and time reduction, and productivity and quality improvement, have expanded in recent years to include the supply chain. Opportunity now lies largely with procurement, distribution, and logistics—the supply chain.

2. **Increasing levels of outsourcing.** Organizations are increasing their levels of **outsourcing**, buying goods or services instead of producing or providing them themselves. As outsourcing increases, organizations are spending increasing amounts on supply-related activities (wrapping, packaging, moving, loading and unloading, and sorting). A significant amount of the cost and time spent on these and other related activities may be unnecessary. Issues with imported products, including tainted food products, toothpaste, and pet foods, as well as unsafe tires and toys, have led to questions of liability and the need for companies to take responsibility for monitoring the safety of outsourced goods.

   outsourcing Buying goods or services instead of producing or providing them in-house.

3. **Increasing transportation costs.** Transportation costs are increasing, and they need to be more carefully managed.

4. **Competitive pressures.** Competitive pressures have led to an increasing number of new products, shorter product development cycles, and increased demand for customization. And in some industries, most notably consumer electronics, product life cycles are relatively short. Added to this are adoption of quick-response strategies and efforts to reduce lead times.

5. **Increasing globalization.** Increasing globalization has expanded the physical length of supply chains. A global supply chain increases the challenges of managing a supply chain. Having far-flung customers and/or suppliers means longer lead times and greater opportunities for disruption of deliveries. Often currency differences and monetary fluctuations are factors, as well as language and cultural differences. Also, tightened border security in some instances has slowed shipments of goods.

   In Kachchh, India, Fairtrade allows cotton farmers to have the assurance of a minimum price, which gives them more security to plan their business and invest in their communities.

6. **Increasing importance of e-business.** The increasing importance of e-business has added new dimensions to business buying and selling and has presented new challenges.

7. **The complexity of supply chains.** Supply chains are complex; they are dynamic, and they have many inherent uncertainties that can adversely affect them, such as inaccurate forecasts, late deliveries, substandard quality, equipment breakdowns, and canceled or changed orders.

8. **The need to manage inventories.** Inventories play a major role in the success or failure of a supply chain, so it is important to coordinate inventory levels throughout a supply chain. Shortages can severely disrupt the timely flow of work and have far-reaching impacts, while excess inventories add unnecessary costs. It would not be unusual to find inventory shortages in some parts of a supply chain and excess inventories in other parts of the same supply chain.

© Pixtal/AGE Fotostock

Elements of Supply Chain Management

Supply chain management involves coordinating activities across the supply chain. Central to this is taking customer demand and translating it into corresponding activities at each level of the supply chain.

The key elements of supply chain management are listed in Table 1.6. The first element, customers, is the driving element. Typically, marketing is responsible for determining what customers want as well as forecasting the quantities and timing of customer demand. Product and service design must match customer wants with operations capabilities.

Processing occurs in each component of the supply chain: it is the core of each organization. The major portion of processing occurs in the organization that produces the product or service for the final customer (the organization that assembles the computer, services the car, etc.). A major aspect of this for both the internal and external portions of a supply chain is scheduling.

Inventory is a staple in most supply chains. Balance is the main objective; too little causes delays and disrupts schedules, but too much adds unnecessary costs and limits flexibility.

Purchasing is the link between an organization and its suppliers. It is responsible for obtaining goods and/or services that will be used to produce products or provide services for the organization's customers. Purchasing selects suppliers, negotiates contracts, establishes alliances, and acts as liaison between suppliers and various internal departments.

The supply portion of a value chain is made up of one or more suppliers, all links in the chain, and each one capable of having an impact on the effectiveness—or the ineffectiveness—of the supply chain. Moreover, it is essential that the planning and execution be carefully coordinated between suppliers and all members of the demand portion of their chains.

Location can be a factor in a number of ways. Where suppliers are located can be important, as can location of processing facilities. Nearness to market, nearness to sources of supply, or nearness to both may be critical. Also, delivery time and cost are usually affected by location.

Two types of decisions are relevant to supply chain management—strategic and operational. The strategic decisions are the design and policy decisions. The operational decisions relate to day-to-day activities: managing the flow of material and product and other aspects of the supply chain in accordance with strategic decisions.

The major decision areas in supply chain management are location, production, distribution, and inventory. The *location* decision relates to the choice of locations for both production and distribution facilities. Production and transportation costs and delivery lead times are important. *Production* and *distribution* decisions focus on what customers want, when they want it, and how much is needed. Outsourcing can be a consideration. Distribution decisions are strongly influenced by transportation cost and delivery times, because transportation costs

TABLE 1.6
Elements of supply chain management

Element	Typical Issues	Chapter(s)
Customers	Determining what products and/or services customers want	3, 4
Forecasting	Predicting the quantity and timing of customer demand	3
Design	Incorporating customers, wants, manufacturability, and time to market	4
Capacity planning	Matching supply and demand	5, 11
Processing	Controlling quality, scheduling work	10, 16
Inventory	Meeting demand requirements while managing the costs of holding inventory	12, 13, 14
Purchasing	Evaluating potential suppliers, supporting the needs of operations on purchased goods and services	15
Suppliers	Monitoring supplier quality, on-time delivery, and flexibility; maintaining supplier relations	15
Location	Determining the location of facilities	8
Logistics	Deciding how to best move information and materials	15

often represent a significant portion of total cost. Moreover, shipping alternatives are closely tied to production and inventory decisions. For example, using air transport means higher costs but faster deliveries and less inventory in transit than sea, rail, or trucking options. Distribution decisions must also take into account capacity and quality issues. Operational decisions focus on scheduling, maintaining equipment, and meeting customer demand. Quality control and workload balancing are also important considerations. *Inventory* decisions relate to determining inventory needs and coordinating production and stocking decisions throughout the supply chain. Logistics management plays the key role in inventory decisions.

Enterprise Resource Planning (ERP) is being increasingly used to provide information sharing in real time among organizations and their major supply chain partners. This important topic is discussed in more detail in Chapter 12.

Operations Tours

Throughout the book you will discover operations tours that describe operations in all sorts of companies. The tour you are about to read is Wegmans Food Markets, a major regional supermarket chain. Wegmans has been consistently ranked high on *Fortune* magazine's list of the 100 Best Companies to Work For since the inception of the survey a decade ago.

OPERATIONS TOUR   WEGMANS FOOD MARKETS

Wegmans Food Markets, Inc., is one of the premier grocery chains in the United States. Headquartered in Rochester, New York, Wegmans operates about 100 stores, mainly in Rochester, Buffalo, and Syracuse. There are also a handful of stores elsewhere in New York State as well as in New Jersey, Massachusetts, North Carolina, Pennsylvania, and Virginia. The company employs over 45,000 people, and has annual sales of over $3 billion.

Wegmans has a strong reputation for offering its customers high product quality and excellent service. Through a combination of market research, trial and error, and listening to its customers, Wegmans has evolved into a very successful organization. Its sales per square foot are 50 percent higher than the industry average.

Superstores

Many of the company's stores are giant 100,000-square-foot superstores, double or triple the size of average supermarkets. You can get an idea about the size of these stores from this: they usually have between 25 and 35 checkout lanes, and during busy periods, all of the checkouts are in operation. A superstore typically employs from 500 to 600 people.

Individual stores differ somewhat in terms of actual size and some special features. Aside from the features normally found in supermarkets, they generally have a full-service deli (typically a 40-foot display case), a 500-square-foot fisherman's wharf that has perhaps 10 different fresh fish offerings most days, a large bakery section (each store bakes its own bread, rolls, cakes, pies, and pastries), and extra-large produce sections. They also offer

film processing, a complete pharmacy, a card shop, video rentals, and an Olde World Cheese section. In-store floral shops range in size up to 800 square feet of floor space and offer a wide variety of fresh-cut flowers, flower arrangements, vases, and plants. In-store card shops cover over 1,000 square feet of floor space. The bulk foods department provides customers with the opportunity to select the quantities they desire from a vast array of foodstuffs and some nonfood items such as birdseed and pet food.

Each store is a little different. Among the special features in some stores are a dry cleaning department, a wokery, and a salad bar. Some stores feature a Market Café that has different food stations, each devoted to preparing and serving a certain type of food. For example, one station will have pizza and other Italian specialties, and another oriental food, and still another chicken or fish. There also will be a sandwich bar, a salad bar, and a dessert station. Customers often wander among stations as they decide what to order. In some Market Cafés, diners can have wine with their meals and have brunch on Sundays. In several affluent locations, customers can stop in on their way home from work and choose from a selection of freshly prepared dinner entrees such as medallions of beef with herb butter, chicken Marsala, stuffed flank steak with mushrooms, Cajun tuna, crab cakes, and accompaniments such as roasted red potatoes, grilled vegetables, and Caesar salad. Many Wegmans stores offer ready-made sandwiches as well as made-to-order sandwiches. Some stores have a coffee-shop section with tables and chairs where shoppers can enjoy regular or specialty coffees and a variety of tempting pastries.

(continued)

Produce Department

The company prides itself on fresh produce. Produce is replenished as often as 12 times a day. The larger stores have produce sections that are four to five times the size of a produce section in an average supermarket. Wegmans offers locally grown produce in season. Wegmans uses a "farm to market" system whereby some local growers deliver their produce directly to individual stores, bypassing the main warehouse. That reduces the company's inventory holding costs and gets the produce into the stores as quickly as possible. Growers may use specially designed containers that go right onto the store floor instead of large bins. This avoids the bruising that often occurs when fruits and vegetables are transferred from bins to display shelves and the need to devote labor to transfer the produce to shelves.

Meat Department

In addition to large display cases of both fresh and frozen meat products, many stores have a full-service butcher shop that offers a variety of fresh meat products and where butchers are available to provide customized cuts of meat for customers.

Meat department employees attend Wegmans' "Meat University," where they learn about different cuts of meat and how to best prepare them. They also learn about other items to pair with various meats, and suggest side dishes, breads, and wine. This helps instill a "selling culture" among employees, who often spend 75 percent of their time talking with customers.

Wegmans continually analyzes store operations to improve processes. In the meat department, a change from in-store cutting and traditional packaging to using a centralized meat processing facility and vacuum packaging extended the shelf life of meats and reduced staffing requirements in meat departments, reducing costs and providing customers with an improved product.

Ordering

Each department handles its own ordering. Although sales records are available from records of items scanned at the checkouts, they are not used directly for replenishing stock. Other factors—such as pricing, special promotions, and local circumstances (e.g., festivals, weather conditions)—must all be taken into account. However, for seasonal periods, such as holidays, managers often check scanner records to learn what past demand was during a comparable period.

The superstores typically receive one truckload of goods per day from the main warehouse. During peak periods, a store may receive two truckloads from the main warehouse. The short lead time greatly reduces the length of time an item might be out of stock, unless the main warehouse is also out of stock.

The company exercises strict control over suppliers, insisting on product quality and on-time deliveries.

Inventory Management

Some stores carry as many as 70,000 individual units. Wegmans uses a companywide system to keep track of inventory. Departments take a monthly inventory count to verify the amount shown in the companywide system. Departments receive a periodic report indicating how many days of inventory the department has on hand. Having an appropriate amount on hand is important to department managers: If they have too much inventory on hand, that will add to their department's costs, whereas having too little inventory will result in shortages and thus lost sales and dissatisfied customers.

(continued)

Benjamin C. Tankersley/For The Washington Post via Getty Images

Suzanne Kreiter/The Boston Globe via Getty Images

Wegmans' Patisserie is an authentic French pastry shop.

Employees

The company recognizes the value of good employees. It typically invests an average of $7,000 to train each new employee. In addition to learning about store operations, new employees learn the importance of good customer service and how to provide it. The employees are helpful, cheerfully answering customer questions or handling complaints. Employees are motivated through a combination of compensation, profit sharing, and benefits. Employee turnover for full-time workers is about 6 percent, compared to the industry average of about 20 percent.

Quality

Quality and customer satisfaction are utmost in the minds of Wegmans' management and its employees. Private-label food items as well as name brands are regularly evaluated in test kitchens, along with potential new products. Managers are responsible for checking and maintaining product and service quality in their departments. Moreover, employees are encouraged to report problems to their managers.

If a customer is dissatisfied with an item, and returns it, or even a portion of the item, the customer is offered a choice of a replacement or a refund. If the item is a Wegmans brand food item, it is then sent to the test kitchen to determine the cause of the problem. If the cause can be determined, corrective action is taken.

Technology

Wegmans continues to adopt new technologies to maintain its competitive edge, including new approaches to tracking inventory and managing its supply chain, and new ways to maintain freshness in the meat and produce departments.

Sustainability

Wegmans began replacing incandescent light bulbs with compact fluorescent bulbs back in 2007, generating 3,000 fewer tons of carbon dioxide each year. Also the company installed sensors in its dairy cases that reduced the time the cooling systems run by 50 percent.

Questions

1. How do customers judge the quality of a supermarket?
2. Indicate how and why each of these factors is important to the successful operation of a supermarket:
   a. Customer satisfaction
   b. Forecasting
   c. Capacity planning
   d. Location
   e. Inventory management
   f. Layout of the store
   g. Scheduling
3. What are some of the ways Wegmans uses technology to gain an edge over its competition?

Robert A. Reeder/The Washington Post/Getty Images
Fresh seafood is delivered daily, often direct from boat to store the same day it was caught.

Mark Gail/The Washington Post via Getty Images
Wegmans' chefs prepare ready-to-eat entrees, side dishes, salads, sandwiches, and ready-to-heat entrees.

SUMMARY

The operations function in business organizations is responsible for producing goods and providing services. It is a core function of every business. Supply chains are the sequential system of suppliers and customers that begins with basic sources of inputs and ends with final customers of the system. Operations and supply chains are interdependent—one couldn't exist without the other, and no business organization could exist without both.

Operations management involves system design and operating decisions related to product and service design, capacity planning, process selection, location selection, work management, inventory and supply management, production planning, quality assurance, scheduling, and project management.

The historical evolution of operations management provides interesting background information on the continuing evolution of this core business function.

The Operations Tours and Readings included in this and subsequent chapters provide insights into actual business operations.

KEY POINTS

1. The operations function is that part of every business organization that produces products and/or delivers services.

2. Operations consists of processes that convert inputs into outputs. Failure to manage those processes effectively will have a negative impact on the organization.

3. A key goal of business organizations is to achieve an economic matching of supply and demand. The operations function is responsible for providing the supply or service capacity for expected demand.

4. All processes exhibit variation that must be managed.

5. Although there are some basic differences between services and products that must be taken into account from a managerial standpoint, there are also many similarities between the two.

6. Environmental issues will increasingly impact operations decision making.

7. Ethical behavior is an integral part of good management practice.

8. All business organizations have, and are part of, a supply chain that must be managed.

KEY TERMS

agility 26	interchangeable parts 22	process 13
craft production 21	lead time 11	services 4
division of labor 23	lean system 26	six sigma 26
e-business 24	mass production 22	supply chain 4
e-commerce 24	model 18	sustainability 27
ethical framework 30	operations management 4	system 20
ethics 29	outsourcing 31	technology 25
goods 4	pareto phenomenon 20	value-added 6

DISCUSSION AND REVIEW QUESTIONS

1. Briefly describe the terms *operations management* and *supply chain*.

2. Identify the three major functional areas of business organizations and briefly describe how they interrelate.

3. Describe the operations function and the nature of the operations manager's job.

4. List five important differences between goods production and service operations; then list five important similarities.

5. Briefly discuss each of these terms related to the historical evolution of operations management:

    a. Industrial Revolution

    b. Scientific management

    c. Interchangeable parts

    d. Division of labor

6. Why are services important? Why is manufacturing important? What are nonmanufactured goods?

Chapter One   Introduction to Operations Management   37

7. What are models and why are they important?

8. Why is the degree of customization an important consideration in process planning?

9. List the trade-offs you would consider for each of these decisions:

   a. Driving your own car versus public transportation.

   b. Buying a computer now versus waiting for an improved model.

   c. Buying a new car versus buying a used car.

   d. Speaking up in class versus waiting to get called on by the instructor.

   e. A small business owner having a website versus newspaper advertising.

10. Describe each of these systems: craft production, mass production, and lean production.

11. Why might some workers prefer not to work in a lean production environment?

12. Discuss the importance of each of the following:

    a. Matching supply and demand

    b. Managing a supply chain

13. List and briefly explain the four basic sources of variation, and explain why it is important for managers to be able to effectively deal with variation.

14. Why do people do things that are unethical?

15. Explain the term *value-added*.

16. Discuss the various impacts of outsourcing.

17. Discuss the term *sustainability*, and its relevance for business organizations.

This item appears at the end of each chapter. It is intended to focus your attention on three key issues for business organizations in general, and operations management in particular. Those issues are trade-off decisions, collaboration among various functional areas of the organization, and the impact of technology. You will see three or more questions relating to these issues. Here is the first set of questions:

TAKING STOCK

1. What are trade-offs? Why is careful consideration of trade-offs important in decision making?

2. Why is it important for the various functional areas of a business organization to collaborate?

3. In what general ways does technology have an impact on operations management decision making?

This item also will appear in every chapter. It allows you to critically apply information you learned in the chapter to a practical situation. Here is the first set of exercises:

CRITICAL THINKING EXERCISES

1. Many organizations offer a combination of goods and services to their customers. As you learned in this chapter, there are some key differences between production of goods and delivery of services. What are the implications of these differences relative to managing operations?

2. Why is it important to match supply and demand? If a manager believes that supply and demand will not be equal, what actions could the manager take to increase the probability of achieving a match?

3. One way that organizations compete is through technological innovation. However, there can be downsides for both the organization and the consumer. Explain.

4. a. What would cause a business person to make an unethical decision?

   b. What are the risks of doing so?

CASE   HAZEL

Hazel had worked for the same *Fortune* 500 company for almost 15 years. Although the company had gone through some tough times, things were starting to turn around. Customer orders were up, and quality and productivity had improved dramatically from what they had been only a few years earlier due to a company-wide quality improvement program. So it came as a real shock to Hazel and about 400 of her coworkers when they were suddenly terminated following the new CEO's decision to downsize the company.

After recovering from the initial shock, Hazel tried to find employment elsewhere. Despite her efforts, after eight months of searching she was no closer to finding a job than the day she started. Her funds were being depleted and she was getting more discouraged. There was one bright spot, though: She was able to bring in a little money by mowing lawns for her neighbors. She got involved quite by chance when she heard one neighbor remark that now that his children were on their own, nobody was around to cut the grass. Almost jokingly, Hazel asked him how much he'd be willing to pay. Soon Hazel was mowing the lawns of five neighbors. Other neighbors wanted her to work on their lawns, but she didn't feel that she could spare any more time from her job search.

However, as the rejection letters began to pile up, Hazel knew she had to make a decision. On a sunny Tuesday morning, she decided, like many others in a similar situation, to go into business for herself—taking care of neighborhood lawns. She was relieved to give up the stress of job hunting, and she was excited about the prospect of being her own boss. But she was also fearful of being completely on her own. Nevertheless, Hazel was determined to make a go of it.

At first, business was a little slow, but once people realized Hazel was available, many asked her to take care of their lawns. Some people were simply glad to turn the work over to her; others switched from professional lawn care services. By the end of her first year in business, Hazel knew she could earn a living this way. She also performed other services such as fertilizing lawns, weeding gardens, and trimming shrubbery. Business became so good that Hazel hired two part-time workers to assist her and, even then, she believed she could expand further if she wanted to.

Questions

1. Hazel is the operations manager of her business. Among her responsibilities are forecasting, inventory management, scheduling, quality assurance, and maintenance.
   a. What kinds of things would likely require forecasts?
   b. What inventory items does Hazel probably have? Name one inventory decision she has to make periodically.
   c. What scheduling must she do? What things might occur to disrupt schedules and cause Hazel to reschedule?
   d. How important is quality assurance to Hazel's business? Explain.
   e. What kinds of maintenance must be performed?
2. In what ways are Hazel's customers most likely to judge the quality of her lawn care services?
3. What are some of the trade-offs that Hazel probably considered relative to:
   a. Working for a company instead of for herself?
   b. Expanding the business?
   c. Launching a website?
4. The town is considering an ordinance that would prohibit putting grass clippings at the curb for pickup because local landfills cannot handle the volume. What options might Hazel consider if the ordinance is passed? Name two advantages and two drawbacks of each option.
5. Hazel decided to offer the students who worked for her a bonus of $25 for ideas on how to improve the business, and they provided several good ideas. One idea that she initially rejected now appears to hold great promise. The student who proposed the idea has left, and is currently working for a competitor. Should Hazel send that student a check for the idea? What are the possible trade-offs?
6. All managers have to cope with variation.
   a. What are the major sources of variation that Hazel has to contend with?
   b. How might these sources of variation impact Hazel's ability to match supply and demand?
   c. What are some ways she can cope with variation?
7. Hazel is thinking of making some of her operations sustainable. What are some ideas she might consider?

SELECTED BIBLIOGRAPHY & FURTHER READINGS

Bloomberg Businessweek

Bowie, Norman E., ed. *The Blackwell Guide to Business Ethics.* Malden, MA: Blackwell, 2002.

Fitzsimmons, James, and Mona Fitzsimmons. *Service Management,* 4th ed. New York: McGraw-Hill/Irwin, 2011.

Fortune magazine.

Womack, James P., Daniel Jones, and Daniel Roos. *The Machine That Changed the World.* New York: Harper Perennial, 1991, 2007.

Wisner, Joel D., and Linda L. Stanley. *Process Management: Creating Value Along the Supply Chain.* Mason, OH: Thomson South-Western, 2008.

Here is a procedure that will help you solve most of the end-of-chapter problems in this book and on exams:

1. Identify the question to be answered. This is critical.

2. Summarize the information given in the problem statement using the appropriate symbols.

3. Determine what type of problem it is so you can select the appropriate problem-solving tools such as a formula or table. Check your notes from class, chapter examples, and the Solved Problems section of the chapter, and any preceding chapter problems you have already solved for guidance.

4. Solve the problem and indicate your answer.

Department A can produce parts at a rate of 50/day. Department B uses those parts are the rate of 10/day. Each day unused parts are added to inventory. At what rate does the inventory of unused parts build up?

Example 1

1. The question to be answered: At what rate does inventory of unused parts build up (i.e., increase) per day?

Solution

2. The given information: Production rate = 50 parts/day
    Usage rate = 10 parts/day

3. For this simple problem, no formula or table is needed. Inventory buildup is simply the difference between the production and usage rates.

4. Production rate   = 50 parts/day
    Usage rate   = 10 parts/day
    Inventory buildup = 40 parts/day

Companies often use this formula to determine how much of a certain item to order:

Example 2

$$Q = \sqrt{\frac{2DS}{H}}$$

where

Q = order quantity
D = annual demand
S = ordering cost
H = annual holding cost per unit

If annual demand is 400 units, ordering cost is $36, and annual holding cost is $2 per unit, what is the order quantity?

1. The question to be answered: What is the order quantity, Q?

Solution

2. The information given in the problem: D = 400 units/year, S = $36, H = $2 per year

3. To solve the problem, substitute the values given in the problem into the formula.

4. Solution:

$$Q = \sqrt{\frac{2(400\ units/yr.)\$36}{\$2/unit/yr.}} = 120\ units$$

Problem-Solving Template
Problem number:
The question to be answered:
Information given:
Solve using:

2

Competitiveness, Strategy, and Productivity

LEARNING OBJECTIVES

After completing this chapter, you should be able to:

LO2.1   List several ways that business organizations compete.

LO2.2   Name several reasons that business organizations fail.

LO2.3   Define the terms *mission* and *strategy* and explain why they are important.

LO2.4   Discuss and compare organization strategy and operations strategy and explain why it is important to link the two.

LO2.5   Describe and give examples of time-based strategies.

LO2.6   Define the term *productivity* and explain why it is important to organizations and to countries.

LO2.7   Describe several factors that affect productivity.

CHAPTER OUTLINE

2.1   **Introduction,** *41*

2.2   **Competitiveness,** *42*
    Why Some Organizations Fail, *43*

2.3   **Mission and Strategies,** *44*
    Strategies and Tactics, *45*
    Strategy Formulation, *46*
    Supply Chain Strategy, *50*
    Sustainability Strategy, *50*
    Global Strategy, *50*

2.4   **Operations Strategy,** *51*
    Strategic Operations
    Management Decision Areas, *52*

    Quality and Time Strategies, *53*

2.5   **Implications of Organization
Strategy for Operations
Management,** *54*

2.6   **Transforming Strategy
into Action: The Balanced
Scorecard,** *54*

2.7   **Productivity,** *56*
    Computing Productivity, *57*
    Productivity in the Service
    Sector, *59*
    Factors That Affect
    Productivity, *60*

    Improving Productivity, *61*

Cases: An American Tragedy: How a
    Good Company Died, *67*
    Home-Style Cookies, *68*
    Hazel Revisited, *69*
    "Your Garden Gloves," *70*

Operations Tour: The U.S. Postal
    Service, *70*

© Peter Charlesworth/LightRocket/Getty

This chapter discusses competitiveness, strategy, and productivity, three separate but related topics that are vitally important to business organizations. *Competitiveness* relates to the effectiveness of an organization in the marketplace relative to other organizations that offer similar products or services. Operations and marketing have a major impact on competitiveness. *Strategy* relates to the plans that determine how an organization pursues its goals. Operations strategy is particularly important in this regard. *Productivity* relates to the effective use of resources, and it has a direct impact on competitiveness. Operations management is chiefly responsible for productivity.

THE COLD HARD FACTS

The name of the game is competition. The playing field is global. Those who understand how to play the game will succeed; those who don't are doomed to failure. And don't think the game is just companies competing with each other. In companies that have multiple factories or divisions producing the same good or service, factories or divisions sometimes find themselves competing with each other. When a competitor—another company or a sister factory or division in the same company—can turn out products better, cheaper, and faster, that spells real trouble for the factory or division that is performing at a lower level. The trouble can be layoffs or even a shutdown if the managers can't turn things around. The bottom line? Better quality, higher productivity, lower costs, and the ability to quickly respond to customer needs are more important than ever, and the bar is getting higher. Business organizations need to develop solid strategies for dealing with these issues.

2.1 INTRODUCTION

In this chapter you will learn about the different ways companies compete and why some firms do a very good job of competing. You will learn how effective strategies can lead to competitive organizations, and you will learn what productivity is, why it is important, and what organizations can do to improve it.

2.2 COMPETITIVENESS

LO2.1 List several ways that business organizations compete.

Competitiveness How effectively an organization meets the wants and needs of customers relative to others that offer similar goods or services.

Companies must be competitive to sell their goods and services in the marketplace. **Competitiveness** is an important factor in determining whether a company prospers, barely gets by, or fails. Business organizations compete through some combination of price, delivery time, and product or service differentiation.

Marketing influences competitiveness in several ways, including identifying consumer wants and needs, pricing, and advertising and promotion.

1. **Identifying consumer wants and/or needs** is a basic input in an organization's decision-making process, and central to competitiveness. The ideal is to achieve a perfect match between those wants and needs and the organization's goods and/or services.

2. **Price and quality** are key factors in consumer buying decisions. It is important to understand the trade-off decision consumers make between price and quality.

3. **Advertising and promotion** are ways organizations can inform potential customers about features of their products or services, and attract buyers.

Operations has a major influence on competitiveness through product and service design, cost, location, quality, response time, flexibility, inventory and supply chain management, and service. Many of these are interrelated.

1. **Product and service design** should reflect joint efforts of many areas of the firm to achieve a match between financial resources, operations capabilities, supply chain capabilities, and consumer wants and needs. Special characteristics or features of a product or service can be a key factor in consumer buying decisions. Other key factors include **innovation** and the **time-to-market** for new products and services.

2. **Cost** of an organization's output is a key variable that affects pricing decisions and profits. Cost-reduction efforts are generally ongoing in business organizations. **Productivity** (discussed later in the chapter) is an important determinant of cost. Organizations with higher productivity rates than their competitors have a competitive cost advantage. A company may outsource a portion of its operation to achieve lower costs, higher productivity, or better quality.

3. **Location** can be important in terms of cost and convenience for customers. Location near inputs can result in lower input costs. Location near markets can result in lower transportation costs and quicker delivery times. Convenient location is particularly important in the retail sector.

4. **Quality** refers to materials, workmanship, design, and service. Consumers judge quality in terms of how well they think a product or service will satisfy its intended purpose. Customers are generally willing to pay more for a product or service if they perceive the product or service has a higher quality than that of a competitor.

5. **Quick response** can be a competitive advantage. One way is quickly bringing new or improved products or services to the market. Another is being able to quickly deliver existing products and services to a customer after they are ordered, and still another is quickly handling customer complaints.

6. **Flexibility** is the ability to respond to changes. Changes might relate to alterations in design features of a product or service, or to the volume demanded by customers, or the mix of products or services offered by an organization. High flexibility can be a competitive advantage in a changeable environment.

7. **Inventory management** can be a competitive advantage by effectively matching supplies of goods with demand.

8. **Supply chain management** involves coordinating internal and external operations (buyers and suppliers) to achieve timely and cost-effective delivery of goods throughout the system.

9. **Service** might involve after-sale activities customers perceive as value-added, such as delivery, setup, warranty work, and technical support. Or it might involve extra attention while work is in progress, such as courtesy, keeping the customer informed, and attention to details. **Service quality** can be a key differentiator; and it is one that is often

Indian operators take calls at Quatro call center in Gurgaon on the outskirts of New Delhi. Companies take advantage of communications and software support offshore to drive down costs. This industry in India already provides over one million jobs.

© Terry Vine/Blend Images/Getty RF

sustainable. Moreover, businesses rated highly by their customers for service quality tend to be more profitable, and grow faster, than businesses that are not rated highly.

10. **Managers** and **workers** are the people at the heart and soul of an organization, and if they are competent and motivated, they can provide a distinct competitive edge by their skills and the ideas they create. One often overlooked skill is answering the telephone. How complaint calls or requests for information are handled can be a positive or a negative. If a person answering is rude or not helpful, that can produce a negative image. Conversely, if calls are handled promptly and cheerfully, that can produce a positive image and, potentially, a competitive advantage.

Why Some Organizations Fail

Organizations fail, or perform poorly, for a variety of reasons. Being aware of those reasons can help managers avoid making similar mistakes. Among the chief reasons are the following:

> **LO2.2** Name several reasons that business organizations fail.

1. Neglecting operations strategy.
2. Failing to take advantage of strengths and opportunities, and/or failing to recognize competitive threats.
3. Putting too much emphasis on short-term financial performance at the expense of research and development.
4. Placing too much emphasis on product and service design and not enough on process design and improvement.
5. Neglecting investments in capital and human resources.
6. Failing to establish good internal communications and cooperation among different functional areas.
7. Failing to consider customer wants and needs.

The key to successfully competing is to determine what customers want and then directing efforts toward meeting (or even exceeding) customer expectations. Two basic issues must be addressed. First: What do the customers want? (Which items on the preceding list of the ways business organizations compete are important to customers?) Second: What is the best way to satisfy those wants?

Operations must work with marketing to obtain information on the relative importance of the various items to each major customer or target market.

Understanding competitive issues can help managers develop successful strategies.

2.3 MISSION AND STRATEGIES

LO2.3 Define the terms *mission* and *strategy* and explain why they are important

Mission The reason for the existence of an organization.

Mission statement States the purpose of an organization.

Goals Provide detail and scope of the mission.

Strategies Plans for achieving organizational goals.

An organization's **mission** is the reason for its existence. It is expressed in its **mission statement**. For a business organization, the mission statement should answer the question "What business are we in?" Missions vary from organization to organization, depending on the nature of their business. Table 2.1 provides several examples of mission statements.

A mission statement serves as the basis for organizational **goals**, which provide more detail and describe the scope of the mission. The mission and goals often relate to how an organization wants to be perceived by the general public, and by its employees, suppliers, and customers. Goals serve as a foundation for the development of organizational strategies. These, in turn, provide the basis for strategies and tactics of the functional units of the organization.

Organizational strategy is important because it guides the organization by providing direction for, and alignment of, the goals and **strategies** of the functional units. Moreover, strategies can be the main reason for the success or failure of an organization.

There are three basic business strategies:

- Low cost
- Responsiveness
- Differentiation from competitors

IS IT A STRATEGIC, TACTICAL, OR OPERATIONAL ISSUE?

Sometimes the same issue may apply to all three levels. However, a key difference is the time frame. From a strategic perspective, long-term implications are most relevant. From tactical and operational perspectives, the time frames are much shorter. In fact, the operational time frame is often measured in days.

Responsiveness relates to ability to respond to changing demands. Differentiation can relate to product or service features, quality, reputation, or customer service. Some organizations focus on a single strategy while others employ a combination of strategies. One company that has multiple strategies is Amazon.com. Not only does it offer low cost and quick, reliable deliveries, it also excels in customer service.

Amazon's service helped propel the company to a double-digit sales increase. Amazon started same-day shipping in major cities, launched a program to urge manufacturers to drop frustrating packaging, and extended its service reach by acquiring free-shipping pioneer Zappos.com.

© Uwe Zucchi/AFP/Getty

TABLE 2.1
Selected portions of company mission statements

Microsoft	To help people and businesses throughout the world to realize their full potential.
Verizon	To help people and businesses communicate with each other.
Starbucks	To inspire and nurture the human spirit—one cup and one neighborhood at a time.
U.S. Dept. of Education	To promote student achievement and preparation for global competitiveness and fostering educational excellence and ensuring equal access.

READING

AMAZON TOPS IN CUSTOMER SERVICE

Amazon received the top spot in customer service in a recent *Business-Week* ranking. Although most Amazon customers never talk with an employee, when something goes wrong, Amazon excels in dealing with the problem. In one case, when a New Jersey woman received a workbook she ordered that was described as "like new," she was surprised to discover that it wasn't even close to new—worksheets had already been filled in. She complained to the merchant but didn't get a response. Then she complained to Amazon. She promptly received a refund, even though she had paid the merchant, not Amazon.

And she wasn't asked to return the book.

Amazon sees its customer service as a way to enhance customer experience, and as a way to identify potential problems with merchants. In fact, if merchants have problems with more than 1 percent of their orders, that can get them removed from the site.

Source: Based on "How Amazon Aims to Keep You Clicking," *BusinessWeek*, March 2009, p. 34.

Strategies and Tactics

If you think of goals as destinations, then strategies are the roadmaps for reaching the destinations. Strategies provide *focus* for decision making. Generally speaking, organizations have overall strategies called *organizational strategies,* which relate to the entire organization. They also have *functional strategies,* which relate to each of the functional areas of the organization. The functional strategies should support the overall strategies of the organization, just as the organizational strategies should support the goals and mission of the organization.

Tactics are the methods and actions used to accomplish strategies. They are more specific than strategies, and they provide guidance and direction for carrying out actual *operations,* which need the most specific and detailed plans and decision making in an organization. You might think of tactics as the "how to" part of the process (e.g., how to reach the destination, following the strategy roadmap) and operations as the actual "doing" part of the process. Much of this book deals with tactical operations.

It should be apparent that the overall relationship that exists from the mission down to actual operations is *hierarchical.* This is illustrated in Figure 2.1.

A simple example may help to put this hierarchy into perspective.

Tactics The methods and actions taken to accomplish strategies.

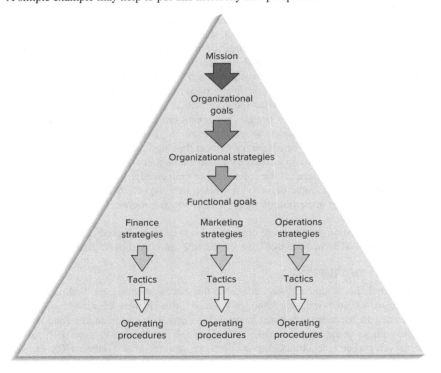

FIGURE 2.1
Planning and decision making are hierarchical in organizations

EXAMPLE 1

Rita is a high school student in Southern California. She would like to have a career in business, have a good job, and earn enough income to live comfortably.

A possible scenario for achieving her goals might look something like this:

Mission: Live a good life.

Goal: Successful career, good income.

Strategy: Obtain a college education.

Tactics: Select a college and a major; decide how to finance college.

Operations: Register, buy books, take courses, study.

Here are some examples of different strategies an organization might choose from:

Low cost. Outsource operations to third-world countries that have low labor costs.

Scale-based strategies. Use capital-intensive methods to achieve high output volume and low unit costs.

Specialization. Focus on narrow product lines or limited service to achieve higher quality.

Newness. Focus on innovation to create new products or services.

Flexible operations. Focus on quick response and/or customization.

High quality. Focus on achieving higher quality than competitors.

Service. Focus on various aspects of service (e.g., helpful, courteous, reliable, etc.).

Sustainability. Focus on environmental-friendly and energy-efficient operations.

A wide range of business organizations are beginning to recognize the strategic advantages of sustainability, not only in economic terms, but also in promotional benefit by publicizing their sustainability efforts and achievements.

Sometimes organizations will combine two or more of these or other approaches into their strategy. However, unless they are careful, they risk losing focus and not achieving advantage in any category. Generally speaking, strategy formulation takes into account the way organizations compete and a particular organization's assessment of its own strengths and weaknesses in order to take advantage of its **core competencies**—those special attributes or abilities possessed by an organization that give it a *competitive edge*.

Core competencies The special attributes or abilities that give an organization a competitive edge.

The most effective organizations use an approach that develops core competencies based on customer needs as well as on what the competition is doing. Marketing and operations work closely to match customer needs with operations capabilities. Competitor competencies are important for several reasons. For example, if a competitor is able to supply high-quality products, it may be necessary to meet that high quality as a baseline. However, merely *matching* a competitor is usually not sufficient to gain market share. It may be necessary to exceed the quality level of the competitor or gain an edge by excelling in one or more other dimensions, such as rapid delivery or service after the sale. Walmart, for example, has been very successful in managing its supply chain, which has contributed to its competitive advantage.

To be effective, strategies and core competencies need to be aligned. Table 2.2 lists examples of strategies and companies that have successfully employed those strategies.

Strategy Formulation

Strategy formulation is almost always critical to the success of a strategy. Walmart discovered that when it opened stores in Japan. Although Walmart thrived in many countries on its reputation for low-cost items, Japanese consumers associated low cost with low quality, causing Walmart to rethink its strategy in the Japanese market. And many felt that Hewlett-Packard (HP) committed a strategic error when it acquired Compaq Computers at a cost of $19 billion. HP's share of the

Organization Strategy	Operations Strategy	Examples of Companies or Services
Low price	Low cost	U.S. first-class postage Walmart Southwest Airlines
Responsiveness	Short processing time	McDonald's restaurants Express Mail, UPS, FedEx One-hour photo
	On-time delivery	Domino's Pizza FedEx
Differentiation: High quality	High-performance design and/or high-quality processing	TV: Sony, Samsung, LG Lexus
	Consistent quality	Disneyland Five-star restaurants or hotels Coca-Cola, PepsiCo Wegmans Electrical power
Differentiation: Newness	Innovation	3M, Apple Google
Differentiation: Variety	Flexibility	Burger King ("Have it your way") Hospital emergency room
	Volume	McDonald's ("Buses welcome") Toyota Supermarkets (additional checkouts)
Differentiation: Service	Superior customer service	Disneyland Amazon IBM Nordstrom
Differentiation: Location	Convenience	Supermarkets, dry cleaners Mall stores Service stations Banks, ATMs

TABLE 2.2
Examples of operations strategies

computer market was less after the merger than the sum of the shares of the separate companies before the merger. In another example, U.S. automakers adopted a strategy in the early 2000s of offering discounts and rebates on a range of cars and SUVs, many of which were on low-margin vehicles. The strategy put a strain on profits, but customers began to expect those incentives, and the companies maintained them to keep from losing additional market share.

On the other hand, Coach, the maker of leather handbags and purses, successfully changed its longtime strategy to grow its market by creating new products. Long known for its highly durable leather goods in a market where women typically owned few handbags, Coach created a new market for itself by changing women's view of handbags by promoting "different handbags for different occasions" such as party bags, totes, clutches, wristlets, overnight bags, purses, and day bags. And Coach introduced many fashion styles and colors.

To formulate an effective strategy, senior managers must take into account the core competencies of the organizations, and they must *scan the environment*. They must determine what competitors are doing, or planning to do, and take that into account. They must critically examine other factors that could have either positive or negative effects. This is sometimes referred to as the **SWOT** approach (strengths, weaknesses, opportunities, and threats). Strengths and weaknesses have an internal focus and are typically evaluated by operations people. Threats and opportunities have an external focus and are typically evaluated by marketing people. SWOT is often regarded as the link between organizational strategy and operations strategy.

SWOT Analysis of strengths, weaknesses, opportunities, and threats.

Chapter Two   Competitiveness, Strategy, and Productivity

An alternative to SWOT analysis is Michael Porter's five forces model,[1] which takes into account the threat of new competition, the threat of substitute products or services, the bargaining power of customers, the bargaining power of suppliers, and the intensity of competition.

In formulating a successful strategy, organizations must take into account both order qualifiers and order winners. **Order qualifiers** are those characteristics that potential customers perceive as minimum standards of acceptability for a product to be considered for purchase. However, that may not be sufficient to get a potential customer to purchase from the organization. **Order winners** are those characteristics of an organization's goods or services that cause them to be perceived as better than the competition.

Characteristics such as price, delivery reliability, delivery speed, and quality can be order qualifiers or order winners. Thus, quality may be an order winner in some situations, but in others only an order qualifier. Over time, a characteristic that was once an order winner may become an order qualifier, and vice versa.

Obviously, it is important to determine the set of order qualifier characteristics and the set of order winner characteristics. It is also necessary to decide on the relative importance of each characteristic so that appropriate attention can be given to the various characteristics. Marketing must make that determination and communicate it to operations.

Environmental scanning is the monitoring of events and trends that present either threats or opportunities for the organization. Generally these include competitors' activities; changing consumer needs; legal, economic, political, and environmental issues; the potential for new markets; and the like.

Another key factor to consider when developing strategies is technological change, which can present real opportunities and threats to an organization. Technological changes occur in products (high-definition TV, improved computer chips, improved cellular telephone systems, and improved designs for earthquake-proof structures); in services (faster order processing, faster delivery); and in processes (robotics, automation, computer-assisted processing, point-of-sale scanners, and flexible manufacturing systems). The obvious benefit is a competitive edge; the risk is that incorrect choices, poor execution, and higher-than-expected operating costs will create competitive *disadvantages*.

Important factors may be internal or external. The following are key external factors:

1. **Economic conditions.** These include the general health and direction of the economy, inflation and deflation, interest rates, tax laws, and tariffs.

2. **Political conditions.** These include favorable or unfavorable attitudes toward business, political stability or instability, and wars.

3. **Legal environment.** This includes antitrust laws, government regulations, trade restrictions, minimum wage laws, product liability laws and recent court experience, labor laws, and patents.

4. **Technology.** This can include the rate at which product innovations are occurring, current and future process technology (equipment, materials handling), and design technology.

5. **Competition.** This includes the number and strength of competitors, the basis of competition (price, quality, special features), and the ease of market entry.

6. **Markets.** This includes size, location, brand loyalties, ease of entry, potential for growth, long-term stability, and demographics.

The organization also must take into account various *internal factors* that relate to possible strengths or weaknesses. Among the key internal factors are the following:

1. **Human resources.** These include the skills and abilities of managers and workers, special talents (creativity, designing, problem solving), loyalty to the organization, expertise, dedication, and experience.

Order qualifiers Characteristics that customers perceive as minimum standards of acceptability to be considered as a potential for purchase.

Order winners Characteristics of an organization's goods or services that cause it to be perceived as better than the competition.

Environmental scanning The monitoring of events and trends that present threats or opportunities for a company.

[1]Michael E. Porter, "The Five Competitive Forces That Shape Strategy," *Harvard Business Review* 86, no. 1 (January 2008), pp. 78–93, 137.

2. **Facilities and equipment.** Capacities, location, age, and cost to maintain or replace can have a significant impact on operations.

3. **Financial resources.** Cash flow, access to additional funding, existing debt burden, and cost of capital are important considerations.

4. **Customers.** Loyalty, existing relationships, and understanding of wants and needs are important.

5. **Products and services.** These include existing products and services, and the potential for new products and services.

6. **Technology.** This includes existing technology, the ability to integrate new technology, and the probable impact of technology on current and future operations.

7. **Suppliers.** Supplier relationships, dependability of suppliers, quality, flexibility, and service are typical considerations.

8. **Other.** Other factors include patents, labor relations, company or product image, distribution channels, relationships with distributors, maintenance of facilities and equipment, access to resources, and access to markets.

After assessing internal and external factors and an organization's distinctive competence, a strategy or strategies must be formulated that will give the organization the best chance of success. Among the types of questions that may need to be addressed are the following:

What role, if any, will the Internet play?

Will the organization have a global presence?

To what extent will *outsourcing* be used?

What will the supply chain management strategy be?

To what extent will new products or services be introduced?

What rate of growth is desirable and *sustainable?*

What emphasis, if any, should be placed on lean production?

How will the organization differentiate its products and/or services from competitors'?

The organization may decide to have a single, dominant strategy (e.g., be the price leader) or to have multiple strategies. A single strategy would allow the organization to concentrate on one particular strength or market condition. On the other hand, multiple strategies may be needed to address a particular set of conditions.

Many companies are increasing their use of outsourcing to reduce overhead, gain flexibility, and take advantage of suppliers' expertise. Dell Computers provides a great example of some of the potential benefits of outsourcing as part of a business strategy.

Growth is often a component of strategy, especially for new companies. A key aspect of this strategy is the need to seek a growth rate that is sustainable. In the 1990s, fast-food company Boston Market dazzled investors and fast-food consumers alike. Fueled by its success, it undertook rapid expansion. By the end of the decade, the company was nearly bankrupt; it had overexpanded. In 2000, it was absorbed by fast-food giant McDonald's.

Companies increase their risk of failure not only by missing or incomplete strategies; they also fail due to poor execution of strategies. And sometimes they fail due to factors beyond their control, such as natural or man-made disasters, major political or economic changes, or competitors that have an overwhelming advantage (e.g., deep pockets, very low labor costs, less rigorous environmental requirements).

A useful resource on successful business strategies is the Profit Impact of Market Strategy (PIMS) database (www.pimsonline.com). The database contains profiles of over 3,000 businesses located primarily in the United States, Canada, and western Europe. It is used by companies and academic institutions to guide strategic thinking. It allows subscribers to answer strategy questions about their business. Moreover, they can use it to generate benchmarks and develop successful strategies.

In 1984, Michael Dell, then a college student, started selling personal computers from his dorm room. He didn't have the resources to make computer components, so he let others do that, choosing instead to concentrate on selling the computers. And, unlike the major computer producers, he didn't sell to dealers. Instead, he sold directly to PC buyers, eliminating some intermediaries, which allowed for lower cost and faster delivery. Although direct selling of PCs is fairly commonplace now, in those days it was a major departure from the norm.

What did Dell do that was so different from the big guys? To start, he bought components from suppliers instead of making them. That gave him tremendous leverage. He had little inventory, no R&D expenditures, and relatively few employees. And the risks of this approach were spread among his suppliers.

Suppliers were willing to do this because Dell worked closely with them, and kept them informed. And because he was in direct contact with his customers, he gained tremendous insight into their expectations and needs, which he communicated to his suppliers.

Having little inventory gave Dell several advantages over his competitors. Aside from the lower costs of inventory, when new, faster computer chips became available, there was little inventory to work off, so he was able to offer the newer models much sooner than competitors with larger inventories. Also, when the prices of various components dropped, as they frequently did, he was able to take advantage of the lower prices, which kept his average costs lower than competitors' costs.

Today the company is worth billions, and so is Michael Dell.

STRATEGY FORMULATION

The key steps in strategy formulation are:

1. Link strategy directly to the organization's mission or vision statement.

2. Assess strengths, weaknesses, threats and opportunities, and identify core competencies.
3. Identify order winners and order qualifiers.
4. Select one or two strategies (e.g., low cost, speed, customer service) to focus on.

According to the PIMS website,

> The *database* is a collection of statistically documented experiences drawn from thousands of businesses, designed to help understand what kinds of strategies (e.g. quality, pricing, vertical integration, innovation, advertising) work best in what kinds of business environments. The data constitute a key resource for such critical management tasks as evaluating business performance, analyzing new business opportunities, evaluating and reality testing new strategies, and screening business portfolios. *The primary role* of the PIMS Program of the Strategic Planning Institute is to help managers understand and react to their business environment. PIMS does this by assisting managers as they develop and test strategies that will achieve an acceptable level of winning as defined by various strategies and financial measures.

Supply Chain Strategy

A supply chain strategy specifies how the supply chain should function to achieve supply chain goals. The supply chain strategy should be aligned with the business strategy. If it is well executed, it can create value for the organization. It establishes how the organization should work with suppliers and policies relating to customer relationships and sustainability. Supply chain strategy is covered in more detail in a later chapter.

Sustainability Strategy

Society is placing increasing emphasis on corporate sustainability practices in the form of governmental regulations and interest groups. For these and other reasons, business organizations are or should be devoting attention to sustainability goals. To be successful, they will need a sustainability strategy. That requires elevating sustainability to the level of organizational governance; formulating goals for products and services, for processes, and for the entire supply chain; measuring achievements and striving for improvements; and possibly linking executive compensation to the achievement of sustainability goals.

Global Strategy

As globalization increased, many companies realized that strategic decisions with respect to globalization must be made. One issue companies must face is that what works in one country or region will not necessarily work in another, and strategies must be carefully crafted to take these variabilities into account. Another issue is the threat of political or social upheaval. Still another issue is the difficulty of coordinating and managing far-flung operations. Indeed, "In today's global markets, you don't have to go abroad to experience international competition. Sooner or later the world comes to you."[2]

At this McDonald's in Singapore, one variable is the use of rice as a staple of the Chinese diet. This ad highlights rice burgers.

McGraw-Hill Education/Christopher Kerrigan

2.4 OPERATIONS STRATEGY

LO2.4 Discuss and compare organization strategy and operations strategy and explain why it is important to link the two.

The organization strategy provides the overall direction for the organization. It is broad in scope, covering the entire organization. **Operations strategy** is narrower in scope, dealing primarily with the operations aspect of the organization. Operations strategy relates to products, processes, methods, operating resources, quality, costs, lead times, and scheduling. Table 2.3 provides a comparison of an organization's mission, its overall strategy, and its operations strategy, tactics, and operations.

In order for operations strategy to be truly effective, it is important to link it to organization strategy; that is, the two should not be formulated independently. Rather, formulation of organization strategy should take into account the realities of operations' strengths and weaknesses, capitalizing on strengths and dealing with weaknesses. Similarly, operations strategy must be consistent with the overall strategy of the organization, and with the other functional units of the organization. This requires that senior managers work with functional units to formulate strategies that will support, rather than conflict with, each other and the overall strategy of the organization. As obvious as this may seem, it doesn't always happen in practice. Instead, we may find power struggles between various functional units. These struggles are detrimental to the organization because they pit functional units against each other rather than focusing their energy on making the organization more competitive and better able to serve the customer. Some of the latest approaches in organizations, involving teams of managers and workers, may reflect a growing awareness of the synergistic effects of working together rather than competing internally.

Operations strategy The approach, consistent with the organization strategy, that is used to guide the operations function.

[2]Christopher A. Bartlett and Sumantra Ghoshal, "Going Global: Lessons from Late Movers," *Harvard Business Review,* March–April 2000, p. 139.

TABLE 2.3

Comparison of mission, organization strategy, and operations strategy

		Management Level	Time Horizon	Scope	Level of Detail	Relates to
The overall organization	Mission	Top	Long	Broad	Low	Survival, profitability
	Strategy	Senior	Long	Broad	Low	Growth rate, market share
Operations	Strategic	Senior	Moderate to long	Broad	Low	Product design, choice of location, choice of technology, new facilities
	Tactical	Middle	Moderate	Moderate	Moderate	Employment levels, output levels, equipment selection, facility layout
	Operational	Low	Short	Narrow	High	Scheduling personnel, adjusting output rates, inventory management, purchasing

In the 1970s and early 1980s, operations strategy in the United States was often neglected in favor of marketing and financial strategies. That may have occurred because many chief executive officers did not come from operations backgrounds and perhaps did not fully appreciate the importance of the operations function. Mergers and acquisitions were common; leveraged buyouts were used, and conglomerates were formed that joined dissimilar operations. These did little to add value to the organization; they were purely financial in nature. Decisions were often made by individuals who were unfamiliar with the business, frequently to the detriment of that business. Meanwhile, foreign competitors began to fill the resulting vacuum with a careful focus on operations strategy.

In the late 1980s and early 1990s, many companies began to realize this approach was not working. They recognized that they were less competitive than other companies. This caused them to focus attention on operations strategy. A key element of both organization strategy and operations strategy is strategy formulation.

Operations strategy can have a major influence on the competitiveness of an organization. If it is well designed and well executed, there is a good chance that the organization will be successful; if it is not well designed or executed, the chances are much less that the organization will be successful.

Strategic Operations Management Decision Areas

Operations management people play a strategic role in many strategic decisions in a business organization. Table 2.4 highlights some key decision areas. Notice that most of the decision areas have cost implications.

TABLE 2.4

Strategic operations management decisions

Decision Area	What the Decisions Affect
1. Product and service design	Costs, quality, liability, and environmental issues
2. Capacity	Cost structure, flexibility
3. Process selection and layout	Costs, flexibility, skill level needed, capacity
4. Work design	Quality of work life, employee safety, productivity
5. Location	Costs, visibility
6. Quality	Ability to meet or exceed customer expectations
7. Inventory	Costs, shortages
8. Maintenance	Costs, equipment reliability, productivity
9. Scheduling	Flexibility, efficiency
10. Supply chains	Costs, quality, agility, shortages, vendor relations
11. Projects	Costs, new products, services, or operating systems

Two factors that tend to have universal strategic operations importance relate to quality and time. The following section discusses quality and time strategies.

Quality and Time Strategies

Traditional strategies of business organizations have tended to emphasize cost minimization or product differentiation. While not abandoning those strategies, many organizations have embraced strategies based on *quality* and/or *time*.

Quality-based strategies focus on maintaining or improving the quality of an organization's products or services. Quality is generally a factor in both attracting and retaining customers. Quality-based strategies may be motivated by a variety of factors. They may reflect an effort to overcome an image of poor quality, a desire to catch up with the competition, a desire to maintain an existing image of high quality, or some combination of these and other factors. Interestingly enough, quality-based strategies can be part of another strategy such as cost reduction, increased productivity, or time, all of which benefit from higher quality.

Time-based strategies focus on reducing the time required to accomplish various activities (e.g., develop new products or services and market them, respond to a change in customer demand, or deliver a product or perform a service). By doing so, organizations seek to improve service to the customer and to gain a competitive advantage over rivals who take more time to accomplish the same tasks.

Time-based strategies focus on reducing the time needed to conduct the various activities in a process. The rationale is that by reducing time, costs are generally less, productivity is higher, quality tends to be higher, product innovations appear on the market sooner, and customer service is improved.

Organizations have achieved time reduction in some of the following:

Planning time: The time needed to react to a competitive threat, to develop strategies and select tactics, to approve proposed changes to facilities, to adopt new technologies, and so on.

Product/service design time: The time needed to develop and market new or redesigned products or services.

Processing time: The time needed to produce goods or provide services. This can involve scheduling, repairing equipment, methods used, inventories, quality, training, and the like.

Changeover time: The time needed to change from producing one type of product or service to another. This may involve new equipment settings and attachments, different methods, equipment, schedules, or materials.

Delivery time: The time needed to fill orders.

Response time for complaints: These might be customer complaints about quality, timing of deliveries, and incorrect shipments. These might also be complaints from employees about working conditions (e.g., safety, lighting, heat or cold), equipment problems, or quality problems.

It is essential for marketing and operations personnel to collaborate on strategy formulation in order to ensure that the buying criteria of the most important customers in each market segment are addressed.

Agile operations is a strategic approach for competitive advantage that emphasizes the use of flexibility to adapt and prosper in an environment of change. Agility involves a blending of several distinct competencies such as cost, quality, and reliability along with flexibility. Processing aspects of flexibility include quick equipment changeovers, scheduling, and innovation. Product or service aspects include varying output volumes and product mix.

Successful agile operations requires careful planning to achieve a system that includes people, flexible equipment, and information technology. Reducing the time needed to perform work is one of the ways an organization can improve a key metric: *productivity*.

LO2.5 Describe and give examples of time-based strategies.

Quality-based strategies Strategy that focuses on quality in all phases of an organization.

Time-based strategies Strategy that focuses on reduction of time needed to accomplish tasks.

2.5 IMPLICATIONS OF ORGANIZATION STRATEGY FOR OPERATIONS MANAGEMENT

Organization strategy has a major impact on operations and supply chain management strategies. For example, organizations that use a low-cost, high-volume strategy limit the amount of variety offered to customers. As a result, variations for operations and the supply chain are minimal, so they are easier to deal with. Conversely, a strategy to offer a wide variety of products or services, or to perform customized work, creates substantial operational and supply chain variations and, hence, more challenges in achieving a smooth flow of goods and services throughout the supply chain, thus making the matching of supply to demand more difficult. Similarly, increasing service reduces the ability to compete on price. Table 2.5 provides a brief overview of variety and some other key implications.

2.6 TRANSFORMING STRATEGY INTO ACTION: THE BALANCED SCORECARD

The Balanced Scorecard (BSC) is a top-down *management system* that organizations can use to clarify their vision and strategy and transform them into action. It was introduced in the early 1990s by Robert Kaplan and David Norton,[3] and it has been revised and improved since then. The idea was to move away from a purely financial perspective of the organization and integrate other perspectives such as customers, internal business processes, and learning and growth. Using this approach, managers develop objectives, metrics, and targets for each objective and initiatives to achieve objectives, and they identify links among the various perspectives. Results are monitored and used to improve strategic performance results. Figure 2.2 illustrates the conceptual framework of this approach. Many organizations employ this or a similar approach.

TABLE 2.5
Organization strategies and their implications for operations management

Organization Strategy	Implications for Operations Management
Low price	Requires low variation in products/services and a high-volume, steady flow of goods results in maximum use of resources through the system. Standardized work, material, and inventory requirements.
High quality	Entails higher initial cost for product and service design, and process design, and more emphasis on assuring supplier quality.
Quick response	Requires flexibility, extra capacity, and higher levels of some inventory items.
Newness/innovation	Entails large investment in research and development for new or improved products and services plus the need to adapt operations and supply processes to suit new products or services.
Product or service variety	Requires high variation in resource and more emphasis on product and service design; higher worker skills needed, cost estimation more difficult; scheduling more complex; quality assurance more involved; inventory management more complex; and matching supply to demand more difficult.
Sustainability	Affects location planning, product and service design, process design, outsourcing decisions, returns policies, and waste management.

[3]Robert S. Kaplan and David P. Norton, *Balanced Scorecard: Translating Strategy into Action* (Cambridge, MA: Harvard Business School Press, 1996).

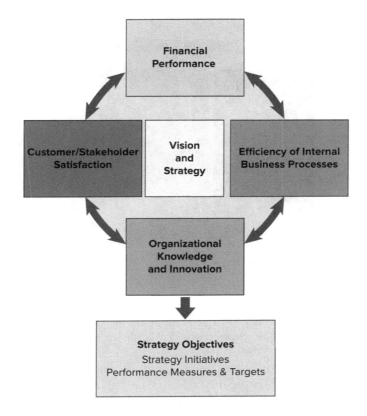

FIGURE 2.2
The Balanced Scorecard

Source: Adapted from Robert S. Kaplan and David P. Norton, "Using the Balanced Scorecard as a Strategic Management System," *Harvard Business Review* (January-February 1996): 76.

As seen in Figure 2.2, the four perspectives are intended to balance not only financial and nonfinancial performance, but also internal and external performance as well as past and future performance. This approach can also help organizations focus on how they differ from the competition in each of the four areas if their vision is realized. Table 2.6 has some examples of factors for key focal points.

Although the Balanced Scorecard helps focus managers' attention on strategic issues and the implementation of strategy, it is important to note that it has no role in strategy formulation.

Moreover, this approach pays little attention to suppliers and government regulations, and community, environmental, and sustainability issues are missing. These are closely linked,

Focal Point	Factors
Suppliers	Delivery performance Quality performance Number of suppliers Supplier locations Duplicate activities
Internal Processes	Bottlenecks Automation potential Turnover
Employees	Job satisfaction Learning opportunities Delivery performance
Customers	Quality performance Satisfaction Retention rate

TABLE 2.6
Balanced scorecard factors Examples

A major key to Apple's continued success is its ability to keep pushing the boundaries of innovation. Apple has demonstrated how to create growth by dreaming up products so new and ingenious that they have upended one industry after another.

Pieter Beens/Shutterstock

and business organizations need to be aware of the impact they are having in these areas and respond accordingly. Otherwise, organizations may be subject to attack by pressure groups and risk damage to their reputation.

2.7 PRODUCTIVITY

LO2.6 Define the term *productivity* and explain why it is important to companies and to countries.

Productivity A measure of the effective use of resources, usually expressed as the ratio of output to input.

One of the primary responsibilities of a manager is to achieve *productive use* of an organization's resources. The term *productivity* is used to describe this. **Productivity** is an index that measures output (goods and services) relative to the input (labor, materials, energy, and other resources) used to produce it. It is usually expressed as the ratio of output to input:

$$\text{Productivity} = \frac{\text{Output}}{\text{Input}} \tag{2-1}$$

Although productivity is important for all business organizations, it is particularly important for organizations that use a strategy of low cost, because the higher the productivity, the lower the cost of the output.

A productivity ratio can be computed for a single operation, a department, an organization, or an entire country. In business organizations, productivity ratios are used for planning workforce requirements, scheduling equipment, financial analysis, and other important tasks.

Productivity has important implications for business organizations and for entire nations. For nonprofit organizations, higher productivity means lower costs; for profit-based organizations, productivity is an important factor in determining how competitive a company is. For a nation, the rate of *productivity growth* is of great importance. Productivity growth is the increase in productivity from one period to the next relative to the productivity in the preceding period. Thus,

$$\text{Productivity growth} = \frac{\text{Current productivity} - \text{Previous productivity}}{\text{Previous productivity}} \times 100 \tag{2-2}$$

For example, if productivity increased from 80 to 84, the growth rate would be

$$\frac{84 - 80}{80} \times 100 = 5\%$$

Courtesy of Hyundai Motor Group

Productivity can be enhanced by the use of robotic equipment. Robots can operate for long periods with consistent precision and high speed. The Hyundai Motor Company manufacturing plant in Montgomery, Alabama, uses robots for assembly work. This $1.4 billion automotive plant is one of the most advanced assembly plants in North America.

Productivity growth is a key factor in a country's rate of inflation and the standard of living of its people. Productivity increases add value to the economy while keeping inflation in check. Productivity growth was a major factor in the long period of sustained economic growth in the United States in the 1990s.

Computing Productivity

Productivity measures can be based on a single input (partial productivity), on more than one input (multifactor productivity), or on all inputs (total productivity). Table 2.7 lists some examples of productivity measures. The choice of productivity measure depends primarily on the purpose of the measurement. If the purpose is to track improvements in labor productivity, then labor becomes the obvious input measure.

Partial measures are often of greatest use in operations management. Table 2.8 provides some examples of partial productivity measures.

The units of output used in productivity measures depend on the type of job performed. The following are examples of labor productivity:

$$\frac{\text{Yards of carpet installed}}{\text{Labor hours}} = \text{Yards of carpet installed per labor hour}$$

$$\frac{\text{Number of motel rooms cleaned}}{\text{Number of workers}} = \text{Number of motel rooms cleaned per worker}$$

Similar examples can be listed for *machine productivity* (e.g., the number of pieces per hour turned out by a machine).

Partial measures	$\dfrac{\text{Output}}{\text{Labor}}$	$\dfrac{\text{Output}}{\text{Machine}}$	$\dfrac{\text{Output}}{\text{Capital}}$	$\dfrac{\text{Output}}{\text{Energy}}$
Multifactor measures	$\dfrac{\text{Output}}{\text{Labor + Machine}}$		$\dfrac{\text{Output}}{\text{Labor + Capital + Energy}}$	
Total measure	$\dfrac{\text{Goods or services produced}}{\text{All inputs used to produce them}}$			

TABLE 2.7

Some examples of different types of productivity measures

TABLE 2.8
Some examples of partial productivity measures

Labor productivity	Units of output per labor hour
	Units of output per shift
	Value-added per labor hour
	Dollar value of output per labor hour
Machine productivity	Units of output per machine hour
	Dollar value of output per machine hour
Capital productivity	Units of output per dollar input
	Dollar value of output per dollar input
Energy productivity	Units of output per kilowatt-hour
	Dollar value of output per kilowatt-hour

EXAMPLE 2

mhhe.com/stevenson13e

Computing Productivity

Determine the productivity for these cases:

a. Four workers installed 720 square yards of carpeting in eight hours.

b. A machine produced 70 pieces in two hours. However, two pieces were unusable.

SOLUTION

a. $\text{Productivity} = \dfrac{\text{Yards of carpet installed}}{\text{Labor hours worked}}$

       $= \dfrac{720 \text{ square yards}}{4 \text{ workers} \times 8 \text{ hours/worker}}$

       $= \dfrac{720 \text{ yards}}{32 \text{ hours}}$

       $= 22.5 \text{ yards/hour}$

b. $\text{Productivity} = \dfrac{\text{Usable pieces}}{\text{Production time}}$

       $= \dfrac{70 - 2 = 68 \text{ usable pieces}}{2 \text{ hours}}$

       $= 34 \text{ pieces/hour}$

Calculations of multifactor productivity measure inputs and outputs using a common unit of measurement, such as cost. For instance, the measure might use cost of inputs and units of the output:

$$\frac{\text{Quantity of production}}{\text{Labor cost} + \text{Materials cost} + \text{Overhead}} \qquad (2\text{–}3)$$

Note: The unit of measure must be the same for all factors in the denominator

---

EXAMPLE 3

eXcel
mhhe.com/stevenson13e

Computing Multifactor Productivity

Determine the multifactor productivity for the combined input of labor and machine time using the following data:

     Output: 7,040 units
     Input

       Labor: $1,000
       Materials: $520
       Overhead: $2,000

SOLUTION

$\text{Multifactor productivity} = \dfrac{\text{Output}}{\text{Labor} + \text{Materials} + \text{Overhead}}$

                       $= \dfrac{7,040 \text{ units}}{\$1,000 + \$520 + \$2,000} = 2 \text{ units per dollar input}$

READING — WHY PRODUCTIVITY MATTERS

It is sometimes easy to overlook the importance of productivity. National figures are often reported in the media. They may seem to be ho-hum; there's nothing glamorous about them to get our attention. But make no mistake; they are key economic indicators—barometers, if you will, that affect everybody. How? High productivity and high standard of living go hand-in-hand. If a country becomes more service-based, as the United States has become, some (but not all) high-productivity manufacturing jobs are replaced by lower-productivity service jobs. That makes it more difficult to support a high standard of living.

Productivity gains can offset inflationary pressures related to wage increases. Productivity increases result in lower cost per unit. Those savings not only generate higher profits, they also help pay for wage increases.

Productivity levels are also important for industries and companies. For companies, a higher productivity relative to their competitors gives them a competitive advantage in the marketplace. With a higher productivity, they can afford to undercut competitors' prices to gain market share or charge the same prices but realize greater profits! For an industry, higher relative productivity means it is less likely to be supplanted by foreign industry.

Questions

1. Why is high productivity important for a nation?
2. Why do you suppose that service jobs have lower productivity than manufacturing jobs?
3. How can a company gain a competitive advantage by having higher productivity than its competitors have?

Productivity measures are useful on a number of levels. For an individual department or organization, productivity measures can be used to track performance *over time*. This allows managers to judge performance and to decide where improvements are needed. For example, if productivity has slipped in a certain area, operations staff can examine the factors used to compute productivity to determine what has changed and then devise a means of improving productivity in subsequent periods.

Productivity measures also can be used to judge the performance of an entire industry or the productivity of a country as a whole. These productivity measures are *aggregate* measures.

In essence, productivity measurements serve as scorecards of the effective use of resources. Business leaders are concerned with productivity as it relates to *competitiveness:* If two firms both have the same level of output but one requires less input because of higher productivity, that one will be able to charge a lower price and consequently increase its share of the market. Or that firm might elect to charge the same price, thereby reaping a greater profit. Government leaders are concerned with national productivity because of the close relationship between productivity and a nation's standard of living. High levels of productivity are largely responsible for the relatively high standards of living enjoyed by people in industrial nations. Furthermore, wage and price increases not accompanied by productivity increases tend to create inflationary pressures on a nation's economy.

Advantages of domestic-based operations for domestic markets often include higher worker productivity, better control of quality, avoidance of intellectual property losses, lower shipping costs, political stability, low inflation, and faster delivery.

Productivity in the Service Sector

Service productivity is more problematic than manufacturing productivity. In many situations, it is more difficult to measure, and thus to manage, because it involves intellectual activities and a high degree of variability. Think about medical diagnoses, surgery, consulting, legal services, customer service, and computer repair work. This makes productivity improvements more difficult to achieve. Nonetheless, because service is becoming an increasingly large portion of our economy, the issues related to service productivity will have to be dealt with. It is interesting to note that government statistics normally do not include service firms.

READING

DUTCH TOMATO GROWERS' PRODUCTIVITY ADVANTAGE

Tomato growers in the Netherlands have a huge productivity advantage over their competitors in Italy and Greece. Although those countries are sun drenched while the Netherlands are anything but, computerized, climate-controlled greenhouses, and a "soil" spun from basalt and chalk that resembles cotton candy, allows for precise control of humidity and nutrition, and enables growers to produce their crops year around. Growers in Italy and Greece generally grow their crops outdoors or in unheated greenhouses, and can only manage two crops a year. Dutch growers are able to achieve yields that are about ten times per square yard of those of Italian and Greek growers. And the Dutch have a supply chain advantage: an integrated Dutch trading company works closely with supermarket chains in Europe and suppliers around the world, so farmers are able to sell their output in high volume, rather than locally the way many farmers in other countries do. That enables Dutch growers to more closely match supply with supermarket demand. Finally, the Dutch tomato has been engineered to achieve a firmness that allows growers to harvest and ship tomatoes at their peak, while the "outdoor" farmers typically need to harvest their tomatoes before they are fully ripe to allow for firmness during shipping.

Questions

1. What factors enable Dutch tomato growers to achieve much higher productivity than the Italian and Greek growers?
2. Discuss the importance of the Dutch growers' supply chain.

Source: Based on "Tomato," *Time,* March 25, 2013, pp. 9–14.

A useful measure closely related to productivity is *process yield.* Where products are involved, process yield is defined as the ratio of output of good product (i.e., defective product is not included) to the quantity of raw material input. Where services are involved, process yield measurement is often dependent on the particular process. For example, in a car rental agency, a measure of yield is the ratio of cars rented to cars available for a given day. In education, a measure for college and university admission yield is the ratio of student acceptances to the total number of students approved for admission. For subscription services, yield is the ratio of new subscriptions to the number of calls made or the number of letters mailed. However, not all services lend themselves to a simple yield measurement. For example, services such as automotive, appliance, and computer repair don't readily lend themselves to such measures.

Factors That Affect Productivity

LO2.7 Describe several factors that affect productivity.

Numerous factors affect productivity. Generally, they are methods, capital, quality, technology, and management.

A commonly held misconception is that workers are the main determinant of productivity. According to that theory, the route to productivity gains involves getting employees to work harder. However, the fact is that many productivity gains in the past have come from *technological* improvements. Familiar examples include:

Drones	Automation	GPS devices
Copiers and scanners	Calculators	Smartphones
The Internet, search engines	Computers	Apps
Voice mail, cellular phones	E-mail	3-D printing
Radio frequency ID tags	Software	Medical imaging

However, technology alone won't guarantee productivity gains; it must be used wisely and thoughtfully. Without careful planning, technology can actually *reduce* productivity, especially if it leads to inflexibility, high costs, or mismatched operations. Another current productivity pitfall results from employees' use of computers or smartphones for nonwork-related activities (playing games or checking stock prices or sports scores on the Internet or smartphones, and texting friends and relatives). Beyond all of these is the dip in productivity that results while employees learn to use new equipment or procedures that will eventually lead to productivity gains after the learning phase ends.

Other factors that affect productivity include the following:

Standardizing processes and procedures wherever possible to reduce variability can have a significant benefit for both productivity and quality.

Quality differences may distort productivity measurements. One way this can happen is when comparisons are made over time, such as comparing the productivity of a factory now with one 30 years ago. Quality is now much higher than it was then, but there is no simple way to incorporate quality improvements into productivity measurements.

Use of the Internet can lower costs of a wide range of transactions, thereby increasing productivity. It is likely that this effect will continue to increase productivity in the foreseeable future.

Computer viruses can have an immense negative impact on productivity.

Searching for lost or misplaced items wastes time, hence negatively affecting productivity.

Scrap rates have an adverse effect on productivity, signaling inefficient use of resources.

New workers tend to have lower productivity than seasoned workers. Thus, growing companies may experience a productivity lag.

Safety should be addressed. Accidents can take a toll on productivity.

A shortage of technology-savvy workers hampers the ability of companies to update computing resources, generate and sustain growth, and take advantage of new opportunities.

Layoffs often affect productivity. The effect can be positive and negative. Initially, productivity may increase after a layoff, because the workload remains the same but fewer workers do the work—although they have to work harder and longer to do it. However, as time goes by, the remaining workers may experience an increased risk of burnout, and they may fear additional job cuts. The most capable workers may decide to leave.

Labor turnover has a negative effect on productivity; replacements need time to get up to speed.

Design of the workspace can impact productivity. For example, having tools and other work items within easy reach can positively impact productivity.

Incentive plans that reward productivity increases can boost productivity.

And there are still other factors that affect productivity, such as *equipment breakdowns* and *shortages* of parts or materials. The education level and training of workers and their health can greatly affect productivity. The opportunity to obtain lower costs due to higher productivity elsewhere is a key reason many organizations turn to *outsourcing*. Hence, an alternative to outsourcing can be improved productivity. Moreover, as a part of their strategy for quality, the best organizations strive for *continuous improvement*. Productivity improvements can be an important aspect of that approach.

Improving Productivity

A company or a department can take a number of key steps toward improving productivity:

1. Develop productivity measures for all operations. Measurement is the first step in managing and controlling an operation.

2. Look at the system as a whole in deciding which operations are most critical. It is overall productivity that is important. Managers need to reflect on the value of potential productivity improvements *before* okaying improvement efforts. The issue is *effectiveness*. There are several aspects of this. One is to make sure the result will be something customers want. For example, if a company is able to increase its output through productivity improvements, but then is unable to sell the increased output, the increase in productivity isn't effective. Second, it is important to adopt a systems viewpoint: A productivity increase in one part of an operation that doesn't increase the productivity of the system would not be effective. For example, suppose a system consists of a sequence of two operations, where the output of the first operation is the input to the second

READING   PRODUCTIVITY IMPROVEMENT

Stryker Howmedica set up a team to improve the running of its packaging line. A strategy focus on productivity improvement was used. The team adopted an approach based on the production system of Toyota. The goal was to satisfy the customer expectations for delivery and quality, while achieving gains in productivity. After the team identified needs and set objectives, a number of improvements were implemented. A one-piece flow was established that reduced bottlenecks in the flow of devices through a clean room and the total time spent blister sealing devices was lowered. Within a short time, productivity nearly doubled from 36 devices per hour to 60 devices per hour, work-in-progress inventory fell, and a 10 percent reduction in the standard cost of product was achieved.

Source: Based on Lauraine Howley, "A Strategy for Company Improvement," *Medical Device Technology* 11, no. 2 (March 2000), p. 33.

operation, and each operation can complete its part of the process at a rate of 20 units per hour. If the productivity of the first operation is increased, but the productivity of the second operation is not, the output of the system will still be 20 units per hour.

3. Develop methods for achieving productivity improvements, such as soliciting ideas from workers (perhaps organizing teams of workers, engineers, and managers), studying how other firms have increased productivity, and reexamining the way work is done.

4. Establish reasonable goals for improvement.

5. Make it clear that management supports and encourages productivity improvement. Consider incentives to reward workers for contributions.

6. Measure improvements and publicize them.

Don't confuse productivity with *efficiency*. Efficiency is a narrower concept that pertains to getting the most out of a *fixed* set of resources; productivity is a broader concept that pertains to effective use of overall resources. For example, an efficiency perspective on mowing a lawn given a hand mower would focus on the best way to use the hand mower; a productivity perspective would include the possibility of using a power mower.

Fracking productivity improvement is another example. Drilling methods have become more effective. Drillers are now adopting a hydraulic fracturing method pioneered by companies such as Liberty Resources and EOG Resources that uses larger amounts of water and minerals. Although it's a more costly process, it has increased production rates in the first year of a well's life, after which output tends to drop off dramatically. Processes such as these have reduced the break-even cost of producing a barrel of oil and kept profitable some acreage that drillers might otherwise have left idle.

SUMMARY

Competition is the driving force in many organizations. It may involve price, quality, special features or services, time, or other factors. To develop effective strategies for business, it is essential for organizations to determine what combinations of factors are important to customers, which factors are order qualifiers, and which are order winners.

It is essential that goals and strategies be aligned with the organization's mission. Strategies are plans for achieving organizational goals. They provide focus for decision making. Strategies must take into account present and future customer wants, as well as the organization's strengths and weaknesses, threats and opportunities. These can run the gamut from what competitors are doing, or are likely to do, to technology, supply chain management, and e-business. Organizations generally have overall strategies that pertain to the entire organization and strategies that pertain to each of the functional areas. Functional strategies are narrower in scope and should be linked to overall strategies. Time-based strategies and quality-based strategies are among the most widely used strategies business organizations employ to serve their customers and to become more productive. The chapter includes a description of the Balanced Scorecard approach, which can be helpful for transforming strategies into actions, and the implications of organization strategy for operations management.

Productivity is a measure of the use of resources. There is considerable interest in productivity both from an organizational standpoint and from a national standpoint. Business organizations want higher productivity because it yields lower costs and helps them to become more competitive. Nations want higher productivity because it makes their goods and services more attractive, offsets inflationary pressures associated with higher wages, and results in a higher standard of living for their people.

1. Competitive pressure often means that business organizations must frequently assess their competitors' strengths and weaknesses, as well as their own, to remain competitive.

2. Strategy formulation is critical because strategies provide direction for the organization, so they can play a role in the success or failure of a business organization.

3. Functional strategies and supply chain strategies need to be aligned with the goals and strategies of the overall organization.

4. The three primary business strategies are low cost, responsiveness, and differentiation.

5. Productivity is a key factor in the cost of goods and services. Increases in productivity can become a competitive advantage.

6. High productivity is particularly important for organizations that have a strategy of low costs.

competitiveness, 42
core competencies, 46
environmental scanning, 48
goals, 44
mission, 44

mission statement, 44
operations strategy, 51
order qualifiers, 48
order winners, 48
productivity, 56

quality-based strategies, 53
strategies, 44
SWOT, 47
tactics, 45
time-based strategies, 53

Computing Productivity

A company that processes fruits and vegetables is able to produce 400 cases of canned peaches in one-half hour with four workers. What is labor productivity?

$$\text{Labor productivity} = \frac{\text{Quantity produced}}{\text{Labor hours}} = \frac{400 \text{ cases}}{4 \text{ workers} \times 1/2 \text{ hour/worker}}$$

$$= 200 \text{ cases per labor hour}$$

Problem 1

mhhe.com/stevenson13e

Solution

Computing Multifactor Productivity

A wrapping-paper company produced 2,000 rolls of paper one day. Labor cost was $160, material cost was $50, and overhead was $320. Determine the multifactor productivity.

$$\text{Multifactor productivity} = \frac{\text{Quantity produced}}{\text{Labor cost} + \text{Material cost} + \text{Overhead}}$$

$$= \frac{2,000 \text{ rolls}}{\$160 + \$50 + \$320} = 3.77 \text{ rolls per dollar input}$$

A variation of the multifactor productivity calculation incorporates the standard price in the numerator by multiplying the units by the standard price.

Problem 2

mhhe.com/stevenson13e

Solution

Computing Multifactor Productivity

Compute the multifactor productivity measure for an eight-hour day in which the usable output was 300 units, produced by three workers who used 600 pounds of materials. Workers have an hourly wage of $20, and material cost is $1 per pound. Overhead is 1.5 times labor cost.

$$\text{Multifactor productivity} = \frac{\text{Usable output}}{\text{Labor cost} + \text{Material cost} + \text{Overhead cost}}$$

$$= \frac{300 \text{ units}}{(3 \text{ workers} \times 8 \text{ hours} \times \$20/\text{hour}) + (600 \text{ pounds} \times \$1/\text{pound}) + (3 \text{ workers} \times 8 \text{ hours} \times \$20/\text{hour} \times 1.50)}$$

$$= \frac{300 \text{ units}}{\$480 + \$600 + \$720}$$

$$= .167 \text{units of output per dollar of input}$$

Problem 3

mhhe.com/stevenson13e

Solution

Problem 4

eXcel
mhhe.com/stevenson13e

Computing Multifactor Productivity

A health club has two employees who work on lead generation. Each employee works 40 hours a week, and is paid $20 an hour. Each employee identifies an average of 400 possible leads a week from a list of 8,000 names. Approximately 10 percent of the leads become members and pay a onetime fee of $100. Material costs are $130 per week, and overhead costs are $1,000 per week. Calculate the multifactor productivity for this operation in fees generated per dollar of input.

Solution

$$\text{MFP} = \frac{(\text{Possible leads})(\text{No. of workers})(\text{Fee})(\text{Conversion percentage})}{\text{Labor cost} + \text{Material cost} + \text{Overhead cost}}$$

$$= \frac{(400)(2)(\$100)(.10)}{2(40)(\$20) + \$130 + \$1,000} = \frac{\$8,000}{\$2,730} = 2.93$$

DISCUSSION AND REVIEW QUESTIONS

1. From time to time, various groups clamor for import restrictions or tariffs on foreign-produced goods, particularly automobiles. How might these be helpful? Harmful?
2. List the key ways that organizations compete.
3. Explain the importance of identifying and differentiating order qualifiers and order winners.
4. Select two stores you shop at, and state how they compete.
5. What is the Balanced Scorecard and how is it useful?
6. Contrast the terms *strategies* and *tactics*.
7. Contrast *organization strategy* and *operations strategy*.
8. Explain the term *time-based strategies* and give three examples.
9. Productivity should be a concern of every business organization.
   a. How is productivity defined?
   b. How are productivity measures used?
   c. Why is productivity important?
   d. What part of the organization has primary responsibility for productivity?
   e. How is efficiency different from productivity?
10. List some factors that can affect productivity and some ways that productivity can be improved.
11. It has been said that a typical Japanese automobile manufacturer produces more cars with fewer workers than its U.S. counterpart. What are some possible explanations for this, assuming that U.S. workers are as hardworking as Japanese workers?
12. Boeing's strategy appears to focus on its 777 midsize plane's ability to fly into smaller, nonhub airports. Rival European Airbus's strategy appears to focus on large planes. Compare the advantages and disadvantages of these two strategies.
13. Name 10 ways that banks compete for customers.
14. Explain the rationale of an operations strategy that seeks to increase the opportunity for use of technology by reducing variability in processing requirements.
15. Identify two companies that have time-based strategies, and two that have quality-based strategies.

TAKING STOCK

1. Who needs to be involved in formulating organizational strategy?
2. Name some of the competitive trade-offs that might arise in a fast-food restaurant.
3. How can technology improve
   a. Competitiveness?
   b. Productivity?

1. In the past there was concern about a "productivity paradox" related to IT services. More recently, there have been few references to this phenomenon. Using the Internet, explain the term *productivity paradox*. Why do you think that the discussion of that topic has faded?

2. A U.S. company has two manufacturing plants, one in the United States and one in another country. Both produce the same item, each for sale in their respective countries. However, their productivity figures are quite different. The analyst thinks this is because the U.S. plant uses more automated equipment for processing while the other plant uses a higher percentage of labor. Explain how that factor can cause productivity figures to be misleading. Is there another way to compare the two plants that would be more meaningful?

3. While it is true that increases in efficiency generate productivity increases, it is possible to get caught in an "efficiency improvement trap." Explain what this means.

4. It is common knowledge that Sam's boss Dom has been fudging the weekly productivity figures. Several employees, including Sam, have spoken to him about this, but he continues to do it. Sam has observed a drop in morale among his coworkers due to this. Sam is thinking about sending an anonymous note to Dom's boss. Would that be ethical? What would you do if you were Sam?

5. Give two examples of what would be considered unethical involving competition and the ethical principles (see Chapter 1) that would be violated.

CRITICAL THINKING EXERCISES

1. A catering company prepared and served 300 meals at an anniversary celebration last week using eight workers. The week before, six workers prepared and served 240 meals at a wedding reception.

   a. For which event was the labor productivity higher? Explain.

   b. What are some possible reasons for the productivity differences?

2. The manager of a crew that installs carpeting has tracked the crew's output over the past several weeks, obtaining these figures:

Week	Crew Size	Yards Installed
1	4	96
2	3	72
3	4	92
4	2	50
5	3	69
6	2	52

Compute the labor productivity for each of the weeks. On the basis of your calculations, what can you conclude about crew size and productivity?

3. Compute the multifactor productivity measure for each of the weeks shown for production of chocolate bars. What do the productivity figures suggest? Assume 40-hour weeks and an hourly wage of $12. Overhead is 1.5 times weekly labor cost. Material cost is $6 per pound.

Week	Output (units)	Workers	Material (lbs)
1	30,000	6	450
2	33,600	7	470
3	32,200	7	460
4	35,400	8	480

4. A company that makes shopping carts for supermarkets and other stores recently purchased some new equipment that reduces the labor content of the jobs needed to produce the shopping carts. Prior to buying the new equipment, the company used five workers, who produced an average of 80 carts per hour. Workers receive $10 per hour, and machine cost was $40 per hour. With the new equipment, it was possible to transfer one of the workers to another department, and equipment cost increased by $10 per hour while output increased by four carts per hour.

   a. Compute labor productivity under each system. Use carts per worker per hour as the measure of labor productivity.

   b. Compute the multifactor productivity under each system. Use carts per dollar cost (labor plus equipment) as the measure.

   c. Comment on the changes in productivity according to the two measures, and on which one you believe is the more pertinent for this situation.

PROBLEMS

5. An operation has a 10 percent scrap rate. As a result, 72 pieces per hour are produced. What is the potential increase in labor productivity that could be achieved by eliminating the scrap?

6. A manager checked production records and found that a worker produced 160 units while working 40 hours. In the previous week, the same worker produced 138 units while working 36 hours. Did the worker's productivity increase, decrease, or remain the same? Explain.

7. The following table shows data on the average number of customers processed by several bank service units each day. The hourly wage rate is $25, the overhead rate is 1.0 times labor cost, and material cost is $5 per customer.

Unit	Employees	Customers Processed/Day
A	4	36
B	5	40
C	8	60
D	3	20

   a. Compute the labor productivity and the multifactor productivity for each unit. Use an eight-hour day for multifactor productivity.

   b. Suppose a new, more standardized procedure is to be introduced that will enable each employee to process one additional customer per day. Compute the expected labor and multifactor productivity rates for each unit.

8. A property title search firm is contemplating using online software to increase its search productivity. Currently an average of 40 minutes is needed to do a title search. The researcher cost is $2 per minute. Clients are charged a fee of $400. Company A's software would reduce the average search time by 10 minutes, at a cost of $3.50 per search. Company B's software would reduce the average search time by 12 minutes at a cost of $3.60 per search. Which option would have the higher productivity in terms of revenue per dollar of input?

9. A company offers ID theft protection using leads obtained from client banks. Three employees work 40 hours a week on the leads, at a pay rate of $25 per hour per employee. Each employee identifies an average of 3,000 potential leads a week from a list of 5,000. An average of 4 percent actually sign up for the service, paying a one-time fee of $70. Material costs are $1,000 per week, and overhead costs are $9,000 per week. Calculate the multifactor productivity for this operation in fees generated per dollar of input.

CASE

AN AMERICAN TRAGEDY: HOW A GOOD COMPANY DIED

ZACHARY SCHILLER

The Rust Belt is back. So say bullish observers as U.S. exports surge, long-moribund industries glow with newfound profits, and unemployment dips to lows not seen in a decade. But in the smokestack citadels, there's disquiet. Too many machine-tool and auto parts factories are silent; too many U.S. industries still can't hold their own.

What went wrong since the heyday of the 1960s? That's the issue Max Holland, a contributing editor of *The Nation*, takes up in his nutsy-boltsy but fascinating study, *When the Machine Stopped.**

The focus of the story is Burgmaster Corp., a Los Angeles–area machine-tool maker founded in 1944 by Czechoslovakian immigrant Fred Burg. Holland's father worked there for 29 years, and the author interviewed 22 former employees. His shop-floor view of this small company is a refreshing change from academic treatises on why America can't compete.

The discussions of spindles and numerical control can be tough going. But Holland compensates by conveying the excitement and innovation of the company's early days and the disgust and cynicism accompanying its decline. Moreover, the fate of Burgmaster and its brethren is crucial to the U.S. industrial economy: Any manufactured item is either made by a machine tool or by a machine made by a machine tool.

Producing innovative turret drills used in a wide variety of metal working tasks, Burgmaster was a thriving enterprise by 1965, when annual sales amounted to about $8 million. The company needed backing to expand, however, so it sold out to Buffalo-based conglomerate Houdaille Industries Inc. Houdaille was in turn purchased in a 1979 leveraged buyout (LBO) led by Kohlberg Kravis Roberts & Co. By 1982, when debt, competition, and a sickly machine-tool market had battered Burgmaster badly, Houdaille went to Washington with a petition to withhold the investment tax credit for certain Japanese-made machine tools.

Thanks to deft lobbying, the Senate passed a resolution supporting Houdaille's position, but President Reagan refused to go along. Houdaille's subsequent attempt to link Burgmaster up with a Japanese rival also failed, and Burgmaster was closed.

Holland uses Burgmaster's demise to explore some key issues of economic and trade policy. Houdaille's charge that a cartel led by the Japanese government had injured U.S. toolmakers, for example, became a rallying point for those who would blame a fearsome Japan Inc. for the problems of U.S. industry.

Holland describes the Washington wrangling over Houdaille in painful detail. But he does show that such government decisions are often made without much knowledge of what's going on in industry. He shows, too, that Japanese producers succeeded less because of government help than because they made better, cheaper machines.

For those who see LBOs as a symptom of what ails the U.S. economy, Holland offers plenty of ammunition. He argues persuasively that the LBO crippled Burgmaster by creating enormous pressure to generate cash. As Burgmaster pushed its products out as fast as possible, he writes, it routinely shipped defective machines. It promised customers features that engineers hadn't yet designed. And although KKR disputes the claim, Holland concludes that the LBO choked off Burgmaster's investment funds just when foreign competition made them most necessary. As for Houdaille, it was recapitalized and sold to Britain's Tube Investments Group.

But Burgmaster's problems had started even before the LBO. Holland's history of the company under Houdaille is a veritable catalog of modern management techniques that flopped. One of the most disastrous was a system for computerizing production scheduling that was too crude for complex machine-tool manufacturing. Holland gives a dramatic depiction of supply snafus that resulted in delays and cost increases.

As an independent company, "Burgmaster thrived because the Burgs knew their business," Holland writes. Their departure under Houdaille was followed by an "endless and ultimately futile search for a better formula." But, he concludes: "No formula was a substitute for management involvement on the shop floor."

In the end, however, Holland puts most of the blame for the industry's decline on government policy. He targets tax laws and macroeconomic policies that encourage LBOs and speculation instead of productive investment. He also criticizes Pentagon procurement policies for favoring exotic, custom machines over standard, low-cost models. This adds up to an industrial policy, Holland writes—a bad one.

The point is well taken, but Holland gives it excessive weight. Like their brethren in Detroit and Pittsburgh, domestic toolmakers in the 1970s were too complacent when imports seized the lower end of the product line. The conservatism that had for years served them in their cyclical industry left them ill-prepared for change. Even now some of the largest U.S. tool-makers are struggling to restructure. Blame the government, yes. But blame the industry, too.

Questions

1. Write a brief report that outlines the reasons (both internal and external) for Burgmaster's demise, and whether operations management played a significant role in the demise.

2. Do you think that inadequate strategic planning was a factor that resulted in the company's asking for trade protection?

3. Can you think of a strategy that could have increased Burgmaster's chance of survival? Explain why you think that strategy would have been effective.

---

*Max Holland, *When the Machine Stopped: A Contemporary Tale from Industrial America* (Boston: Harvard Business School Press, 1988).

CASE HOME-STYLE COOKIES

The Company

The baking company is located in a small town in New York State. The bakery is run by two brothers. The company employs fewer than 200 people, mainly blue-collar workers, and the atmosphere is informal.

The Product

The company's only product is soft cookies, of which it makes over 50 varieties. Larger companies, such as Nabisco, Sunshine, and Keebler, have traditionally produced biscuit cookies, in which most of the water has been baked out, resulting in crisp cookies. The cookies have no additives or preservatives. The high quality of the cookies has enabled the company to develop a strong market niche for its product.

The Customers

The cookies are sold in convenience stores and supermarkets throughout New York, Connecticut, and New Jersey. The company markets its cookies as "good food"—no additives or preservatives—and this appeals to a health-conscious segment of the market. Many customers are over 45 years of age, and prefer a cookie that is soft and not too sweet. Parents with young children also buy the cookies.

The Production Process

The company has two continuous band ovens that it uses to bake the cookies. The production process is called a batch processing system. It begins as soon as management gets orders from distributors. These orders are used to schedule production. At the start of each shift, a list of the cookies to be made that day is delivered to the person in charge of mixing. That person checks a master list, which indicates the ingredients needed for each type of cookie, and enters that information into the computer. The computer then determines the amount of each ingredient needed, according to the quantity of cookies ordered, and relays that information to storage silos located outside the plant where the main ingredients (flour, sugar, and cake flour) are stored. The ingredients are automatically sent to giant mixing machines where the ingredients are combined with proper amounts of eggs, water, and flavorings. After the ingredients have been mixed, the batter is poured into a cutting machine where it is cut into individual cookies. The cookies are then dropped onto a conveyor belt and transported through one of two ovens. Filled cookies, such as apple, date, and raspberry, require an additional step for filling and folding.

The nonfilled cookies are cut on a diagonal rather than round. The diagonal-cut cookies require less space than straight-cut cookies, and the result is a higher level of productivity. In addition, the company recently increased the length of each oven by 25 feet, which also increased the rate of production.

As the cookies emerge from the ovens, they are fed onto spiral cooling racks 20 feet high and 3 feet wide. As the cookies come off the cooling racks, workers place the cookies into boxes manually, removing any broken or deformed cookies in the process. The boxes are then wrapped, sealed, and labeled automatically.

Inventory

Most cookies are loaded immediately onto trucks and shipped to distributors. A small percentage are stored temporarily in the company's warehouse, but they must be shipped shortly because of their limited shelf life. Other inventory includes individual cookie boxes, shipping boxes, labels, and cellophane for wrapping. Labels are reordered frequently, in small batches, because FDA label requirements are subject to change, and the company does not want to get stuck with labels it can't use. The bulk silos are refilled two or three times a week, depending on how quickly supplies are used.

Cookies are baked in a sequence that minimizes downtime for cleaning. For instance, light-colored cookies (e.g., chocolate chip) are baked before dark-colored cookies (e.g., fudge), and oatmeal cookies are baked before oatmeal raisin cookies. This permits the company to avoid having to clean the processing equipment every time a different type of cookie is produced.

Quality

The bakery prides itself on the quality of its cookies. Cookies are sampled randomly by a quality control inspector as they come off the line to assure that their taste and consistency are satisfactory, and that they have been baked to the proper degree. Also, workers on the line are responsible for removing defective cookies when they spot them. The company has also installed an X-ray machine on the line that can detect small bits of metal filings that may have gotten into cookies during the production process. The use of automatic equipment for transporting raw materials and mixing batter has made it easier to maintain a sterile process.

Scrap

The bakery is run very efficiently and has minimal amounts of scrap. For example, if a batch is mixed improperly, it is sold for dog food. Broken cookies are used in the oatmeal cookies. These practices reduce the cost of ingredients and save on waste disposal costs. The company also uses heat reclamation: The heat that escapes from the two ovens is captured and used to boil the water that supplies the heat to the building. Also, the use of automation in the mixing process has resulted in a reduction in waste compared with the manual methods used previously.

(continued)

New Products

Ideas for new products come from customers, employees, and observations of competitors' products. New ideas are first examined to determine whether the cookies can be made with existing equipment. If so, a sample run is made to determine the cost and time requirements. If the results are satisfactory, marketing tests are conducted to see if there is a demand for the product.

Potential Improvements

There are a number of areas of potential improvement at the bakery. One possibility would be to automate packing the cookies into boxes. Although labor costs are not high, automating the process might save some money and increase efficiency. So far, the owners have resisted making this change because they feel an obligation to the community to employ the 30 women who now do the boxing manually. Another possible improvement would be to use suppliers who are located closer to the plant. That would reduce delivery lead times and transportation costs, but the owners are not convinced that local suppliers could provide the same good quality. Other opportunities have been proposed in recent years, but the owners rejected them because they feared that the quality of the product might suffer.

Questions

1. Briefly describe the cookie production process.
2. What are two ways that the company has increased productivity? Why did increasing the length of the ovens result in a faster output rate?
3. Do you think that the company is making the right decision by not automating the packing of cookies? Explain your reasoning. What obligation does a company have to its employees in a situation such as this? What obligation does it have to the community? Is the size of the town a factor? Would it make a difference if the company was located in a large city? Is the size of the company a factor? What if it were a much larger company?
4. What factors cause the company to carry minimal amounts of certain inventories? What benefits result from this policy?
5. As a consumer, what things do you consider in judging the quality of cookies you buy in a supermarket?
6. What advantages and what limitations stem from the company's not using preservatives in cookies?
7. Briefly describe the company's strategy.

CASE   HAZEL REVISITED

(Refer to the Hazel Case at the end of chapter 1.)

1. What competitive advantage does Hazel have over a professional lawn care service?
2. Hazel would like to increase her profits, but she doesn't believe that it would be wise to raise her prices considering the current state of the local economy. Instead, she has given some thought to increasing productivity.
   a. Explain how increased productivity could be an alternative to increased prices.
   b. What are some ways that Hazel could increase productivity?
3. Hazel is thinking about the purchase of new equipment. One would be power sidewalk edgers. She believes edgers will lead to an increase in productivity. Another would be a chain saw, which would be used for tree pruning. What trade-offs should she consider in her analysis?
4. Hazel has been fairly successful in her neighborhood, and now wants to expand to other neighborhoods, including some that are five miles away. What would be the advantages and disadvantages of doing this?
5. Hazel does not have a mission statement or a set of objectives. Take one of the following positions and defend it:
   a. Hazel doesn't need a formal mission statement and objectives. Many small businesses don't have them.
   b. She definitely needs a mission statement and a set of objectives. They would be extremely beneficial.
   c. There may be some benefit to Hazel's business, and she should consider developing one.

CASE   "YOUR GARDEN GLOVES"

JOSEPH MURRAY, GRAND VALLEY STATE UNIVERSITY

"Your Garden Gloves" is a small gardening business located in Michigan. The company plants and maintains flower gardens for both commercial and residential clients. The company was founded about five years ago, and has since grown substantially, averaging about 10 new clients and one new employee a year. The company currently employs eight seasonal employees who are responsible for a certain number of clients.

Each morning crews are assigned to jobs by the owner. Crew sizes range from two to four workers. Crew size and composition are a function of the square footage of the garden and requirements of the job. The owner feels that large jobs should be assigned to crews of four workers in order to complete the job in a reasonable amount of time.

From time to time, the owner noticed that some jobs, especially the largest ones, took longer than she had estimated, based on the square footage of the garden space involved. The owner's son, Joe, decided to investigate. He kept records of job times and crew sizes, and then used those records to compute labor productivity. The results were:

Crew Size	Average Productivity per Crew
2	4,234 square feet per day
3	5,352 square feet per day
4	7,860 square feet per day

The company operates on a small profit margin, so it is especially important to take worker productivity into account.

Questions

1. Which crew size had the highest productivity per worker? Which crew size had the lowest productivity per worker? What are some possible explanations for these results?
2. After a recent storm, a customer called in a panic, saying that she had planned a garden party for the upcoming weekend and her garden was in shambles. The owner decided to send a crew of four workers, even though a two-worker crew would have a higher productivity. Explain the rationale for this decision.
3. What is a possible qualitative issue that may very well influence productivity levels that the productivity ratios fail to take into account?

OPERATIONS TOUR   THE U.S. POSTAL SERVICE

"Neither rain, nor snow . . ."

The U.S. Postal Service (USPS) is the largest postal service in the world, handling about 41 percent (630 million pieces a day) of the world's mail volume. The second largest is Japan's, which handles only about 6 percent of the world's mail. The USPS is huge by any standard. It employs over 760,000 workers, making it the largest civilian employer in the United States. It has over 300,000 mail collection boxes, 38,000 post offices, 130 million mail delivery points, more than 300 processing plants to sort and ship mail, and more than 75,000 pieces of mail processing equipment. It handles over 100 billion pieces of first-class mail a year, and ships about 3 billion pounds of mail on commercial airline flights, making it the airlines' largest shipper.

Processing First-Class Mail

The essence of processing the mail is sorting, which means organizing the mail into smaller and smaller subgroups to facilitate its timely delivery. Sorting involves a combination of manual and automatic operations. Much of the mail that is processed is first-class mail.

Most first-class mail is handled using automated equipment. A small portion that cannot be handled by automated equipment must be sorted by hand, just the way it was done in colonial times.

The majority of first-class mail begins at the advanced facer canceling system. This system positions each letter so that it is face up, with the stamp in the upper corner, checks to see if the address is handwritten, and pulls the hand-addressed letters off the line. It also rejects letters that have the stamp covered by tape, have no postage, are third-class mail, or have meter impressions that are too light to read. The rejects are handled manually. The remaining letters are cancelled and date stamped, and then sorted to one of seven stackers.

Next the letters go to the multiline optical character readers, which can handle both printed and pre–bar-coded mail, but not

(continued)

hand-addressed mail. The optical reader sprays a bar code on the mail that hasn't been pre–bar-coded, which represents up to an 11-digit zip code. For hand-addressed mail, a camera focuses on the front of the letter, and the image is displayed on a remote terminal, often in another city, where an operator views the image and provides the information that the optical readers could not determine so that a bar code can be added.

Bar-code readers then sort the mail into one of 96 stackers, doing this at a rate of more than 500 a minute. The mail goes through another sort using manually controlled mechanical equipment. At that point, the mail is separated according to whether it is local or out-of-town mail. The out-of-town mail is placed into appropriate sacks according to its destination, and moved to the outgoing send area where it will be loaded on trucks.

The local mail is moved to another machine that not only sorts the mail into local carrier delivery routes, it sorts it according to delivery walk sequence!

Small parcels, bundles of letters, and bundles of flats are sorted by a bundle-sorting machine.

Productivity

Over the years, the USPS has experienced an ever-increasing volume of mail. Productivity has been an important factor for the USPS in keeping postal rates low and maintaining rapid delivery service. Two key factors in improved productivity have been the increased use of automation and the introduction of zip codes.

Mail processing underwent a major shift to mechanization during the 1950s and 1960s, which led to more rapid processing and higher productivity. In 1978, an expanded zip code was introduced. That was followed in 1983 by a four-digit expansion in zip codes. These changes required new, automated processing equipment, and the use of bar codes and optical readers. All of these changes added greatly to productivity. But even with these improvements, the USPS faced increasing competitive pressures.

Competition

In the late 1980s, the USPS experienced a slowdown in the volume of mail. Some of this was due to a slowing of the economy, but most of it was the result of increasing competition. Delivery giants FedEx and UPS, as well as other companies that offer speedy delivery and package tracking, gave businesses and the general public convenient alternatives for some mail services. At the same time, there was a growing use of fax machines and electronic communications and increased use of alternate forms of advertising such as cable TV, all of which cut into the volume of mail. Early in this century, e-mail and automated bill paying also cut into mail volume.

Strategies and Tactics Used to Make the Postal Service More Competitive

To meet these challenges, the USPS developed several strategies to become more competitive. These included reorganizing, continuing to seek ways to keep costs down, increasing productivity, and emphasizing quality and customer service. Here is an overview of the situation and the strategies and tactics used by the USPS.

The USPS began working more closely with customers to identify better ways to meet their needs and expanded customer conveniences such as stamps on consignment. With the help of business mailers, the USPS continued support for rates reflecting customer work-sharing features, many tied to automation, to give customers more flexibility. At the same time, the USPS began forming Customer Advisory Councils—groups of citizens who volunteered to work with local postal management on postal issues of interest to the community. In 1990, the USPS awarded two contracts to private firms to measure first-class mail service and customer satisfaction. In 1992, the USPS stepped up its quest to become more competitive by reducing bureaucracy and overhead in order to improve service and customer satisfaction, and to reduce the need to increase postage rates.

To help accomplish these goals, the USPS underwent a reorganization. Layers of management were eliminated and overhead positions were cut by about 30,000. Five regions and 73 field divisions were replaced by 10 areas, each with a manager for customer services and a manager for processing and distribution. Ten customer service areas were established, with managers for customer service and processing and distribution in each area, as well as a marketing and sales office. The new structure allowed postal managers to be focused, improved communications, and empowered employees to meet customer needs. The USPS also took other steps to improve service. In 1993, it implemented improvements in processing and mail delivery at major postal facilities, expanded retail hours, and developed a more user-friendly Domestic Mail Manual. In cooperation with business customers, the USPS began to develop new services to meet specific mailer needs and to overhaul and simplify its complex rate structure. It also awarded contracts for two more external tracking systems, one to measure satisfaction levels of business mailers, and the other to measure service performance of third-class mail.

The reorganization eliminated some programs, cut costs, attracted new business, and reduced the USPS's projected deficit.

The postal services' sustainability scorecard for 2015 is shown as follows.

(continued)

**United States
Postal Service**

January 2015 OMB Scorecard on
Sustainability/Energy

Scope 1&2 GHG Emission Reduction Target

For Scope 1&2 GHG Reduction Target of 20% by 2020:
17% reduction in 2014 and on track

Score: **GREEN**

Scope 3GHG Emission Reduction Target

For Scope 3GHG Reduction Target of 20% by 2020:
24% reduction in 2014 and on track

Score: **GREEN**

Reduction in Energy Intensity

Reduction inenergy intensity in goal-subject facilities compared with 2003:
32% and on track for 30% by 2015

Score: **GREEN**

Use of Renewable Energy

Not applicable

Score: **N/A**

Reduction in Potable Water Intensity

Reduction inpotable water intensity compared with 2007:
30% and on track for 26% in 2020

Score: **GREEN**

Reduction in Fleet Petroleum Use

Reduction infleet petroleum use compared to 2005:
10.1% increase and not ontrack

Score: **RED**

Green Buildings

Not applicable

Score: **N/A**

(continued)

Questions

1. Why is it important for the USPS to have a high volume of mail to process?
2. What caused productivity to increase?
3. What impact did competitive pressures have on the USPS?
4. What measures did the USPS adopt to increase competitiveness?
5. What results were achieved by the USPS's changes?
6. What effect does the increased use of e-mail have on postal productivity?
7. How does the use of standard shipping containers and flat-rate mailers help competitiveness?

Source: http://about.usps.com/what-we-are-doing/green/pdf/omb-scorecard-2015.pdf

Standards for Success — *Red Standard, Yellow Standard, Green Standard*

Scope 1&2 GHG Emission Reduction Target

GREEN: On track to achieve agency's proposed 2020 GHG Scopes 1&2 emissions reduction target.

YELLOW: Less than a year behind glide path to achieve agency's 2020 target for GHG Scopes 1&2.

RED: More than a year behind glide path to achieve agency's 2020 target for GHG Scopes 1&2.

Scope 3 GHG Emission Reduction Target

GREEN: On track to achieve agency's proposed 2020 GHG Scope 3 emissions reduction target.

YELLOW: Less than a year behind glide path to achieve agency's 2020 target for GHG Scope 3.

RED: More than a year behind glide path to achieve agency's 2020 target for GHG Scope 3.

Reduction in Energy Intensity

GREEN: Reduced energy intensity (Btu/GSF*) in EISA goal-subject facilities by at least 27 percent compared with 2003 and is on track for 30 percent reduction by 2015.

YELLOW: Reduced energy intensity (Btu/GSF) in EISA goal-subject facilities by at least 24 percent compared with 2003.

RED: Did not reduce energy intensity (Btu/GSF) in EISA goal-subject facilities by at least 24 percent compared with 2003.

Use of Renewable Energy

GREEN: Uses at least 7.5 percent electricity from renewable sources as a percentage of facility electricity use & at least 3.75 percent of facility electricity use comes from new sources (post-1999). (Thermal and mechanical renewable can be included in the 3.75 percent new requirement, but not the 7.5 percent goal; i.e., an agency meets all new sources requirement with thermal or mechanical energy (3.75 percent) but would still need an additional 7.5 percent from renewable electricity sources.)

YELLOW: Uses at least 7.5 percent renewable energy from electric, thermal or mechanical sources to power facilities and equipment; but less than half was obtained from new sources (post-1999) or part of the requirement was met with thermal and mechanical renewable energy.

RED: Did not use at least 7.5 percent renewable energy from electric, thermal or mechanical sources to power facilities and equipment.

Reduction in Potable Water Intensity

GREEN: Reduced water intensity by at least 14 percent from final approved 2007 baseline and is on track for 26 percent reduction by 2020.

YELLOW: Reduced water intensity by at least 12 percent from final approved 2007 baseline.

RED: Did not reduce water intensity by at least 12 percent from final approved 2007 baseline.

Reduction in Fleet Petroleum Use

GREEN: Achieved an 18 percent reduction in petroleum use in its entire vehicle fleet compared to 2005 and is on track for 20 percent reduction by 2015.

YELLOW: Achieved at least 16 percent reduction in petroleum use in the entire vehicle fleet compared to 2005.

RED: Did not achieve at least 16 percent reduction in petroleum use in its entire vehicle fleet since 2005.

Green Buildings

GREEN: Demonstrates implementation of Guiding Principles for Federal Leadership in High Performance and Sustainable Buildings (GP) for new, existing and leased buildings; and is on track to meet 15% goal by 2015 by reporting that at least 13% of buildings >5,000 GSF meet GP as reported in the Federal Real Property Profi (FRPP).

YELLOW: Incorporates Guiding Principles into all new design contracts for construction, major renovations and leases and at least 13 percent of GSF of its building inventory over 5,000 GSF meets GP as reported in FRPP.

RED: Cannot demonstrate compliance with GP on new construction, major renovations, or leases; and/or less than 13 percent of building inventory, either by number of buildings or GSF, over 5,000 GSF meets GP as reported in FRPP.

*GSF = Gross Square Footage

Fortune.

Hammer, Michael, and Steven Stanton. "Ignore Operations at Your Peril." *Harvard Business Review* 6565 (April 2004).

Hill, Terry. *Manufacturing Strategy: Text and Cases,* 3rd ed. New York: McGraw-Hill, 2000.

Michael E. Porter, "The Five Competitive Forces That Shape Strategy," *Harvard Business Review* 86, no. 1 (January 2008), pp. 78–93, 137.

Slack, Nigel, and Michael Lewis. *Operations Strategy,* 4e. Upper Saddle River, NJ: Prentice-Hall, 2011. Global Competitiveness Report.

Werbach, Adam. *Strategy for Sustainability: A Business Manifesto.* Boston: Harvard Business Press, 2009.

SELECTED BIBLIOGRAPHY AND FURTHER READINGS

6

Process Selection and Facility Layout

LEARNING OBJECTIVES

After completing this chapter, you should be able to:

LO6.1   Explain the strategic importance of process selection and the influence it has on the organization and its supply chain.

LO6.2   Name the two main factors that influence process selection.

LO6.3   Compare the four basic processing types.

LO6.4   Explain the need for management of technology.

LO6.5   List some reasons for redesign of layouts.

LO6.6   Describe product layouts and their main advantages and disadvantages.

LO6.7   Describe process layouts and their main advantages and disadvantages.

LO6.8   Solve simple line-balancing problems.

LO6.9   Develop simple process layouts.

CHAPTER OUTLINE

6.1 Introduction, *243*

6.2 Process Selection, *244*
Process Types: 244
Operations Tour: Morton Salt, *248*
Product and Service Profiling, *249*
Sustainable Production of Goods and Services, *250*
Lean Process Design, *250*

6.3 Technology, *250*
Automation, 251
3D Printing, *255*
Drones, 256

6.4 Process Strategy, *257*

6.5 Strategic Resource Organization: Facilities Layout, *257*
Repetitive Processing: Product Layouts, *258*
Nonrepetitive Processing: Process Layouts, *260*
Fixed-Position Layouts, *262*
Combination Layouts, *262*
Cellular Layouts, *263*
Service Layouts, *266*

6.6 Designing Product Layouts: Line Balancing, *269*

Some Guidelines for Line Balancing, *274*
Other Factors, *277*
Other Approaches, *277*

6.7 Designing Process Layouts, *278*
Measures of Effectiveness, *279*
Information Requirements, *279*
Minimizing Transportation Costs or Distances, *279*
Closeness Ratings, *281*

© Jeff Gilbert/Alamy

Product and service choices, capacity planning, process selection, and layout of facilities are among the most basic decisions managers make because they have long-term consequences for business organizations, and they impact a wide range of activities and capabilities.

This chapter is about process selection and facility layout (i.e., the arrangement of the workplace). Processes convert inputs into outputs; they are at the core of operations management. But the impact of process selection goes beyond operations management: It affects the entire organization and its ability to achieve its mission, and it affects the organization's supply chain. So process selection choices very often have strategic significance. Different process types have different capacity ranges, and once a process type is functioning, changing it can be difficult, time consuming, and costly. Obviously, long-term forecasts as well as an organization's mission and goals are important in developing a process strategy.

Process selection has operational and supply chain implications. Operational implications include equipment and labor requirements, operations costs, and both the ability to meet demand and the ability to respond to variations in demand. Supply chain implications relate to the volume and variety of inputs and outputs and the degree of flexibility that is required.

Technology is often a factor in process selection and layout. Three aspects of technology can be factors: product technology, processing technology, and information technology.

Process selection and facility layout are closely tied, and for that reason, these two topics are presented in a single chapter. The first part of the chapter covers the basic options for processing work. This is followed by a discussion of how processes and layout are linked. The remainder of the chapter is devoted to layout design.

6.1 INTRODUCTION

Process selection refers to deciding on the way production of goods or services will be organized. It has major implications for capacity planning, layout of facilities, equipment, and design of work systems. Process selection occurs as a matter of course when new products or services are being planned. However, it also occurs periodically due to technological changes in products or equipment, as well as competitive pressures. Figure 6.1 provides an overview

> **LO6.1** Explain the strategic importance of process selection and the influence it has on the organization and its supply chain.

244   **Chapter Six**   Process Selection and Facility Layout

FIGURE 6.1
Process selection and
capacity planning influence
system design

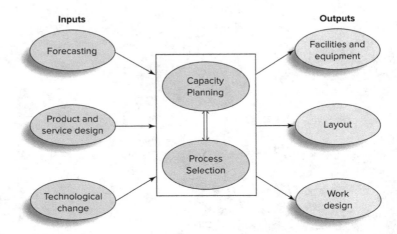

of where process selection and capacity planning fit into system design. Forecasts, product and service design, and technological considerations all influence capacity planning and process selection. Moreover, capacity and process selection are interrelated, and are often done in concert. They, in turn, affect facility and equipment choices, layout, and work design.

How an organization approaches process selection is determined by the organization's *process strategy*. Key aspects include:

- Capital intensity: The mix of equipment and labor that will be used by the organization.
- Process flexibility: The degree to which the system can be adjusted to changes in processing requirements due to such factors as changes in product or service design, changes in volume processed, and changes in technology.

6.2 PROCESS SELECTION

LO6.2 Name the two main factors that influence process selection.

Process choice is demand driven. The two key questions in process selection are:

1. How much variety will the process need to be able to handle?
2. How much volume will the process need to be able to handle?

Answers to these questions will serve as a guide to selecting an appropriate process. Usually, volume and variety are *inversely* related; a higher level of one means a lower level of the other. However, the need for flexibility of personnel and equipment is *directly* related to the level of variety the process will need to handle: the lower the variety, the less the need for flexibility, while the higher the variety, the greater the need for flexibility.

There is another aspect of variety that is important. Variety means either having separate operations for each product or service, with a steady demand for each, or being willing to live with some idle time, or to get equipment ready every time there is the need to change the product being produced or the service being provided.

Process Types

There are five basic process types: job shop, batch, repetitive, continuous, and project.

Job Shop. A job shop usually operates on a relatively small scale. It is used when a low volume of high-variety goods or services will be needed. Processing is *intermittent;* work includes small jobs, each with somewhat different processing requirements. High flexibility using general-purpose equipment and skilled workers are important characteristics of a job shop. A manufacturing example of a job shop is a tool and die shop that is able to produce

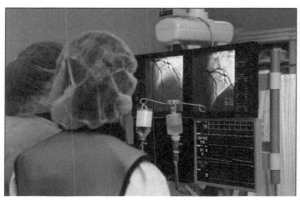

© vilevi/123RF

A job shop process: A hospital medical team performs a non-invasive diagnostic surgery.

© Don Tremain/Getty RF

A batch process: Menu items are prepared in batches, in the kitchen of the Spago Restaurant in the Forum at Caesar's Palace, Las Vegas, Nevada.

© Keith Dannemiller/Alamy Stock Photo

A repetitive process: Motorcycles on an assembly line with parts added in a sequential order.

© Kevin Burke/Corbis/Getty Images Plus

A continuous process: An oil refinery performs a continuous process, mixing and separating crude oil into gas, fuel oil, chemicals, and many other products.

one-of-a-kind tools. A service example is a veterinarian's office, which is able to process a variety of animals and a variety of injuries and diseases.

Batch. Batch processing is used when a moderate volume of goods or services is desired, and it can handle a moderate variety in products or services. The equipment need not be as flexible as in a job shop, but processing is still intermittent. The skill level of workers doesn't need to be as high as in a job shop because there is less variety in the jobs being processed. Examples of batch systems include bakeries, which make bread, cakes, or cookies in batches; movie theaters, which show movies to groups (batches) of people; and airlines, which carry planeloads (batches) of people from airport to airport. Other examples of products that lend themselves to batch production are paint, ice cream, soft drinks, beer, magazines, and books. Other examples of services include plays, concerts, music videos, radio and television programs, and public address announcements.

Repetitive. When higher volumes of more standardized goods or services are needed, repetitive processing is used. The standardized output means only slight flexibility of equipment is needed. Skill of workers is generally low. Examples of this type of system include

246   **Chapter Six**   Process Selection and Facility Layout

production lines and assembly lines. In fact, this type of process is sometimes referred to as *assembly*. Familiar products made by these systems include automobiles, television sets, pencils, and computers. An example of a service system is an automatic carwash. Other examples of service include cafeteria lines and ticket collectors at sports events and concerts. Also, *mass customization* is an option.

Continuous. When a very high volume of nondiscrete, highly standardized output is desired, a continuous system is used. These systems have almost no variety in output and, hence, no need for equipment flexibility. Workers' skill requirements can range from low to high, depending on the complexity of the system and the expertise workers need. Generally, if equipment is highly specialized, worker skills can be lower. Examples of nondiscrete products made in continuous systems include petroleum products, steel, sugar, flour, and salt. Continuous services include air monitoring, supplying electricity to homes and businesses, and the Internet.

These process types are found in a wide range of manufacturing and service settings. The ideal is to have process capabilities match product or service requirements. Failure to do so can result in inefficiencies and higher costs than are necessary, perhaps creating a competitive disadvantage. Table 6.1 provides a brief description of each process type along with advantages and disadvantages of each.

Figure 6.2 provides an overview of these four process types in the form of a matrix, with an example for each process type. Note that job variety, process flexibility, and unit cost are highest for a job shop and get progressively lower moving from job shop to continuous processing. Conversely, volume of output is lowest for a job shop and gets progressively higher moving from job shop to continuous processing. Note, too, that the examples fall along the diagonal. The implication is that the diagonal represents the ideal choice of processing system for a given set of circumstances. For example, if the goal is to be able to process a small volume of jobs that will involve high variety, job shop processing is most appropriate. For less variety and a higher volume, a batch system would be most appropriate, and so on. Note that combinations far from the diagonal would not even be considered, such as using a job shop for high-volume, low-variety jobs, or continuous processing for low-volume, high-variety jobs, because that would result in either higher than necessary costs or lost opportunities.

Another consideration is that products and services often go through *life cycles* that begin with low volume, which increases as products or services become better known. When that happens, a manager must know when to shift from one type of process (e.g., job shop) to the next (e.g., batch). Of course, some operations remain at a certain level (e.g., magazine publishing), while others increase (or decrease as markets become saturated) over time. Again, it is important for a manager to assess his or her products and services and make a judgment on whether to plan for changes in processing over time.

All of these process types (job shop, batch, repetitive, and continuous) are typically ongoing operations. However, some situations are not ongoing but instead are of limited duration. In such instances, the work is often organized as a *project*.

LO6.3 Compare the four basic processing types.

TABLE 6.1
Types of processing

	Job Shop	Batch	Repetitive/ Assembly	Continuous
Description	Customized goods or services	Semi-standardized goods or services	Standardized goods or services	Highly standardized goods or services
Advantages	Able to handle a wide variety of work	Flexibility; easy to add or change products or services	Low unit cost, high volume, efficient	Very efficient, very high volume
Disadvantages	Slow, high cost per unit, complex planning and scheduling	Moderate cost per unit, moderate scheduling complexity	Low flexibility, high cost of downtime	Very rigid, lack of variety, costly to change, very high cost of downtime

Product or Service and Flexibility Variety and Equipment Flexibility

	High	Moderate	Low	Very low
Low or very low volume	**Job Shop** repair shop emergency room			
Moderate volume		**Batch** commercial bakery classroom lecture		
High volume			**Repetitive** assembly line automatic car wash	
Very high volume				**Continuous Flow** petroleum refining water treatment

FIGURE 6.2
Volume and variety influence process choice

Project. A **project** is used for work that is nonroutine, with a unique set of objectives to be accomplished in a limited time frame. Examples range from simple to complicated, including such things as putting on a play, consulting, making a motion picture, launching a new product or service, publishing a book, building a dam, and building a bridge. Equipment flexibility and worker skills can range from low to high.

The type of process or processes used by an organization influences a great many activities of the organization. Table 6.2 briefly describes some of those influences.

Process type also impacts supply chain requirements. Repetitive and continuous processes require steady inputs of high-volume goods and services. Delivery reliability in terms of quality and timing is essential. Job shop and batch processing may mean that suppliers have to be able to deal with varying order quantities and timing of orders. In some instances seasonality is a factor, so suppliers must be able to handle periodic large demand.

The processes discussed do not always exist in their "pure" forms. It is not unusual to find hybrid processes—processes that have elements of other process types embedded in them. For instance, companies that operate primarily in a repetitive mode, or a continuous mode,

Project A nonrepetitive set of activities directed toward a unique goal within a limited time frame.

TABLE 6.2
Process choice affects numerous activities/functions

Activity/ Function	Job Shop	Batch	Repetitive	Continuous	Projects
Cost estimation	Difficult	Somewhat routine	Routine	Routine	Simple to complex
Cost per unit	High	Moderate	Low	Low	Very high
Equipment used	General purpose	General purpose	Special purpose	Special purpose	Varied
Fixed costs	Low	Moderate	High	Very high	Varied
Variable costs	High	Moderate	Low	Very low	High
Labor skills	High	Moderate	Low	Low to high	Low to high
Marketing	Promote capabilities	Promote capabilities; semi-standardized goods and services	Promote standardized goods/services	Promote standardized goods/services	Promote capabilities
Scheduling	Complex	Moderately complex	Routine	Routine	Complex, subject to change
Work-in-process inventory	High	High	Low	Low	Varied

OPERATIONS TOUR   MORTON SALT

Introduction

Morton Salt is a subsidiary of Morton International, a manufacturer of specialty chemicals, air bags, and salt products. The Morton salt-processing facility in Silver Springs, New York, between Buffalo and Rochester, is one of six similar Morton salt-processing facilities in the United States. The Silver Springs plant employs about 200 people, ranging from unskilled to skilled. It produces salt products for water conditioning, grocery, industrial, and agricultural markets. The grocery business consists of 26-oz. round cans of iodized salt. Although the grocery business represents a relatively small portion of the total output (approximately 15 percent), it is the most profitable.

Salt Production

The basic raw material, salt, is obtained by injecting water into salt caverns that are located some 2,400 feet below the surface. There, the salt deposits dissolve in the water. The resulting brine is pumped to the surface where it is converted into salt crystals. The brine is boiled, and much of the liquid evaporates, leaving salt crystals and some residual moisture, which is removed in a drying process. This process is run continuously for about six weeks at a time. Initially, salt is produced at the rate of 45 tons per hour. But the rate of output decreases due to scale buildup, so that by the sixth week, output is only 75 percent of the initial rate. At that point, the process is halted to perform maintenance on the equipment and remove the scale, after which salt production resumes.

The salt is stored in silos until it is needed for production, or it is shipped in bulk to industrial customers. Conveyors move the salt to each of the four dedicated production areas, one of which is round can production. (See diagram.) The discussion here focuses exclusively on round can production.

Round Can Production

Annual round can production averages roughly 3.8 million cans. Approximately 70 percent of the output is for the Morton label, and the rest is for private label. There are two parallel, high-speed production lines. The two lines share common processes at the beginning of the lines, and then branch out into two identical lines. Each line is capable of producing 9,600 cans per hour (160 cans per minute). The equipment is not flexible, so the production rate is fixed. The operations are completely standardized; the only variable is the brand label that is applied. One line requires 12 production workers, while both lines together can be operated by 18 workers because of the common processes. Workers on the line perform low-skilled, repetitive tasks.

The plant produces both the salt and the cans the salt is packaged in. The cans are essentially a cylinder with a top and a bottom; they are made of cardboard, except for a plastic pour spout in the top. The cylinder portion is formed from two sheets of chip board that are glued together and then rolled into a continuous tube. The glue not only binds the material, it also provides a moisture barrier. The tube is cut in a two-step process: it is first cut into long sections, and those sections are then cut into can-size pieces. The top and bottom pieces for the cans are punched from a continuous strip of cardboard. The separate pieces move along conveyor belts to the lines where the components are assembled into cans and glued. The cans are then filled with salt and the pour spout is added. Finally, the cans are loaded onto pallets and placed into inventory, ready to be shipped to distributors.

Quality

Quality is checked at several points in the production process. Initially, the salt is checked for purity when it is obtained from the wells. Iodine and an anti-caking compound are added to the salt, and their levels are verified using chemical analysis. Crystal size is important. In order to achieve the desired size and to remove lumps, the salt is forced through a scraping screen, which can cause very fine pieces of metal to mix with the salt. However, these pieces are effectively removed by magnets that are placed at appropriate points in the process. If, for any reason, the salt is judged to be contaminated, it is diverted to a nonfood product.

Checking the quality of the cans is done primarily by visual inspection, including verifying the assembly operation is correct, checking filled cans for correct weight, inspecting cans to see that labels are properly aligned, and checking to see that plastic pour spouts are correctly attached.

The equipment on the production line is sensitive to misshapen or damaged cans, and frequently jams, causing production delays. This greatly reduces the chance of a defective can getting through the process, but it reduces productivity, and the salt in the defective cans must be scrapped. The cost of quality is fairly high, owing to the amount of product that is scrapped, the large number of inspectors, and the extensive laboratory testing that is needed.

Production Planning and Inventory

The plant can sell all of the salt it produces. The job of the production scheduler is to distribute the salt that is stored in the silos to the various production areas, taking into account production capacities in each area and available inventory levels of those products. A key consideration is to make sure there is sufficient storage capacity in the silos to handle the incoming salt from brine production.

Equipment Maintenance and Repair

The equipment is 1950s vintage, and it requires a fair amount of maintenance to keep it in good working order. Even so, breakdowns occur as parts wear out. The plant has its own tool shop where skilled workers repair parts or make new parts because replacement parts are no longer available for the old equipment.

(continued)

(continued)

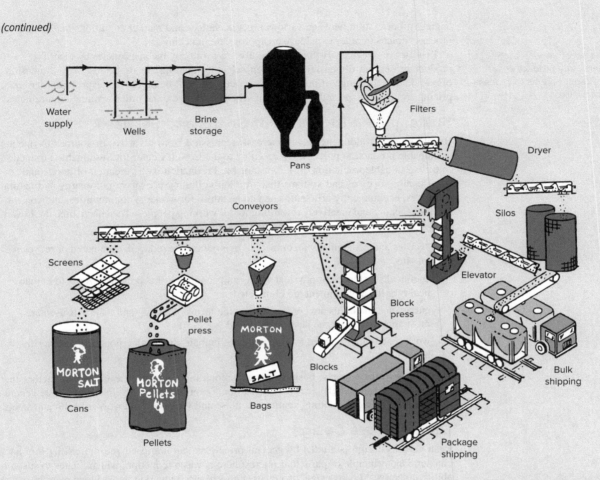

Questions

1. Briefly describe salt production, from brine production to finished round cans.
2. Briefly describe quality assurance efforts in round can production.
3. What are some of the possible reasons why the company continues to use the old processing equipment instead of buying new, more modern equipment?
4. Where would you place salt production in the product-process spectrum?
5. Determine the approximate number of tons of salt produced annually for the grocery market. *Hints:* one ton = 2,000 pounds, and one pound = 16 ounces.
6. What improvements can you suggest for the plant?

will often have repair shops (i.e., job shops) to fix or make new parts for equipment that fails. Also, if volume increases for some items, an operation that began, say, in a job shop or as a batch mode may evolve into a batch or repetitive operation. This may result in having some operations in a job shop or batch mode, and others in a repetitive mode.

Product and Service Profiling

Process selection can involve substantial investment in equipment and have a very specific influence on the layout of facilities, which also require heavy investment. Moreover, mismatches between operations capabilities and market demand and pricing or cost strategies can have a significant negative impact on the ability of the organization to compete or, in government agencies, to effectively service clients. Therefore, it is highly desirable to assess the degree of correlation between various process choices and market conditions *before* making process choices in order to achieve an appropriate matching.

Product or service profiling
Linking key product or service requirements to process capabilities.

Product or service profiling can be used to avoid any inconsistencies by identifying key product or service dimensions and then selecting appropriate processes. Key dimensions often relate to the range of products or services that will be processed, expected order sizes, pricing strategies, expected frequency of schedule changes, and order-winning requirements.

Sustainable Production of Goods and Services

Business organizations are facing increasing pressure from a variety of sources to operate sustainable production processes. According to the Lowell Center for Sustainable Production (http://sustainableproduction.org), "Sustainable Production is the creation of goods and services using processes and systems that are: non-polluting; conserving of energy and natural resources; economically efficient; safe and healthful for workers, communities, and consumers; and socially and creatively rewarding for all working people." To achieve this, the Lowell Center advocates designing and operating processes in ways that:

- "wastes and ecologically incompatible byproducts are reduced, eliminated or recycled on-site;
- chemical substances or physical agents and conditions that present hazards to human health or the environment are eliminated;
- energy and materials are conserved, and the forms of energy and materials used are most appropriate for the desired ends; and
- work spaces are designed to minimize or eliminate chemical, ergonomic and physical hazard."

To achieve these goals, business organizations must focus on a number of factors that include energy use and efficiency, CO_2 (carbon footprint) and toxic emissions, waste generation, lighting, heating, cooling, ventilation, noise and vibration, and worker health and safety.

Lean Process Design

Lean process design is guided by general principles that are discussed more fully in a later chapter. One principle of particular interest here is waste reduction, which relates to sustainability objectives. Lean design also focuses on variance reduction in workload over the entire process to achieve level production and thereby improve process flow. Successful lean design results in reduced inventory and floor space; quicker response times and shorter lead times; reduced defects, rework, and scrap; and increased productivity. Lean design is often translated into practice using cellular layouts, which are discussed later in this chapter.

Lean process design has broad applications in seemingly diverse areas such as health care delivery systems, manufacturing, construction projects, and process reengineering.

LO6.4 Explain the need for management of technology.

6.3 TECHNOLOGY

Technological innovation
The discovery and development of new or improved products, services, or processes for producing or providing them.

Technology The application of scientific discoveries to the development and improvement of products and services and operations processes.

Technology and technological innovation often have a major influence on business processes. **Technological innovation** refers to the discovery and development of new or improved products, services, or processes for producing or providing them. **Technology** refers to applications of scientific knowledge to the development and improvement of goods and services and/or the processes that produce or provide them. The term *high technology* refers to the most advanced and developed equipment and/or methods.

Process technology and information technology can have a major impact on costs, productivity, and competitiveness. *Process technology* includes methods, procedures, and equipment used to produce goods and provide services. This not only involves processes within an organization, it also extends to supply chain processes. *Information technology (IT)* is the science and use of computers and other electronic equipment to store, process, and send information. IT is heavily ingrained in today's business operations. This includes electronic data processing, the use of bar codes and radio frequency tags to identify and track goods, devices used to obtain point-of-sale information, data transmission, the Internet, e-commerce, e-mail, and more.

With radio frequency (RFID) tags, items can be tracked during production and in inventory. For outbound goods, readers at a packing station can verify that the proper items and quantities were picked before shipping the goods to a customer or a distribution center. In a hospital setting, RFID tags can be used in several ways. One is to facilitate keeping accurate track of hospital garments, automating the process by which clean garments are inventoried and disbursed. An RFID tag can be worn by each hospital employee. The tag contains a unique ID number which is associated with each wearer. When an employee comes to the counter to pick up garments, the employee's tag is scanned and software generates data regarding garment, type, size, location on racks, and availability for that employee. The garments are then picked from the specified racks, their RFID tag is read by a nearby scanner and processed, and the database is automatically updated.

Technological innovation in processing technology can produce tremendous benefits for organizations by increasing quality, lowering costs, increasing productivity, and expanding processing capabilities. Among the examples are laser technology used in surgery and laser measuring devices, advances in medical diagnostic equipment, high-speed Internet connections, high-definition television, online banking, information retrieval systems, and high-speed search engines. Processing technologies often come through acquisition rather than through internal efforts of an organization.

While process technology can have enormous benefits, it also carries substantial risk unless a significant effort is made to fully understand both the downside and the upside of a particular technology. It is essential to understand what the technology will and won't do. Also, there are economic considerations (initial cost, space, cash flow, maintenance, consultants), integration considerations (cost, time, resources), and human considerations (training, safety, job loss).

Automation

An increasingly asked question in process design is whether to automate. **Automation** is machinery that has sensing and control devices that enable it to operate automatically. If a company decides to automate, the next question is how much. Automation can range from factories that are completely automated to a single automated operation.

Automated services are becoming increasingly important. Examples range from automated teller machines (ATMs) to automated heating and air conditioning and include automated inspection, automated storage and retrieval systems, package sorting, mail processing, e-mail, online banking, and E-Z pass.

Automation offers a number of advantages over human labor. It has low variability, whereas it is difficult for a human to perform a task in exactly the same way, in the same amount of time, and on a repetitive basis. In a production setting, variability is detrimental to quality and to meeting schedules. Moreover, machines do not get bored or distracted, nor do they go out on strike, ask for higher wages, or file labor grievances. Still another advantage of automation is reduction of variable costs. In order for automated processing to be an option, job-processing requirements must be *standardized* (i.e., have very little or no variety).

Both manufacturing and service organizations are increasing their use of automation as a way to reduce costs, increase productivity, and improve quality and consistency.

Automation is frequently touted as a strategy necessary for competitiveness. However, automation also has certain disadvantages and limitations compared to human labor. To begin with, it can be costly. Technology is expensive; usually it requires high volumes of output to offset high costs. In addition, automation is much less flexible than human labor. Once a process has been automated, there is substantial reason for not changing it. Moreover, workers sometimes fear automation because it might cause them to lose their jobs. That can have an adverse effect on morale and productivity.

Decision makers must carefully examine the issue of whether to automate or the degree to which to automate, so that they clearly understand all the ramifications. Also, much thought

Automation Machinery that has sensing and control devices that enable it to operate automatically.

READING   FOXCONN SHIFTS ITS FOCUS TO AUTOMATION

Foxconn operates a network of factories across the Chinese main-land, employing 1.2 million people, that makes products for tech companies that include Apple, Hewlett Packard, and Dell. The electronics manufacturing giant has been on a steady course for a while to replace manpower with robotic systems.

"Foxconn (has) vowed to install up to 1 million robots in its fac-tories over the next three years, which analysts suggested was in part to address long-time scandals such as high suicide rates among employees and exploitation of workers."

Foreign manufacturers in China are also viewing upgrades as vital to their operations in the country. In fact, numerous mul-tinational companies have recognized the long-term benefits of replacing human labor with robots.

Questions

1. As Foxconn cuts jobs as it shifts to greater use of automation, jobs will be created in other companies. In what types of com-panies would you expect to see jobs created?
2. Many companies outsourced their manufacturing activities to Foxconn due to its low labor costs. Does Foxconn's shift to automation make it likely that some of those companies will reconsider outsourcing in favor of shifting to automation? What are some reasons for staying with Foxconn, and what are some reasons that favor shifting to their own automated processes?

Source: Based on "Foxconn halts recruitment as focus shifts to automation," He Wei in Shanghai, *China Daily*, February 2, 2013, p. 9.

and careful planning are necessary to successfully *integrate* automation into a production system. Otherwise, it can lead to major problems. Automation has important implications not only for cost and flexibility, but also for the fit with overall strategic priorities. If the decision is made to automate, care must be taken to remove waste from the system prior to automating, to avoid building the waste into the automated system. Table 6.3 has a list of questions for organizations that are considering automation.

Generally speaking, there are three kinds of automation: fixed, programmable, and flexible.

Fixed automation is the least flexible. It uses high-cost, specialized equipment for a fixed sequence of operations. Low cost and high volume are its primary advantages; minimal vari-ety and the high cost of making major changes in either product or process are its primary limitations.

Programmable automation involves the use of high-cost, general-purpose equipment con-trolled by a computer program that provides both the sequence of operations and specific details about each operation. This type of automation has the capability of economically pro-ducing a fairly wide variety of low-volume products in small batches. Numerically controlled (N/C) machines and some robots are applications of programmable automation.

Computer-aided manufacturing (CAM) refers to the use of computers in process control, ranging from robots to automated quality control. **Numerically controlled (N/C) machines** are programmed to follow a set of processing instructions based on mathematical relationships that tell the machine the details of the operations to be performed. The instruc-tions are stored on a device such as magnetic tape or microprocessor. Although N/C machines have been used for many years, they are an important part of new approaches to manufactur-ing. Individual machines often have their own computer; this is referred to as *computerized numerical control (CNC)*. Or one computer may control a number of N/C machines, which is referred to as *direct numerical control (DNC)*.

N/C machines are best used in cases where parts are processed frequently and in small batches, where part geometry is complex, close tolerances are required, mistakes are costly, and there is the possibility of frequent changes in design. The main limitations of N/C

Computer-aided manufactur-ing (CAM) The use of com-puters in process control.

Numerically controlled (N/C) machines Machines that perform operations by follow-ing mathematical processing instructions.

TABLE 6.3
Automation questions

1. What level of automation is appropriate? (Some operations are more suited to being automated than others, so partial automation can be an option.)
2. How would automation affect the flexibility of an operation system?
3. How can automation projects be justified?
4. How should changes be managed?
5. What are the risks of automating?
6. What are some of the likely effects of implementing automation on market share, costs, quality, customer satisfaction, labor relations, and ongoing operations?

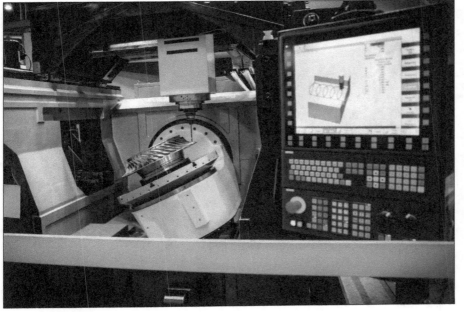

© Andrey Armyagov/Shutterstock

Computer numerical control (CNC) refers to a computer that reads instructions and drives a machine tool. CNC machines are controlled directly from files created by CAM software packages. With increased automation of manufacturing processes with CNC machining, considerable improvements in consistency and quality have been achieved. CNC automation reduces the frequency of errors and provides operators with time to perform additional tasks. The intelligence of CNC controllers has dramatically increased job shop cell production. Some machines might even make 1,000 parts on a weekend with no operator, checking each part with lasers and sensors.

machines are the higher skill levels needed to program the machines and their inability to detect tool wear and material variation.

The use of robots in manufacturing is sometimes an option. Robots can handle a wide variety of tasks, including welding, assembly, loading and unloading of machines, painting, and testing. They relieve humans from heavy or dirty work and often eliminate drudgery tasks.

Some uses of robots are fairly simple, others are much more complex. At the lowest level are robots that follow a fixed set of instructions. Next are programmable robots, which can repeat a set of movements after being led through the sequence. These robots "play back" a mechanical sequence much as a video recorder plays back a visual sequence. At the next level up are robots that follow instructions from a computer. Below are robots that can recognize objects and make certain simple decisions.

Flexible automation evolved from programmable automation. It uses equipment that is more customized than that of programmable automation. A key difference between the two is that flexible automation requires significantly less changeover time. This permits almost continuous operation of equipment *and* product variety without the need to produce in batches.

In practice, flexible automation is used in several different formats.

A **flexible manufacturing system (FMS)** is a group of machines that include supervisory computer control, automatic material handling, and robots or other automated processing equipment. Reprogrammable controllers enable these systems to produce a variety of *similar* products. Systems may range from three or four machines to more than a dozen. They are designed to handle intermittent processing requirements with some of the benefits of automation and some of the flexibility of individual, or stand-alone, machines (e.g., N/C machines). Flexible manufacturing systems offer reduced labor costs and more consistent quality when compared with more traditional manufacturing methods, lower capital investment and higher flexibility than "hard" automation, and relatively quick changeover time. Flexible manufacturing systems often appeal to managers who hope to achieve both the flexibility of job shop processing and the productivity of repetitive processing systems.

Flexible manufacturing system (FMS) A group of machines designed to handle intermittent processing requirements and produce a variety of similar products.

254   **Chapter Six**   Process Selection and Facility Layout

Tmsuk's receptionist robot is used for medical purposes. These robots can guide a hospital visitor to a nearby elevator. If a human touches the panel on the robot's body or speaks to it, the robot can display or print directions.

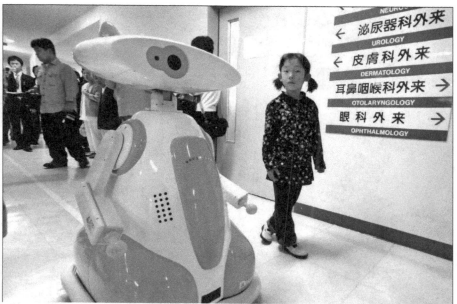

© AFP/Getty Images

Although these are important benefits, an FMS also has certain limitations. One is that this type of system can handle a relatively narrow range of part variety, so it must be used for a family of similar parts, which all require similar machining. Also, an FMS requires longer planning and development times than more conventional processing equipment because of its increased complexity and cost. Furthermore, companies sometimes prefer a gradual approach to automation, and FMS represents a sizable chunk of technology.

Computer-integrated manufacturing (CIM) is a system that uses an integrating computer system to link a broad range of manufacturing activities, including engineering design, flexible manufacturing systems, purchasing, order processing, and production planning and control. Not all elements are absolutely necessary. For instance, CIM might be as simple as linking two or more FMSs by a host computer. More encompassing systems can link scheduling, purchasing, inventory control, shop control, and distribution. In effect, a CIM system integrates information from other areas of an organization with manufacturing.

The overall goal of using CIM is to link various parts of an organization to achieve rapid response to customer orders and/or product changes, to allow rapid production, and to reduce *indirect* labor costs.

A shining example of how process choices can lead to competitive advantages can be found at Allen-Bradley's computer-integrated manufacturing process in Milwaukee, Wisconsin. The company converted a portion of its factory to a fully automated "factory within a factory" to assemble contactors and relays for electrical motors. A handful of humans operate the factory, although once an order has been entered into the system, the machines do virtually all the work, including packaging and shipping, and quality control. Any defective items are removed from the line, and replacement parts are automatically ordered and scheduled to compensate for the defective items. The humans program the machines, monitor operations, and attend to any problems signaled by a system of warning lights.

As orders come into the plant, computers determine production requirements and schedules and order the necessary parts. Bar-coded labels that contain processing instructions are automatically placed on individual parts. As the parts approach a machine, a sensing device reads the bar code and communicates the processing instructions to the machine. The factory can produce 600 units an hour.

Computer-integrated manufacturing (CIM) A system for linking a broad range of manufacturing activities through an integrating computer system.

At the Ford Motor plant in Michigan, in the final assembly area, flexibility means that the build sequence is the same, regardless of model, on one or more platforms. This allows for efficient use of people and equipment.

© Bill Pugliano/Getty

The company has realized substantial competitive advantages from the system. Orders can be completed and shipped within 24 hours of entry into the system, indirect labor costs and inventory costs have been greatly reduced, and quality is very high.

3D Printing

A 3D printer is a type of *industrial robot* that is controlled using computer assisted design (CAD). **3D printing**, also known as *additive manufacturing,* involves processes that create three-dimensional objects by applying successive layers of materials to create the objects. The objects can be of almost any size or shape. These processes are different than many familiar processes that use *subtractive manufacturing* to create objects: material is removed by methods such as cutting, grinding, sanding, drilling, and milling. And producing an object using 3D printing is generally much slower than the time that would be needed using more conventional techniques in a factory setting.

In early applications, material was deposited onto a powder bed using inkjet printer heads; hence the name *3D printing*. Today, the term 3D printing refers to a wide range of techniques such as *extrusion* (the deformation of either metal or plastic forced under pressure through a die to create a shape) and *sintering* (using heat or pressure or both to form a solid material from powder without causing it to liquefy).

3D printers come in a wide variety of sizes and shapes. Some printers look very much like a microwave oven, while others look completely different.

The use of *3D scanning* technologies allows the replication of objects without the use of molds. That can be beneficial in cases where molding techniques are difficult or costly, or where contact with substances used in molding processes could harm the original item. 3D objects can also be created from photographs of an existing object. That involves taking a series of photographs of the object (usually about 20) from various angles in order to capture adequate detail of the object for reproduction.

It is possible that in the long term, 3D printing technologies could have a significant impact on where and how production occurs and on supply chains.

3D printing A process that creates a three-dimensional object by adding successive layers of material.

Applications Commercial applications of 3D technology are occurring in in a wide array of businesses, along with a few consumer applications, some of which are shown in Table 6.4.

Benefits Although 3D printing is unlikely to replace more widespread forms of high-volume production in the foreseeable future, mainly because of its relative slowness, it does offer an alternate form of production that provides value in a wide range of applications. In some of those applications, manufacturers have been able to substantially reduce the cost and/or time needed to develop or produce items. Among the examples is production of replacement parts in the case of equipment failure when no spare parts are available. Replacement occurs much faster than the time it would take to receive the part from a supplier, thereby avoiding costly production delays. Other examples include economical production of small quantities of items, and the avoidance of shipping costs and time when the application is not near a supplier.

3D printing will become even more useful through development in three areas: printers and printing methods, software to design and print, and materials used in printing.

Drones

Drones are remotely-controlled unmanned aircraft, usually small. An important benefit is providing an "eye-in-the sky" to obtain visual detail in places that are hazardous to humans or that are not readily accessible. For example, drones are proving to be very helpful in assessing storm and earthquake damage, especially in situations where access by vehicles or on foot is difficult or impossible due to the terrain, debris, or where roads or bridges are impassable. They are also useful for assessing crop damage, monitoring forest fires, and inspecting pipelines, cell towers, railroad tracks, and power lines. And when medicines and medical supplies are urgently needed in remote areas, drones can be used to deliver them. Despite these many benefits, to use of drones poses a number of issues. There is the possibility of collisions with other drones, power lines, birds, or other objects, as well as mechanical failure or operator error, any of which can result in failure to accomplish the intended task. In addition, crashes have the potential to injure nearby humans or cause damage to property.

TABLE 6.4
Some examples of applications of 3D technology

Industrial Applications
Mass customization: Customers can create unique designs for standard goods (e.g., cell phone cases)
Distributed manufacturing: Local 3D printing centers that can produce goods on demand for pickup
Computers: Computers, motherboards, other parts
Robots: Robots and robot parts
Rapid prototyping: Rapid fabrication of a scale model of a physical part or assembly
Rapid manufacturing: Inexpensive production of one or a small number of items
Medical devices: Prosthetics
Dental: Crowns, implants
Pharmaceutical: Pills and medicines
Food products: Candy, chocolate, crackers, and pasta
Apparel: Custom-designed footwear, eyeglass frames
Space exploration: Tools and parts can be made on the international space station as needed instead
    of the cost and time needed to transport them from earth
Vehicles: Automotive parts, and replacement parts at repair shops; airplane parts and spare parts;
    also, combine multiple parts into a single part
Construction: Architectural scale models

Consumer Applications
Hobbyists: Models, parts, and replacement parts (e.g., for drones)
Appliances and tools: Replacement parts

READING   **SELF-DRIVING VEHICLES ARE ON THE HORIZON**

Self-driving vehicles, sometimes referred to as *autonomous vehicles,* are expected to populate the roadways in the not too distant future. They will be equipped with multiple cameras and sensors, GPS and other guidance systems, giving them the ability to operate vehicles with little or no human assistance. They will be able to communicate with similarly equipped nearby vehicles, which will add to their ability to operate safely with other vehicles. Among the expected benefits are a reducing traffic congestion due to their ability to operate closely to other vehicles safely, reducing the number of accidents and injuries, and providing transportation for those unable to drive. There is the very likely possibility that self-driving trucks or other vehicles will be used to make deliveries without the need for drivers.

However, issues remain before the vehicles are ready for prime time, including figuring out how to keep sensors clean of dirt and snow so they can function as intended, how they will be able to maneuver on roads when snow or dirt cover lane markers, how to enable them to operate when it is snowing, raining heavily, or foggy, and how to compensate when they coexist with human-operated vehicles.

Questions

1. Drones have been mentioned as possible ways to deliver packages to customers. What advantages might self-driving delivery vehicles have compared to drones for package delivery?
2. What conflicts do you envision when self-driving vehicles coexist with human-operated vehicles?

6.4 PROCESS STRATEGY

Throughout this book, the importance of *flexibility* as a competitive strategy is stressed. However, flexibility does not always offer the best choice in processing decisions. Flexible systems and equipment are often more expensive and not as efficient as less flexible alternatives. In certain instances, flexibility is unnecessary because products are in mature stages, requiring few design changes, and there is a steady volume of output. Ordinarily, this type of situation calls for specialized processing equipment, with no need for flexibility. The implication is clear: Flexibility should be adopted with great care; its applications should be matched with situations in which a *need* for flexibility clearly exists.

In practice, decision makers choose flexible systems for either of two reasons: Demand variety or uncertainty exists about demand. The second reason can be overcome through improved forecasting.

6.5 STRATEGIC RESOURCE ORGANIZATION: FACILITIES LAYOUT

> **LO6.5** List some reasons for redesign of layouts.

Layout refers to the configuration of departments, work centers, and equipment, with particular emphasis on movement of work (customers or materials) through the system. This section describes the main types of layout designs and the models used to evaluate design alternatives.

As in other areas of system design, layout decisions are important for three basic reasons: (1) they require substantial investments of money and effort; (2) they involve long-term commitments, which makes mistakes difficult to overcome; and (3) they have a significant impact on the cost and efficiency of operations.

The need for layout planning arises both in the process of designing new facilities and in redesigning existing facilities. The most common reasons for redesign of layouts include inefficient operations (e.g., high cost, bottlenecks), accidents or safety hazards, changes in the design of products or services, introduction of new products or services, changes in the volume of output or mix of outputs, changes in methods or equipment, changes in environmental or other legal requirements, and morale problems (e.g., lack of face-to-face contact).

Poor layout design can adversely affect system performance. For example, a change in the layout at the Minneapolis–St. Paul International Airport solved a problem that had plagued travelers. In the former layout, security checkpoints were located in the boarding area. That meant that arriving passengers who were simply changing planes had to pass through a security checkpoint before being able to board their connecting flight, along with other passengers whose journeys were originating at Minneapolis–St. Paul. This created excessive waiting times for both sets of passengers. The new layout relocated the security checkpoints, moving them from the boarding area to a position close to the ticket counters. Thus, the need for passengers who were making connecting flights to pass through security was eliminated, and in the process, the waiting time for passengers departing from Minneapolis–St. Paul was considerably reduced.[1]

The basic objective of layout design is to facilitate a smooth flow of work, material, and information through the system. Supporting objectives generally involve the following:

1. To facilitate attainment of product or service quality.
2. To use workers and space efficiently.
3. To avoid bottlenecks.
4. To minimize material handling costs.
5. To eliminate unnecessary movements of workers or materials.
6. To minimize production time or customer service time.
7. To design for safety.

The three basic types of layout are product, process, and fixed-position. *Product layouts* are most conducive to repetitive processing, *process layouts* are used for intermittent processing, and *fixed-position layouts* are used when projects require layouts. The characteristics, advantages, and disadvantages of each layout type are described in this section, along with hybrid layouts, which are combinations of these pure types. These include cellular layouts and flexible manufacturing systems.

Repetitive Processing: Product Layouts

LO6.6 Describe product layouts and their main advantages and disadvantages.

Product layout Layout that uses standardized processing operations to achieve smooth, rapid, high-volume flow.

Product layouts are used to achieve a smooth and rapid flow of large volumes of goods or customers through a system. This is made possible by highly standardized goods or services that allow highly standardized, repetitive processing. The work is divided into a series of standardized tasks, permitting specialization of equipment and division of labor. The large volumes handled by these systems usually make it economical to invest substantial sums of money in equipment and job design. Because only one or a few very similar items are involved, it is feasible to arrange an entire layout to correspond to the technological processing requirements of the product or service. For instance, if a portion of a manufacturing operation required the sequence of cutting, sanding, and painting, the appropriate pieces of equipment would be arranged in that same sequence. And because each item follows the same sequence of operations, it is often possible to utilize fixed-path material-handling equipment such as conveyors to transport items between operations. The resulting arrangement forms a line like the one depicted in Figure 6.3. In manufacturing environments, the lines are referred to as **production lines** or **assembly lines,** depending on the type of activity involved. In service processes, the term *line* may or may not be used. It is common to refer to a cafeteria line as such but not a car wash, although from a conceptual standpoint the two are nearly identical. Figure 6.4 illustrates the layout of a typical cafeteria serving line. Examples of this type of layout are less plentiful in service environments because processing requirements usually exhibit too much variability to make standardization feasible. Without high standardization, many of the benefits of repetitive processing are lost. When lines are used, certain compromises may be made. For instance, an automatic car wash provides equal treatment to all cars—the same amount of soap, water, and scrubbing—even though cars may differ considerably in cleaning needs.

Product layouts achieve a high degree of labor and equipment utilization, which tends to offset their high equipment costs. Because items move quickly from operation to operation, the amount of work-in-process is often minimal. Consequently, operations are so closely

Production line Standardized layout arranged according to a fixed sequence of production tasks.

Assembly line Standardized layout arranged according to a fixed sequence of assembly tasks.

[1]Based on "Airport Checkpoints Moved to Help Speed Travelers on Their Way," *Minneapolis—St. Paul Star Tribune,* January 13, 1995, p. 1B.

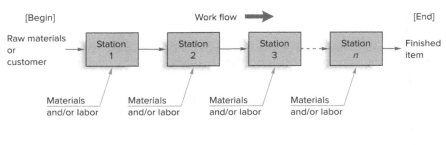

FIGURE 6.3
A flow line for production or service

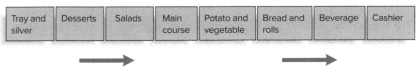

FIGURE 6.4
Cafeteria line

tied to each other that the entire system is highly vulnerable to being shut down because of mechanical failure or high absenteeism. Maintenance procedures are geared to this. *Preventive maintenance*—periodic inspection and replacement of worn parts or those with high failure rates—reduces the probability of breakdowns during the operations. Of course, no amount of preventive activity can completely eliminate failures, so management must take measures to provide quick repair. These include maintaining an inventory of spare parts and having repair personnel available to quickly restore equipment to normal operation. These procedures are fairly expensive; because of the specialized nature of equipment, problems become more difficult to diagnose and resolve, and spare-part inventories can be extensive.

Repetitive processing can be machine paced (e.g., automatic car wash, automobile assembly), worker paced (e.g., fast-food restaurants such as McDonald's, Burger King), or even customer paced (e.g., cafeteria line).

The main advantages of product layouts are:

1. A high rate of output.
2. Low unit cost due to high volume. The high cost of specialized equipment is spread over many units.

Floto+Warner/OTTO

Workers assemble "Wizard of Oz" pinball machines at Jersey Jack Pinball.

3. Labor specialization, which reduces training costs and time, and results in a wide span of supervision.

4. Low material-handling cost per unit. Material handling is simplified because units follow the same sequence of operations. Material handling is often automated.

5. A high utilization of labor and equipment.

6. The establishment of routing and scheduling in the initial design of the system. These activities do not require much attention once the system is operating.

7. Fairly routine accounting, purchasing, and inventory control.

The primary disadvantages of product layouts include the following:

1. The intensive division of labor usually creates dull, repetitive jobs that provide little opportunity for advancement and may lead to morale problems and to repetitive stress injuries.

2. Poorly skilled workers may exhibit little interest in maintaining equipment or in the quality of output.

3. The system is fairly inflexible in response to changes in the volume of output or changes in product or process design.

4. The system is highly susceptible to shutdowns caused by equipment breakdowns or excessive absenteeism because workstations are highly interdependent.

5. Preventive maintenance, the capacity for quick repairs, and spare-parts inventories are necessary expenses.

6. Incentive plans tied to individual output are impractical since they would cause variations among outputs of individual workers, which would adversely affect the smooth flow of work through the system.

U-Shaped Layouts. Although a straight production line may have intuitive appeal, a U-shaped line (see Figure 6.5) has a number of advantages that make it worthy of consideration. One disadvantage of a long, straight line is that it interferes with cross-travel of workers and vehicles. A U-shaped line is more compact; it often requires approximately half the length of a straight production line. In addition, a U-shaped line permits increased communication among workers on the line because workers are clustered, thus facilitating teamwork. Flexibility in work assignments is increased because workers can handle not only adjacent stations but also stations on opposite sides of the line. Moreover, if materials enter the plant at the same point that finished products leave it, a U-shaped line minimizes material handling.

Of course, not all situations lend themselves to U-shaped layouts: On highly automated lines there is less need for teamwork and communication. And entry and exit points may be on opposite sides of the building. Also, operations may need to be separated because of noise or contamination factors.

LO6.7 Describe process layouts and their main advantages and disadvantages.

Process layouts Layouts that can handle varied processing requirements.

Nonrepetitive Processing: Process Layouts

Process layouts (functional layouts) are designed to process items or provide services that involve a variety of processing requirements. The variety of jobs that are processed requires frequent adjustments to equipment. This causes a discontinuous work flow, which is referred

FIGURE 6.5
A U-shaped production line

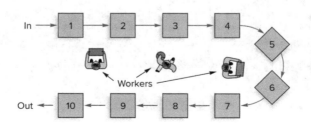

to as **intermittent processing.** The layouts feature departments or other *functional* groupings in which similar kinds of activities are performed. A manufacturing example of a process layout is the *machine shop,* which has separate departments for milling, grinding, drilling, and so on. Items that require those operations are frequently moved in lots or batches to the departments in a sequence that varies from job to job. Consequently, variable-path material-handling equipment (forklift trucks, jeeps, tote boxes) is needed to handle the variety of routes and items. The use of *general-purpose equipment* provides the *flexibility* necessary to handle a wide range of processing requirements. Workers who operate the equipment are usually skilled or semiskilled. Figure 6.6 illustrates the departmental arrangement typical of a process layout.

Intermittent processing Non-repetitive processing.

Process layouts are quite common in service environments. Examples include hospitals, colleges and universities, banks, auto repair shops, airlines, and public libraries. For instance, hospitals have departments or other units that specifically handle surgery, maternity, pediatrics, psychiatric, emergency, and geriatric care. And universities have separate schools or departments that concentrate on one area of study such as business, engineering, science, or math.

Because equipment in a process layout is arranged by type rather than by processing sequence, the system is much less vulnerable to shutdown caused by mechanical failure or absenteeism. In manufacturing systems especially, idle equipment is usually available to replace machines that are temporarily out of service. Moreover, because items are often processed in lots (batches), there is considerably less interdependence between successive operations than with a product layout. Maintenance costs tend to be lower because the equipment is less specialized than that of product layouts, and the grouping of machinery permits repair personnel to become skilled in handling that type of equipment. Machine similarity reduces the necessary investment in spare parts. On the negative side, routing and scheduling must be done on a continual basis to accommodate the variety of processing demands typically imposed on these systems. Material handling is inefficient, and unit handling costs are generally much higher than in product layouts. In-process inventories can be substantial due to batch processing and capacity mismatches. Furthermore, it is not uncommon for such systems to have equipment utilization rates under 50 percent because of routing and scheduling complexities related to the variety of processing demands being handled.

In sum, process layouts have both advantages and disadvantages. The advantages of process layouts include the following:

1. The systems can handle a variety of processing requirements.

2. The systems are not particularly vulnerable to equipment failures.

3. General-purpose equipment is often less costly than the specialized equipment used in product layouts and is easier and less costly to maintain.

4. It is possible to use individual incentive systems.

FIGURE 6.6
Comparison of process and product layouts

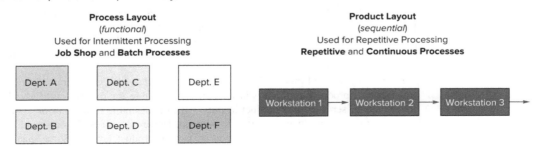

The disadvantages of process layouts include the following:

1. In-process inventory costs can be high if batch processing is used in manufacturing systems.
2. Routing and scheduling pose continual challenges.
3. Equipment utilization rates are low.
4. Material handling is slow and inefficient, and more costly per unit than in product layouts.
5. Job complexities often reduce the span of supervision and result in higher supervisory costs than with product layouts.
6. Special attention necessary for each product or customer (e.g., routing, scheduling, machine setups) and low volumes result in higher unit costs than with product layouts.
7. Accounting, inventory control, and purchasing are much more involved than with product layouts.

Fixed-Position Layouts

Fixed-position layout Layout in which the product or project remains stationary, and workers, materials, and equipment are moved as needed.

In **fixed-position layouts**, the item being worked on remains stationary, and workers, materials, and equipment are moved about as needed. This is in marked contrast to product and process layouts. Almost always, the nature of the product dictates this kind of arrangement: Weight, size, bulk, or some other factor makes it undesirable or extremely difficult to move the product. Fixed-position layouts are used in large construction projects (buildings, power plants, dams), shipbuilding, and production of large aircraft and space mission rockets. In those instances, attention is focused on timing of material and equipment deliveries so as not to clog up the work site and to avoid having to relocate materials and equipment around the work site. Lack of storage space can present significant problems, for example, at construction sites in crowded urban locations. Because of the many diverse activities carried out on large projects and because of the wide range of skills required, special efforts are needed to coordinate the activities, and the span of control can be quite narrow. For these reasons, the administrative burden is often much higher than it would be under either of the other layout types. Material handling may or may not be a factor; in many cases, there is no tangible product involved (e.g., designing a computerized inventory system). When goods and materials are involved, material handling often resembles process-type, variable-path, general-purpose equipment. Projects might require use of earth-moving equipment and trucks to haul materials to, from, and around the work site, for example.

Fixed-position layouts are widely used in farming, firefighting, road building, home building, remodeling and repair, and drilling for oil. In each case, compelling reasons bring workers, materials, and equipment to the product's location instead of the other way around.

Combination Layouts

The three basic layout types are ideal models, which may be altered to satisfy the needs of a particular situation. It is not hard to find layouts that represent some combination of these pure types. For instance, supermarket layouts are essentially process layouts, yet we find that most use fixed-path material-handling devices such as roller-type conveyors in the stockroom and belt-type conveyors at the cash registers. Hospitals also use the basic process arrangement, although frequently patient care involves more of a fixed-position approach, in which nurses, doctors, medicines, and special equipment are brought to the patient. By the same token, faulty parts made in a product layout may require off-line reworking, which involves customized processing. Moreover, conveyors are frequently observed in both farming and construction activities.

Process layouts and product layouts represent two ends of a continuum from small jobs to continuous production. Process layouts are conducive to the production of a wider range of products or services than product layouts, which is desirable from a customer standpoint where customized products are often in demand. However, process layouts tend to be less efficient and have higher unit production costs than product layouts. Some manufacturers

© Alain Denantes/Gamma-Rapho via Getty Images

The Queen Mary 2 when under construction at the Chantiers de l'Atlantique shipyard in St. Nazaire, France. When a large project must remain stationary, workers and equipment come to the site. The QM2 weighs 150,000 tons, is 1,132 feet long, and is 147.6 feet wide. Its capacity is 2,620 passengers and 1,253 officers and crew.

are moving away from process layouts in an effort to capture some of the benefits of product layouts. Ideally, a system is flexible and yet efficient, with low unit production costs. Cellular manufacturing, group technology, and flexible manufacturing systems represent efforts to move toward this ideal.

Cellular Layouts

Cellular Production. Cellular production is a type of layout in which workstations are grouped into what is referred to as a *cell.* Groupings are determined by the operations needed to perform work for a set of similar items, or *part families,* that require similar processing. The cells become, in effect, miniature versions of product layouts. The cells may have no conveyorized movement of parts between machines, or they may have a flow line connected by a conveyor (automatic transfer). All parts follow the same route, although minor variations (e.g., skipping an operation) are possible. In contrast, the functional layout involves multiple paths for parts. Moreover, there is little effort or need to identify part families.

Cellular manufacturing enables companies to produce a variety of products with as little waste as possible. A cell layout provides a smooth flow of work through the process with minimal transport or delay. Benefits frequently associated with cellular manufacturing include minimal work in process, reduced space requirements and lead times, productivity and quality improvement, and increased flexibility.

Figure 6.7 provides a comparison between a traditional process layout (6.7A) and a cellular layout (6.7B). To get a sense of the advantage of the cellular layout, trace the movement of an order in the traditional layout (6.7A) that is depicted by the path of the arrow. Begin on the bottom left at Shipping/Receiving, then follow the arrow to Warehouse, where a batch of raw

Cellular production Layout in which workstations are grouped into a cell that can process items that have similar processing requirements.

Production & Operations Management

FIGURE 6.7
Comparison of process
and cellular layouts

Source: Adapted from U.S. Environmental
Protection Agency, "Lean Manufacturing and
the Environment," www.epa.gov/innovation/
lean/thinking/cellular.htm.

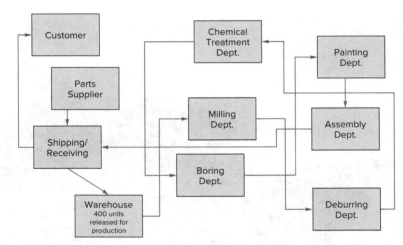

A. Example of an order processed in a traditional process layout.

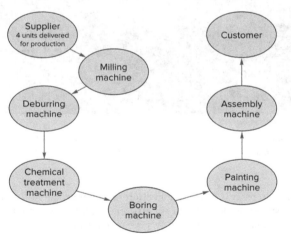

B. The same example of an order processed in a cellular layout.

material is released for production. Follow the path (shown by the arrows) that the batch takes
as it moves through the system to Shipping/Receiving and then to the Customer. Now turn to
Figure 6.7B. Note the simple path the order takes as it moves through the system.

Several techniques facilitate effective cellular layout design. Among them are the following two:

Single-minute exchange of die (SMED) enables an organization to quickly convert a
machine or process to produce a different (but similar) product type. Thus, a single cell
can produce a variety of products without the time-consuming equipment changeover
associated with large batch processes, enabling the organization to quickly respond to
changes in customer demand.

Right-sized equipment is often smaller than equipment used in traditional process layouts, and mobile, so that it can quickly be reconfigured into a different cellular layout in
a different location.

Table 6.5 lists the benefits of cellular layouts compared to functional layouts.

The biggest challenges of implementing cellular manufacturing involve issues of equipment and layout and issues of workers and management. Equipment and layout issues relate

Dimension	Functional	Cellular
Number of moves between departments	Many	Few
Travel distances	Longer	Shorter
Travel paths	Variable	Fixed
Job waiting time	Greater	Shorter
Throughput time	Higher	Lower
Amount of work in process	Higher	Lower
Supervision difficulty	Higher	Lower
Scheduling complexity	Higher	Lower
Equipment utilization	Lower	Higher

TABLE 6.5
A comparison of functional (process) layouts and cellular layouts

to design and cost. The costs of work stoppages during implementation can be considerable, as can the costs of new or modified equipment and the rearrangement of the layout. The costs to implement cellular manufacturing must be weighed against the cost savings that can be expected from using cells. Also, the implementation of cell manufacturing often requires employee training and the redefinition of jobs. Each of the workers in each cell should ideally be able to complete the entire range of tasks required in that cell, and often this means being more multiskilled than they were previously. In addition, cells are often expected to be self-managing, and therefore workers will have to be able to work effectively in teams. Managers have to learn to be less involved than with more traditional work methods.

Group Technology. Effective cellular manufacturing must have groups of identified items with similar processing characteristics. This strategy for product and process design is known as **group technology** and involves identifying items with similarities in either *design characteristics* or *manufacturing characteristics,* and grouping them into *part families.* Design characteristics include size, shape, and function; manufacturing or processing characteristics involve the type and sequence of operations required. In many cases, design and processing characteristics are correlated, although this is not always the case. Thus, design families may be different from processing families. Figure 6.8 illustrates a group of parts with similar processing characteristics but different design characteristics.

Group technology The grouping into part families of items with similar design or manufacturing characteristics.

FIGURE 6.8
A group of parts with similar manufacturing process requirements but different design attributes

Source: © McGraw-Hill Education/Mark Dierker, photographer

Once similar items have been identified, items can be classified according to their families; then a system can be developed that facilitates retrieval from a database for purposes of design and manufacturing. For instance, a designer can use the system to determine if there is an existing part similar or identical to one that needs to be designed. It may happen that an existing part, with some modification, is satisfactory. This greatly enhances the productivity of design. Similarly, planning the manufacturing of a new part can include matching it with one of the part families in existence, thereby alleviating much of the burden of specific processing details.

The conversion to group technology and cellular production requires a systematic analysis of parts to identify the part families. This is often a major undertaking; it is a time-consuming job that involves the analysis of a considerable amount of data. Three primary methods for accomplishing this are visual inspection, examination of design and production data, and production flow analysis.

Visual inspection is the least accurate of the three but also the least costly and the simplest to perform. Examination of design and production data is more accurate but much more time-consuming; it is perhaps the most commonly used method of analysis. Production flow analysis has a manufacturing perspective and not a design perspective, because it examines operations sequences and machine routings to uncover similarities. Moreover, the operation sequences and routings are taken as givens; in reality the existing procedures may be far from optimal.

Conversion to cellular production can involve costly realignment of equipment. Consequently, a manager must weigh the benefits of a switch from a process layout to a cellular one against the cost of moving equipment as well as the cost and time needed for grouping parts.

Flexible manufacturing systems, discussed earlier, are more fully automated versions of cellular manufacturing.

Service Layouts

As is the case with manufacturing, service layouts can often be categorized as product, process, or fixed-position layouts. In a fixed-position service layout (e.g., appliance repair, roofing, landscaping, home remodeling, copier service), materials, labor, and equipment are brought to the customer's residence or office. Process layouts are common in services due mainly to the high degree of variety in customer processing requirements. Examples include hospitals, supermarkets and department stores, vehicle repair centers, and banks. If the service is organized sequentially, with all customers or work following the same or similar sequence, as it is in a car wash or a cafeteria line, a product layout is used.

However, service layout requirements are somewhat different from manufacturing layout requirements. The degree of customer contact and the degree of customization are two key factors in service layout design. If contact and customization are both high, as in health care and personal care, the service environment is a job shop, usually with high labor content and flexible equipment, and a layout that supports this. If customization is high but contact low (e.g., picture framing, tailoring), the layout can be arranged to facilitate workers and equipment. If contact is high but customization is low (e.g., supermarkets, gas stations), self-service is a possibility, in which case layout must take into account ease of obtaining the service as well as customer safety. If the degree of contact and the need for customization are low, the core service and the customer can be separated, making it easier to achieve a high degree of efficiency in operations. Highly standardized services may lend themselves to automation (e.g., Web services, online banking, ATM machines).

Let's consider some of these layouts.

Warehouse and Storage Layouts. The design of storage facilities presents a different set of factors than the design of factory layouts. Frequency of order is an important consideration; items that are ordered frequently should be placed near the entrance to the facility, and those ordered infrequently should be placed toward the rear of the facility. Any correlations between items are also significant (i.e., item A is usually ordered with item B), suggesting that placing those two items close together would reduce the cost and time of *picking* (retrieving) those

READING **A SAFE HOSPITAL ROOM OF THE FUTURE**

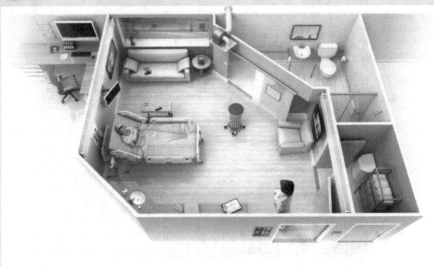

No one expects a stay in a hospital room to be unsafe or having to endure disruptions in their care, although today, there is need for improvement in hospital room safety and patient care. The following are suggestions for an improved hospital room of the future.

1. **Double-sided linen closets** allow staff to restock supplies without disturbing the patient.
2. **Bar codes** increase safety by matching the right medicine to the right patient.
3. **A two-bin supply system** ensures that providers don't run out of critical supplies.
4. **A hand-washing station** in every room gives providers a place to wash their hands.
5. **A sliding glass door** doubles as a **whiteboard** for information exchanges.
6. **Hand bars** on all sides of the bathroom help patients navigate more safely.
7. **Bed alarms** alert nurses that a patient may be attempting to get out of bed unassisted.
8. **Disinfecting units** use ultra-violet light to kill germs.
9. **Checklists** give providers a set of proven rules for preventing infections.
10. **Vents** suck the air out of the room of sick patients, filter it and then release it from the building.
11. **"Smart" pumps** deliver fluids, nutrients, and medicines to patients at precisely controlled rates.
12. **Kits for fall prevention** include color-coded nonslip socks, lap blanket and wristband.
13. Frequently touched surfaces, such as IV poles, bed rails and faucets, are made with **germ-resistant copper alloys,** which are naturally antimicrobial.
14. **Infrared technology** that lights up the sink reminds health care providers to wash their hands.
15. Beds with **translation technology** help staff speak with all patients.
16. **Real-time vital signs**—heart rate, blood pressure—can be monitored from computers outside the room.—*B.H.*

Questions

1. If you have experienced a hospital room, either as a patient or a visitor, which of these features was present in that room?
2. If you have experienced a hospital room, which of these features was missing, but would have been desirable additions?

Source: "Real Possibilities," *AARP The Magazine,* April/May 2013, p. 54.

items. Other considerations include the number and widths of aisles, the height of storage racks, rail and/or truck loading and unloading, and the need to periodically make a physical count of stored items.

268   **Chapter Six**   Process Selection and Facility Layout

Kiosks benefit customers by speeding up tedious processes and reducing waiting time. At McDonald's, kiosks actually increase sales by an average of $1 over face-to-face purchases. Managers explain this by the kiosk's ability to prompt customers for more purchases by showing pictures of products they might want to buy.

© Rick Wilking/Reuters

Retail Layouts. The objectives that guide design of manufacturing layouts often pertain to cost minimization and product flow. However, with retail layouts such as department stores, supermarkets, and specialty stores, designers must take into account the presence of customers and the opportunity to influence sales volume and customer attitudes through carefully designed layouts. Traffic patterns and traffic flow are important factors to consider. Some large retail chains use standard layouts for all or most of their stores. This has several advantages. Most obvious is the ability to save time and money by using one layout instead of custom designing one for each store. Another advantage is to avoid confusing consumers who visit more than one store. In the case of service retail outlets, especially small ones such as dry cleaners, shoe repair, and auto service centers, layout design is much simpler.

Office Layouts. Office layouts are undergoing transformations as the flow of paperwork is replaced with the increasing use of electronic communications. This lessens the need to place office workers in a layout that optimizes the physical transfer of information or paperwork. Another trend is to create an image of openness; office walls are giving way to low-rise partitions, which also facilitate communication among workers.

Restaurant Layouts. There are many different types of restaurants, ranging from food trucks to posh establishments. Many belong to chains, and some of those are franchises. That type of restaurant typically adheres to a floor plan established by the company. Independent restaurants and bars have their own floor plans. Some have what could be considered very good designs, while others do not. Ed Norman of MVP Services Group, Inc., in Dubuque, IA, offers this valuable observation: "The single most important element is process workflow. Food and non-food products should transition easily through the operation from the receiving door to the customer with all phases of storage, pre-preparation, cooking, holding, and service, unimpaired or minimized due to good design."

Hospital Layouts. Key elements of hospital layout design are patient care and safety, with easy access to critical resources such as X-ray, CAT scan, and MRI equipment. General layout of the hospital is one aspect of layout, while layout of patient rooms is another. The following reading illustrates a safe hospital room of the future.

© Oleksiy Maksymenko/Getty

© PhotoInc/Getty RF

From self check-in at the airport to depositing a check from anywhere, automation speeds up service and reduces the need to stand in line.

Automation in Services. One way to improve productivity and reduce costs in services is to remove the customer from the process as much as possible. Automated services is one increasingly used alternative. For example, financial services use ATMs, automated call answering, online banking, and electronic funds transfers; retail stores use optical scanning to process sales; and the travel industry uses electronic reservation systems. Other examples of automated services include shipping, mail processing, communication, and health care services.

Automating services means more-standardized services and less need to involve the customer directly. However, service standardization brings trade-offs. Generally, costs are reduced and productivity increases, but the lack of customization and the inability to deal with a real person raise the risk of customer dissatisfaction.

6.6 DESIGNING PRODUCT LAYOUTS: LINE BALANCING

> **LO6.8** Solve simple line-balancing problems.

The goal of a product layout is to arrange workers or machines in the sequence that operations need to be performed. The sequence is referred to as a production line or an assembly line. These lines range from fairly short, with just a few operations, to long lines that have a large number of operations. Automobile assembly lines are examples of long lines. At the assembly line for Ford Mustangs, a Mustang travels about nine miles from start to finish!

Because it is difficult and costly to change a product layout that is inefficient, design is a critical issue. Many of the benefits of a product layout relate to the ability to divide required work into a series of elemental tasks (e.g., "assemble parts C and D") that can be performed quickly and routinely by low-skilled workers or specialized equipment. The durations of these elemental tasks typically range from a few seconds to 15 minutes or more. Most time requirements are so brief that it would be impractical to assign only one task to each worker. For one thing, most workers would quickly become bored by the limited job scope. For another, the number of workers required to complete even a simple product or service would be enormous. Instead, tasks are usually grouped into manageable bundles and assigned to workstations staffed by one or two operators.

Line balancing The process of assigning tasks to workstations in such a way that the workstations have approximately equal time requirements.

The process of deciding how to assign tasks to workstations is referred to as **line balancing**. The goal of line balancing is to obtain task groupings that represent approximately equal time requirements. This minimizes the idle time along the line and results in a high utilization of labor and equipment. Idle time occurs if task times are not equal among workstations; some stations are capable of producing at higher rates than others. These "fast" stations will experience periodic waits for the output from slower stations or else be forced into idleness to avoid buildups of work between stations. Unbalanced lines are undesirable in terms of inefficient utilization of labor and equipment and because they may create morale problems at the slower stations for workers who must work continuously.

Lines that are perfectly balanced will have a smooth flow of work as activities along the line are synchronized to achieve maximum utilization of labor and equipment. The major obstacle to attaining a perfectly balanced line is the difficulty of forming task bundles that have the same duration. One cause of this is that it may not be feasible to combine certain activities into the same bundle, either because of differences in equipment requirements or because the activities are not compatible (e.g., risk of contamination of paint from sanding). Another cause of difficulty is that differences among elemental task lengths cannot always be overcome by grouping tasks. A third cause of an inability to perfectly balance a line is that a required technological sequence may prohibit otherwise desirable task combinations. Consider a series of three operations that have durations of two minutes, four minutes, and two minutes, as shown in the following diagram. Ideally, the first and third operations could be combined at one workstation and have a total time equal to that of the second operation. However, it may not be possible to combine the first and third operations. In the case of an automatic car wash, scrubbing and drying operations could not realistically be combined at the same workstation due to the need to rinse cars between the two operations.

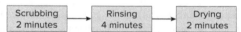

Line balancing involves assigning tasks to workstations. Usually, each workstation has one worker who handles all of the tasks at that station, although an option is to have several workers at a single workstation. For purposes of illustration, however, all of the examples and problems in this chapter have workstations with one worker. A manager could decide to use anywhere from one to five workstations to handle five tasks. With one workstation, all tasks would be done at that station; with five stations, for example, one task would be assigned to each station. If two, three, or four workstations are used, some or all of the stations will have multiple tasks assigned to them. How does a manager decide how many stations to use?

Cycle time The maximum time allowed at each workstation to complete its set of tasks on a unit.

The primary determinant is what the line's **cycle time** will be. The cycle time is the *maximum* time allowed at each workstation to perform assigned tasks before the work moves on. The cycle time also establishes the output rate of a line. For instance, if the cycle time is two minutes, units will come off the end of the line at the rate of one every two minutes. Hence, the line's capacity is a function of its cycle time.

We can gain some insight into task groupings and cycle time by considering a simple example.

Suppose that the work required to fabricate a certain product can be divided up into five elemental tasks, with the task times and precedence relationships as shown in the following diagram:

The task times govern the range of possible cycle times. The *minimum* cycle time is equal to the *longest* task time (1.0 minute), and the *maximum* cycle time is equal to the sum of the task times ($0.1 + 0.7 + 1.0 + 0.5 + 0.2 = 2.5$ minutes). The minimum cycle time would apply if there were five workstations. The maximum cycle time would apply if all tasks were performed at a single workstation. The minimum and maximum cycle times are important because they establish the potential range of output for the line, which we can compute using the following formula:

$$\text{Output rate} = \frac{\text{Operating time per day}}{\text{Cycle time}} \qquad (6\text{--}1)$$

Assume that the line will operate for eight hours per day (480 minutes). With a cycle time of 1.0 minute, output would be

$$\frac{480 \text{ minutes per day}}{1.0 \text{ minute per unit}} = 480 \text{ units per day}$$

With a cycle time of 2.5 minutes, the output would be

$$\frac{480 \text{ minutes per day}}{2.5 \text{ minute per unit}} = 192 \text{ units per day}$$

Assuming that no parallel activities are to be employed (e.g., two lines), the output selected for the line must fall in the range of 192 units per day to 480 units per day.

As a general rule, the cycle time is determined by the desired output; that is, a desired output rate is selected, and the cycle time is computed. If the cycle time does not fall between the maximum and minimum bounds, the desired output rate must be revised. We can compute the cycle time using this equation:

$$\text{Cycle time} = \frac{\text{Operating time per day}}{\text{Desired output rate}} \qquad (6\text{--}2)$$

For example, suppose that the desired output rate is 480 units. Using Formula 6–2, the necessary cycle time is

$$\frac{480 \text{ minutes per day}}{480 \text{ units per day}} = 1.0 \text{ minute per minute}$$

The number of workstations that will be needed is a function of both the desired output rate and our ability to combine elemental tasks into workstations. We can determine the *theoretical minimum* number of stations necessary to provide a specified rate of output as follows:

$$N_{\min} = \frac{\Sigma t}{\text{Cycle time}} \qquad (6\text{--}3)$$

where

$N_{\min}$ = Theoretical minimum number of stations
Σt = Sum of task times

Suppose the desired rate of output is the maximum of 480 units per day.[2] (This will require a cycle time of 1.0 minute.) The minimum number of stations required to achieve this goal is

$$N_{\min} = \frac{2.5 \text{ minutes per unit}}{1 \text{ minute per unit per station}} = 2.5 \text{ stations}$$

Because 2.5 stations is not feasible, it is necessary to *round up* (because 2.5 is the minimum) to three stations. Thus, the actual number of stations used will equal or exceed three, depending on how successfully the tasks can be grouped into workstations.

A very useful tool in line balancing is a **precedence diagram**. Figure 6.9 illustrates a simple precedence diagram. It visually portrays the tasks that are to be performed along with

Precedence diagram A diagram that shows elemental tasks and their precedence requirements.

---

[2] At first glance, it might seem that the desired output would logically be the maximum possible output. However, you will see why that is not always the best alternative.

272   **Chapter Six**   Process Selection and Facility Layout

FIGURE 6.9
A simple precedence
diagram

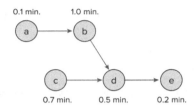

the *sequential* requirements, that is, the *order* in which tasks must be performed. The diagram is read from left to right, so the initial task(s) are on the left and the final task is on the right. In terms of precedence requirements, we can see from the diagram, for example, that the only requirement to begin task *b* is that task *a* must be finished. However, in order to begin task *d*, tasks *b* and *c* must *both* be finished. Note that the elemental tasks are the same ones that we have been using.

Now let's see how a line is balanced. This involves assigning tasks to workstations. Generally, no techniques are available that guarantee an optimal set of assignments. Instead, managers employ *heuristic (intuitive) rules,* which provide good and sometimes optimal sets of assignments. A number of line-balancing heuristics are in use, two of which are described here for purposes of illustration:

1. Assign tasks in order of most following tasks.
2. Assign tasks in order of greatest positional weight. Positional weight is the sum of each task's time and the times of all following tasks.

EXAMPLE 1

mhhe.com/stevenson13e

Assigning Tasks According to Greatest Number of Following Tasks

Arrange the tasks shown in Figure 6.9 into three workstations. Use a cycle time of 1.0 minute.
    Assign tasks in order of the greatest number of followers.

SOLUTION

1. Begin with task *a;* it has the most following tasks. Assign it to workstation 1.
2. Next, tasks *b* and *c* each have two following tasks, but only task *c* will fit in the time remaining at workstation 1, so assign task *c* to workstation 1.
3. Task *b* now has the most followers, but it will not fit at workstation 1, so assign it to workstation 2.
4. There is no time left at workstation 2, so we move on to workstation 3, assigning task *d* and then task *e* to that workstation.

Workstation	Time Remaining	Eligible	Assign Task	Revised Time Remaining	Station Idle Time
1	1.0	a, c	a	0.9	
	0.9	b, c	c	0.2	
	0.2	none	—		0.2
2	1.0	b	b	0.0	0.0
3	1.0	d	d	0.5	
	0.5	e	e	0.3	
	0.3	—	—		<u>0.3</u>
					0.5

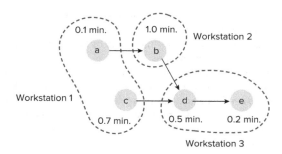

The initial "time remaining" for each workstation is equal to the cycle time. For a task to be eligible, tasks preceding it must have been assigned, and the task's time must not exceed the station's remaining time.

Example 1 is purposely simple; it is designed to illustrate the basic procedure. Later examples will illustrate tiebreaking, constructing precedence diagrams, and the positional weight method. Before considering those examples, let us first consider some measures of effectiveness that can be used for evaluating a given set of assignments.

Two widely used measures of effectiveness are

1. The **percentage of idle time** of the line. This is sometimes referred to as the **balance delay**. It can be computed as follows:

    Balance delay Percentage of idle time of a line.

$$\text{Percentage of idle time} = \frac{\text{Idle time per cycle}}{N_{actual} \times \text{Cycle time}} \times 100 \qquad (6\text{--}4)$$

where

$$N_{actual} = \text{Actual number of stations}$$

For the preceding example, the value is

$$\text{Percentage of idle time} = \frac{.5}{3 \times 1.0} \times 100 = 16.7\%$$

In effect, this is the average idle time divided by the cycle time, multiplied by 100. Note that cycle time refers to the actual cycle time that is achieved. When the calculated cycle time in Formula 6–2 and the actual bottleneck station time differ, the actual bottleneck station time should be used in all idle time, efficiency, and output (throughput) calculations. The actual bottleneck time dictates the actual pace of the line, whereas the calculated cycle time is just an upper limit on the amount of time that can be loaded into any station.

2. The **efficiency** of the line. This is computed as follows:

$$\text{Efficiency} = 100\% - \text{Percent idle time} \qquad (6\text{--}5a)$$

Here, Efficiency = 100% − 16.7% = 83.3%. Alternatively, efficiency could be computed using Formula 6–5b:

$$\text{Efficiency} = \frac{N_{actual} \times \text{Cycle time} - \text{Idle time}}{N_{actual} \times \text{Cycle time}} \times 100 \qquad (6\text{--}5b)$$

Now let's consider the question of whether the selected level of output should equal the maximum output possible. The minimum number of workstations needed is a function of the desired output rate and, therefore, the cycle time. Thus, a lower rate of output (hence, a longer cycle time) may result in a need for fewer stations. Hence, the manager must consider whether the potential savings realized by having fewer workstations would be greater than the decrease in profit resulting from producing fewer units.

The preceding examples serve to illustrate some of the fundamental concepts of line balancing. They are rather simple; in most real-life situations, the number of branches and tasks is often much greater. Consequently, the job of line balancing can be a good deal more complex. In many instances, the number of alternatives for grouping tasks is so great that it is virtually impossible to conduct an exhaustive review of all possibilities. For this reason, many real-life problems of any magnitude are solved using heuristic approaches. The purpose of a heuristic approach is to reduce the number of alternatives that must be considered, but it does not guarantee an optimal solution.

Some Guidelines for Line Balancing

In balancing an assembly line, tasks are assigned *one at a time* to the line, starting at the first workstation. At each step, the unassigned tasks are checked to determine which are eligible for assignment. Next, the eligible tasks are checked to see which of them will fit in the workstation being loaded. A heuristic is used to select one of the tasks that will fit, and the task is assigned. This process is repeated until there are no eligible tasks that will fit. Then the next workstation can be loaded. This continues until all tasks are assigned. The objective is to minimize the idle time for the line subject to technological and output constraints.

Technological constraints tell us which elemental tasks are *eligible* to be assigned at a particular position on the line. Technological constraints can result from the precedence or ordering relationships among the tasks. The precedence relationships require that certain tasks must be performed before others (and so, must be assigned to workstations before others). Thus, in a car wash, the rinsing operation must be performed before the drying operation. The drying operation is not eligible for assignment until the rinsing operation has been assigned. Technological constraints may also result from two tasks being incompatible (e.g., space restrictions or the nature of the operations may prevent their being placed in the same work center). For example, sanding and painting operations would not be assigned to the same work center because dust particles from the sanding operation could contaminate the paint.

Output constraints, on the other hand, determine the maximum amount of work that a manager can assign to each workstation, and this determines whether an eligible task *will fit* at a workstation. The desired output rate determines the cycle time, and the sum of the task times assigned to any workstation must not exceed the cycle time. If a task can be assigned to a workstation without exceeding the cycle time, then the task will fit.

Once it is known which tasks are *eligible* and *will fit*, the manager can select the task to be assigned (if there is more than one to choose from). This is where the heuristic rules help us decide which task to assign from among those that are eligible and will fit.

To clarify the terminology, *following tasks* are all tasks that you would encounter by following all paths from the task in question through the precedence diagram. *Preceding tasks* are all tasks you would encounter by tracing all paths *backward* from the task in question. In the following precedence diagram , tasks *b, d, e,* and *f* are followers of task *a.* Tasks *a, b,* and *c* are preceding tasks for *e.*

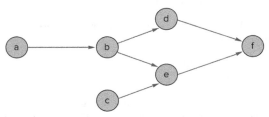

The *positional weight* for a task is the sum of the task times for itself and all its following tasks.

Neither of the heuristics *guarantees* the *best* solution, or even a good solution to the line-balancing problem, but they do provide guidelines for developing a solution. It may be useful to apply several different heuristics to the same problem and pick the best (least idle time) solution out of those developed.

EXAMPLE 2

eXcel
mhhe.com/stevenson13e

Drawing a Precedence Diagram, Computing Cycle Time and the Minimum Number of Workstations Needed, and Assigning Tasks Using Greatest Number of Following Tasks

Using the information contained in the table shown, do each of the following:

1. Draw a precedence diagram.

2. Assuming an eight-hour workday, compute the cycle time needed to obtain an output of 400 units per day.

3. Determine the minimum number of workstations required.

4. Assign tasks to workstations using this rule: Assign tasks according to greatest number of following tasks. In case of a tie, use the tiebreaker of assigning the task with the longest processing time first.

Task	Immediate Predecessor	Task Time (in minutes)
a	—	0.2
b	a	0.2
c	—	0.8
d	c	0.6
e	b	0.3
f	d, e	1.0
g	f	0.4
h	g	0.3
		$\Sigma t = 3.8$

5. Compute the resulting percent idle time and efficiency of the system.

SOLUTION

1. Drawing a precedence diagram is a relatively straightforward task. Begin with activities with no predecessors. We see from the list that tasks *a* and *c* do not have predecessors. We build from here.

Step 1:

Step 2: Task *b* follows *a*, and *d* follows *c*.

Step 3: Task *e* follows *b*.

step 4: Task *f* follows *e*, and *d*.

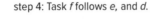

276 **Chapter Six** Process Selection and Facility Layout

Step 5: Task *g* follows *f*, and *h* follows *g*.

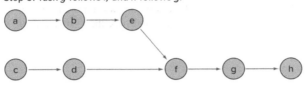

2. $\text{Cycle time} = \dfrac{\text{Operating time}}{\text{Desired output rate}} = \dfrac{480 \text{ minutes per day}}{400 \text{ units per day}} = 1.2 \text{ minutes per cycle}$

3. $N_{\min} = \dfrac{\sum t}{\text{Cycle time}} = \dfrac{3.8 \text{ minutes per unit}}{1.2 \text{ minutes per cycle per station}} = 3.17 \text{ stations (round to 4)}$

4. Beginning with station 1, make assignments following this procedure: Determine from the precedence diagram which tasks are eligible for assignment. Then determine which of the eligible tasks will fit the time remaining for the station. Use the tiebreaker if necessary. Once a task has been assigned, remove it from consideration. When a station cannot take any more assignments, go on to the next station. Continue until all tasks have been assigned.

Station	Time Remaining	Eligible	Will Fit	Assign (task time)	Revised Time Remaining	Idle
1	1.2	a, c*	a, c*	a (0.2)		
	1.0	c, b**	c, b**	c (0.8)	0.2	
	0.2	b, d	b	b (0.2)	0.0	
	0	e, d	None	—		0.0
2	1.2	e, d	e, d	d (0.6)	0.6	
	0.6	e	e	e (0.3)	0.3	
	0.3***	f	None	—		0.3
3	1.2	f	f	f (1.0)	0.2	
	0.2	g	None	—		0.2
4	1.2	g	g	g (0.4)	0.8	
	0.8	h	h	h (0.3)	0.5	
	0.5	—	—	—		0.5
						1.0 min.

*Neither *a* nor *c* has any predecessors, so both are eligible. Task *a* was assigned since it has more followers.
**Once *a* is assigned, *b* and *c* are now eligible. Both will fit in the time remaining of 1.0 minute. The tie cannot be broken by the "most followers" rule, so the longer task is assigned.
***Although *f* is eligible, this task will not fit, so station 2 is left with 0.3 minute of idle time per 1.2-minute cycle.

These assignments are shown in the following diagram. *Note:* One should not expect that heuristic approaches will always produce optimal solutions; they merely provide a practical way to deal with complex problems that may not lend themselves to optimizing techniques. Moreover, different heuristics often yield different answers.

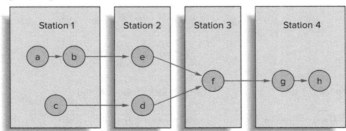

5. $\text{Percent idle time} = \dfrac{1.0 \text{ min.}}{4 \times 1.2 \text{ min.}} \times 100 = 20.83\%$

$\text{Efficiency} = 100\% - 20.83\% = 79.17\%$

Other Factors

The preceding discussion on line balancing presents a relatively straightforward approach to approximating a balanced line. In practice, the ability to do this usually involves additional considerations, some of which are technical.

Technical considerations include skill requirements of different tasks. If skill requirements of tasks are quite different, it may not be feasible to place the tasks in the same workstation. Similarly, if the tasks themselves are incompatible (e.g., the use of fire and flammable liquids), it may not be feasible even to place them in stations that are near each other.

Developing a workable plan for balancing a line may also require consideration of human factors as well as equipment and space limitations.

Although it is convenient to treat assembly operations as if they occur at the same rate time after time, it is more realistic to assume that whenever humans are involved, task completion times will be variable. The reasons for the variations are numerous, including fatigue, boredom, and failure to concentrate on the task at hand. Absenteeism also can affect line balance. Minor variability can be dealt with by allowing some slack along the line. However, if more variability is inherent in even a few tasks, that will severely impact the ability to achieve a balanced line.

For these reasons, lines that involve human tasks are more of an ideal than a reality. In practice, lines are rarely perfectly balanced. However, this is not entirely bad, because some unbalance means that slack exists at points along the line, which can reduce the impact of brief stoppages at some workstations. Also, workstations that have slack can be used for new workers who may not be "up to speed."

Other Approaches

Companies use a number of other approaches to achieve a smooth flow of production. One approach is to use *parallel workstations*. These are beneficial for bottleneck operations which would otherwise disrupt the flow of product as it moves down the line. The bottlenecks may be the result of difficult or very long tasks. Parallel workstations increase the work flow and provide flexibility.

Consider this example.[3] A job has four tasks; task times are 1 minute, 1 minute, 2 minutes, and 1 minute. The cycle time for the line would be 2 minutes, and the output rate would be 30 units per hour:

$$\frac{60 \text{ minutes per hour}}{2 \text{ minutes per unit}} = 30 \text{ units per hour}$$

Bottleneck

| 1 min. | 30/hr | 1 min. | 30/hr | 2 min. | 30/hr | 1 min. | 30/hr |

Using parallel stations for the third task would result in a cycle time of 1 minute because the output rate at the parallel stations would be equal to that of a single station and allow an output rate for the line of 60 units per hour:

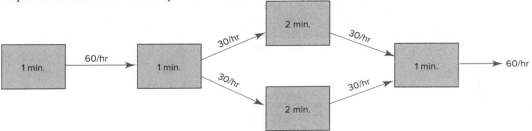

[3] Adapted from Mikell P. Groover, *Automation, Production Systems, and Computer-Aided Manufacturing,* 2nd ed. © 1987. Reprinted by permission of Pearson Education, Inc., Upper Saddle River, NJ.

 **BMW'S STRATEGY: FLEXIBILITY**

The assembly line in Dingolfing, Germany, where BMW assembles its 7-Series, has built-in flexibility that allows it to easily produce multiple models. Rival car producers typically configure their assembly lines to produce just a single model at a time. In order for them to produce a different model, the line must be shut down so that it can be changed over to be able to produce the different model. BMW's production flexibility enables its line to easily respond to market fluctuations while avoiding the costly change-overs that its rivals' more rigid lines require.

Source: Based on "Betting on the S," *The Wall Street Journal,* July 11, 2005, p. B1.

Another approach to achieving a balanced line is to *cross-train* workers so that they are able to perform more than one task. Then, when bottlenecks occur, the workers with temporarily increased idle time can assist other workers who are temporarily overburdened, thereby maintaining an even flow of work along the line. This is sometimes referred to as *dynamic line balancing,* and it is used most often in lean production systems.

Still another approach is to design a line to handle more than one product on the same line. This is referred to as a *mixed model line.* Naturally, the products have to be fairly similar, so that the tasks involved are pretty much the same for all products. This approach offers great flexibility in varying the amount of output of the products. The following reading describes one such line.

6.7 DESIGNING PROCESS LAYOUTS

LO6.9 Develop simple process layouts.

The main issue in designing process layouts concerns the relative positioning of the departments involved. As illustrated in Figure 6.10, departments must be assigned to locations. The problem is to develop a reasonably good layout; some combinations will be more desirable than others. For example, some departments may benefit from adjacent locations whereas others should be separated. A lab with delicate equipment would not be located near a department that had equipment with strong vibrations. Conversely, two departments that share some of the same equipment would benefit from being close together.

Layouts can also be influenced by external factors such as the location of entrances, loading docks, elevators, windows, and areas of reinforced flooring. Also important are noise levels, safety, and the size and locations of restrooms.

In some instances (e.g., the layouts of supermarkets, gas stations, and fast-food chains), a sufficient number of installations having similar characteristics justify the development of standardized layouts. For example, the use of the same basic patterns in McDonald's fast-food locations facilitates construction of new structures and employee training. Food preparation, order taking, and customer service follow the same pattern throughout the chain. Installation and service of equipment are also standardized. This same concept has been successfully employed in computer software products such as Microsoft Windows and the Macintosh Operating System. Different applications are designed with certain basic features in common, so that a user familiar with one application can readily use other applications without having to start from scratch with each new application.

The majority of layout problems involve single rather than multiple locations, and they present unique combinations of factors that do not lend themselves to a standardized approach. Consequently, these layouts require customized designs.

FIGURE 6.10
Work centers must be assigned to locations

Locations

A	B	C
D	E	F

Work centers to be assigned

1
2
3
4
5
6

A major obstacle to finding the most efficient layout of departments is the large number of possible assignments. For example, there are more than 87 billion different ways that 14 departments can be assigned to 14 locations if the locations form a single line. Different location configurations (e.g., 14 departments in a 2×7 grid) often reduce the number of possibilities, as do special requirements (e.g., the stamping department may have to be assigned to a location with reinforced flooring). Still, the remaining number of layout possibilities is quite large. Unfortunately, no algorithms exist to identify the best layout arrangement under all circumstances. Often planners must rely on heuristic rules to guide trial-and-error efforts for a satisfactory solution to each problem.

Measures of Effectiveness

One advantage of process layouts is their ability to satisfy a variety of processing requirements. Customers or materials in these systems require different operations and different sequences of operations, which causes them to follow different paths through the system. Material-oriented systems necessitate the use of variable-path material-handling equipment to move materials from work center to work center. In customer-oriented systems, people must travel or be transported from work center to work center. In both cases, transportation costs or time can be significant. Because of this factor, one of the major objectives in process layout is to minimize transportation cost, distance, or time. This is usually accomplished by locating departments with relatively high interdepartmental work flow as close together as possible.

Other concerns in choosing among alternative layouts include initial costs in setting up the layout, expected operating costs, the amount of effective capacity created, and the ease of modifying the system.

In situations that call for improvement of an existing layout, costs of relocating any work center must be weighed against the potential benefits of the move.

Information Requirements

The design of process layouts requires the following information:

1. A list of departments or work centers to be arranged, their approximate dimensions, and the dimensions of the building or buildings that will house the departments.

2. A projection of future work flows between the various work centers.

3. The distance between locations and the cost per unit of distance to move loads between locations.

4. The amount of money to be invested in the layout.

5. A list of any special considerations (e.g., operations that must be close to each other or operations that must be separated).

6. The location of key utilities, access and exit points, loading docks, and so on, in existing buildings.

The ideal situation is to first develop a layout and then design the physical structure around it, thus permitting maximum flexibility in design. This procedure is commonly followed when new facilities are constructed. Nonetheless, many layouts must be developed in existing structures where floor space, the dimensions of the building, location of entrances and elevators, and other similar factors must be carefully weighed in designing the layout. Note that multilevel structures pose special problems for layout planners.

Minimizing Transportation Costs or Distances

The most common goals in designing process layouts are minimization of transportation costs or distances traveled. In such cases, it can be very helpful to summarize the necessary data in *from-to charts* like those illustrated in Tables 6.6 and 6.7. Table 6.6 indicates the distance between each of the locations, and Table 6.7 indicates actual or projected work flow between each pair. For instance, the distance chart reveals that a trip from location A to location B will involve a distance of 20 meters. (Distances are often measured between department centers.) Oddly enough,

280 **Chapter Six** Process Selection and Facility Layout

TABLE 6.6
Distance between locations (meters)

From \ To	A	B	C
A		20	40
B			30
C			

TABLE 6.7
Interdepartmental work flow (loads per day)

From \ To	1	2	3
Dept. 1		30	170
Dept. 2			100
Dept. 3			

the length of a trip between locations A and B may differ depending on the *direction* of the trip, due to one-way routes, elevators, or other factors. To simplify the discussion, assume a constant distance between any two locations regardless of direction. However, it is not realistic to assume that interdepartmental work flows are equal—there is no reason to suspect that department 1 will send as much work to department 2 as department 2 sends to 1. For example, several departments may send goods to packaging, but packaging may send only to the shipping department.

Transportation costs can also be summarized in from-to charts, but we shall avoid that complexity, assuming instead that costs are a direct, linear function of distance.

EXAMPLE 3

mhhe.com/stevenson13e

Assigning Locations that Minimize Transportation Cost

Assign the three departments shown in Table 6.7 to locations A, B, and C, which are separated by the distances shown in Table 6.6, in such a way that transportation cost is minimized. Note that Table 6.7 summarizes the flows in both directions. Use this heuristic: Assign departments with the greatest interdepartmental work flow first to locations that are closest to each other.

SOLUTION

Ranking departments according to highest work flow and locations according to highest inter-location distances helps in making assignments.

Trip	Distance (meters)	Department Pair	Work Flow
A–B	20	1–3	170
B–C	30	2–3	100
A–C	40	1–2	30

From these listings, you can see that departments 1 and 3 have the highest interdepartmental work flow, and that locations A and B are the closest. Thus, it seems reasonable to consider assigning 1 and 3 to locations A and B, although it is not yet obvious which department should be assigned to which location. Further inspection of the work flow list reveals that 2 and 3 have higher work flow than 1 and 2, so 2 and 3 should probably be located more closely than 1 and 2. Hence, it would seem reasonable to place 3 between 1 and 2, or at least centralize that department with respect to the other two. The resulting assignments might appear as illustrated in Figure 6.11.

If the cost per meter to move any load is $1, you can compute the total daily transportation cost for this assignment by multiplying each department's number of loads by the trip distance, and summing those quantities:

Department	Number of Loads Between	Location	Distance To:	Loads × Distance
1	2: 30	A	C: 40	30 × 40 = 1,200
	3: 170		B: 20	170 × 20 = 3,400
2	3: 100	C	B: 30	100 × 30 = 3,000
			B: 30	100 × 30 = 3,000
				7,600

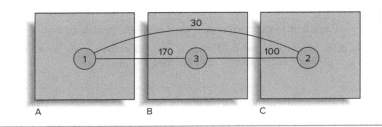

FIGURE 6.11
Interdepartmental work flows for assigned departments

At $1 per load meter, the cost for this plan is $7,600 per day. Even though it might appear that this arrangement yields the lowest transportation cost, you cannot be absolutely positive of that without actually computing the total cost for every alternative and comparing it to this one. Instead, rely on the choice of reasonable heuristic rules such as those demonstrated previously to arrive at a satisfactory, if not optimal, solution.

Closeness Ratings

Although the preceding approach is widely used, it suffers from the limitation of focusing on only one objective, and many situations involve multiple criteria. Richard Muther developed a more general approach to the problem, which allows for subjective input from analysis or managers to indicate the relative importance of each combination of department pairs.[4] That information is then summarized in a grid like that shown in Figure 6.12. Read the grid in the same way as you would read a mileage chart on a road map, except that letters rather than distances appear at the intersections. The letters represent the importance of closeness for each department pair, with A being the most important and X being an undesirable pairing. Thus, in the grid it is "absolutely necessary" to locate 1 and 2 close to each other because there is an A at the intersection of those departments on the grid. On the other hand, 1 and 4 should not be close together because their intersection has an X. In practice, the letters on the grid are often accompanied by numbers that indicate the reason for each assignment; they are omitted here to simplify the illustration. Muther suggests the following list:

1. They use same equipment or facilities.
2. They share the same personnel or records.
3. Required sequence of work flow.
4. Needed for ease of communication.
5. Would create unsafe or unpleasant conditions.
6. Similar work is performed.

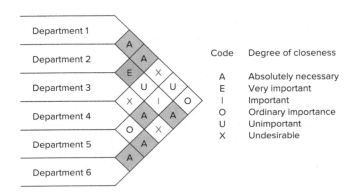

FIGURE 6.12
A Muther grid

Code	Degree of closeness
A	Absolutely necessary
E	Very important
I	Important
O	Ordinary importance
U	Unimportant
X	Undesirable

[4]Richard Muther and John Wheeler, "Simplified Systematic Layout Planning," *Factory* 120, nos. 8, 9, and 10 (August, September, October 1962), pp. 68–77, 111–119, 101–113, respectively.

EXAMPLE 4   **Assign Departments in Order of Criticalness**

Assign the six departments in Figure 6.12 to a 2 × 3 set of locations using the heuristic rule: Assign critical departments first, because they are the most important.

SOLUTION

Critical pairs of departments are those with A or X ratings. Prepare a list of those by referring to the grid:

A Links	X Links
1–2	1–4
1–3	3–6
2–6	3–4
3–5	
4–6	
5–6	

Next, form a cluster of A links, beginning with the department that appears most frequently in the A list (in this case, 6). For instance:

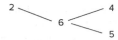

Take the remaining A links in order, and add them to this main cluster where possible, rearranging the cluster as necessary. Form separate clusters for departments that do not link with the main cluster. In this case, all link with the main cluster.

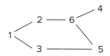

Next, graphically portray the X links:

Observe that, as it stands, the cluster of A links also satisfies the X separations. It is a fairly simple exercise to fit the cluster into a 2 × 3 arrangement:

1	2	6
3	5	4

Note that the lower-level ratings have also been satisfied with this arrangement, even though no attempt was made to explicitly consider the E and I ratings. Naturally, not every problem will yield the same results, so it may be necessary to do some additional adjusting to see if improvements can be made, keeping in mind that the A and X assignments deserve the greatest consideration.

Note that departments are considered close not only when they touch side to side but also when they touch corner to corner.

The value of this rating approach is that it permits the use of multiple objectives and subjective inputs. Its limitations relate to the use of subjective inputs in general: They are imprecise and unreliable.

Chapter Six   Process Selection and Facility Layout   **283**

Process selection choices often have strategic implications for organizations. They can affect cost, quality, productivity, customer satisfaction, and competitive advantage. Process types include job shop, batch processing, repetitive processing, continuous processing, and projects. Process type determines how work is organized, and it has implications for the entire organization and its supply chain. Process type and layout are closely related. Except for projects, process selection is usually a function of the volume and variety needed.

SUMMARY

Layout decisions are an important aspect of the design of operations systems, affecting operating costs and efficiency. Layout decisions are often closely related to process selection decisions.

Product layouts are geared to high-volume output of standardized items. Workers and equipment are arranged according to the technological sequence required by the product or service involved. Emphasis in design is on work flow through the system, and specialized processing and handling equipment is often used. Product layouts are highly vulnerable to breakdowns. Preventive maintenance is used to reduce the occurrence of breakdowns. Software is available for large or complex designs.

Process layouts group similar activities into departments or other work centers. These systems can handle a wide range of processing requirements and are less susceptible to breakdowns. However, the variety of processing requirements necessitates continual routing and scheduling and the use of variable-path material-handling equipment. The rate of output is generally much lower than that of product layouts.

Fixed-position layouts are used when size, fragility, cost, or other factors make it undesirable or impractical to move a product through a system. Instead, workers, equipment, and materials are brought to the product.

The main design efforts in product layout development focus on dividing up the work required to produce a product or service into a series of tasks that are as nearly equal as possible. The goal is to achieve a high degree of utilization of labor and equipment. In process layout, design efforts often focus on the relative positioning of departments to minimize transportation costs or to meet other requirements concerning the proximity of certain department pairs.

The large number of possible alternatives to layout problems prevents an examination of each one. Instead, heuristic rules guide discovery of alternatives. The solutions thus obtained are usually satisfactory although not necessarily optimal. Software packages are available to reduce the effort required to obtain solutions to layout problems, but these too rely largely on heuristic methods.

KEY POINTS

1. Process choice is demand driven.

2. Process type and layout are a function of expected demand volume and the degree of customization that will be needed.

3. Each process type and layout type has advantages and limitations that should be clearly understood when making process selection and layout decisions.

4. Process design is critical in a product-focused system, whereas managing is critical in a process-focused system.

KEY TERMS

3D printing, 255
assembly line, 258
automation, 251
balance delay, 273
cellular Production, 263
computer-aided manufacturing (CAM), 252
computer-integrated manufacturing (CIM), 254

cycle time, 270
fixed-position layout, 262
flexible manufacturing system (FMS), 253
group technology, 265
intermittent processing, 261
line balancing, 270
numerically controlled (N/C) machines, 252

precedence diagram, 271
process layouts, 260
production line, 258
product layouts, 262
product or service profiling, 250
project, 247
technological innovation, 250
technology, 250

SOLVED PROBLEMS

The tasks shown in the following precedence diagram are to be assigned to workstations with the intent of minimizing idle time. Management has designed an output rate of 275 units per day. Assume 440 minutes are available per day.

Problem 1

a. Determine the appropriate cycle time.

b. What is the minimum number of stations possible?

284 **Chapter Six** Process Selection and Facility Layout

c. Assign tasks using the "positional weight" rule: Assign tasks with highest following times (including a task's own time) first. Break ties using greatest number of following tasks.

d. Compute efficiency.

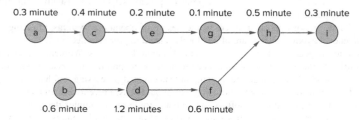

Solution

a. Cycle time $= \dfrac{\text{Operating time}}{\text{Desired output}} = \dfrac{440 \text{ minutes per day}}{275 \text{ units per day}} = 1.6$ minutes per unit

b. $N = \dfrac{\sum t}{\text{Cycle time}} = \dfrac{4.2}{1.6 \text{ minutes}} = 2.625$ (round to 3)

c. Add positional weights (task time plus the sum of all following times) to the diagram. Start at the right end and work backward:

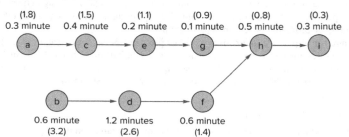

Station	Time Remaining*	Eligible	Will Fit	Assign Task/Time	Station Idle Time
1	1.6	a, b	a, b	b/0.6	
	1.0	a, d	a	a/0.3	
	0.7	c, d	c	c/0.4	
	0.3	e, d	e	e/0.2	
	0.1	g, d	g	g/0.1	
	0	—	—	—	0
2	1.6	d	d	d/1.2	
	0.4	f	none	none	0.4
3	1.6	f	f	f/0.6	
	1.0	h	h	h/0.5	
	0.5	i	i	i/0.3	
	0.2	—	—	—	0.2
					0.6

*The initial time for each station is the cycle time computed in part a.

The resulting assignments are shown as follows.

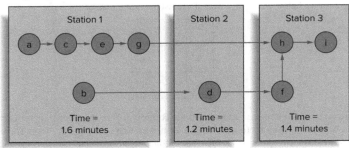

d.   Efficiency $= 100\% -$ Percent idle time $= 100\% - \dfrac{0.6 \text{ min.}}{3 \times 1.6 \text{ min.}} \times 100 = 87.5\%$

Problem 2

Assign nine automobile service departments to bays in a 3×3 grid so that the closeness ratings in the following matrix are satisfied. (The unimportant and ordinary-importance ratings have been omitted to simplify the example.) The location of department 4 must be in the upper right-hand corner of the grid to satisfy a town ordinance.

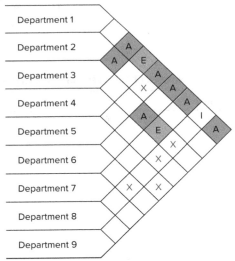

Solution

Note that department 1 has many A ratings, making it a strong candidate for the center position in the grid. We can form a cluster of departments that should be close together:

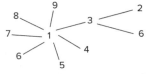

Next, we can identify departmental pairings that should be avoided:

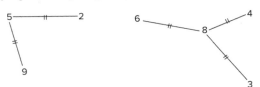

286 **Chapter Six** Process Selection and Facility Layout

These departments should be spaced around the perimeter of the grid. After a bit of trial and error, the final grid shown below emerged. Check it against the rating matrix to see if it satisfies the ratings.

2	3	4
9	1	6
8	7	5

Problem 3 Five departments are to be assigned to locations B through F in the grid. (For technical reasons, department 6 must be assigned to location A.) Transportation cost is $2 per foot. The objective is to minimize total transportation cost. Information on interdepartmental work flows and distances between locations is shown in the following tables. Assign departments with the greatest interdepartmental work flow first.

DISTANCE BETWEEN LOCATIONS (FEET)

From	To	A	B	C	D	E	F
A		—	50	100	50	80	130
B			—	50	90	40	70
C				—	140	60	50
D					—	50	120
E						—	50
F							—

NUMBER OF TRIPS PER DAY BETWEEN CENTERS

From	To	1	2	3	4	5	6
1		—	125	62	64	25	50
2			—	10	17	26	54
3				—	2	0	20
4					—	13	2
5						—	5
6							—

A Dept. 6	B	C
D	E	F

Solution First either rank or arrange the work flows from high to low. Here they have been arranged from high to low.

Dept.	Work Flow	Dept.	Work Flow
1–2	125	2–4	17
1–4	64	4–5	13
1–3	62	2–3	10
2–6	54	5–6	5
1–6	50	3–4	2
2–5	26	4–6	2
1–5	25	3–5	0
3–6	20		

From this, we can see that departments 1 and 2 have the greatest interdepartmental work flow, so they should be close, perhaps at B and E. Next, work flows for 1–3 and 1–4 are high. Note, though, that the work flow for 3–4 is low, suggesting that they need not be close. Instead, we would place them on either side of department 1. Note also that 3–4 is only 2, 3–5 is 0, while 3–6 is 20 and 4–5 is 13. Hence, place department 3 at location D, department 4 at location F, and department 5 at location C.

A Dept. 6	B Dept. 2	C Dept. 5
D Dept. 3	E Dept. 1	F Dept. 4

Total cost:

Trip		b Distance	c Frequency	(b × c × $2) Cost
1–2	(B–E)	40	125	$10,000
1–3	(D–E)	50	62	6,200
1–4	(F–E)	50	64	6,400
1–5	(E–C)	60	25	3,000
1–6	(A–E)	80	50	8,000
2–3	(B–D)	90	10	1,800
2–4	(B–F)	70	17	2,380
2–5	(B–C)	50	26	2,600
2–6	(A–B)	50	54	5,400
3–4	(F–D)	120	2	480
3–5	(D–C)	140	0	0
3–6	(A–D)	50	20	2,000
4–5	(C–F)	50	13	1,300
4–6	(A–F)	130	2	520
5–6	(A–C)	100	5	1,000
				$51,080

DISCUSSION & REVIEW QUESTIONS

1. Explain the importance of process selection in system design.
2. Briefly describe the five process types, and indicate the kinds of situations in which each would be used.
3. Briefly discuss the advantages and disadvantages of automation.
4. Briefly describe computer-assisted approaches to production.
5. What is a flexible manufacturing system, and under what set of circumstances is it most appropriate?
6. Why is management of technology important?
7. Why might the choice of equipment that provides flexibility sometimes be viewed as a management cop-out?
8. What are the trade-offs that occur when a process layout is used? What are the trade-offs that occur when a product layout is used?
9. List some common reasons for redesigning layouts.
10. Briefly describe the two main layout types.
11. What are the main advantages of a product layout? The main disadvantages?
12. What are the main advantages of a process layout? The main disadvantages?
13. What is the goal of line balancing? What happens if a line is unbalanced?
14. Why are routing and scheduling continual problems in process layouts?
15. Compare equipment maintenance strategies in product and process layouts.
16. Briefly outline the impact that job sequence has on each of the layout types.

288   **Chapter Six**   Process Selection and Facility Layout

17. The City Transportation Planning Committee must decide whether to begin a long-term project to build a subway system or to upgrade the present bus service. Suppose you are an expert in fixed-path and variable-path material-handling equipment, and the committee seeks your counsel on this matter. What are the advantages and limitations of the subway and bus systems?

18. Identify the fixed-path and variable-path material-handling equipment commonly found in supermarkets.

19. What are heuristic approaches, and why are they used in designing layouts?

20. Why are product layouts atypical in service environments?

21. According to a study by the Alliance of American Insurers, it costs more than three times the original purchase price in parts and labor to reconstruct a wrecked Chevrolet. Explain the reasons for this large discrepancy in terms of the processes used to assemble the original car and those required to reconstruct the wrecked car.

22. Name some ways that a layout can help or hinder productivity.

23. What is cellular manufacturing? What are its main benefits and limitations?

24. What is group technology?

25. Explain the consequences of task time variability on line balancing.

TAKING STOCK

1. Name three major trade-offs in process selection.
2. What trade-offs are involved when deciding how often to rebalance an assembly line?
3. Who needs to be involved in process selection?
4. Who needs to be involved in layout design?
5. In what ways does technology have an impact on process selection? How can technology impact layout decisions?

CRITICAL THINKING EXERCISES

1. Name two unethical behaviors related to process selection and two related to layout, and the ethical principles they violate (see Chapter 1).
2. Layout decisions affect a wide range of facilities, from factories, supermarkets, offices, department stores, and warehouses, to malls, parking lots and garages, and kitchens. Layout is also important in the design of some products such as the interiors of automobiles and the arrangement of components inside computers and other electronic devices. Select three different items from this list, or other similar items, and explain for each what the four or five key considerations for layout design are.
3. What are the risks of automating a production process? What are the risks for a service process?
4. Consider an assembly line such as the burrito assembly line at Chipotle Mexican Grill. During slow times of the day, one server can handle assembly, but during very busy times, having many servers would be prudent. Explain why either approach wouldn't work all the time, and the benefit of matching the number of servers to the pace of customer arrivals.

PROBLEMS

1. An assembly line with 17 tasks is to be balanced. The longest task is 2.4 minutes, and the total time for all tasks is 18 minutes. The line will operate for 450 minutes per day.

   a. What are the minimum and maximum cycle times?

   b. What range of output is theoretically possible for the line?

   c. What is the minimum number of workstations needed if the maximum output rate is to be sought?

   d. What cycle time will provide an output rate of 125 units per day?

   e. What output potential will result if the cycle time is (1) 9 minutes? (2) 15 minutes?

2. A manager wants to assign tasks to workstations as efficiently as possible and achieve an hourly output of 33⅓ units. Assume the shop works a 60-minute hour. Assign the tasks shown in the accompanying precedence diagram (times are in minutes) to workstations using the following rules:

   a. In order of most following tasks. Tiebreaker: greatest positional weight.

   b. In order of greatest positional weight. Tiebreaker: most following tasks.

   c. What is the efficiency?

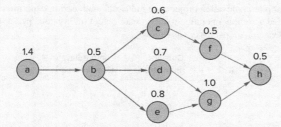

3. A manager wants to assign tasks to workstations as efficiently as possible and achieve an hourly output of four units. The department uses a working time of 56 minutes per hour. Assign the tasks shown in the accompanying precedence diagram (times are in minutes) to workstations using the following rules:

a. In order of most following tasks. Tiebreaker: greatest positional weight.

b. In order of greatest positional weight. Tiebreaker: most following tasks.

c. What is the efficiency?

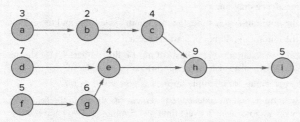

4. A producer of inkjet printers is planning to add a new line of printers, and you have been asked to balance the process, given the following task times and precedence relationships. Assume that cycle time is to be the minimum possible.

Task	Length (minutes)	Immediate (Predecessor)
a	0.2	—
b	0.4	a
c	0.3	—
d	1.3	b, c
e	0.1	—
f	0.8	e
g	0.3	d, f
h	1.2	g

a. Do each of the following:

(1) Draw the precedence diagram.

(2) Assign tasks to stations in order of most following tasks. Tiebreaker: greatest positional weight.

(3) Determine the percentage of idle time.

(4) Compute the rate of output in printers per day that could be expected for this line assuming a 420-minute working day.

b. Answer these questions:

(1) What is the shortest cycle time that will permit use of only two workstations? Is this cycle time feasible? Identify the tasks you would assign to each station.

(2) Determine the percentage of idle time that would result if two stations were used.

(3) What is the daily output under this arrangement?

(4) Determine the output rate that would be associated with the maximum cycle time.

5. As part of a major plant renovation project, the industrial engineering department has been asked to balance a revised assembly operation to achieve an output of 240 units per eight-hour day. Task times and precedence relationships are as follows:

Task	Duration (minutes)	Immediate (Predecessor)
a	0.2	—
b	0.4	a
c	0.2	b
d	0.4	—
e	1.2	d
f	1.2	c
g	1.0	e, f

Do each of the following:

a. Draw the precedence diagram.

b. Determine the minimum cycle time, the maximum cycle time, and the calculated cycle time.

c. Determine the minimum number of stations needed.

d. Assign tasks to workstations on the basis of most following tasks. Use shortest processing time as a tiebreaker. If ties still exist, assume indifference in choice.

e. Compute the percentage of idle time for the assignment in part *d*.

6. Twelve tasks, with times and precedence requirements as shown in the following table, are to be assigned to workstations using a cycle time of 1.5 minutes. Two heuristic rules will be tried: (1) greatest positional weight, and (2) most following tasks.

In each case, the tiebreaker will be shortest processing time.

Task	Length (minutes)	Immediate Predecessor
a	0.1	—
b	0.2	a
c	0.9	b
d	0.6	c
e	0.1	—
f	0.2	d, e
g	0.4	f
h	0.1	g
i	0.2	h
j	0.7	i
k	0.3	j
l	0.2	k

a. Draw the precedence diagram for this line.

b. Assign tasks to stations under each of the two rules.

c. Compute the percentage of idle time for each rule.

7. For the given set of tasks, do the following:

a. Develop the precedence diagram.

b. Determine the minimum cycle time and then calculate the cycle time for a desired output of 500 units in a seven-hour day. Why might a manager use a cycle time of 50 seconds?

c. Determine the minimum number of workstations for output of 500 units per day.

   d. Balance the line using the *greatest positional weight* heuristic. Break ties with the *most following tasks* heuristic. Use a cycle time of 50 seconds.

   e. Calculate the percentage idle time for the line.

Task	Task Time (seconds)	Immediate Predecessor
A	45	—
B	11	A
C	9	B
D	50	—
E	26	D
F	11	E
G	12	C
H	10	C
I	9	F, G, H
J	10	I
	193	

8. A shop works a 400-minute day. The manager of the shop wants an output of 200 units per day for the assembly line that has the elemental tasks shown in the table. Do the following:

   a. Construct the precedence diagram.

   b. Assign tasks according to the *most following tasks* rule. Break ties with the *greatest positional weight* rule.

   c. Assign tasks according to the *greatest positional weight* rule. Break ties with the *most following tasks* rule.

   d. Compute the balance delay for each rule. Which one yields the better set of assignments in this instance?

Task	Immediate Predecessor	Task Time
a	—	0.5
b	a	1.4
c	a	1.2
d	a	0.7
e	b, c	0.5
f	d	1.0
g	e	0.4
h	g	0.3
i	f	0.5
j	e, i	0.8
k	h, j	0.9
m	k	0.3

9. Arrange six departments into a 2 × 3 grid so that these conditions are satisfied: 1 close to 2, 5 close to 2 and 6, 2 close to 5, and 3 not close to 1 or 2.

10. Using the information given in the preceding problem, develop a Muther-type grid using the letters A, O, and X. Assume that any pair of combinations not mentioned have an O rating.

11. Using the information in the following grid, determine if the department locations shown are appropriate. If not, modify the assignments so that the conditions are satisfied.

Chapter Six Process Selection and Facility Layout

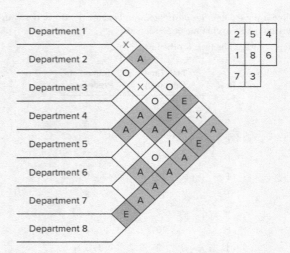

12. Arrange the eight departments shown in the accompanying Muther grid into a 2 × 4 format. *Note:* Department 1 must be in the location shown.

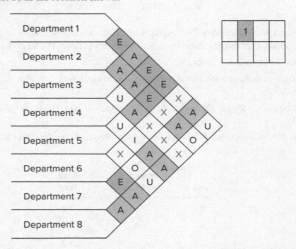

13. Arrange the departments so they satisfy the conditions shown in the following rating grid into a 3 × 3 format. Place department 5 in the lower left corner of the 3 × 3 grid.

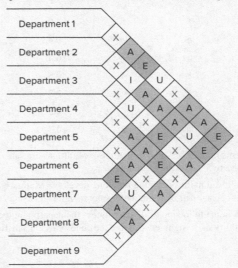

14. a. Determine the placement of departments for a newly designed facility that will minimize total transportation costs using the data in the following tables. Assume that reverse distances are the same. The locations are shown in the grid. Use a cost of $1 per trip yard.

Location A	Location B	Location C
	Location D	

DISTANCE BETWEEN LOCATIONS (yards)				
From \ To	A	B	C	D
A	—	40	80	70
B		—	40	50
C			—	60
D				—

NUMBER OF TRIPS PER DAY BETWEEN DEPARTMENTS				
From \ To	1	2	3	4
1	—	10	20	80
2		—	40	90
3			—	55
4				—

b. Suppose the company has revised its plans for the processes described in part *a* to accommodate technological process changes. Determine the placement of departments that will now minimize total travel cost. Use the distances shown in part *a*, but use the following new matrix of daily trips between departments.

NUMBER OF TRIPS PER DAY BETWEEN DEPARTMENTS				
From \ To	1	2	3	4
1	—	20	20	40
2		—	10	50
3			—	60
4				—

15. Eight work centers must be arranged in an L-shaped building. The locations of centers 1 and 3 are assigned as shown in the accompanying diagram. Assuming transportation selection costs are $1 per load per meter, develop a suitable layout that minimizes transportation costs using the given information. Compute the total cost. (Assume the reverse distances are the same.)

DISTANCE (meters)								
From \ To	A	B	C	D	E	F	G	H
A	—	40	40	60	120	80	100	110
B		—	60	40	60	140	120	130
C			—	45	85	40	70	90
D				—	40	50	40	45
E					—	90	50	40
F						—	40	60
G							—	40
H								—

Chapter Six Process Selection and Facility Layout

From	To	1	2	3	4	5	6	7	8
					LOADS PER DAY				
1		—	10	5	90	370	135	125	0
2			—	360	120	40	115	45	120
3				—	350	110	40	20	200
4					—	190	70	50	190
5						—	10	40	10
6							—	50	20
7								—	20
8									—

16. Develop a process layout that will minimize the total distance traveled by patients at a medical clinic, using the following information on projected departmental visits by patients and distance between locations. Assume a distance of 35 feet between the reception area and each potential location. Use the format shown.

DISTANCE BETWEEN LOCATIONS (feet)

From	To	A	B	C	D	E	F
A		—	40	80	100	120	160
B			—	40	60	80	120
C				—	20	40	80
D					—	20	40
E						—	40
F							—

TRIPS BETWEEN DEPARTMENTS (per day)

	To	Reception	1	2	3	4	5	6
Reception		—	20	50	210	20	10	130
1		10	—	0	40	110	80	50
2		40		—	0	50	40	120
3		10		0	—	10	250	10
4		0				—	40	90
5		10					—	20
6		30						—

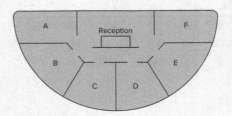

Chapter Six   Process Selection and Facility Layout   **295**

17. Ten labs will be assigned to the circular layout shown. Recalling a similar layout's congestion in the halls, the new lab manager has requested an assignment that will minimize traffic between offices. Department 1 must be at location A. Develop a suitable layout using the following information.

NUMBER OF TRIPS PER DAY BETWEEN DEPARTMENTS

From \ TO	1	2	3	4	5	6	7	8	9	10
1	—	40	51	26	23	9	20	12	11	35
2		—	37	16	27	15	18	18	18	36
3			—	18	20	14	50	18	25	36
4				—	35	14	14	22	23	31
5					—	24	14	13	21	25
6						—	17	44	42	25
7							—	14	33	40
8								—	43	35
9									—	47
10										—

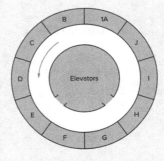

18. Rebalance the assembly line in Problem 7. This time, use the *longest operation time* heuristic. Break ties with the *most following tasks* heuristic. What is the percentage idle time for your line?

Francis, Richard L., Leon F. McGinnis Jr., and John A. White. *Facility Layout and Location: An Analytical Approach,* 3rd ed. Upper Saddle River, NJ: Prentice Hall, 2001.

Groover, Mikell P. *Automation, Production Systems, and Computer-Aided Manufacturing,* 3rd ed. Upper Saddle River, NJ: Prentice Hall, 2007.

Pinto, J. *A Short History of Automation Growth.* JimPinto.com

Stephens, Matthew P., and Fred E. Meyers. *Manufacturing Facilities Design & Material Handling,* 5th ed. West Lafayette, IN: Purdue University Press, 2013.

Zijlstra, Emma, and Mark P. Mobach. "The Influence of Facility Layout on Operations Explored." *Journal of Facilities Management* 9 (2011), pp. 127–144.

SELECTED BIBLIOGRAPHY & FURTHER READINGS

9 Management of Quality

LEARNING OBJECTIVES

After completing this chapter, you should be able to:

LO9.1   Discuss the philosophies of quality gurus.

LO9.2   Define the term *quality* as it relates to products and as it relates to services.

LO9.3   Identify the determinants of quality.

LO9.4   Explain why quality is important and the consequences of poor quality.

LO9.5   Describe and give examples of the costs associated with quality.

LO9.6   Discuss the importance of ethics in managing quality.

LO9.7   Compare the quality awards.

LO9.8   Discuss quality certification and its importance.

LO9.9   Describe TQM.

LO9.10   Give an overview of problem solving.

LO9.11   Give an overview of process improvement.

LO9.12   Describe the Six Sigma methodology.

LO9.13   Describe and use various quality tools.

CHAPTER OUTLINE

9.1   Introduction 373

9.2   The Evolution of Quality Management 374

9.3   The Foundations of Modern Quality Management: The Gurus 375

9.4   Insights on Quality Management 378
      Defining Quality: The Dimensions of Quality 378

Assessing Service Quality 380
The Determinants of Quality 381
Responsibility for Quality 382
Benefits of Good Quality 383
The Consequences of Poor Quality 383
The Costs of Quality 384
Ethics and Quality Management 386

9.5   Quality Awards 386
      The Baldrige Award 387
      The European Quality Award 387
      The Deming Prize 387

9.6   Quality Certification 387
      ISO 9000, 14000, and 24700 387

9.7   Quality and the Supply Chain 389

© Thomas Samson/AFP/Getty

9.8   Total Quality Management *390*

Obstacles to Implementing
TQM *392*

Criticisms of TQM *393*

**9.9   Problem Solving, and Process
Improvement** *394*

The Plan-Do-Study-Act
Cycle *394*

Six Sigma *396*

9.10   Quality Tools *398*

Illustrations of the Use of
Graphical Tools *403*

Methods for Generating
Ideas *404*

9.11   Operations Strategy *406*

Cases: Chick-n-Gravy Dinner Line *411*
         Tip Top Markets *412*

This chapter is the first of two chapters on quality. In this chapter you will learn about the evolution of quality management, definitions of quality, the costs of quality and the consequences of poor quality, some quality awards and quality certification, total quality management, and quality tools.

The importance of quality cannot be overstated; two key elements of every purchasing decision are price and quality. Consequently, having a focus on quality and quality improvement should be a part of every business organization, whether the organization's business is making cars, selling electronic goods, providing financial services, providing medical services, or baking cookies.

9.1 INTRODUCTION

Broadly defined, **quality** refers to the ability of a product or service to consistently meet or exceed customer requirements or expectations. However, different customers will have different requirements, so a working definition of quality is customer-dependent.

For a decade or so, quality was an important focal point in business. But after a while, the emphasis on quality began to fade, and quality took a backseat to other concerns. However, there has been an upsurge recently in the need for attention to quality. Much of this has been driven by recent experience with costs and adverse publicity associated with wide-ranging recalls that have included automobiles, ground meat, toys, produce, dog food, and pharmaceuticals.

Quality The ability of a product or service to consistently meet or exceed customer expectations.

Quality is more than just a statistical analysis tool for manufacturing lines. When done right, quality should encompass the entire enterprise.

Some 50 years after the advent of the total quality management (TQM) movement championed by W. Edwards Deming, manufacturers of all different sizes and stripes are still being dogged by high-profile manufacturing quality defects. The list is long, and getting longer every week, and crosses every manufacturing vertical. At least a token "quality program" is de rigueur for U.S. manufacturers, but many are still at lip-service level agreement with the means required to reach the necessary ends. However, talk is cheap—recalls are not.

From tainted beef to spinach, from lead-painted toys to poisoned pet food and blood thinners to exploding laptop batteries and malfunctioning medical devices, the costs in scrapped product, consumer lawsuits, and lost brand equity from defects and recalls are huge. Persistent, expensive and well-publicized recalls are striking companies with even the most stellar quality reputations. Toyota, the progenitor of a legendary quality-focused production system, has suffered a rash of defects that have caused the company to drop in *Consumer Reports'* Annual Car Reliability Survey ratings—an important market barometer for its consumers.

On a perhaps less dangerous but equally costly front, Microsoft's Xbox 360 video gaming platform suffered a high-profile manufacturing defect that at one point had up to one-third of all units suffering from a "fatal error" (device owners called it "the red ring of death") that led at least indirectly to markedly weaker competitive positioning in the crucial holiday selling season, as well as a warranty extension that is estimated at more than $6 billion in unplanned accruals.

Many of these manufacturing problems are coming from global supply chains, which is a failure as much of management as it is the defective products themselves. However bleak the situation may seem, all is not lost. Indeed, the responsibility for quality manufacturing finally seems to be taking hold across all levels of the enterprise.

Quality Goes Upstream

Talk to the manufacturing community about quality's place in today's environment and a clear pattern emerges—companies are finally grasping the "shared responsibility" aspect of Deming's teachings. If quality is truly everyone's responsibility, then the idea goes beyond the shop floor and into the front office, the service department and everywhere else that provides value to customers and shareholders.

Ron Atkinson, chairman of the American Society for Quality (ASQ), has been watching this trend unfold. He describes the path that the idea of quality management in manufacturing has taken over the years.

"When I started in manufacturing 35 years ago, there was a policeman installed at the end of the line who looked at the parts and said, 'That one is OK, that can be shipped and that one can't.' Gradually, it got to, 'Let's find better ways to do the checking,' and then to, 'Let's find a way to predict what the parts are going to look like when they hit the end of the line,' so we started doing defect prevention. Now where we're at is that quality is expanding to cover everything, including outside of the actual manufacturing process, to how do we improve the quality of our HR services and support services? How do we improve the quality of the decisions that are made?"

According to Atkinson, concepts crucial to establishing a top-quality manufacturing line have been driven upstream, and expanded to become part of an overall continuous improvement strategy. "Quality has become a systems approach, rather than focusing on one part at a time and whether it's dimensionally correct. Quality is continuous improvement."

Source: Excerpted from Brad Kenney, *Industry Week,* April 1, 2008.

9.2 THE EVOLUTION OF QUALITY MANAGEMENT

Prior to the Industrial Revolution, skilled craftsmen performed all stages of production. Pride of workmanship and reputation often provided the motivation to see that a job was done right. Lengthy guild apprenticeships caused this attitude to carry over to new workers. Moreover, one person or a small group of people were responsible for an entire product.

A division of labor accompanied the Industrial Revolution; each worker was then responsible for only a small portion of each product. Pride of workmanship became less meaningful because workers could no longer identify readily with the final product. The responsibility for quality shifted to the foremen. Inspection was either nonexistent or haphazard, although in some instances 100 percent inspection was used.

Frederick Winslow Taylor, the "Father of Scientific Management," gave new emphasis to quality by including product inspection and gauging in his list of fundamental areas of manufacturing management. G. S. Radford improved Taylor's methods. Two of his most significant contributions were the notions of involving quality considerations early in the product design stage and making connections among high quality, increased productivity, and lower costs.

In 1924, Bell Telephone Laboratories introduced statistical control charts that could be used to monitor production. Around 1930, H. F. Dodge and H. G. Romig, also of Bell Labs, introduced tables for sampling. Nevertheless, statistical quality control procedures were not widely used until World War II, when the U.S. government began to require vendors to use them.

World War II caused a dramatic increase in emphasis on quality control. The U.S. Army refined sampling techniques for dealing with large shipments of arms from many suppliers. By the end of the 1940s, the U.S. Army, Bell Labs, and major universities were training engineers in other industries in the use of statistical sampling techniques. About the same time, professional quality organizations were emerging throughout the country. One of these organizations was the American Society for Quality Control (ASQC, now known as ASQ). Over the years, the society has promoted quality with its publications, seminars and conferences, and training programs.

During the 1950s, the quality movement evolved into quality assurance. In the mid-1950s, total quality control efforts enlarged the realm of quality efforts from its primary focus on manufacturing to include product design and incoming raw materials. One important feature of this work was greater involvement of upper management in quality.

During the 1960s, the concept of "zero defects" gained favor. This approach focused on employee motivation and awareness, and the expectation of perfection from each employee. It evolved from the success of the Martin Company in producing a "perfect" missile for the U.S. Army.

In the 1970s, quality assurance methods gained increasing emphasis in services including government operations, health care, banking, and the travel industry.

Something else happened in the 1970s that had a global impact on quality. An embargo on oil sales instituted by the Organization of Petroleum Exporting Countries (OPEC) caused an increase in energy costs, and automobile buyers became more interested in fuel-efficient, lower-cost vehicles. Japanese auto producers, who had been improving their products, were poised to take advantage of these changes, and they captured an increased share of the automobile market. The quality of their automobiles enhanced the reputation of Japanese producers, opening the door for a wide array of Japanese-produced goods.

American producers, alarmed by their loss of market share, spent much of the late 1970s and the 1980s trying to improve the quality of their goods while lowering their costs.

The evolution of quality took a dramatic shift from quality assurance to a strategic approach to quality in the late 1970s. Up until that time, the main emphasis had been on finding and correcting defective products before they reached the market. It was still a reactive approach. The strategic approach is proactive, focusing on preventing mistakes from occurring in the first place. The idea is to design quality into products, rather than to find and correct defects after the fact. This approach has now expanded to include processes and services. Quality and profits are more closely linked. This approach also places greater emphasis on customer satisfaction, and it involves all levels of management as well as workers in a continuing effort to increase quality.

9.3 THE FOUNDATIONS OF MODERN QUALITY MANAGEMENT: THE GURUS

LO9.1 Discuss the philosophies of quality gurus.

A core of quality pioneers shaped current thinking and practice. This section describes some of their key contributions to the field.

Walter Shewhart. Walter Shewhart was a genuine pioneer in the field of quality control, and he became known as the "father of statistical quality control." He developed control charts for analyzing the output of processes to determine when corrective action was necessary.

© Richard Drew/AP Images

W. Edwards Deming.

Deming Prize Prize established by the Japanese and awarded annually to firms that distinguish themselves with quality management programs.

Shewhart had a strong influence on the thinking of two other gurus, W. Edwards Deming and Joseph Juran.

W. Edwards Deming. Deming, a statistics professor at New York University in the 1940s, went to Japan after World War II to assist the Japanese in improving quality and productivity. The Union of Japanese Scientists, who had invited Deming, were so impressed that in 1951, after a series of lectures presented by Deming, they established the **Deming Prize**, which is awarded annually to firms that distinguish themselves with quality management programs.

Although the Japanese revered Deming, he was largely unknown to business leaders in the United States. In fact, he worked with the Japanese for almost 30 years before he gained recognition in his own country. Before his death in 1993, U.S. companies turned their attention to Deming, embraced his philosophy, and requested his assistance in setting up quality improvement programs.

Deming compiled a famous list of 14 points he believed were the prescription needed to achieve quality in an organization (see Table 9.1). His message was that the cause of inefficiency and poor quality is the *system,* not the employees. Deming felt that it was *management's responsibility* to correct the system to achieve the desired results. In addition to the 14 points, Deming stressed the need to reduce variation in output (deviation from a standard), which can be accomplished by distinguishing between *special causes* of variation (i.e., correctable) and *common causes* of variation (i.e., random). Deming's concept of profound knowledge incorporates the beliefs and values about learning that guided Japan's rise to a world economic power.

Joseph M. Juran. Juran, like Deming, taught Japanese manufacturers how to improve the quality of their goods, and he, too, can be regarded as a major force in Japan's success in quality.

Juran viewed quality as fitness-for-use. He also believed that roughly 80 percent of quality defects are management controllable; thus, management has the responsibility to correct this deficiency. He described quality management in terms of a *trilogy* consisting of quality planning, quality control, and quality improvement. According to Juran, quality planning is necessary to establish processes that are *capable* of meeting quality standards; quality control is necessary in order to know when corrective action is needed; and quality improvement will help to find better ways of doing things. A key element of Juran's philosophy is the commitment of management to continual improvement.

TABLE 9.1
Deming's 14 points

1. Create constancy of purpose toward improvement of product and service.
2. Reduce levels of delays, mistakes, defective materials, and defective workmanship.
3. Cease dependence on mass inspection. (*Prevent* defects rather than *detect* defects.)
4. Eliminate suppliers that cannot qualify with statistical evidence of quality.
5. Find problems. It is management's job to work continually on system improvement.
6. Institute modern methods of training on the job.
7. Emphasize quality instead of volume alone. Management must prepare to take immediate action on reports from foremen concerning barriers such as inherent defects, machines not maintained, poor tools, and fuzzy operational definitions.
8. Drive out fear, so that everyone may work effectively for the company.
9. Break down barriers between departments. People in research, design, sales, and production must work as a team.
10. Eliminate goals and slogans asking for new levels of productivity without providing methods.
11. Eliminate work standards that prescribe numerical quotas.
12. Remove barriers that stand between the hourly worker and his right to pride of workmanship.
13. Institute a vigorous program of education and retraining.
14. Create a structure in top management that will push every day on the above 13 points.

Source: Adapted from W. Edwards Deming, *Out of the Crisis,* pp. 23 and 24. Copyright © 2000 MIT Press. Used with permission.

Juran is credited as one of the first to measure the cost of quality, and he demonstrated the potential for increased profits that would result if the costs of poor quality could be reduced.

Armand Feigenbaum. Feigenbaum was instrumental in advancing the "cost of nonconformance" approach as a reason for management to commit to quality. He recognized that quality was not simply a collection of tools and techniques, but a "total field." According to Feigenbaum, it is the customer who defines quality.

Philip B. Crosby. Crosby developed the concept of *zero defects* and popularized the phrase "Do it right the first time." He stressed prevention, and he argued against the idea that "there will always be some level of defectives." The quality-is-free concept presented in his book, *Quality Is Free,* is that the costs of poor quality are much greater than traditionally defined. According to Crosby, these costs are so great that rather than viewing quality efforts as costs, organizations should view them as a way to reduce costs, because the improvements generated by quality efforts will more than pay for themselves.

Crosby believes that any level of defects is too high and that achieving quality can be relatively easy, as explained in his book *Quality Without Tears: The Art of Hassle-Free Management.*

Kaoru Ishikawa. The late Japanese expert on quality was strongly influenced by both Deming and Juran, although he made significant contributions of his own to quality management. Among his key contributions were the development of the cause-and-effect diagram (also known as a fishbone diagram) for problem solving and the implementation of quality circles, which involve workers in quality improvement. He was the first quality expert to call attention to the *internal customer*—the next person in the process, the next operation, within the organization.

Genichi Taguchi. Taguchi is best known for the Taguchi loss function, which involves a formula for determining the cost of poor quality. The idea is that the deviation of a part from a standard causes a loss, and the combined effect of deviations of all parts from their standards can be large, even though each individual deviation is small. An important part of his philosophy is the cost to society of poor quality.

Taiichi Ohno and Shigeo Shingo. Taiichi Ohno and Shigeo Shingo both developed the philosophy and methods of *kaizen,* a Japanese term for continuous improvement (defined more fully later in this chapter), at Toyota. Continuous improvement is one of the hallmarks of successful quality management.

Table 9.2 provides a summary of the important contributions of the gurus to modern quality management.

Contributor	Key Contributions
Shewhart	Control charts; variance reduction
Deming	14 points; special versus common causes of variation
Juran	Quality is fitness-for-use; quality trilogy
Feigenbaum	Quality is a total field; the customer defines quality
Crosby	Quality is free; zero defects
Ishikawa	Cause-and-effect diagrams; quality circles
Taguchi	Taguchi loss function
Ohno and Shingo	Continuous improvement

TABLE 9.2
A summary of key contributors to quality management

9.4 INSIGHTS ON QUALITY MANAGEMENT

Successful management of quality requires that managers have insights on various aspects of quality. These include defining quality in operational terms, understanding the costs and benefits of quality, recognizing the consequences of poor quality, and recognizing the need for ethical behavior. We begin with defining quality.

Defining Quality: The Dimensions of Quality

One way to think about quality is the degree to which performance of a product or service meets or exceeds customer expectations. The difference between these two, that is Performance—Expectations, is of great interest. If these two measures are equal, the difference is zero, and expectations have been met. If the difference is negative, expectations have not been met, whereas if the difference is positive, performance has exceeded customer expectations.

Customer expectations can be broken down into a number of categories, or *dimensions,* that customers use to judge the quality of a product or service. Understanding these helps organizations in their efforts to meet or exceed customer expectations. The dimensions used for goods are somewhat different from those used for services.

LO9.2 Define the term *quality* as it relates to products and as it relates to services.

Product Quality. Product quality is often judged on nine dimensions of quality:[1]

Performance—main characteristics of the product

Aesthetics—appearance, feel, smell, taste

Special features—extra characteristics

Conformance—how well a product corresponds to design specifications

Reliability—dependable performance

Durability—ability to perform over time

Perceived quality—indirect evaluation of quality (e.g., reputation)

Serviceability—handling of complaints or repairs

Consistency—quality doesn't vary

These dimensions are further described by the examples presented in Table 9.3. When referring to a product, a customer sometimes judges the first four dimensions by its *fitness for use.*

Notice that price is *not* a dimension of quality.

TABLE 9.3
Examples of product quality

Dimensions	Examples
1. Performance	Everything works: fit and finish, ride, handling, acceleration
2. Aesthetics	Exterior and interior design
3. Features	Convenience: placement of gauges High tech: GPS system Safety: anti-skid, airbags
4. Conformance	Car matches manufacturer's specifications
5. Reliability	Infrequent need for repairs
6. Durability	Useful life in miles, resistance to rust
7. Perceived quality	Top-rated
8. Serviceability	Ease of repair
9. Consistency	Quality doesn't vary from car to car

[1]Adapted from David Garvin, "Competing on the Eight Dimensions of Quality," *Harvard Business Review* 65, no. 6 (1987). Copyright © 1987 by the Harvard Business School Publishing Corporation; all rights reserved.

Service Quality. The dimensions of product quality don't adequately describe service quality. Instead, service quality is often described using the following dimensions:[2]

Convenience—the availability and accessibility of the service

Reliability—the ability to perform a service dependably, consistently, and accurately

Responsiveness—the willingness of service providers to help customers in unusual situations and to deal with problems

Time—the speed with which service is delivered

Assurance—the knowledge exhibited by personnel who come into contact with a customer and their ability to convey trust and confidence

Courtesy—the way customers are treated by employees who come into contact with them

Tangibles—the physical appearance of facilities, equipment, personnel, and communication materials

Consistency—the ability to provide the same level of good quality repeatedly

Expectations—meet (or exceed) customer expectations

Table 9.4 illustrates how the dimensions of service quality might apply to having an automobile repaired.

The dimensions of both product and service quality establish a *conceptual* framework for thinking about quality, but even they are too abstract to be applied operationally for purposes of product or service design, or actually producing a product or delivering a service. They must be stated in terms of specific, *measurable* characteristics. For example, when buying a car, a customer would naturally be interested in the car's performance. But what does that mean? In more specific terms, it might refer to a car's estimated miles per gallon, how quickly it can go from 0 to 60 miles per hour, or its stopping distance when traveling at 60 mph. Each of these can be stated in measurable terms (e.g., estimated miles per gallon: city = 25, highway = 30). Similar measurable characteristics can often be identified for each of the other product dimensions, as well as for the service dimensions. This is the sort of detailed information that is needed to both design and produce high-quality goods and services.

Information on customer wants in service can sometimes be difficult to pin down, creating challenges for designing and managing service quality. For example, customers may use words such as *friendly, considerate,* and *professional* to describe what they expect from service providers. These and similar descriptors are often difficult to translate into exact service specifications. Moreover in many instances, customer wants are often industry specific. Thus, the expectations would be quite different for health care versus dry cleaning. Furthermore, customer complaints may be due in part to unrelated factors (e.g., customer's mood or general health, the weather).

Dimension	Examples
1. Convenience	Was the service center conveniently located?
2. Reliability	Was the problem fixed and will the "fix" last?
3. Responsiveness	Were customer service personnel willing and able to answer questions?
4. Time	How long did the customer have to wait?
5. Assurance	Did the customer service personnel seem knowledgeable about the repair?
6. Courtesy	Were customer service personnel and the cashier friendly and courteous?
7. Tangibles	Were the facilities clean? Were personnel neat?
8. Consistency	Was the service quality good, and was it consistent with previous visits?
9. Expectations	Were customer expectations met?

TABLE 9.4

Examples of service quality dimensions for having a car repaired

[2]Adapted from Valerie A. Zeithaml, A. Parasuraman, and Leonard L. Berry, *Delivering Quality Service and Balancing Customer Expectations* (New York: The Free Press, 1990); and J. R. Evans and W. M. Lindsey, *The Management and Control of Quality,* 3rd ed. (St. Paul, MN: West Publishing, 1996).

Consumers often associate quiet operation as a sign of product quality, and they are willing to pay extra to get it. Such is the case with clothes washers, dishwashers, air conditioners, shredders, and automobiles. In the case of automobiles, designers know that buyers associate a quiet ride with quality, so doors, hood, windshield and exhaust systems have extra soundproofing and sealing to keep noise out. They also know that buyers value safety, and that buyers associate safety with how solid a car door sounds when it is closed, so designers have given extra attention to those sorts of details. A sign of the growing importance of sound in the auto industry is that J.D. Power & Associates measures "pleasantness of sound" for doors, signals, and engine acceleration in its Initial Quality Study.

Likewise, cell phone manufacturers are giving careful attention to ring tones and other sounds emitted by their products, as are manufacturers of other electronic gadgets.

Source: Based on David Kiley, "Fine-Tuning a Brand's Signature Sound," *Business-Week,* August 13, 2007.

Other challenges with service quality include the reality that customer expectations often change over time and that different customers tend to have different expectations, so what one customer might view as good service quality, another customer might not be satisfied with at all. Couple these with the fact that each contact with a customer is a "moment of truth" in which service quality is instantly judged, and you begin to understand some of the challenges of achieving a consistently high perception of service quality.

If customers participate in a service system (i.e., self-service), there can be increased potential for a negative perception of quality. Consequently, adequate care must be taken to make the necessary customer acts simple and safe, especially since customers cannot be trained. So error prevention must be designed into the system.

It should also be noted that in most instances, some quality dimensions of a product or service will be more important than others, so it is important to identify customer priorities, especially when it is likely that trade-off decisions will be made at various points in design and production. Quality function deployment (described in Chapter 4) is a tool that can be helpful for that purpose.

Assessing Service Quality

A widely used tool for assessing service quality is SERVQUAL,[3] an instrument designed to obtain feedback on an organization's ability to provide quality service to customers. It focuses on five of the previously mentioned service dimensions that influence customers' perceptions of service quality: tangibles, reliability, responsiveness, assurance, and empathy. The results of this service quality audit help management identify service strengths and weaknesses. Of particular interest are any *gaps* or discrepancies in service quality. There may be discrepancies between:

1. Actual customer expectations and management perceptions of those expectations
2. Management perceptions of customer expectations and service-quality specifications
3. Service quality and service actually delivered
4. Service actually delivered and what is communicated about the service to customers
5. Customers' expectations of the service provider and their perceptions of provider delivery.

If gaps are found, they can be related to tangibles or other service quality dimensions to address the discrepancies.

[3]Valarie A. Zeithaml, A. Parasuraman, and Leonard L. Berry, *Delivering Quality Service: Balancing Customer Perceptions and Expectations* (New York: The Free Press, 1990), p. 26.

The Determinants of Quality

The degree to which a product or a service successfully satisfies its intended purpose has four primary determinants:

1. Design
2. How well the product or service conforms to the design
3. Ease of use
4. Service after delivery

LO9.3 Identify the determinants of quality.

The design phase is the starting point for the level of quality eventually achieved. Design involves decisions about the specific characteristics of a product or service such as size, shape, and location. **Quality of design** refers to the intention of designers to include or exclude certain features in a product or service. For example, many different models of automobiles are on the market today. They differ in size, appearance, roominess, fuel economy, comfort, and materials used. These differences reflect choices made by designers that determine the quality of design. Design decisions must take into account customer wants, production or service capabilities, safety and liability (both during production and after delivery), costs, and other similar considerations.

Quality of design Intention of designers to include or exclude features in a product or service.

Designers may determine customer wants from information provided by marketing, perhaps through the use of consumer surveys or other market research. Marketing may organize focus groups of consumers to express their views on a product or service (what they like and don't like, and what they would like to have).

Designers must work closely with representatives of operations to ascertain that designs can be produced; that is, that production or service has the equipment, capacity, and skills necessary to produce or provide a particular design.

A poor design can result in difficulties in production or service. For example, materials might be difficult to obtain, specifications difficult to meet, or procedures difficult to follow. Moreover, if a design is inadequate or inappropriate for the circumstances, the best workmanship in the world may not be enough to achieve the desired quality. Also, we cannot expect a worker to achieve good results if the given tools or procedures are inadequate. Similarly, a superior design usually cannot offset poor workmanship.

Quality of conformance refers to the degree to which goods and services conform to (i.e., *achieve*) the intent of the designers. This is affected by factors such as the capability of

Quality of conformance The degree to which goods or services conform to the intent of the designers.

Customers shopping for appliances at an Abt Electronics store in Glenview, Illinois. Abt is an independent, family-owned retailer known for quality products and great customer service.

© John Zich/Bloomberg via Getty

equipment used; the skills, training, and motivation of workers; the extent to which the design lends itself to production; the monitoring process to assess conformance; and the taking of corrective action (e.g., through problem solving) when necessary. One important key to quality is reducing the variability in process outputs (i.e., reducing the degree to which individual items or individual service acts vary from one another). This will be discussed in detail in Chapter 10.

The determination of quality does not stop once the product or service has been sold or delivered. *Ease of use* and user instructions are important. They increase the chances, but do not guarantee, that a product will be used for its intended purposes and in such a way that it will continue to function properly and safely. (When faced with liability litigation, companies often argue that injuries and damages occurred because the user misused the product.) Much of the same reasoning can be applied to services. Customers, patients, clients, or other users must be clearly informed on what they should or should not do; otherwise, there is the danger that they will take some action that will adversely affect quality. Some examples include the doctor who fails to specify that a medication should be taken *before* meals and *not* with orange juice and the attorney who neglects to inform a client of a deadline for filing a claim.

Much consumer education takes the form of printed instructions and labeling. Thus, manufacturers must ensure that directions for unpacking, assembling, using, maintaining, and adjusting the product—and what to do if something goes wrong (e.g., flush eyes with water, call a physician, induce vomiting, do not induce vomiting, disconnect set immediately)—are *clearly visible* and *easily understood.*

For a variety of reasons, products do not always perform as expected, and services do not always yield the desired results. Whatever the reason, it is important from a quality standpoint to remedy the situation—through recall and repair of the product, adjustment, replacement or buyback, or reevaluation of a service—and do whatever is necessary to bring the product or service up to standard.

Responsibility for Quality

It is true that all members of an organization have some responsibility for quality, but certain parts of the organization are key areas of responsibility:

Top management. Top management has the ultimate responsibility for quality. While establishing strategies for quality, top management must institute programs to improve quality; guide, direct, and motivate managers and workers; and set an example by being involved in quality initiatives. Examples include taking training in quality, issuing periodic reports on quality, and attending meetings on quality.

Design. Quality products and services begin with design. This includes not only features of the product or service; it also includes attention to the *processes* that will be required to produce the products and/or the services that will be required to deliver the service to customers.

Procurement. The procurement department has responsibility for obtaining goods and services that will not detract from the quality of the organization's goods and services.

Production/operations. Production/operations has responsibility to ensure that processes yield products and services that conform to design specifications. Monitoring processes and finding and correcting root causes of problems are important aspects of this responsibility.

Quality assurance. Quality assurance is responsible for gathering and analyzing data on problems and working with operations to solve problems.

Packaging and shipping. This department must ensure that goods are not damaged in transit, that packages are clearly labeled, that instructions are included, that all parts are included, and that shipping occurs in a timely manner.

Marketing and sales. This department has the responsibility to determine customer needs and to communicate them to appropriate areas of the organization. In addition, it has the responsibility to report any problems with products or services.

Customer service. Customer service is often the first department to learn of problems. It has the responsibility to communicate that information to appropriate departments, deal in a reasonable manner with customers, work to resolve problems, and follow up to confirm that the situation has been effectively remedied.

Poor quality increases certain *costs* incurred by the organization. The following section provides further detail on costs associated with quality.

Benefits of Good Quality

Business organizations with good or excellent quality typically benefit in a variety of ways: an enhanced reputation for quality, the ability to command premium prices, an increased market share, greater customer loyalty, lower liability costs, and fewer production or service problems—which yields higher productivity, fewer complaints from customers, lower production costs, and higher profits. Annual studies by the National Institute of Standards indicate that winners of the Baldrige quality award, described later in the chapter, outperform the S&P 500 Index by a significant amount.[4]

The Consequences of Poor Quality

LO9.4 Explain why quality is important and the consequences of poor quality.

It is important for management to recognize the different ways in which the quality of a firm's products or services can affect the organization and to take these into account in developing and maintaining a quality assurance program. Some of the major areas affected by quality are:

1. Loss of business
2. Liability
3. Productivity
4. Costs

Poor designs or defective products or services can result in *loss of business*. Failure to devote adequate attention to quality can damage a profit-oriented organization's reputation and lead to a decreased share of the market, or it can lead to increased criticism and/or controls for a government agency or nonprofit organization.

In the retail sector, managers might not be fully aware of poor product or service quality because customers do not always report their dissatisfaction. Even so, dissatisfied customers do tend to voice their dissatisfaction to friends and relatives, which can have negative implications for customer perceptions and future business.

Organizations must pay special attention to their potential *liability* due to damages or injuries resulting from either faulty design or poor workmanship. This applies to both products and services. Thus, a poorly designed steering arm on a car might cause the driver to lose control of the car, but so could improper assembly of the steering arm. However, the net result is the same. Similarly, a tree surgeon might be called to cable a tree limb. If the limb later falls and causes damage to a neighbor's car, the accident might be traced to a poorly designed procedure for cabling or to improper workmanship. Liability for poor quality has been well established in the courts. An organization's liability costs can often be substantial, especially if large numbers of items are involved, as in the automobile industry, or if potentially widespread injury or damage is involved (e.g., an accident at a nuclear power plant). Express written warranties as well as implied warranties generally guarantee the product as safe when used as intended. The courts have tended to extend this to *foreseeable* uses, even if these uses were not intended by the producer. In the health care field, medical malpractice claims and insurance costs are contributing to skyrocketing costs and have become a major issue nationwide. It's been estimated that medical mistakes result in about 98,000 deaths annually in the United States. Surprisingly, this number has remained fairly steady for more than a few years. If medical errors were classified as a disease, they would rank about sixth on the list of major causes of death.

---

[4]"Baldrige Index' Outperforms S&P 500 by Almost 5 to 1," press release, available at www.quality.nist.gov.

READING   HYUNDAI: KISSING CLUNKERS GOODBYE

**MOON IHLWAN, WITH LARRY ARMSTRONG
AND MICHAEL EIDAM**

When Hyundai Motor Co. Chairman Chung Mong Koo said his company could increase the quality of its cars to "Toyota levels," few took him seriously. After all, Hyundai was the butt of talk-show jokes and a target of industry disdain for tinny cars that were about as reliable as a go-kart. So when J. D. Power & Associates Inc. announced the Korean carmaker had virtually caught up with Toyota in terms of quality, jaws dropped from Detroit to Tokyo. "We still have a long way to go," says Suh Byung Kee, the senior executive vice-president heading Hyundai's quality-control team. "But we have completed the first phase of our task."

The second phase could well be tougher. The eye-opening survey measured initial quality—the number of complaints customers had in the first 90 days of ownership. Hyundai owners reported just 102 problems per 100 cars sold—earning a tie with Honda as the second-best carmaker on the list and falling just below Toyota's tally of 101. And its Sonata sedan was the top-ranked car in the "entry mid-sized" category. On longer-term measures, though, Hyundai remains a laggard: In a later Power's Vehicle Dependability Study, Hyundai tallied 342 problems per 100 vehicles after three years of ownership, versus an industry average of 273. Hyundai execs counter that it will take time before the recent improvement shows up in the longer-term statistics.

There's reason to agree with Hyundai's optimism. First wooed by the company's generous warranty—10 years for the drive train and five years for everything else—U.S. consumers are starting to believe that Hyundai is a changed brand. Sales have increased steadily. . . . Jeff Ball, a pharmacist from Laurence Harbor, N.J., has four of them: He and his wife share a Santa Fe SUV and a Sonata sedan ("I call it my Jaguar without the cat," he says), and

he has bought smaller models for his sons. Sales like that are helping Hyundai's bottom line.

A Team with Teeth

Hyundai's focus on quality comes straight from the top. Since 1999, Chairman Chung has boosted the quality team to 865 workers from 100, and virtually all employees have had to attend special seminars on improving Hyundai's cars. Chung presides over twice-monthly quality meetings in a special conference room and an adjacent workshop, with vehicle lifts and high-intensity spotlights for comparing Hyundais head-to-head with rivals. And this team has teeth: In the past year, the introduction of three new models was delayed by months as engineers scrambled to boost quality in response to problems found by the team.

The focus is on the details. When customers reported faulty warning lights and difficulty starting engines, Chung set up a $30 million computer center where 71 engineers simulate harsh conditions to test electronics and pinpoint defects. The result: In a Power's initial quality survey, Hyundai had only 9.6 problems in these areas per 100 vehicles, versus an industry average of 13.8. Three years ago Hyundai had 23.4 problems, versus the industry's 17.9. "This is not a shotgun approach," says Robert Cosmai, president of the company's U.S. affiliate, Hyundai Motor America.

The big test came when Hyundai began building redesigned Santa Fes and Sonatas in Alabama. One encouraging sign: DaimlerChrysler and Mitsubishi Motors Corp. planned to use a Hyundai-designed four-cylinder engine in their own small and midsize cars. "This is a vote of confidence for Hyundai's engine quality," says Ahn Soo Woong, an auto analyst at Han-wha Securities Co. Now it's up to consumers to decide whether Hyundai really makes the grade.

Productivity and quality are often closely related. Poor quality can adversely affect productivity during the manufacturing process if parts are defective and have to be reworked or if an assembler has to try a number of parts before finding one that fits properly. Also, poor quality in tools and equipment can lead to injuries and defective output, which must be reworked or scrapped, thereby reducing the amount of usable output for a given amount of input. Similarly, poor service can mean having to redo the service and reduce service productivity.

Cost to remedy a problem is a major consideration in quality management. The earlier a problem is identified in the process, the cheaper the cost to fix it. The cost to fix a problem at the customer end has been estimated at about five times the cost to fix a problem at the design or production stages.

The Costs of Quality

Any serious attempt to deal with quality issues must take into account the costs associated with quality. Those costs can be classified into three categories: appraisal, prevention, and failure.

Appraisal costs Costs of activities designed to ensure quality or uncover defects.

Appraisal costs relate to inspection, testing, and other activities intended to uncover defective products or services, or to assure that there are none. They include the cost of inspectors, testing, test equipment, labs, quality audits, and field testing.

Prevention costs relate to attempts to prevent defects from occurring. They include costs such as planning and administration systems, working with vendors, training, quality control procedures, and extra attention in both the design and production phases to decrease the probability of defective workmanship.

Failure costs are incurred by defective parts or products or by faulty services. **Internal failures** are those discovered during the production process; **external failures** are those discovered after delivery to the customer. Internal failures occur for a variety of reasons, including defective material from vendors, incorrect machine settings, faulty equipment, incorrect methods, incorrect processing, carelessness, and faulty or improper material handling procedures. The costs of internal failures include lost production time, scrap and rework, investigation costs, possible equipment damage, and possible employee injury. Rework costs involve the salaries of workers and the additional resources needed to perform the rework (e.g., equipment, energy, raw materials). Beyond those costs are items such as inspection of reworked parts, disruption of schedules, the added costs of parts and materials in inventory waiting for reworked parts, and the paperwork needed to keep track of the items until they can be reintegrated into the process. External failures are defective products or poor service that go undetected by the producer. Resulting costs include warranty work, handling of complaints, replacements, liability/litigation, payments to customers or discounts used to offset the inferior quality, loss of customer goodwill, and opportunity costs related to lost sales.

External failure costs are typically much greater than internal failure costs on a per-unit basis. Table 9.5 summarizes quality costs.

Internal and external failure costs represent costs related to poor quality, whereas appraisal and prevention costs represent investments for achieving good quality.

An important issue in quality management is the value received from expenditures on prevention. There are two schools of thought on this. One is that prevention costs will be outweighed by savings in appraisal and failure costs. This is espoused by such people as Crosby and Juran, discussed in further detail later in this chapter. They believe that as the costs of defect prevention are increased, the costs of appraisal and failure decrease by much more. What this means, if true, is that the net result is lower total costs, and, thus, as Crosby suggests, quality is free. On the other hand, some managers believe that by attempting to go beyond a certain point, such expenditures on quality reduce the funds available for other objectives such as reducing product development times and upgrading technology. The **return on quality** (ROQ) approach focuses on the economics of quality efforts. In this approach, quality improvement projects are viewed as investments, and, as such, they are evaluated like any other investment, using metrics related to return on investment (ROI).

Prevention costs Costs of preventing defects from occurring.

Failure costs Costs caused by defective parts or products or by faulty services.

Internal failures Failures discovered during production.

External failures Failures discovered after delivery to the customer.

Return on quality An approach that evaluates the financial return of investments in quality.

Category	Description	Examples
Appraisal costs	Costs related to measuring, evaluating, and auditing materials, parts, products, and services to assess conformance with quality standards	Inspection equipment, testing, labs, inspectors, and the interruption of production to take samples
Prevention costs	Costs related to reducing the potential for quality problems	Quality improvement programs, training, monitoring, data collection and analysis, and design costs
Internal failure costs	Costs related to defective products or services before they are delivered to customers	Rework costs, problem solving, material and product losses, scrap, and downtime
External failure costs	Costs related to delivering substandard products or services to customers	Returned goods, reworking costs, warranty costs, loss of goodwill, liability claims, and penalties

TABLE 9.5
Summary of quality costs

LO9.5 Describe and give examples of the costs associated with quality.

READING  REWORK AND MORALE

Larry Coburn, vice president of operations at high-tech audio equipment manufacturer Crown Audio, has seen the need for strong management and employee commitment in his company's recent quality improvements. The market in his industry was driving the development of more complex products that need to be produced more cheaply, and these twin trends put so much pressure on his manufacturing operations that things were breaking down. Their first-pass yields had gotten so bad that their rework inventory had piled up, and even became a major line item on the balance sheet.

"We had areas that were designated for rework that were so large that they were getting on our inventory control list because they were major entities in terms of dollars in inventory," he recounts. In fact, the problem was large enough to conceal what Coburn and his team call "hidden factories"—millions of dollars of untapped production and sales potential existing within their production line. "We started analyzing these hidden factories and we actually identified $4 million of cost related to poor quality," Coburn says.

To stem the tide of red ink, Crown Audio embarked on a drastic plant-floor triage process that involved stopping production entirely, so as not to generate any more rework. They then analyzed and tested the defective inventory, broke the components up into groups based on the common problems they exhibited, and used those groupings to analyze potential process improvements and defect reduction strategies before plugging them back through the process. Once they finished, they not only had saleable inventory to get out the door, but also had a pretty good handle on the parts of their process that needed changing, says Coburn. "When we started, we had months and sometimes close to a year of backlog

that needed to be fixed and repaired," he relates. "Now we are talking in terms of hours of rework in front of us."

However positive and dramatic this change, Coburn and his management team also realized that it wouldn't help much if the scrap and rework inventory piles kept growing, he says, which is where he says the less-tangible "employee engagement" part of the equation comes in.

The first aspect is enabling them to do their jobs. "We're continuing to empower our workers to get real-time data at their fingertips so they're making good decisions without two-week-old data, or without estimating or just evading what they think the problem is," he says. Rather than having his workers hanging their heads, Crown Audio's management team is now in the enviable situation of having different lines and shifts brag about their first-pass yields to each other.

Sustaining this motivated, engaged workforce is itself a team effort, says Coburn, who says that he has learned over the course of Crown Audio's continuing quality initiative that solidly designed manufacturing processes backed up by an engaged and empowered workforce is the essential combination to move any company forward. Quality truly is everyone's responsibility, and everyone appreciates a job well done.

"There is nothing more frustrating than working hard and then knowing that what you did, did not work out or did not come through." Coburn stresses this point in no uncertain terms. "Morale is everything in quality," he says. "People want to do a good job, and we have to enable that."

Source: Excerpted from Brad Kenney, Industry Week, April 1, 2008.

Ethics and Quality Management

LO9.6 Discuss the importance of ethics in managing quality.

All members of an organization have an obligation to perform their duties in an ethical manner. Ethical behavior comes into play in many situations that involve quality. One major category is substandard work, including defective products and substandard service, poor designs, shoddy workmanship, and substandard parts and raw materials. Having knowledge of this and failing to correct and *report it* in a timely manner is unethical and can have a number of negative consequences. These can include increased costs for organizations in terms of decreased productivity, an increase in the accident rate among employees, inconveniences and injuries to customers, and increased liability costs.

A related issue is how an organization chooses to deal with information about quality problems in products that are already in service. For example, automakers and tire makers in recent years have been accused of withholding information about actual or potential quality problems; they failed to issue product recalls, or failed to divulge information, choosing instead to handle any complaints that arose on an individual basis.

9.5 QUALITY AWARDS

Quality awards have been established to generate improvement in quality. The Malcolm Baldrige Award, the European Quality Award, and the Deming Prize are well-known awards given annually to recognize firms that have integrated quality management into their operations.

The Baldrige Award

Named after the late Malcolm Baldrige, an industrialist and former secretary of commerce, the annual **Baldrige Award** is administered by the National Institute of Standards and Technology. The purpose of the award competition is to stimulate efforts to improve quality, to recognize quality achievements, and to publicize successful programs.

When the award was first presented in 1988, the award categories were manufacturing and small business. A few years later a service category was added, and then categories for education and health care were added a few years after that. The earliest winners included Motorola, Globe Metallurgical, Xerox Corporation, and Milliken & Company. Since then, many companies have been added to the list. For a complete listing of current and former winners, go to www.patapsco.nist.gov/Award_Recipients.

Applicants are evaluated in seven main areas: leadership, information and analysis, strategic planning, human resource management, customer and market focus, process management, and business results.

Examiners check the extent to which top management incorporates quality values in daily management; whether products or services are at least as good as those of competitors; whether employees receive training in quality techniques; if the business works with suppliers to improve quality; and if customers are satisfied. Even organizations that don't win benefit from applying for the award: All applicants receive a written summary of the strengths and weaknesses of their quality management and suggestions for improvement.

Most states have quality award programs based on the Baldrige criteria. These award programs can serve as an entry point for organizations that want to eventually apply for the national award.

For more information, visit www.nist.gov/baldrige.

Baldrige Award Annual award given by the U.S. government to recognize quality achievements of U.S. companies.

NIST

LO9.7 Compare the quality awards.

The European Quality Award

The **European Quality Award** is Europe's most prestigious award for organizational excellence. The European Quality Award sits at the top of regional and national quality awards, and applicants have often won one or more of those awards prior to applying for the European Quality Award.

European Quality Award European award for organizational excellence.

The Deming Prize

The Deming Prize, named in honor of the late W. Edwards Deming, is Japan's highly coveted award recognizing successful quality efforts. It is given annually to any company that meets the award's standards. Although typically given to Japanese firms, in 1989, Florida Power and Light became the first U.S. company to win the award.

The major focus of the judging is on statistical quality control, making it much narrower in scope than the Baldrige Award, which focuses more on customer satisfaction. Companies that win the Deming Prize tend to have quality programs that are detailed and well-communicated throughout the company. Their quality improvement programs also reflect the involvement of senior management and employees, customer satisfaction, and training.

9.6 QUALITY CERTIFICATION

Many firms that do business internationally recognize the importance of quality certification.

LO9.8 Discuss quality certification and its importance.

ISO 9000, 14000, and 24700

The International Organization for Standardization (ISO) promotes worldwide standards for the improvement of quality, productivity, and operating efficiency through a series of standards and guidelines. Used by industrial and business organizations, regulatory agencies, governments, and trade organizations, the standards have important economic and social benefits. Not only are they tremendously important for designers, manufacturers, suppliers, service providers, and customers, but the standards make a tremendous contribution to society in general: They increase the levels of quality and reliability, productivity, and safety, while making products and services affordable. The standards help facilitate international trade. They provide governments with a basis for health, safety, and environmental legislation. And they aid in transferring technology to developing countries.

Two of the most well-known of these are ISO 9000 and ISO 14000. **ISO 9000** pertains to quality management. It concerns what an organization does to ensure that its products or services conform to its customers' requirements. **ISO 14000** concerns what an organization does to minimize harmful effects to the environment caused by its operations. Both ISO 9000 and ISO 14000 relate to an organization's *processes* rather than its products and services, and both stress continual improvement. Moreover, the standards are meant to be generic; no matter what the organization's business, if it wants to establish a quality management system or an environmental management system, the system must have the essential elements contained in ISO 9000 or in ISO 14000. The ISO 9000 standards are critical for companies doing business internationally, particularly in Europe. They must go through a process that involves documenting quality procedures and on-site assessment. The process often takes 12 to 18 months. With certification comes *registration* in an ISO directory that companies seeking suppliers can refer to for a list of certified companies. They are generally given preference over unregistered companies. More than 40,000 companies are registered worldwide; three-fourths of them are located in Europe.

A key requirement for registration is that a company review, refine, and map functions such as process control, inspection, purchasing, training, packaging, and delivery. Similar to the Baldrige Award, the review process involves considerable self-appraisal, resulting in problem identification and improvement. Unlike the Baldrige Award, registered companies face an ongoing series of audits, and they must be re-registered every three years.

In addition to the obvious benefits of certification for companies that want to deal with the European Union, the ISO 9000 certification and registration process is particularly helpful for companies that do not currently have a quality management system; it provides guidelines for establishing the system and making it effective.

Eight quality management principles form the basis of the latest version of ISO 9000:

1. A customer focus
2. Leadership
3. Involvement of people
4. A process approach
5. A system approach to management
6. Continual improvement
7. Use of a factual approach to decision making
8. Mutually beneficial supplier relationships

The standards for ISO 14000 certification bear upon three major areas:

Management systems—systems development and integration of environmental responsibilities into business planning

Operations—consumption of natural resources and energy

Environmental systems—measuring, assessing, and managing emissions, effluents, and other waste streams

ISO 24700 pertains to the quality and performance of office equipment that contains reused components. ISO/IEC 24700 specifies product characteristics for use in an original equipment manufacturer's or authorized third-party's declaration of conformity to demonstrate that a marketed product that contains reused components performs equivalent to new, meeting equivalent-to-new component specifications and performance criteria, and continues to meet all the safety and environmental criteria required by responsibly built products. It is relevant to marketed products whose manufacturing and recovery processes result in the reuse of components.

ISO 9000 A set of international standards on quality management and quality assurance, critical to international business.

ISO 14000 A set of international standards for assessing a company's environmental performance.

ISO 24700 A set of international standards that pertains to the quality and performance of office equipment that contains reused components.

If you'd like to learn more about ISO standards, visit the International Organization for Standardization website at www.ISO.org/ISO/en/ISOonline.frontpage or the American Society for Quality website at www.asq.org.

9.7 QUALITY AND THE SUPPLY CHAIN

Business leaders are increasingly recognizing the importance of their supply chains in achieving their quality goals. Achievement requires measuring customer perceptions of quality, identifying problem areas, and correcting those problems.

When dealing with supplier quality in global supply chains, companies are finding a wide range in the degree of sophistication concerning quality assurance. Although developed countries often have a fair level of sophistication, little or no awareness of modern quality practices may be found in some less-developed countries. This poses important liability issues for companies that outsource to those areas.

An interesting situation is outsourcing in the pharmaceutical industry. Offshore suppliers offer low prices that domestic producers can't match. However, the cost advantage of offshore producers is not based solely on lower labor costs; a significant "advantage" is the fact that domestic producers undergo strict and costly government quality regulations and unannounced inspections that offshore producers are not subject to. While this lowers the costs to importers, it also increases their liability risks.

Increasingly, the emphasis in supply chain quality management is on reducing outsourcing risk as well as product or service variation and overhead. Risk comes from the use of substandard materials or work methods, which can lead to inferior product quality and potential product liability. Tighter control of vendors and worker training can reduce these risks. Variation results from processes that are not in control; it can be reduced through statistical quality control.

The acting chair of the Consumer Product Safety Commission spoke at a press conference on a recall of Mattel Inc. toys manufactured in China. Mattel recalled 18.6 million products around the world because they contained magnets that could fall out and be swallowed by children.

© Jay Mallin/Bloomberg via Getty

READING   IMPROVING QUALITY AND REDUCING RISK IN OFFSHORING

William E. Mitchell, chairman, president and CEO of Arrow Electronics, offered 10 guidelines on how to reduce product quality and related risks in an offshore supply chain. The guidelines were nominally targeted at electronics suppliers, but offer a good starting point for many companies looking to reduce risk and potential quality problems.

1. Source from reputable, well-established companies with tight internal controls.
2. Conduct comprehensive background checks, including checking trade references and past business history, of supply chain partners before conducting business with them.
3. Implement site inspections of supply chain partners and find out what systems have been put in place to track quality.
4. Conduct ongoing performance reviews of supply chain partners and engage in ongoing communications with them to benchmark against preset goals and define improvement plans.
5. Only source from companies that are willing to provide a guarantee for products in writing.

6. Be cautious of buying from companies that do not have franchised relationships with distribution partners to avoid a greater potential risk of counterfeit product.
7. Beware of unusually low pricing.
8. Look for International Organization for Standardization (ISO) or other equivalent, globally recognized certifications in a supply chain partner's operations.
9. Establish relationships with third-party organizations.
10. Translate quality into measurable and clearly defined targets with supply chain partners and ensure these metrics are communicated regularly with employees.

As the *Supply Chain Digest* notes, to do this right will involve greater costs, reducing the relative price advantage of offshore strategies to a degree, and requiring companies to build a substantial infrastructure to develop and maintain these monitoring programs.

Overhead can be reduced by assigning quality assurance responsibility to vendors, while customers operate in a quality audit mode, with some monitoring of vendor quality efforts.

Supply chain quality management can benefit from a collaborative relationship with suppliers that includes helping suppliers with quality assurance efforts as well as information sharing on quality-related matters. Ideally, improving supply chain quality can become part of an organization's continuous improvement efforts.

The following reading offers some guidelines for improving quality and reducing outsourcing risk.

9.8 TOTAL QUALITY MANAGEMENT

LO9.9 Describe TQM.

Total quality management (TQM) A philosophy that involves everyone in an organization in a continual effort to improve quality and achieve customer satisfaction.

A primary role of management is to lead an organization in its daily operation and to maintain it as a viable entity into the future. Quality has become an important factor in both of these objectives.

The term **total quality management (TQM)** refers to a quest for quality in an organization. There are three key philosophies in this approach. One is a never-ending push to improve, which is referred to as *continuous improvement;* the second is the *involvement of everyone* in the organization; and the third is a goal of *customer satisfaction,* which means meeting or exceeding customer expectations. TQM expands the traditional view of quality—looking only at the quality of the final product or services—to *looking at the quality of every aspect of the process* that produces the product or service. TQM systems are intended to prevent poor quality from occurring.

We can describe the TQM approach as follows:

1. Find out what customers want. This might involve the use of surveys, focus groups, interviews, or some other technique that integrates the customer's voice in the decision-making process. Be sure to include the *internal customer* (the next person in the process) as well as the *external customer* (the final customer).
2. Design a product or service that will meet (or exceed) what customers want. Make it easy to use and easy to produce.

3. Design processes that facilitate doing the job right the first time. Determine where mistakes are likely to occur and try to prevent them. When mistakes do occur, find out why so that they are less likely to occur again. Strive to make the process "mistake-proof." This is sometimes referred to as a **fail-safing**: Elements are incorporated in product or service design that make it virtually impossible for an employee (or sometimes a customer) to do something incorrectly. The Japanese term for this is *pokayoke*. Examples include parts that fit together one way only and appliance plugs that can be inserted into a wall outlet the correct way only. Another term that is sometimes used is *foolproofing*, but use of this term may be taken to imply that employees (or customers) are fools—not a wise choice!

Fail-safing Incorporating design elements that prevent incorrect procedures.

4. Keep track of results, and use them to guide improvement in the system. Never stop trying to improve.

5. Extend these concepts throughout the supply chain.

6. Top management must be involved and committed. Otherwise, TQM will just be another fad that fails and fades away.

Many companies have successfully implemented TQM programs. Successful TQM programs are built through the dedication and combined efforts of everyone in the organization.

The preceding description provides a good idea of what TQM is all about, but it doesn't tell the whole story. A number of other elements of TQM are important:

1. **Continuous improvement.** The *philosophy* that seeks to improve all factors related to the process of converting inputs into outputs on an ongoing basis is called **continuous improvement**. It covers equipment, methods, materials, and people. Under continuous improvement, the old adage "If it ain't broke, don't fix it" gets transformed into "Just because it isn't broke doesn't mean it can't be improved."

   The concept of continuous improvement was not new, but it did not receive much interest in the United States for a while, even though it originated here. However, many Japanese companies used it for years, and it became a cornerstone of the Japanese approach to production. The Japanese use the term *kaizen* to refer to continuous improvement. The successes of Japanese companies caused other companies to reexamine many of their approaches. This resulted in a strong interest in the continuous improvement approach.

Continuous improvement Philosophy that seeks to make never-ending improvements to the process of converting inputs into outputs.

Kaizen Japanese term for continuous improvement.

2. **Competitive benchmarking.** This involves identifying other organizations that are the best at something and studying how they do it to learn how to improve your operation. The company need not be in the same line of business. For example, Xerox used the mail-order company L.L. Bean to benchmark order filling.

3. **Employee empowerment.** Giving workers the responsibility for improvements and the authority to make changes to accomplish them provides strong motivation for employees. This puts decision making into the hands of those who are closest to the job and have considerable insight into problems and solutions.

4. **Team approach.** The use of teams for problem solving and to achieve consensus takes advantage of group synergy, gets people involved, and promotes a spirit of cooperation and shared values among employees.

5. **Decisions based on facts rather than opinions.** Management gathers and analyzes data as a basis for decision making.

6. **Knowledge of tools.** Employees and managers are trained in the use of quality tools.

7. **Supplier quality.** Suppliers must be included in quality assurance and quality improvement efforts so that their processes are capable of delivering quality parts and materials in a timely manner.

8. **Champion.** A TQM champion's job is to promote the value and importance of TQM principles throughout the company.

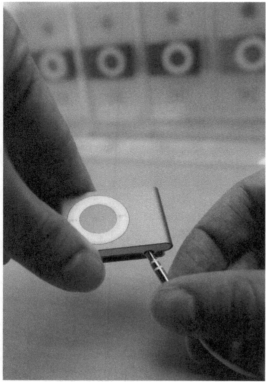

© Paul Sakuma/AP Images

The iPod Shuffle stops playing music when the earphone jack is unplugged. When the earphones are plugged back in, the music resumes right where it left off. This keeps the battery from running down and is an example of mistake proofing.

Quality at the source The philosophy of making each worker responsible for the quality of his or her work.

9. **Quality at the source.** Quality at the source refers to the philosophy of making each worker responsible for the quality of his or her work. The idea is to "Do it right the first time." Workers are expected to provide goods or services that meet specifications and to find and correct mistakes that occur. In effect, each worker becomes a quality inspector for his or her work. When the work is passed on to the next operation in the process (the internal customer) or, if that step is the last in the process, to the ultimate customer, the worker is "certifying" that it meets quality standards.

    This accomplishes a number of things: (a) it places direct responsibility for quality on the person(s) who directly affect it; (b) it removes the adversarial relationship that often exists between quality control inspectors and production workers; and (c) it motivates workers by giving them control over their work as well as pride in it.

10. **Suppliers** are partners in the process, and long-term relationships are encouraged. This gives suppliers a vital stake in providing quality goods and services. Suppliers, too, are expected to provide quality at the source, thereby reducing or eliminating the need to inspect deliveries from suppliers.

It would be incorrect to think of TQM as merely a collection of techniques. Rather, TQM reflects a whole new attitude toward quality. It is about the *culture* of an organization. To truly reap the benefits of TQM, the organization must change its culture.

Table 9.6 illustrates the differences between cultures of a TQM organization and a more traditional organization.

Obstacles to Implementing TQM

Companies have had varying success in implementing TQM. Some have been quite successful, but others have struggled. Part of the difficulty may be with the process by which it is implemented rather than with the principles of TQM. Among the factors cited in the literature are the following:

1. Lack of a companywide definition of quality: Efforts aren't coordinated; people are working at cross-purposes, addressing different issues, and using different measures of success.

2. Lack of a strategic plan for change: Without such a plan the chance of success is lessened and the need to address strategic implications of change is ignored.

3. Lack of a customer focus: Without a customer focus, there is a risk of customer dissatisfaction.

4. Poor intraorganizational communication: The left hand doesn't know what the right hand is doing; frustration, waste, and confusion ensue.

5. Lack of employee empowerment: Not empowering employees gives the impression of not trusting employees to fix problems, adds red tape, and delays solutions.

6. View of quality as a "quick fix": Quality needs to be a long-term, continuing effort.

7. Emphasis on short-term financial results: "Duct-tape" solutions often treat symptoms; spend a little now—a lot more later.

8. Inordinate presence of internal politics and "turf" issues: These can sap the energy of an organization and derail the best of ideas.

9. Lack of strong motivation: Managers need to make sure employees are motivated.

Aspect	Traditional	TQM
Overall mission	Maximize return on investment	Meet or exceed customer expectations
Objectives	Emphasis on short term	Balance of long term and short term
Management	Not always open; sometimes inconsistent objectives	Open; encourages employee input; consistent objectives
Role of manager	Issue orders; enforce	Coach; remove barriers; build trust
Customer requirements	Not highest priority; may be unclear	Highest priority; important to identify and understand
Problems	Assign blame; punish	Identify and resolve
Problem solving	Not systematic; individuals	Systematic; teams
Improvement	Erratic	Continuous
Suppliers	Adversarial	Partners
Jobs	Narrow, specialized; much individual effort	Broad, more general; much team effort
Focus	Product oriented	Process oriented

TABLE 9.6
Comparing the cultures of TQM and traditional organizations

10. Lack of time to devote to quality initiatives: Don't add more work without adding additional resources.

11. Lack of leadership: Managers need to be leaders.[5]

This list of potential problems can serve as a guideline for organizations contemplating implementing TQM or as a checklist for those having trouble implementing it.

Criticisms of TQM

TQM programs are touted as a way for companies to improve their competitiveness, which is a very worthwhile objective. Nonetheless, TQM programs are not without criticism. The following are some of the major criticisms:

1. Overzealous advocates may pursue TQM programs blindly, focusing attention on quality even though other priorities may be more important (e.g., responding quickly to a competitor's advances).

2. Programs may not be linked to the strategies of the organization in a meaningful way.

3. Quality-related decisions may not be tied to market performance. For instance, customer satisfaction may be emphasized to the extent that its cost far exceeds any direct or indirect benefit of doing so.

4. Failure to carefully plan a program before embarking on it can lead to false starts, employee confusion, and meaningless results.

5. Organizations sometimes pursue continuous improvement (i.e., *incremental* improvement) when *dramatic* improvement is needed.

6. Quality efforts may not be tied to results.

Note that there is nothing inherently wrong with TQM; the problem is how some individuals or organizations misuse it. Let's turn our attention to problem solving and process improvement.

[5] Excerpt from Gary Salegna and Farzaneh Fazel, "Obstacles to Implementing Quality," *Quality Progress*, July 2000, p. 53. Copyright © 2000 American Society for Quality. Reprinted with permission from *Quality Progress* magazine.

9.9 PROBLEM SOLVING AND PROCESS IMPROVEMENT

LO9.10 Give an overview of problem solving.

Problem solving is one of the basic procedures of TQM. In order to be successful, problem-solving efforts should follow a standard approach. Table 9.7 describes the basic steps in the TQM problem-solving process.

An important aspect of problem solving in the TQM approach is *eliminating* the cause so that the problem does not recur. This is why users of the TQM approach often like to think of problems as "opportunities for improvement."

The Plan-Do-Study-Act Cycle

Plan-do-study-act (PDSA) cycle A framework for problem solving and improvement activities.

The **plan-do-study-act (PDSA) cycle**, also referred to as either the Shewhart cycle or the Deming wheel, is the conceptual basis for problem-solving activities. The cycle is illustrated in Figure 9.1. Representing the process with a circle underscores its continuing nature. There are four basic steps in the cycle:

Plan. Begin by studying the current process. Document that process. Then collect data on the process or problem. Next, analyze the data and develop a plan for improvement. Specify measures for evaluating the plan.

Do. Implement the plan, on a small scale if possible. Document any changes made during this phase. Collect data systematically for evaluation.

Study. Evaluate the data collection during the *do* phase. Check how closely the results match the original goals of the *plan* phase.

Act. If the results are successful, *standardize* the new method and communicate the new method to all people associated with the process. Implement training for the new method. If the results are unsuccessful, revise the plan and repeat the process or cease this project.

Employing this sequence of steps provides a systematic approach to continuous improvement.

Process improvement A systematic approach to improving a process.

Process improvement is a *systematic* approach to improving a process. It involves documentation, measurement, and analysis for the purpose of improving the functioning of a

TABLE 9.7
Basic steps in problem solving

Step 1	**Define the problem and establish an improvement goal.** Give problem definition careful consideration; don't rush through this step because this will serve as the focal point of problem-solving efforts.
Step 2	**Develop performance measures and collect data.** The solution must be based on *facts*. Possible tools include check sheet, scatter diagram, histogram, run chart, and control chart.
Step 3	**Analyze the problem.** Possible tools include Pareto chart, cause-and-effect diagram.
Step 4	**Generate potential solutions.** Methods include brainstorming, interviewing, and surveying.
Step 5	**Choose a solution.** Identify the criteria for choosing a solution. (Refer to the goal established in Step 1.) Apply criteria to potential solutions and select the best one.
Step 6	**Implement the solution.** Keep everyone informed.
Step 7	**Monitor the solution to see if it accomplishes the goal.** If not, modify the solution, or return to Step 1. Possible tools include control chart and run chart.

A. The PDSA cycle

B. The PDSA cycle applied to problem solving

FIGURE 9.1

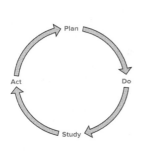

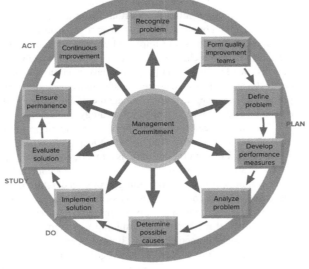

Source: Figure from Donna Summers, *Quality,* 2nd ed., p. 67. Copyright © 2000 Prentice Hall, Inc. Reprinted by permission of Pearson Education, Inc., Upper Saddle River, NJ.

process. Typical goals of process improvement include increasing customer satisfaction, achieving higher quality, reducing waste, reducing cost, increasing productivity, and reducing processing time.

Table 9.8 provides an overview of process improvement.

A. Map the process
 1. Collect information about the process; identify each step in the process. For each step, determine:
    The inputs and outputs.
    The people involved.
    The decisions that are made.
    Document such measures as time, cost, space used, waste, employee morale and any employee turnover, accidents and/or safety hazards, working conditions, revenues and/or profits, quality, and customer satisfaction, as appropriate.
 2. Prepare a flowchart that *accurately* depicts the process. Make sure that key activities and decisions are represented.

B. Analyze the process
 1. Ask these questions about the process:
    Is the flow logical?
    Are any steps or activities missing?
    Are there any duplications?
 2. Ask these questions about each step:
    Could it be eliminated?
    Does the step add value?
    Does any waste occur at this step?
    Could the time be shortened?
    Could the cost to perform the step be reduced?
    Could two (or more) steps be combined?

C. Redesign the process
 Using the results of the analysis, redesign the process. Document the improvements; potential measures include reductions in time, cost, space, waste, employee turnover, accidents, safety hazards, and increases/ improvements in employee morale, working conditions, revenues/profits, quality, and customer satisfaction.

TABLE 9.8
Overview of process improvement

LO9.11 Give an overview of process improvement.

Six Sigma

Six Sigma A business process for improving quality, reducing costs, and increasing customer satisfaction.

The term **Six Sigma** has several meanings. Statistically, Six Sigma means having no more than 3.4 defects per million opportunities in any process, product, or service. Conceptually, the term is much broader, referring to a program designed to reduce the occurrence of defects to achieve lower costs and improved customer satisfaction. It is based on the application of certain tools and techniques to selected projects to achieve strategic business results. In the business world, Six-Sigma programs have become a key way to improve quality, save time, cut costs, and improve customer satisfaction. Six-Sigma programs can be employed in design, production, service, inventory management, and delivery. It is important for Six-Sigma projects to be aligned with organization strategy.

Motorola pioneered the concept of a Six-Sigma program in the 1980s and actually trademarked the term. Today, Six Sigma concepts are widely used by businesses, governments, consultants, and even the military as a business performance methodology.

There are management and technical components of Six-Sigma programs. The management component involves providing strong leadership, defining performance metrics, selecting projects likely to achieve business results, and selecting and training appropriate people. The technical component involves improving process performance, reducing variation, utilizing statistical methods, and designing a structured improvement strategy, which involves definition, measurement, analysis, improvement, and control.

For Six Sigma to succeed in any organization, buy-in at the top is essential. Top management must formulate and communicate the company's overall objectives and lead the program for a successful deployment. Other key players in Six-Sigma programs are program champions, "master black belts," "black belts," and "green belts." Champions identify and rank potential projects, help select and evaluate candidates, manage program resources, and serve as advocates for the program. Master black belts have extensive training in statistics and use of quality tools. They are teachers and mentors of black belts. Black belts are project team leaders responsible for implementing process improvement projects. They have typically completed four weeks of Six-Sigma training and have demonstrated mastery of the subject matter through an exam and successful completion of one or more projects. Green belts are members of project teams.

Black belts play a pivotal role in the success of Six-Sigma programs. They influence change, facilitate teamwork, provide leadership in applying tools and techniques, and convey knowledge and skills to green belts. Black belt candidates generally have a proven strength in either a technical discipline such as engineering or a business discipline. Candidates also must have strong "people skills" and be able to facilitate change. And they must be proficient in applying continuous improvement and statistical methods and tools. A black belt must understand the technical aspects of process improvement as well as the expected business results (time, money, and quality improvement).

Six Sigma is based on these guiding principles:

LO9.12 Describe the six sigma methodology.

1. Reduction of variation is an important goal.
2. The methodology is data driven; it requires valid measurements.
3. Outputs are determined by inputs; focus on modifying and/or controlling inputs to improve outputs.
4. Only a critical few inputs have a significant impact on outputs (the Pareto effect); concentrate on those.

DMAIC (define-measure-analyze-improve-control) is a formalized problem-solving process of Six Sigma. It is composed of five steps that can be applied to any process to improve its effectiveness. The steps are:

1. Define: Set the context and objectives for improvement.
2. Measure: Determine the baseline performance and capability of the process.
3. Analyze: Use data and tools to understand the cause-and-effect relationships of the process.
4. Improve: Develop the modifications that lead to a validated improvement in the process.
5. Control: Establish plans and procedures to ensure that improvements are sustained.

READING

WHAT KEEPS SIX SIGMA PRACTITIONERS UP AT NIGHT?

BILL KOWALSKI

It may be the most widely acclaimed performance improvement system across the business world, yet Six Sigma is not immune to a paradox common to most large-scale change efforts:

> *You can't expect to sustain top executive support without producing consistent bottom-line results . . . yet consistent results aren't likely without sustained top executive support.*

This conundrum is a key finding from a recent survey of more than 240 Six Sigma practitioners across industries and around the globe. Sponsored by Leap Technologies, the survey was conducted anonymously over the Web through iSixSigma.com, the leading Six Sigma information portal.

The survey gauged perceptions of Six Sigma practitioners on two primary issues:

1. What causes Six Sigma projects to fail to produce desired results?
2. What would most help to improve Six Sigma project results?

We know these are issues keeping practitioners up at night because these same people are under increasingly heavy pressure to produce and sustain bottom-line results from their projects.

The "Catch 22" for Six Sigma Practitioners

The most often cited reason for Six Sigma project failure was "lack of sustained executive sponsorship and commitment." It is clearly evident that there is no substitute for top leadership support to achieve sustained Six Sigma success. In close second ranking was "lack of buy-in, cooperation and ownership by frontline managers and employees for implementing and sustaining results on Six Sigma project solutions." These top two barriers to success create a classic "Catch 22" for Six Sigma practitioners. On the one hand, executive commitment is critical to the funding and mandate Six Sigma practitioners need to challenge the status quo.

On the other hand, sustaining executive support is nearly impossible without consistent delivery of results. Yet this payoff can't be sustained without active support by those most impacted by Six Sigma solutions . . . *frontline managers and employees!*

Six Sigma is, with its dedicated Belt infrastructure and standardized *DMAIC methodology,* a more sophisticated and effective approach than past quality improvement methods. But, if there is a chink to be found in Six Sigma's armor, it is the issue of non-Belt participation and ownership. This problem, however, rarely surfaces in the first 12 to 18 months of a *Six Sigma Deployment.* In fact, we've observed that, initially, many Six Sigma Deployment Leaders experience a false sense of security about results. Why? Because most of the projects taken on by newly trained Black and Green Belts rarely require high levels of frontline support and, for the most part, don't challenge top management's ingrained cultural biases.

At the same time, it's also not uncommon for organizations adopting Six Sigma to "hit the wall" once "low touch" projects are completed. Top management's appetite for results has been whetted, but the foundational support in terms of skills, experience and commitment may not be there to tackle the projects that present bigger change management challenges.

More Tools Are Needed

According to the Six Sigma practitioners completing the survey, the path to better Six Sigma project results requires equipping practitioners with an expanded set of tools to both tackle more complex projects and improve Belt productivity by getting more non-Belt involvement. This finding is not likely to be a revelation to many of the early pioneers who paved the way to the popularity of Six Sigma. Companies like Motorola, Allied Signal (now merged with Honeywell), and GE, along with other big players, such as DuPont and 3M (among others), have already taken steps to strengthen their Six Sigma Deployments by enhancing the skills of Belts and expanding the tool kit.

At the same time, the survey results indicate there is more work to do in advancing Six Sigma into a robust and sustainable method for *transformational change.* The top priority appears to be the expansion of the Six Sigma practitioner's tool kit to break free of the "Catch 22" syndrome. In fact, the integration of *Lean principles* by numerous Six Sigma users is a big step in the right direction. However, in addition to Lean tools there also appears to be a growing recognition that more tools are needed to deal with the *change management* aspects of Six Sigma. Ninety percent of the survey respondents rated the need for a structured tool set for engaging "non-Belts" in projects, particularly those with significant behavior change requirements.

The preceding finding is linked to the second most important reason practitioners stated as the cause for Six Sigma projects falling short (i.e., lack of buy-in, cooperation, or ownership by frontline employees and managers). The relationship between these two findings correlates with the anecdotal evidence from more experienced Six Sigma organizations about the keys to accelerating results and reducing project cycle times. As they move down the experience curve and tackle larger and more complex change projects, the most successful Six Sigma organizations have expanded their tool sets and integrated other improvement disciplines such as Lean seamlessly into deployments.

The Keys to a Better Night's Sleep

Six Sigma practitioners can break free of the "Catch 22" syndrome by designing their deployments to deliver consistent results and sustain consistent executive support. The keys are:

1. Expand the tool set early in deployment with methods to get more non-Belt participation and faster results. The key to avoiding confusion or overload is to integrate Lean, Innovation, and other improvement methods into the DMAIC framework.
2. Engage senior leaders to go beyond the rubber-stamping of project selections to actually designing the project plan with the Belts. The benefits are a more realistic appraisal of project requirements and deeper understanding of where and how to apply other tool sets to drive bigger and faster results.

(continued)

3. Engage non-Belt managers and employees early on projects where there is existing motivation for change.

Taking actions such as these will provide a steadier stream of results, sustained executive support, and a better night's sleep for Six Sigma practitioners!

About the Author
Bill Kowalski is a Senior Partner with Leap Technologies, the leading provider of Change Acceleration Tools for Six Sigma Deployment. For more articles and information on accelerating organization change, visit Leap Technologies on the Web at www. actionworkout.com.

Source: Bill Kowalski, "What Keeps Six Sigma Practitioners Up at Night?" Copyright © Leap Technologies, Inc., 2003. Used with permission.

9.10 QUALITY TOOLS

LO9.13 Describe and use various quality tools.

There are a number of tools that an organization can use for problem solving and process improvement. This section describes eight of these tools. The tools aid in data collection and interpretation, and provide the basis for decision making.

The first seven tools are often referred to as the *seven basic quality tools*. Figure 9.2 provides a quick overview of the seven tools.

Flowchart A diagram of the steps in a process.

Flowcharts. A **flowchart** is a visual representation of a process. As a problem-solving tool, a flowchart can help investigators in identifying possible points in a process where problems occur. Figure 9.3 illustrates a flowchart for catalog telephone orders in which potential failure points are highlighted.

The diamond shapes in the flowchart represent decision points in the process, and the rectangular shapes represent procedures. The arrows show the direction of "flow" of the steps in the process.

To construct a simple flowchart, begin by listing the steps in a process. Then classify each step as either a procedure or a decision (or check) point. Try to not make the flowchart too detailed or it may be overwhelming, but be careful not to omit any key steps.

Check sheet A tool for recording and organizing data to identify a problem.

Check sheets. A **check sheet** is a simple tool frequently used for problem identification. Check sheets provide a format that enables users to record and organize data in a way that facilitates collection and analysis. This format might be one of simple checkmarks. Check sheets are designed on the basis of what the users are attempting to learn by collecting data.

Many different formats can be used for a check sheet, and there are many different types of sheets. One frequently used form of check sheet deals with type of defect, another with location of defects. These are illustrated in Figures 9.4 and 9.5

Figure 9.4 shows tallies that denote the type of defect and the time of day each occurred. Problems with missing labels tend to occur early in the day and smeared print tends to occur late in the day, whereas off-center labels are found throughout the day. Identifying types of defects and when they occur can help in pinpointing causes of the defects.

Figure 9.5 makes it easy to see where defects on the product—in this case, a glove—are occurring. Defects seem to be occurring on the tips of the thumb and first finger, in the finger valleys (especially between the thumb and first finger), and in the center of the gloves. Again, this may help determine why the defects occur and lead to a solution.

Histogram A chart of an empirical frequency distribution.

Histograms. A **histogram** can be useful in getting a sense of the distribution of observed values. Among other things, one can see if the distribution is symmetrical, what the range of values is, and if there are any unusual values. Figure 9.6 illustrates a histogram. Note the two peaks. This suggests the possibility of *two* distributions with different centers. Possible causes might be two workers or two suppliers with different quality.

Pareto analysis Technique for classifying problem areas according to degree of importance, and focusing on the most important.

Pareto Analysis. **Pareto analysis** is a technique for focusing attention on the most important problem areas. The Pareto concept, named after the 19th-century Italian economist Vilfredo Pareto, is that a relatively few factors generally account for a large percentage of the

FIGURE 9.2   The seven basic quality tools

Flowchart

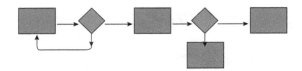

A diagram of the steps in a process

Check sheet

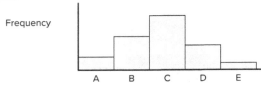

A tool for organizing and collecting data; a tally of problems or other events by category

Histogram

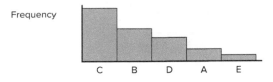

A chart that shows an empirical frequency distribution

Pareto chart

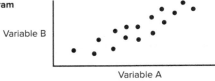

A diagram that arranges categories from highest to lowest frequency of occurrence

Scatter diagram

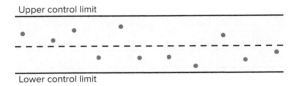

A graph that shows the degree and direction of relationship between two variables

Control chart

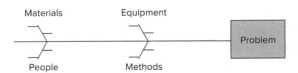

A statistical chart of time-ordered values of a sample statistic (e.g., sample means)

Cause-and-effect diagram

A diagram used to organize a search for the cause(s) of a problem; also known as a *fishbone* diagram

FIGURE 9.3
Flowchart of catalog call

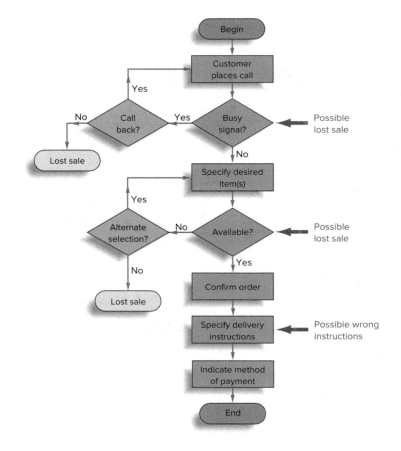

FIGURE 9.4
An example of a check sheet

| Day | Time | Type of Defect | | | | | Total |
		Missing label	Off-center	Smeared print	Loose or folded	Other	
M	8–9	IIII	II				6
	9–10		III				3
	10–11	I	III	I			5
	11–12		I		I	I (Torn)	3
	1–2		I				1
	2–3		II	III	I		6
	3–4		II	IIIII			8
Total		5	14	10	2	1	32

FIGURE 9.5
A special-purpose check sheet

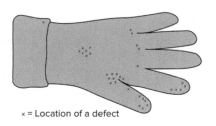

x = Location of a defect

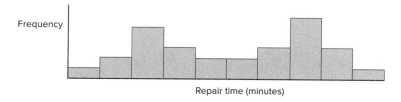

Frequency

Repair time (minutes)

FIGURE 9.6
A histogram

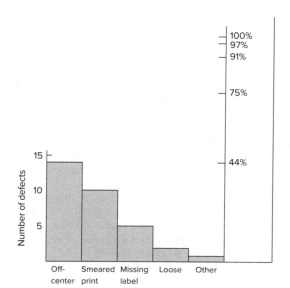

FIGURE 9.7
A Pareto diagram based on
data in Figure 9.4

total cases (e.g., complaints, defects, problems). The idea is to classify the cases according to degree of importance and focus on resolving the most important, leaving the less important. Often referred to as the 80–20 rule, the Pareto concept states that approximately 80 percent of the problems come from 20 percent of the items. For instance, 80 percent of machine break-downs come from 20 percent of the machines, and 80 percent of the product defects come from 20 percent of the causes of defects.

Often, it is useful to prepare a chart that shows the number of occurrences by category, arranged in order of frequency. Figure 9.7 illustrates such a chart corresponding to the check sheet shown in Figure 9.4. The dominance of the problem with off-center labels becomes apparent. Presumably, the manager and employees would focus on trying to resolve this prob-lem. Once they accomplished that, they could address the remaining defects in similar fash-ion; "smeared print" would be the next major category to be resolved, and so on. Additional check sheets would be used to collect data to verify that the defects in these categories have been eliminated or greatly reduced. Hence, in later Pareto diagrams, categories such as "off-center" may still appear but would be much less prominent.

Scatter Diagrams. A **scatter diagram** can be useful in deciding if there is a correlation between the values of two variables. A correlation may point to a cause of a problem. Figure 9.8 shows an example of a scatter diagram. In this particular diagram, there is a *positive* (upward-sloping) relationship between the humidity and the number of errors per hour. High values of humidity correspond to high numbers of errors, and vice versa. On the other hand, a *negative* (downward-sloping) relationship would mean that when values of one variable are low, values of the other variable are high, and vice versa.

The higher the correlation between the two variables, the less scatter in the points; the points will tend to line up. Conversely, if there were little or no relationship between two

Scatter diagram A graph that shows the degree and direc-tion of relationship between two variables.

FIGURE 9.8
A scatter diagram

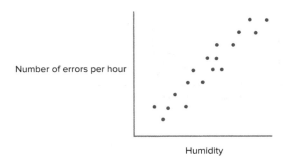

Number of errors per hour

Humidity

variables, the points would be completely scattered. In Figure 9.8, the correlation between humidity and errors seems strong because the points appear to scatter along an imaginary line.

Control chart A statistical chart of time-ordered values of a sample statistic.

Control Charts. A **control chart** can be used to monitor a process to see if the process output is random. It can help detect the presence of *correctable* causes of variation. Figure 9.9 illustrates a control chart. Control charts also can indicate when a problem occurred and give insight into what caused the problem. Control charts are described in detail in Chapter 10.

Cause-and-effect diagram A diagram used to search for the cause(s) of a problem; also called fishbone diagram.

Cause-and-Effect Diagrams. A **cause-and-effect diagram** offers a structured approach to the search for the possible cause(s) of a problem. It is also known as a *fishbone diagram* because of its shape, or an *Ishikawa diagram*, after the Japanese professor who developed the approach to aid workers overwhelmed by the number of possible sources of problems when problem solving. This tool helps to organize problem-solving efforts by identifying *categories* of factors that might be causing problems. Often this tool is used after brainstorming sessions to organize the ideas generated. Figure 9.10 illustrates one form of a cause-and-effect diagram.

Some errors are more likely causes than others, depending on the nature of the errors. If the cause is still not obvious at this point, additional investigation into the *root cause* may be necessary, involving a more in-depth analysis. Often, more detailed information can be

FIGURE 9.9
A control chart

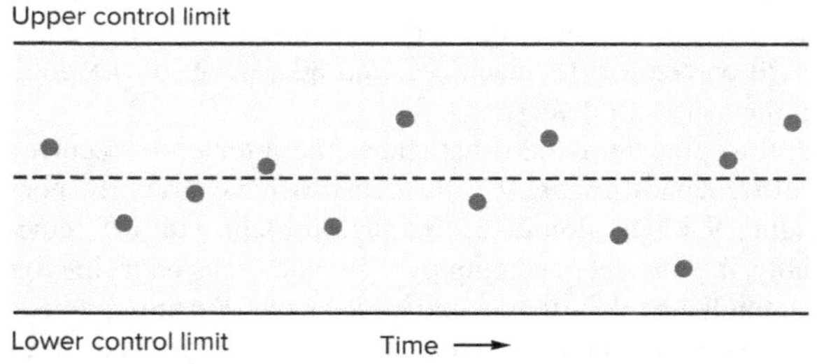

Upper control limit

Lower control limit   Time →

FIGURE 9.10
One format of a cause-and-effect diagram

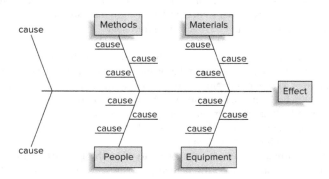

FIGURE 9.11   A run chart shows performance over time

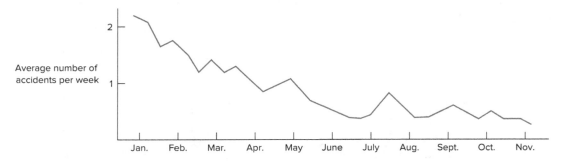

obtained by asking *who, what, where, when, why,* and *how* questions about factors that appear to be the most likely sources of problems.

Run Charts. A **run chart** can be used to track the values of a variable over time. This can aid in identifying trends or other patterns that may be occurring. Figure 9.11provides an example of a run chart showing a decreasing trend in accident frequency over time. Important advantages of run charts are ease of construction and ease of interpretation.

Run chart Tool for tracking results over a period of time.

Illustrations of the Use of Graphical Tools

This section presents some illustrations of the use of graphical tools in process or product improvement. Figure 9.12 begins with a check sheet that can be used to develop a Pareto chart of the types of errors found. That leads to a more focused analysis of the most frequently occurring type of error using a cause-and-effect diagram. Additional cause-and-effect diagrams, such as errors by location, might also be used.

FIGURE 9.12   Employing graphical tools in problem solving

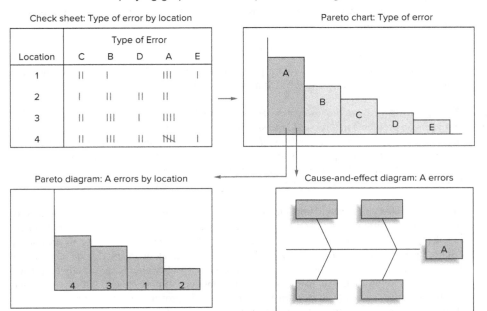

404   **Chapter Nine**   Management of Quality

FIGURE 9.13
Comparison of before and after using Pareto charts

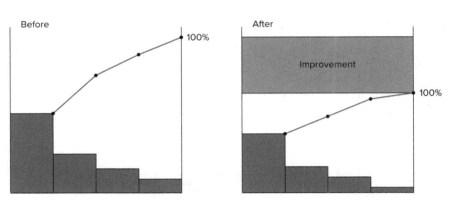

FIGURE 9.14
Using a control chart to track improvements

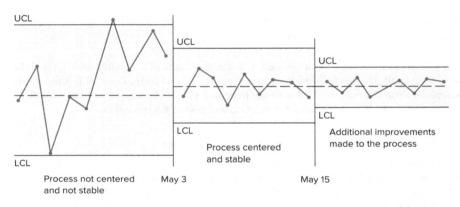

UCL = Upper Control Limit
LCL = Lower Control Limit

Figure 9.13 shows how Pareto charts measure the amount of improvement achieved in a before-and-after scenario of errors.

Figure 9.14 illustrates how control charts track two phases of improvement in a process that was initially out of control.

Methods for Generating Ideas

Some additional tools that are useful for problem solving and/or for process improvement are brainstorming, quality circles, and benchmarking.

Brainstorming Technique for generating a free flow of ideas in a group of people.

Brainstorming. **Brainstorming** is a technique in which a group of people share thoughts and ideas on problems in a relaxed atmosphere that encourages unrestrained collective thinking. The goal is to generate a free flow of ideas on identifying problems, and finding causes, solutions, and ways to implement solutions. In successful brainstorming, criticism is absent, no single member is allowed to dominate sessions, and all ideas are welcomed. Structured brainstorming is an approach to assure that everyone participates.

Quality circles Groups of workers who meet to discuss ways of improving products or processes.

Quality Circles. One way companies have tapped employees for ideas concerning quality improvement is through **quality circles**. The circles comprise a number of workers who get together periodically to discuss ways of improving products and processes. Not only are quality circles a valuable source of worker input, they also can motivate workers, if handled properly, by demonstrating management interest in worker ideas. Quality circles are usually less structured and more informal than teams involved in continuous improvement, but in some organizations quality circles have evolved into continuous improvement teams. Perhaps a major distinction between quality circles and teams is the amount of authority given to the teams.

Chapter Nine Management of Quality   **405**

1. What organizations do it the best?
2. How do they do it?
3. How do we do it now?
4. How can we change to match or exceed the best?

TABLE 9.9
The benchmarking approach

Typically, quality circles have had very little authority to implement any but minor changes; continuous improvement teams are sometimes given a great deal of authority. Consequently, continuous improvement teams have the added motivation generated by *empowerment.*

Benchmarking. **Benchmarking** is an approach that can inject new energy into improvement efforts. Summarized in Table 9.9, benchmarking is the process of measuring an organization's performance on a key customer requirement against the best in the industry, or against the best in any industry. Its purpose is to establish a standard against which performance is judged, and to identify a model for learning how to improve. A benchmark demonstrates the degree to which customers of other organizations are satisfied. Once a benchmark has been identified, the goal is to meet or exceed that standard through improvements in appropriate processes. The benchmarking process usually involves these steps:

Benchmarking Process of measuring performance against the best in the same or another industry.

1. Identify a critical process that needs improvement (e.g., order entry, distribution, service after sale).

2. Identify an organization that excels in the process, preferably the best.

3. Contact the benchmark organization, visit it, and study the benchmark activity.

4. Analyze the data.

5. Improve the critical process at your own organization.

Selecting an industry leader provides insight into what competitors are doing; but competitors may be reluctant to share this information. Several organizations are responding to this difficulty by conducting benchmarking studies and providing that information to other organizations without revealing the sources of the data.

Selecting organizations that are world leaders in different industries is another alternative. For example, the Xerox Corporation uses many benchmarks: For employee involvement, Procter & Gamble; for quality process, Florida Power and Light and Toyota; for high-volume production, Canon; for billing collection, American Express; for research and development, AT&T and Hewlett-Packard; for distribution, L.L. Bean and Hershey Foods; and for daily scheduling, Cummins Engine.

Hewlett-Packard (HP), a world leader in research and development, created the TouchSmart PC. Joint research with universities, customers, and partners meets the scientific and business objectives of HP. This model is a benchmark for other companies.

BENCHMARKING CORPORATE WEBSITES OF FORTUNE 500 COMPANIES

More and more people are using the Internet. And when these people want information about a company's products or services, they often go to the company's website. In a study of the home pages of Fortune 500 companies, 13 factors were deemed critical to quality. Those factors, and the survey results, are shown as follows.

1. Use of meta tags (e.g., keywords used by search engines): yes, 70%; no, 30%
2. Meaningful home page title: yes, 97%; no, 3%
3. Unique domain name: yes, 91%; no, 9%
4. Search engine site registration: 97% (average)
5. Server reliability: 99% (average)
6. Average speed of loading (seconds): 28k, 19.3; 56k, 10.9; T1, 2.6 sec.
7. Average number of bad links: .40
8. Average number of spelling errors: .16
9. Visibility of contact information: yes, 74%; no, 26%
10. Indication of last update date: yes, 17%; no, 83%
11. A privacy policy: yes, 53%; no, 47%
12. Presence of a search engine: yes, 59%; no, 41%
13. Translation to multiple languages: yes, 11%; no, 89%

The corporations are doing well on most factors, but they need improvement on the last five.

The list is a handy reference other organizations can use to benchmark their existing home pages to see where improvements are needed or to develop effective home pages.

Question   Give one reason for the importance of each factor.

Source: Based on Nabil Tamimi, Murli Rajan, and Rose Sebastianelli, "Benchmarking the Home Pages of 'Fortune 500' Companies." Reprinted with permission from *Quality Progress* © 2000 American Society for Quality. No further distribution allowed without permission.

9.11 OPERATIONS STRATEGY

All customers are concerned with the quality of goods or services they receive. For this reason alone, business organizations have a vital, strategic interest in achieving and maintaining high quality standards. Moreover, there is a positive link between quality and productivity, giving an additional incentive for achieving high quality and being able to present that image to current and potential customers.

The best business organizations view quality as a never-ending journey. That is, they strive for continual improvement with the attitude that no matter how good quality is, it can always be improved, and there are benefits for doing so.

In order for total quality management to be successful, it is essential that a majority of those in an organization buy in to the idea. Otherwise, there is a risk that a significant portion of the benefits of the approach will not be realized. Therefore, it is important to give this sufficient attention, and to confirm that concordance exists before plunging ahead. A key aspect of this is a top-down approach: Top management needs to be visibly involved and needs to be supportive, both financially and emotionally. Also important is education of managers and workers in the concepts, tools, and procedures of quality. Again, if education is incomplete, there is the risk that TQM will not produce the desired benefits.

And here's a note of caution: Although customer retention rates can have a dramatic impact on profitability, customer satisfaction does not always guarantee customer loyalty. Consequently, organizations may need to develop a retention strategy to deal with this possibility.

It is not enough for an organization to incorporate quality into its operations; the entire supply chain has to be involved. Problems such as defects in purchased parts, long lead times, and late or missed deliveries of goods or services all negatively impact an organization's ability to satisfy its customers. So it is essential to incorporate quality throughout the supply chain.

SUMMARY

This chapter presents philosophies and tools that can be used to achieve high quality and continually improve quality. Quality is the culmination of efforts of the entire organization and its supply chain. It begins with careful assessment of what the customers want, then translating this information into technical specifications to which goods or services must conform. The specifications guide product and service design, process design, production of goods and delivery of services, and service after the sale or delivery.

The consequences of poor quality include loss of market share, liability claims, a decrease in productivity, and an increase in costs. Quality costs include costs related to prevention, appraisal, and failure. Determinants of quality are design, conformance to design, ease of use, and service after delivery.

Modern quality management is directed at preventing mistakes rather than finding them after they occur and reducing process output variation. Currently, the business community shows widespread interest in improving quality and competitiveness.

The chapter includes a description of the key contributors to quality management, and it outlines the ISO 9000, ISO 14000, and ISO 24700 international quality standards.

Three awards of distinction—the Baldrige Award, the European Quality Award, and the Deming Prize—are given annually to organizations that have shown great achievement in quality management.

Total quality management is a never-ending pursuit of quality that involves everyone in an organization. The driving force is customer satisfaction; a key philosophy is continuous improvement. Training of managers and workers in quality concepts, tools, and procedures is an important aspect of the approach. Teams are an integral part of TQM.

Two major aspects of the TQM approach are problem solving and process improvement. Six-Sigma programs are a form of TQM. They emphasize the use of statistical and management science tools on selected projects to achieve business results.

KEY POINTS

1. Price and quality are the two primary considerations in every buying transaction, so quality is extremely important.
2. Quality gurus have made important contributions to the way business organizations view quality and achieve quality.
3. Quality certification and quality awards are important because they can provide some degree of assurance to customers about quality.
4. Many simple-to-use tools are available for problem solving and process improvement.

KEY TERMS

appraisal costs 384
Baldrige Award 387
benchmarking 405
brainstorming 404
cause-and-effect (fishbone)
   diagram 402
check sheet 398
continuous improvement 391
control chart 402
Deming Prize 376
European Quality Award 387
external failures 385
fail-safing 391

failure costs 385
flowchart 398
histogram 398
internal failures 385
ISO 9000 388
ISO 14000 388
ISO 24700 388
kaizen 391
Pareto analysis 398
plan-do-study-act (PDSA)
   cycle 394
prevention costs 385
process improvement 394

quality 373
quality at the source 392
quality circles 404
quality of conformance 381
quality of design 381
return on quality 385
run chart 403
scatter diagram 401
Six Sigma 396
total quality management
   (TQM) 390

SOLVED PROBLEM

The county sheriff's department handed out the following tickets on a summer weekend. Make a check sheet and a Pareto diagram for the types of infractions.

Problem

Ticket Number	Infraction
1	Excessive speed
2	Expired inspection
3	Improper turn
4	Excessive speed
5	Parking violation
6	Parking violation
7	Excessive speed

Ticket Number	Infraction
8	Parking violation
9	Improper turn
10	Parking violation
11	Expired inspection
12	Parking violation
13	Improper turn
14	Parking violation
15	Excessive speed
16	Parking violation
17	Parking violation
18	Parking violation
19	Excessive speed
20	Parking violation

Solution

Check sheet (list the types of infractions, tally, summarize frequencies):

Infraction	Tally	Frequency
Excessive speed	////	5
Expired inspection	//	2
Improper turn	///	3
Parking violation	//// ////	10

Pareto diagram (arrange infractions from highest frequency to lowest):

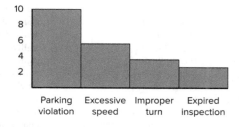

**DISCUSSION AND
REVIEW QUESTIONS**

1. List and briefly explain:
   a. The dimensions of service quality
   b. The determinants of quality

2. Define the terms *quality of design* and *quality of conformance.*

3. What are some possible consequences of poor quality?

4. Use the dimensions of quality to describe typical characteristics of these products and services:
   a. A television set
   b. A restaurant meal (product)
   c. A restaurant meal (service)
   d. Painting a house
   e. Surgery and postsurgery care

5. Many product reviews are available on the Internet. Two examples are reviews on electronics products such as DVD players and high-definition televisions. There are often both positive and negative reviews.
   a. Do such reviews (positive and negative) influence your purchasing decisions? Why or why not?
   b. Why do you suppose consumers take the time and effort to write such reviews?
   c. There is often a feedback button asking if you found the review helpful. Do you usually respond? Why or why not?

6. Describe the quality–ethics connection.

7. Select one of the quality gurus and briefly describe his major contributions to quality management.

8. a. What is ISO 9000, and why is it important for global businesses to have ISO 9000 certification?
   b. Compare the Baldrige Award and ISO certification. If an organization were going to seek both, which one should it seek first? Why?

9. Briefly explain how a company can achieve lower production costs and increase productivity by improving the quality of its products or services.

10. What are the key elements of the TQM approach? What is the driving force behind TQM?

11. Briefly describe each of the seven quality tools.

12. Briefly define or explain each of these tools:
    a. Brainstorming
    b. Benchmarking
    c. Run charts

13. Explain the plan-do-study-act cycle.

14. List the steps of problem solving.

15. Select four tools and describe how they could be used in problem solving.

16. List the steps of process improvement.

17. Select four tools and describe how they could be used for process improvement.

1. What trade-offs are involved in deciding on whether to offer a product or service guarantee?

2. Who needs to be involved in setting priorities for quality improvement?

3. Name several ways that technology has had an impact on quality.

TAKING STOCK

1. A computer repair shop had received a number of complaints on the length of time it took to make repairs. The manager responded by increasing the repair staff by 10 percent. Complaints on repair time quickly decreased, but then complaints on the cost of repairs suddenly increased. Oddly enough, when repair costs were analyzed, the manager found that the average cost of repair had actually decreased relative to what it was before the increase in staff. What are some possible explanations for the complaints, and what actions might the manager contemplate?

2. As a manager, how would you deal with the possibility that customer satisfaction does not always lead to customer retention?

3. What quality-related trade-offs might there be between having a single large, centralized produce-processing facility and having many small, decentralized produce-processing facilities?

4. Give three examples of what would be considered unethical behavior involving management of quality, and state which ethical principle (see Chapter 1) is violated.

CRITICAL THINKING EXERCISES

1. Make a check sheet and then a Pareto diagram for the following car repair shop data.

PROBLEMS

Ticket No.	Work	Ticket No.	Work	Ticket No.	Work
1	Tires	11	Brakes	21	Lube & oil
2	Lube & oil	12	Lube & oil	22	Brakes
3	Tires	13	Battery	23	Transmission
4	Battery	14	Lube & oil	24	Brakes
5	Lube & oil	15	Lube & oil	25	Lube & oil
6	Lube & oil	16	Tires	26	Battery
7	Lube & oil	17	Lube & oil	27	Lube & oil
8	Brakes	18	Brakes	28	Battery
9	Lube & oil	19	Tires	29	Brakes
10	Tires	20	Brakes	30	Tires

2. An air-conditioning repair department manager has compiled data on the primary reason for 41 service calls for the previous week, as shown in the table. Using the data, make a check sheet for the problem types for each customer type, and then construct a Pareto diagram for each type of customer.

410 **Chapter Nine** Management of Quality

Key Problem type:
N = Noisy
F = Equipment failure
W = Runs warm
O = Odor
Customer type:
C = Commercial customer
R = Residential customer

Job Number	Problem/ Customer Type	Job Number	Problem/ Customer Type	Job Number	Problem/ Customer Type
301	F/R	315	F/C	329	O/C
302	O/R	316	O/C	330	N/R
303	N/C	317	W/C	331	N/R
304	N/R	318	N/R	332	W/R
305	W/C	319	O/C	333	O/R
306	N/R	320	F/R	334	O/C
307	F/R	321	F/R	335	N/R
308	N/C	322	O/R	336	W/R
309	W/R	323	F/R	337	O/C
310	N/R	324	N/C	338	O/R
311	N/R	325	F/R	339	F/R
312	F/C	326	O/R	340	N/R
313	N/R	327	W/C	341	O/C
314	W/C	328	O/C		

3. Prepare a run chart similar to Figure 9.11 for the occurrences of defective computer monitors based on the following data, which an analyst obtained from the process for making the monitors. Workers are given a 15-minute break at 10:15 a.m. and 3:15 p.m., and a lunch break at noon. What can you conclude?

Interval Start Time	Number of Defects	Interval Start Time	Number of Defects	Interval Start Time	Number of Defects
8:00	1	10:45	0	2:15	0
8:15	0	11:00	0	2:30	2
8:30	0	11:15	0	2:45	2
8:45	1	11:30	1	3:00	3
9:00	0	11:45	3	3:30	0
9:15	1	1:00	1	3:45	1
9:30	1	1:15	0	4:00	0
9:45	2	1:30	0	4:15	0
10:00	3	1:45	1	4:30	1
10:30	1	2:00	1	4:45	3

4. Prepare a run diagram for this emergency call data. Use five-minute intervals (i.e., count the calls received in each five-minute interval. Use intervals of 0 to 4, 5 to 9, etc.). *Note:* Two or more calls may occur in the same minute; there were three operators on duty this night. What can you conclude from the run chart?

Call	Time	Call	Time	Call	Time	Call	Time
1	1:03	12	1:36	23	1:56	34	2:08
2	1:06	13	1:39	24	2:00	35	2:11
3	1:09	14	1:42	25	2:00	36	2:12
4	1:11	15	1:43	26	2:01	37	2:12
5	1:12	16	1:44	27	2:02	38	2:13
6	1:17	17	1:47	28	2:03	39	2:14
7	1:21	18	1:48	29	2:03	40	2:14
8	1:27	19	1:50	30	2:04	41	2:16
9	1:28	20	1:52	31	2:06	42	2:19
10	1:29	21	1:53	32	2:07		
11	1:31	22	1:56	33	2:08		

Chapter Nine Management of Quality   **411**

5. Suppose that a table lamp fails to light when turned on. Prepare a simple cause-and-effect diagram to analyze possible causes.

6. Prepare a cause-and-effect diagram to analyze the possible causes of late delivery of parts ordered from a supplier.

7. Prepare a cause-and-effect diagram to analyze why a machine has produced a large run of defective parts.

8. Prepare a scatter diagram for each of these data sets and then express in words the apparent relationship between the two variables. Put the first variable on the horizontal axis and the second variable on the vertical axis.

a.

Age	24	30	22	25	33	27	36	58	37	47	54	28	42	55
Absenteeism rate	6	5	7	6	4	5	4	1	3	2	2	5	3	1

b.

Temperature (°F)	65	63	72	66	82	58	75	86	77	65	79
Error rate	1	2	0	0	3	3	1	5	2	1	3

9. Prepare a flowchart that describes going to the library to study for an exam. Your flowchart should include these items: finding a place at the library to study; checking to see if you have your book, paper, highlighter, and so forth; traveling to the library; and the possibility of moving to another location if the place you chose to study starts to get crowded.

10. College students trying to register for a course sometimes find that the course has been closed, or the section they want has been closed. Prepare a cause-and-effect diagram for this problem.

11. The county sheriff's department responded to an unusually large number of vehicular accidents along a quarter-mile stretch of highway in recent months. Prepare a cause-and-effect diagram for this problem.

12. Suppose you are going to have a prescription filled at a local pharmacy. Referring to the dimensions of service quality for each dimension, give an example of how you would judge the quality of the service.

CASE   CHICK-N-GRAVY DINNER LINE

The operations manager of a firm that produces frozen dinners had received numerous complaints from supermarkets about the firm's Chick-n-Gravy dinners. The manager then asked her assistant, Ann, to investigate the matter and to report her recommendations.

Ann's first task was to determine what problems were generating the complaints. The majority of complaints centered on five

defects: underfilled packages, a missing label, spills/mixed items, unacceptable taste, and improperly sealed packages.

Next, she took samples of dinners from the two production lines and examined each sample, making note of any defects that she found. A summary of those results is shown in the table.

The data resulted from inspecting approximately 800 frozen dinners. What should Ann recommend to the manager?

DEFECT OBSERVED

Date	Time	Line	Underfilled	Missing Label	Spill/ Mixed	Unacceptable Taste	Improperly Sealed
5/12	0900	1		✓✓	✓	✓✓✓	
5/12	1330	2			✓✓		✓✓
5/13	1000	2				✓	✓✓✓
5/13	1345	1	✓✓		✓✓		
5/13	1530	2		✓✓	✓✓✓		✓
5/14	0830	1		✓✓✓		✓✓✓	
5/14	1100	2	✓		✓		✓✓
5/14	1400	1			✓		✓
5/15	1030	1		✓✓✓		✓✓✓✓	

(continued)

412   **Chapter Nine**   Management of Quality

(*concluded*)

			DEFECT OBSERVED				
Date	Time	Line	Underfilled	Missing Label	Spill/ Mixed	Unacceptable Taste	Improperly Sealed
5/15	1145	2			✓	✓✓	
5/15	1500	1	✓		✓		
5/16	0845	2				✓✓	✓✓
5/16	1030	1		✓✓✓	✓	✓✓✓	
5/16	1400	1					
5/16	1545	2	✓	✓✓✓✓	✓	✓	✓✓

CASE   TIP TOP MARKETS

Tip Top Markets is a regional chain of supermarkets located in the southeastern United States. Karen Martin, manager of one of the stores, was disturbed by the large number of complaints from customers at her store, particularly on Tuesdays, so she obtained complaint records from the store's customer service desk for the last nine Tuesdays.

Assume you have been asked to help analyze the data and to make recommendations for improvement. Analyze the data using a check sheet, a Pareto diagram, and run charts. Then construct a

cause-and-effect diagram for the leading category on your Pareto diagram.

On July 15, changes were implemented to reduce out-of-stock complaints, improve store maintenance, and reduce checkout lines/pricing problems. Do the results of the last two weeks reflect improvement?

Based on your analysis, prepare a list of recommendations that will address customer complaints.

June 1

out of orange yogurt	produce not fresh
bread stale	lemon yogurt past sell date
checkout lines too long	couldn't find rice
overcharged	milk past sell date
double charged	stock clerk rude
meat smelled strange	cashier not friendly
charged for item not purchased	out of maple walnut ice cream
couldn't find the sponges	something green in meat
meat tasted strange	didn't like music
store too cold	checkout lines too slow
light out in parking lot	

June 8

fish smelled funny	undercharged
out of diet bread	out of roses
dented can	meat spoiled
out of hamburger rolls	overcharged on two items
fish not fresh	store too warm
cashier not helpful	out of ice
meat tasted bad	telephone out of order
ATM ate card	overcharged
slippery floor	rolls stale
music too loud	bread past sale date

June 15

wanted smaller size	overcharged on special
too cold in store	couldn't find aspirin
out of Wheaties	undercharged
out of Minute Rice	checkout lines too long
cashier rude	out of diet cola
fish tasted fishy	meat smelled bad
ice cream thawed	overcharged on eggs
double charged on hard rolls	bread not fresh
long wait at checkout	didn't like music
wrong price on item	lost wallet
overcharged	overcharged on bread
fish didn't smell right	

June 22

milk past sales date	couldn't find oatmeal
store too warm	out of Bounty paper towels
foreign object in meat	overcharged on orange juice
store too cold	lines too long at checkout
eggs cracked	couldn't find shoelaces
couldn't find lard	out of Smucker's strawberry jam
out of 42 oz. Tide	out of Frosty Flakes cereal
fish really bad	out of Thomas' English Muffins
windows dirty	

(*continued*)

(*concluded*)

June 29

checkout line too long	restroom not clean
out of Dove soap	couldn't find sponges
out of Bisquick	checkout lines slow
eggs cracked	out of 18 oz. Tide
store not clean	out of Campbell's turkey soup
store too cold	out of pepperoni sticks
cashier too slow	checkout lines too long
out of skim milk	meat not fresh
charged wrong price	overcharged on melon

July 6

out of straws	store too warm
out of bird food	price not as advertised
overcharged on butter	need to open more checkouts
out of masking tape	shopping carts hard to steer
stockboy was not helpful	debris in aisles
lost child	out of Drano
meat looked bad	out of Chinese cabbage
overcharged on butter	store too warm
out of Swiss chard	floors dirty and sticky
too many people in store	out of Diamond chopped walnuts
out of bubble bath	
out of Dial soap	

July 13

wrong price on spaghetti	undercharged
water on floor	out of brown rice
store looked messy	out of mushrooms
store too warm	overcharged
checkout lines too long	checkout wait too long
cashier not friendly	shopping cart broken
out of Cheese Doodles	couldn't find aspirin
triple charged	out of Tip Top lunch bags
out of Saran Wrap	out of Tip Top straws
out of Dove Bars	

July 20

out of cucumbers	out of Tip Top toilet paper
checkout lines too slow	out of red peppers
found keys in parking lot	out of Tip Top napkins
lost keys	out of apricots
wrong price on sale item	telephone out of order
overcharged on corn	out of cocktail sauce
wrong price on baby food	water on floor
out of 18 oz. Tide	out of onions
out of Tip Top tissues	out of squash
checkout lines too long	out of iceberg lettuce
out of romaine lettuce	out of Tip Top paper towels

July 27

out of bananas	wanted to know who won the lottery
reported accident in parking lot	store too warm
wrong price on cranapple juice	oatmeal spilled in bulk section
out of carrots	telephone out of order
out of fresh figs	out of Tip Top tissues
out of Tip Top napkins	water on floor
out of Tip Top straws	out of Tip Top paper towels
windows dirty	out of Tip Top toilet paper
out of iceberg lettuce	spaghetti sauce on floor
dislike store decorations	out of Peter Pan crunchy peanut butter
out of Tip Top lunch bags	
out of vanilla soy milk	

414   **Chapter Nine** Management of Quality

SELECTED BIBLIOGRAPHY AND FURTHER READINGS

Besterfield, Dale H., Carol Besterfield-Micha, Glen Besterfield, and Mary Besterfield-Sacre. *Total Quality Management,* 3rd ed. Upper Saddle River, NJ: Prentice Hall, 2011.

Brassard, Michael, and Diane Ritter. *The Memory Jogger II: A Pocket Guide of Tools for Continuous Improvement and Effective Planning.* Methuen, MA: Goal/QPC, 1994.

Butman, John. *Juran: A Lifetime of Influence.* New York: John Wiley & Sons, 1997.

El-Haik, Basem, and David M. Roy. *Service Design for Six Sigma: A Roadmap for Excellence.* Hoboken, NJ: John Wiley and Sons, 2005.

Garvin, David A. *Managing Quality.* New York: Free Press, 1988.

Goetsch, David L., and Stanley B. Davis. *Quality Management for Organizational Excellence: Introduction to Total Quality Management,* 6th ed. Upper Saddle River, NJ: Prentice Hall, 2010.

Gygi, Craig, Neil DeCarlo, and Bruce Williams. *Six Sigma for Dummies,* 2nd ed. Hoboken, NJ: John Wiley and Sons, 2012.

Scherkenbach, W. W. *The Deming Route to Quality and Productivity: Roadmaps and Roadblocks.* Rockville, MD: Mercury Press/Fairchild Publications, 1990.

Snee, Ronald D., and Roger W. Hoerl. *Six Sigma beyond the Factory Floor: Deployment Strategies for Financial Services, Health Care, and the Rest of the Real Economy.* Upper Saddle River, NJ: Pearson/Prentice Hall, 2005.

Stevenson, William J. "Supercharging Your Pareto Analysis." *Quality Progress.* October 2000, pp. 51–55.

Summers, Donna. *Quality,* 5th ed. Upper Saddle River, NJ: Prentice Hall, 2010.

Trusko, Brett, Carolyn Pexton, Jim Harrington, and Praveen Gupta. *Improving Healthcare Quality and Cost with Six Sigma.* FT Press, 2007.

10 Quality Control

LEARNING OBJECTIVES

After completing this chapter, you should be able to:

LO10.1   Explain the need for quality control.

LO10.2   Discuss the basic issues of inspection.

LO10.3   List and briefly explain the elements of the control process.

LO10.4   Explain how control charts are used to monitor a process and the concepts that underlie their use.

LO10.5   Use and interpret control charts.

LO10.6   Perform run tests to check for nonrandomness in process output.

LO10.7   Assess process capability.

CHAPTER OUTLINE

10.1 **Introduction** 417

10.2 **Inspection** 418
   How Much to Inspect and How Often 419
   Where to Inspect in the Process 420
   Centralized versus On-Site Inspection 422

10.3 **Statistical Process Control** 423
   Process Variability 423
   Sampling and Sampling Distributions 424

The Control Process 425
Control Charts: The Voice of the Process 426
Control Charts for Variables 428
Control Charts for Attributes 433
Managerial Considerations Concerning Control Charts 436
Run Tests 437
Using Control Charts and Run Tests Together 441
What Happens When a Process Exhibits Possible Nonrandom Variation? 441

10.4 **Process Capability** 441
   Capability Analysis 442
   C_p 443
   C_{pk} 445
   Improving Process Capability 445
   Taguchi Loss Function 446
   Limitations of Capability Indexes 446

10.5 **Operations Strategy** 446
   Cases: Toys, Inc. 460
          Tiger Tools 460

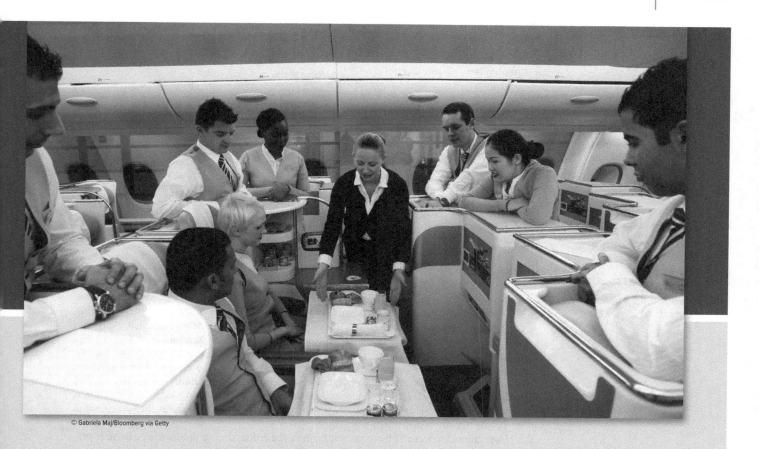

This chapter covers quality control. The purpose of quality control is to assure that processes are performing in an acceptable manner. Companies accomplish this by monitoring process output using statistical techniques. **Quality control** is a process that measures output relative to a standard and takes corrective action when output does not meet standards. If the results are acceptable, no further action is required; unacceptable results call for corrective action.

Every process generates output that exhibits random variability. That is natural and cannot be corrected. However, if there are nonrandom variations in process output, that can be corrected. Quality control tools are used to decide when corrective action is needed.

> **Quality control** A process that evaluates output relative to a standard and takes corrective action when output doesn't meet standards.

10.1 INTRODUCTION

> **LO10.1** Explain the need for quality control.

Quality assurance that relies primarily on inspection of lots (batches) of previously produced items is referred to as *acceptance sampling*. It is described in the chapter supplement. Quality control efforts that occur during production are referred to as *statistical process control*, and these we examine in the following sections.

The best companies emphasize *designing quality into the process*, thereby greatly reducing the need for inspection or control efforts. As you might expect, different business organizations are in different stages of this evolutionary process: Some rely heavily on inspection. However, inspection alone is generally not sufficient to achieve a reasonable level of quality. Many occupy a middle ground that involves some inspection and a great deal of process control. Figure 10.1 illustrates these phases of quality assurance.

FIGURE 10.1
Approaches to quality
assurance

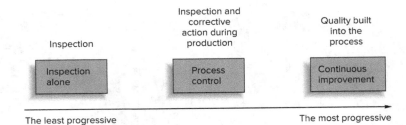

10.2 INSPECTION

Inspection Appraisal of
goods or services.

Inspection is an appraisal activity that compares goods or services to a standard. Inspection is a vital but often unappreciated aspect of quality control. Although for well-designed processes little inspection is necessary, inspection cannot be completely eliminated. And with increased outsourcing of products and services, inspection has taken on a new level of significance. In lean organizations, inspection is less of an issue than it is for other organizations because lean organizations place extra emphasis on quality in the design of both products and processes. Moreover, in lean operations, workers have responsibility for quality (quality at the source). However, many organizations do not operate in a lean mode, so inspection is important for them. This is particularly true of service operations, where quality continues to be a challenge for management.

Inspection can occur at three points: before production, during production, and after production. The logic of checking conformance before production is to make sure that inputs are acceptable. The logic of checking conformance during production is to make sure that the conversion of inputs into outputs is proceeding in an acceptable manner. The logic of checking conformance of output is to make a final verification of conformance before passing goods on to customers.

Inspection before and after production often involves *acceptance sampling* procedures; monitoring during the production process is referred to *as process control*. Figure 10.2 gives an overview of where these two procedures are applied in the production process.

To determine whether a process is functioning as intended or to verify that a batch or lot of raw materials or final products does not contain more than a specified percentage of defective goods, it is necessary to physically examine at least some of the items in question. The purpose of inspection is to provide information on the degree to which items conform to a standard. The basic issues are:

LO10.2 Discuss the basic
issues of inspection.

1. How much to inspect and how often
2. At what points in the process inspection should occur
3. Whether to inspect in a centralized or on-site location
4. Whether to inspect attributes (i.e., *count* the number of times something occurs) or variables (i.e., *measure* the value of a characteristic)

Consider, for example, inspection at an intermediate step in the manufacture of personal computers. Because inspection costs are often significant, questions naturally arise on whether one needs to inspect every computer or whether a small sample of computers will suffice.

FIGURE 10.2
Acceptance sampling and
process control

A Toyota technician prepares to remove the accelerator assembly in a recalled Toyota Avalon.

© Tim Boyle/Bloomberg via Getty

Moreover, although inspections could be made at numerous points in the production process, it is not generally cost-effective to make inspections at every point. Hence, the question comes up of which points should be designated for inspections. Once these points have been identified, a manager must decide whether to remove the computers from the line and take them to a lab, where specialized equipment might be available to perform certain tests, or to test them where they are being made. We will examine these points in the following sections.

How Much to Inspect and How Often

The amount of inspection can range from no inspection whatsoever to inspection of each item numerous times. Low-cost, high-volume items such as paper clips, roofing nails, and wooden pencils often require little inspection because (1) the cost associated with passing defective items is quite low and (2) the processes that produce these items are usually highly reliable, so defects are rare. Conversely, high-cost, low-volume items that have large costs associated with passing defective products often require more intensive inspections. Thus, critical components of a manned-flight space vehicle are closely scrutinized because of the risk to human safety and the high cost of mission failure. In high-volume systems, *automated* inspection is one option that may be employed.

The majority of quality control applications lie somewhere between the two extremes. Most require some inspection, but it is neither possible nor economically feasible to critically examine every part of a product or every aspect of a service for control purposes. The cost of inspection, resulting interruptions of a process or delays caused by inspection, and the manner of testing typically outweigh the benefits of 100 percent inspection. Note that for manual inspection, even 100 percent inspection does not guarantee that all defects will be found and removed. Inspection is a process, and hence, subject to variation. Boredom and fatigue are factors that cause inspection mistakes. Moreover, when destructive testing is involved (items are destroyed by testing), that must be taken into account. However, the cost of letting undetected defects slip through is sufficiently high that inspection cannot be completely ignored. The amount of inspection needed is governed by the costs of inspection and the expected costs of passing defective items. As illustrated in Figure 10.3, if inspection activities increase, inspection costs increase, but the costs of undetected defects decrease. The traditional goal

420   **Chapter Ten**   Quality Control

FIGURE 10.3

Traditional view: The amount of inspection is optimal when the sum of the costs of inspection and passing defectives is minimized

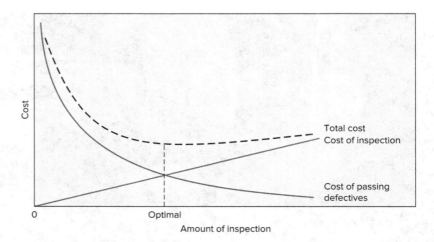

was to minimize the sum of these two costs. In other words, it may not pay to attempt to catch every defect, particularly if the cost of inspection exceeds the penalties associated with letting some defects get through. Current thinking is that every reduction in defective output reduces costs, although not primarily by inspection.

As a rule, operations with a high proportion of human involvement necessitate more inspection effort than mechanical operations, which tend to be more reliable.

The frequency of inspection depends largely on the rate at which a process may go out of control or on the number of lots being inspected. A stable process will require only infrequent checks, whereas an unstable one or one that has recently given trouble will require more frequent checks. Likewise, many small lots will require more samples than a few large lots because it is important to obtain sample data from each lot. For high-volume, repetitive operations, computerized automatic inspections at critical points in a process are cost effective.

Where to Inspect in the Process

Many operations have numerous possible inspection points. Because each inspection adds to the cost of the product or service, it is important to restrict inspection efforts to the points where they can do the most good. In manufacturing, some of the typical inspection points are:

1. **Raw materials and purchased parts.** There is little sense in paying for goods that do not meet quality standards and in expending time and effort on material that is bad to begin with. Supplier certification programs can reduce or eliminate the need for inspection.

2. **Finished products.** Customer satisfaction and the firm's image are at stake here, and repairing or replacing products in the field is usually much more costly than doing it at the factory. Likewise, the seller is usually responsible for shipping costs on returns, and payments for goods or service may be held up pending delivery of satisfactory goods or remedial service. Well-designed processes, products and services, quality at the source, and process monitoring can reduce or eliminate the need for inspection.

3. **Before a costly operation.** The point is to not waste costly labor or machine time on items that are already defective.

4. **Before an irreversible process.** In many cases, items can be reworked up to a certain point; beyond that point they cannot. For example, pottery can be reworked prior to firing. After that, defective pottery must be discarded or sold as seconds at a lower price.

5. **Before a covering process.** Painting, plating, and assemblies often mask defects.

Inspection can be used as part of an effort to improve process yield. One measure of process yield is the ratio of output of good product to the total output. Inspection at key points can help guide process improvement efforts to reduce the scrap rate and improve the overall process yield, and reduce or eliminate the need for inspection.

In the service sector, inspection points are incoming purchased materials and supplies, personnel, service interfaces (e.g., service counter), and outgoing completed work (e.g., repaired appliances). Table 10.1 illustrates a number of examples.

Type of Business	Inspection Points	Characteristics
Fast food	Cashier	Accuracy
	Counter area	Appearance, productivity
	Eating area	Cleanliness, no loitering
	Building and grounds	Appearance, safety hazards
	Kitchen	Cleanliness, purity of food, food storage, health regulations
	Parking lot	Safety, good lighting
Hotel/motel	Accounting/billing	Accuracy, timeliness
	Building and grounds	Appearance and safety
	Main desk	Appearance, waiting times, accuracy of bills
	Maid service	Completeness, productivity
	Personnel	Appearance, manners, productivity
	Reservations/occupancy	Over/underbooking, percent occupancy
	Restaurants	Kitchen, menus, meals, bills
	Room service	Waiting time, quality of food
	Supplies	Ordering, receiving, inventories
Supermarket	Cashiers	Accuracy, courtesy, productivity
	Deliveries	Quality, quantity
	Produce	Freshness, ample stock
	Aisles and stockrooms	Uncluttered layout
	Inventory control	Stock-outs
	Shelf stock	Ample supply, rotation of perishables
	Shelf displays	Appearance
	Checkouts	Waiting time
	Shopping carts	Good working condition, ample supply, theft/vandalism
	Parking lot	Safety, good lighting
	Personnel	Appearance, productivity
Doctor's office	Waiting room	Appearance, comfortable
	Examination room	Clean, temperature controlled
	Doctor	Neat, friendly, concerned, skillful, knowledgeable
	Doctor's assistant	Neat, friendly, concerned, skillful
	Patient records	Accurate, up-to-date
	Billing	Accurate
	Other	Waiting time minimal, adequate time with doctor

TABLE 10.1
Examples of inspection points in service organizations

READING   MAKING POTATO CHIPS

A potato chip is a delicate thing. Fragile. A pound of pressure will crush it. So when you're making potato chips, you need to have a system. If you aren't careful, instead of potato chips, you'll end up with potato chip crumbs.

The Jays company in Chicago was a producer of a variety of snack products, one of which was potato chips. The company is now owned by Snyders. Nonetheless, there is much to be learned from a description of Jay's operations.

To avoid the tendency of potato chips to crush into crumbs, Jays used a system of conveyor belts, radial filling chutes and gently vibrating slides, where masses of chips, a yard deep, were gently moved through the process.

The process started with the arrival of semi-trailers full of potatoes; usually about a dozen a day.

The potatoes were separated into big and small sizes; big potatoes for big chips that go into large bags; and small potatoes for small chips for lunch-size bags.

Computers keep track of everything, shunting potatoes to 15,000-pound holding bins. Each bin feeds into a pipe containing a turning screw—a version of the ancient Archimedes screw used to pump water—that moves the potatoes from the bin to conveyor belts, to where they are washed and skinned—the skin scrubbed off by metal bristle brushes.

No machine can detect if a potato is rotten inside. So a pair of human inspectors gave the potatoes a quick squeeze as they moved along a conveyor, and removed those likely to have rot.

The cleaned potatoes were sent into high-speed chippers—spinning brass rings, each with eight blades inside, straight blades for straight chips, ripple blades for ripple chips.

The blades cut the potatoes, but cutting dulled the blades, so every three hours the line had to be stopped so that the blades could be replaced.

The raw chips spent three minutes cooking in hot corn oil, which was constantly circulated and filtered. Then they were salted, and any flavorings such as barbecue were added.

After the chips were fried, there was another quality check, in which workers removed burned and deformed chips out of the masses passing by.

© Jay Reeves/AP Images

The chips also were laser-inspected. Chips with dark spots or holes were removed by a puff of air that knocked them off the line, into a discard bin.

The discards—about 3 percent of production—were gathered up and used: Starch was drawn out and sold to cornstarch makers; the rest went to hog feed.

Getting the chips in the bags was another challenge: You can't just fill up bags and seal them; the chips would be smashed. Rather, a conveyor poured chips—gently—onto the central hub of a large, wheel-like device, where the chips scattered into 15 buckets that were essentially scales. A computer monitored the weight of each bucket to assure there would be just the right amount to fill a 14-ounce bag. The bags were packed into boxes that read: "HANDLE LIKE EGGS."

While not exactly perishable, potato chips do have a shelf life of about eight weeks, only one day of which is spent at the plant.

Questions

1. What characteristics of potato chips concern Jays in terms of quality?
2. Do you feel that Jays is overdoing it with its concern for quality? Explain.

Centralized versus On-Site Inspection

Some situations require that inspections be performed *on site*. For example, inspecting the hull of a ship for cracks requires inspectors to visit the ship. At other times, specialized tests can best be performed in a lab (e.g., performing medical tests, analyzing food samples, testing metals for hardness, running viscosity tests on lubricants).

The central issue in the decision concerning on-site or lab inspections is whether the advantages of specialized lab tests are worth the time and interruption needed to obtain the results. Reasons favoring on-site inspection include quicker decisions and avoidance of introduction of extraneous factors (e.g., damage or other alteration of samples during transportation to the lab).

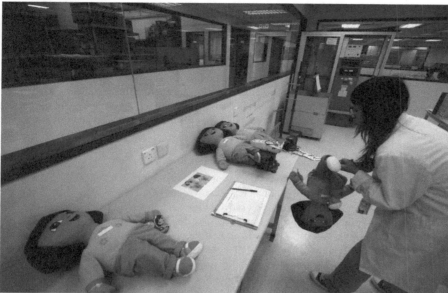

A Mattel technician in China does a pulling test with a Dora the Explorer doll in the name of product safety. Mattel has 10 labs in six countries and has set up strict requirements for vendors because of safety recalls.

© Chang W. Lee/The New York Times/Redux

On the other hand, specialized equipment and a more favorable test environment (less noise and confusion, lack of vibrations, absence of dust, and no workers "helping" with inspections) offer strong arguments for using a lab.

Some companies rely on self-inspections by operators if errors can be traced back to specific operators. This places responsibility for errors at their source (*quality at the source*).

10.3 STATISTICAL PROCESS CONTROL

Quality control is concerned with the **quality of conformance** of a process: Does the output of a process conform to the intent of design? Variations in characteristics of process output provide the rationale for process control. **Statistical process control (SPC)** is used to evaluate process output to decide if a process is "in control" or if corrective action is needed.

Quality of conformance A product or service conforms to specifications.

Statistical process control (SPC) Statistical evaluation of the output of a process.

Process Variability

All processes generate output that exhibits some degree of variability. The issue is whether the output variations are within an acceptable range. The issue is addressed by answering two basic questions about the process variations:

1. Are the variations random? If nonrandom variations are present, the process is considered to be unstable. Corrective action will need to be taken to improve the process by eliminating the causes of nonrandomness to achieve a stable process.

2. Given a stable process, is the inherent variability of process output within a range that conforms to performance criteria? This involves assessment of a process's capability to meet standards. If a process is not capable, that situation will need to be addressed.

The natural or inherent process variations in process output are referred to as *chance* or **random variations**. Such variations are due to the combined influences of countless minor factors, each one so unimportant that even if it could be eliminated, the impact on process variations would be negligible. In Deming's terms, this is referred to as *common variability*. The amount of inherent variability differs from process to process. For instance, older

Random variation Natural variation in the output of a process, created by countless minor factors.

machines generally exhibit a higher degree of natural variability than newer machines, partly because of worn parts and partly because new machines may incorporate design improvements that lessen the variability in their output.

Assignable variation In process output, a variation whose cause can be identified. A nonrandom variation.

A second kind of variability in process output is called **assignable variation**, or *nonrandom variation*. In Deming's terms, this is referred to as *special variation*. Unlike natural variation, the main sources of assignable variation can usually be identified (assigned to a specific cause) and eliminated. Tool wear, equipment that needs adjustment, defective materials, human factors (carelessness, fatigue, noise and other distractions, failure to follow correct procedures, and so on) and problems with measuring devices are typical sources of assignable variation.

Sampling and Sampling Distributions

In statistical process control, periodic samples of process output are taken and sample statistics, such as sample means or the number of occurrences of a certain type of outcome, are determined. The sample statistics can be used to judge randomness of process variations. The sample statistics exhibit variation, just as processes do. The variability of sample statistics can be described by its **sampling distribution**, a theoretical distribution that describes the *random* variability of sample statistics. For a variety of reasons, the most frequently used distribution is the normal distribution.

Sampling distribution A theoretical distribution of sample statistics.

Figure 10.4A illustrates a sampling distribution and a process distribution (i.e., the distribution of process variations). Note three important things in Figure 10.4A: (1) both distributions have the same mean; (2) the variability of the sampling distribution is less than the variability of the process; and (3) the sampling distribution is normal. This is true even if the process distribution is not normal.

Central limit theorem The distribution of sample averages tends to be normal regardless of the shape of the process distribution.

In the case of sample means, the **central limit theorem** states that as the sample size increases, the distribution of sample averages approaches a normal distribution regardless of the shape of the sampled population. This tends to be the case even for fairly small sample sizes. For other sample statistics, the normal distribution serves as a reasonable approximation to the shape of the actual sampling distribution.

Figure 10.4B illustrates what happens to the shape of the sampling distribution relative to the sample size. The larger the sample size, the narrower the sampling distribution. This means that the likelihood that a sample statistic is close to the true value in the population is higher for large samples than for small samples.

A sampling distribution serves as the theoretical basis for distinguishing between random and nonrandom values of a sampling statistic. Very simply, limits are selected within which

FIGURE 10.4A The sampling distribution of means is normal, and it has less variability than the process distribution, which might not be normal

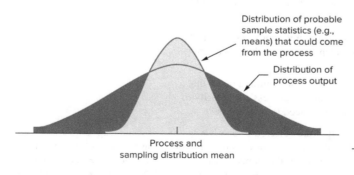

Distribution of probable sample statistics (e.g., means) that could come from the process

Distribution of process output

Process and sampling distribution mean

FIGURE 10.4B The larger the sample size, the narrower the sampling distribution

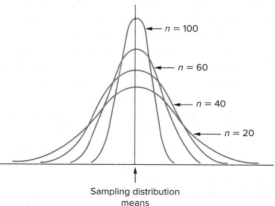

$n = 100$

$n = 60$

$n = 40$

$n = 20$

Sampling distribution means

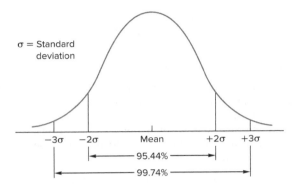

FIGURE 10.5
Percentage of values within given ranges in a normal distribution

most values of a sample statistic should fall if its variations are random. The limits are stated in terms of number of standard deviations from the distribution mean. Typical limits are ± 2 standard deviations or ± 3 standard deviations. Figure 10.5 illustrates these possible limits and the probability that a sample statistic would fall within those limits if only random variations are present. Conversely, if the value of a sample statistic falls outside those limits, there is only a small probability ($1 - 99.74 = .0026$ for ± 3 limits, and $1 - 95.44 = .0456$ for ± 2 limits) that the value reflects randomness. Instead, such a value would suggest nonrandomness.

The Control Process

Sampling and corrective action are only a part of the control process. Effective control requires the following steps:

Define. The first step is to define in sufficient detail what is to be controlled. It is not enough, for example, to simply refer to a painted surface. The paint can have a number of important characteristics such as its thickness, hardness, and resistance to fading or chipping. Different characteristics may require different approaches for control purposes.

LO10.3 List and briefly explain the elements of the control process.

Food and beverage companies use Omron Electronics' fiber optic sensors to monitor processes and to perform quality inspections such as checking beverage content and caps.

426 **Chapter Ten** Quality Control

Measure. Only those characteristics that can be counted or measured are candidates for control. Thus, it is important to consider how measurement will be accomplished.

Compare. There must be a standard of comparison that can be used to evaluate the measurements. This will relate to the level of quality being sought.

Evaluate. Management must establish a definition of *out of control.* Even a process that is functioning as it should will not yield output that conforms exactly to a standard, simply because of the natural (i.e., random) variations inherent in all processes, manual or mechanical—a certain amount of variation is inevitable. The main task of quality control is to distinguish random from *nonrandom* variability, because nonrandom variability means that a process is out of control.

Correct. When a process is judged to be out of control, corrective action must be taken. This involves uncovering the cause of nonrandom variability (e.g., worn equipment, incorrect methods, failure to follow specified procedures) and correcting it.

Monitor results. To ensure that corrective action is effective, the output of a process must be monitored for a sufficient period of time to verify that the problem has been eliminated.

In sum, control is achieved by checking a portion of the goods or services, comparing the results to a predetermined standard, evaluating departures from the standard, taking corrective action when necessary, and following up to ensure that problems have been corrected.

Control Charts: The Voice of the Process

An important tool in statistical process control is the control chart, which was developed by Walter Shewhart. A **control chart** is a *time-ordered* plot of sample statistics. It is used to distinguish between random variability and nonrandom variability. It has upper and lower limits, called *control limits,* that define the range of acceptable (i.e., random) variation for the sample statistic. A control chart is illustrated in Figure 10.6. The purpose of a control chart is to monitor process output to see if it is random. A necessary (but not sufficient) condition for a process to be deemed "in control," or stable, is for all the data points to fall between the upper and lower control limits. Conversely, a data point that falls outside of either limit would be taken as evidence that the process output may be nonrandom and, therefore, not "in control." If that happens, the process would be halted to find and correct the cause of the nonrandom variation. The essence of statistical process control is to assure that the output of a process is random so *that future output* will be random.

The basis for the control chart is the sampling distribution, which essentially describes random variability. There is, however, one minor difficulty relating to the use of a normal sampling distribution. The theoretical distribution extends in either direction to *infinity.* Therefore, *any* value is theoretically possible, even one that is a considerable distance from the mean of the distribution. However, as a practical matter, we know that, say, 99.7 percent of the values will be within ± 3 standard deviations of the mean of the distribution.

Control chart A visual tool for monitoring forecast errors.

LO10.4 Explain how control charts are used to monitor a process and the concepts that underlie their use.

FIGURE 10.6
Example of a control chart

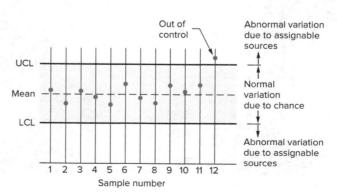

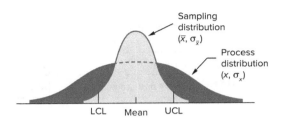

FIGURE 10.7
Control limits are based on the sampling distribution

Therefore, we could decide to set the limit, so to speak, at values that represent ± 3 standard deviations from the mean, and conclude that any value that was farther away than these limits was a nonrandom variation.

In effect, these limits are **control limits**: the dividing lines between what will be designated as random deviations from the mean of the distribution and what will be designated as nonrandom deviations from the mean of the distribution. Figure 10.7 illustrates how control limits are based on the sampling distribution.

Control limits The dividing lines between random and nonrandom deviations from the mean of the distribution.

Control charts have two limits that separate random variation and nonrandom variation. The larger value is the *upper control limit* (UCL), and the smaller value is the *lower control limit* (LCL). A sample statistic that falls between these two limits suggests (but does not prove) randomness, while a value outside or on either limit suggests (but does not prove) nonrandomness.

It is important to recognize that because any limits will leave some area in the *tails* of the distribution, there is a small probability that a value will fall outside the limits *even though only random variations are present*. For example, if ± 2 sigma (standard deviation) limits are used, they would include 95.5 percent of the values. Consequently, the complement of that number (100 percent = 95.5 percent = 4.5 percent) would not be included. That percentage (or *probability*) is sometimes referred to as the probability of a **Type I error**, where the "error" is concluding that nonrandomness is present when only randomness is present. It is also referred to as an *alpha* risk, where alpha (α) is the sum of the probabilities in the two tails. Figure 10.8 illustrates this concept.

Type I error Concluding a process is not in control when it actually is.

Using wider limits (e.g., ± 3 sigma limits) reduces the probability of a Type I error because it decreases the area in the tails. However, wider limits make it more difficult to detect non-random variations *if* they are present. For example, the mean of the process might shift (an assignable cause of variation) enough to be detected by two-sigma limits, but not enough to be readily apparent using three-sigma limits. That could lead to a second kind of error, known as a **Type II error**, which is concluding that a process is in control when it is really out of control (i.e., concluding nonrandom variations are not present, when they are). In theory, the costs of making each error should be balanced by their probabilities. However, in practice, two-sigma limits and three-sigma limits are commonly used without specifically referring to the probability of a Type II error.

Type II error Concluding a process is in control when it is not.

Table 10.2 illustrates how Type I and Type II errors occur.

Each sample is represented by a single value (e.g., the sample mean) on a control chart. Moreover, each value is compared to the extremes of the sampling distribution (the control

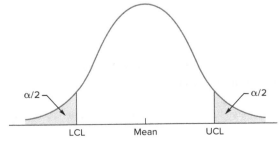

FIGURE 10.8
The probability of a Type I error

α = Probability of a Type I error

TABLE 10.2
Type I and Type II errors

		And the conclusion is that it is:	
		In Control	Out of Control
If a process is actually:	In control	No error	**Type I error** (producer's risk)
	Out of control	**Type II error** (consumer's risk)	No error

FIGURE 10.9
Each observation is compared to the selected limits of the sampling distribution

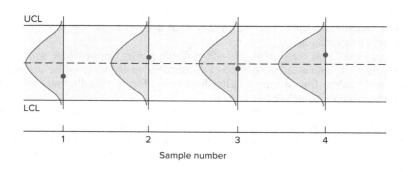

limits) to judge if it is within the acceptable (random) range. Figure 10.9 illustrates this concept.

There are four commonly used control charts. Two are used for **variables**, and two are used for **attributes**. Attribute data are *counted* (e.g., the number of defective parts in a sample, the number of calls per day); variables data are *measured,* usually on a continuous scale (e.g., amount of time needed to complete a task, length or width of a part).

Variables Generate data that are *measured.*

Attributes Generate data that are *counted.*

The two control charts for variables data are described in the next section, and the two control charts for attribute data are described in the section following that.

Control Charts for Variables

Mean and range charts are used to monitor variables. Control charts for means monitor the *central tendency* of a process, and range charts monitor the *dispersion* of a process.

Mean control chart Control chart used to monitor the central tendency of a process.

Mean Charts. A **mean control chart**, sometimes referred to as an $\bar{x}$ ("*x*-bar") chart, is based on a normal distribution. It can be constructed in one of two ways. The choice depends on what information is available. Although the value of the standard deviation of a process, σ, is often unknown, if a reasonable estimate is available, one can compute control limits using these formulas:

$$\text{Upper control limit (UCL): } = \bar{\bar{x}} + z\sigma_{\bar{x}}$$
$$\text{Lower control limit (LCL): } = \bar{\bar{x}} - z\sigma_{\bar{x}}$$

(10–1)

where

$\sigma_{\bar{x}} = \sigma/\sqrt{n}$

$\sigma_{\bar{x}}$ = Standard deviation of distribution of sample means

σ = Estimate of the process standard deviation

n = Sample size

z = The number of standard deviations that control limits are based on

$\bar{\bar{x}}$ = Average of sample means

The following example illustrates the use of these formulas.

Determining Control Limits for Means

EXAMPLE 1

mhhe.com/stevenson13e

A quality inspector took five samples, each with four observations ($n = 4$), of the length of time for glue to dry. The analyst computed the mean of each sample and then computed the grand mean. All values are in minutes. Use this information to obtain three-sigma (i.e., $z = 3$) control limits for means of future times. It is known from previous experience that the standard deviation of the process is .02 minute.

		SAMPLE				
		1	2	3	4	5
	1	12.11	12.15	12.09	12.12	12.09
Observation	2	12.10	12.12	12.09	12.10	12.14
	3	12.11	12.10	12.11	12.08	12.13
	4	12.08	12.11	12.15	12.10	12.12
	$\bar{X}$	12.10	12.12	12.11	12.10	12.12

SOLUTION

$$\bar{\bar{x}} = \frac{12.10 + 12.12 + 12.11 + 12.10 + 12.12}{5} = 12.11$$

Using Formula 10–1, with $z = 3$, $n = 4$ observations per sample, and $\sigma = .02$, we find

$$\text{UCL:} \quad 12.11 + 3\left(\frac{.02}{\sqrt{4}}\right) = 12.14$$

$$\text{LCL:} \quad 12.11 - 3\left(\frac{.02}{\sqrt{4}}\right) = 12.08$$

Note: If one applied these control limits to the means, one would judge the process to be *in control* because all of the sample means have values that fall within the control limits. The fact that some of the *individual* measurements fall outside of the control limits (e.g., the first observation in Sample 2 and the last observation in Sample 3) is irrelevant. You can see why by referring to Figure 10.7: *Individual* values are represented by the process distribution, a large portion of which lies outside of the control limits for *means*.

This and similar problems can also be solved using the Excel templates that are available on the book's website. The solution for Example 1 using Excel is shown here.

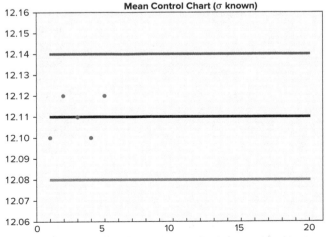

Note: To display more data on the above graph, right click on the x-axis, select Format Axis, and set Maximum to higher value. The size of the graph may also be increased.

LO10.5 Use and interpret control charts.

If an observation on a control chart is on or outside of either control limit, the process is stopped to investigate the cause of that value, such as operator error, machine out of adjustment, or similar assignable cause of variation. If no source of error is found, the value could simply be due to chance, and the process will be restarted. However, the output should then be monitored to see if additional values occur that are beyond the control limits, in which case a more thorough investigation would be needed to uncover the source of the problem so that it could be corrected.

If the standard deviation of the process is unknown, another approach is to use the sample *range* as a measure of process variability. The appropriate formulas for control limits are

$$\text{UCL} = \bar{\bar{x}} + A_2 \bar{R}$$
$$\text{LCL} = \bar{\bar{x}} - A_2 \bar{R}$$

(10–2)

where

$A_2 =$ A factor from Table 10.3
$\bar{R} =$ Average of sample ranges

E X A M P L E   2

mhhe.com/stevenson13e

Using Table 10.3 to Compute Control Limits for Means

Refer to the data given in Example 1. In order to use Formula 10–2, we need to compute the grand mean for the data and the average sample range. In Example 1, the grand mean is 12.11. The range for each sample is the difference between the largest and smallest sample values. For the first sample, the largest value is 12.11 and the smallest value is 12.08. The range is the difference between these two values, which is $12.11 - 12.08 = .03$. For Sample 2, the range is $12.15 - 12.10 = 0.05$. The other ranges can be computed in similar fashion. The average range is:

$$\bar{R} = (.03 + .05 + .06 + .04 + .05)/5 = .046.$$

S O L U T I O N

$\bar{x} = 12.11$, $\bar{R} = .046$ and $A_2 = .73$ for $n = 4$ (from Table 10.3). Using Formula 10-2, we can compute the upper and lower limits for a mean control chart:

UCL $= 12.11 + .73(.046) = 12.14$ minutes
LCL $= 12.11 - .73(.046) = 12.08$ minutes

Except for rounding, these results are the same as those computed in Example 1. Usually that will be the case, but not always.

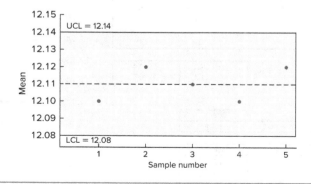

Range control chart Control chart used to monitor process dispersion.

Range Charts. **Range control charts** (*R*-charts) are used to monitor process dispersion; they are sensitive to changes in process dispersion. Although the underlying sampling distribution is not normal, the concepts for the use of range charts are much the same as those for the use of mean charts. Control limits for range charts are found using the average sample range in conjunction with these formulas:

$$\text{UCL} = D_4\overline{R}$$
$$\text{LCL} = D_3\overline{R} \qquad\qquad (10\text{–}3)$$

where values of D_3 and D_4 are obtained from Table 10.3.[1]

Using Table 10.3 to Compute Control Limits for Ranges

EXAMPLE 3

Using the average range found in Example 2 and Formula 10–3, we can compute the control limits for a range chart.

SOLUTION

From Table 10.3, for $n = 4$, $D_4 = 2.28$ and $D_3 = 0$. Thus,

$$\text{UCL} = 2.28(.046) = .105 \text{ minutes}$$
$$\text{LCL} = 0(.046) \quad\;\; = 0 \text{ minutes}$$

Note that the five sample ranges shown in Example 2 are within these control limits.

Number of Observations in Sample, n	Factor for Chart, A_2	FACTORS FOR R CHARTS	
		Lower Control Limit, D_3	Upper Control Limit, D_4
2	1.88	0	3.27
3	1.02	0	2.57
4	0.73	0	2.28
5	0.58	0	2.11
6	0.48	0	2.00
7	0.42	0.08	1.92
8	0.37	0.14	1.86
9	0.34	0.18	1.82
10	0.31	0.22	1.78
11	0.29	0.26	1.74
12	0.27	0.28	1.72
13	0.25	0.31	1.69
14	0.24	0.33	1.67
15	0.22	0.35	1.65
16	0.21	0.36	1.64
17	0.20	0.38	1.62
18	0.19	0.39	1.61
19	0.19	0.40	1.60
20	0.18	0.41	1.59

TABLE 10.3
Factors for three-sigma control limits for $\overline{X}$ and R charts

Source: Adapted from Eugene Grant and Richard Leavenworth, *Statistical Quality Control,* 5th ed. Copyright © 1980 McGraw-Hill Companies, Inc. Used with permission

[1] If the process standard deviation is known, control limits for a range chart can be calculated using values from Table 10.3:

$$\text{LCL} = \frac{3D_3\sigma}{A_2\sqrt{n}}, \; \text{UCL} = \frac{3D_4\sigma}{A_2\sqrt{n}}$$

432   **Chapter Ten**   Quality Control

© Brian Brainerd/Denver Post/Getty Images

Food inspectors check the temperature of food during a health inspection.

Using Mean and Range Charts. Mean control charts and range control charts provide different perspectives on a process. As we have seen, mean charts are sensitive to shifts in the process mean, whereas range charts are sensitive to changes in process dispersion. Because of this difference in perspective, both types of charts might be used to monitor the same process. The logic of using both is readily apparent in Figure 10.10 . In Figure 10.10A, the mean chart picks up the shift in the process mean, but because the dispersion is not changing, the range chart fails to indicate a problem. Conversely, in Figure 10.10B, a change in process dispersion is less apt to be detected by the mean chart than by the range chart. Thus, use of both charts provides more complete information than either chart alone. Even so, a single chart may suffice in some cases. For example, a process may be more susceptible to changes in the process mean than to changes in dispersion, so it might be unnecessary to monitor dispersion. Because of the time and cost of constructing control charts, gathering the necessary data, and evaluating the results, only those aspects of a process that tend to cause problems should be monitored.

FIGURE 10.10
Mean and range charts used together complement each other

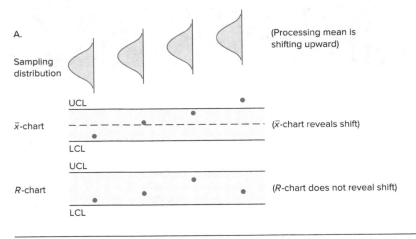

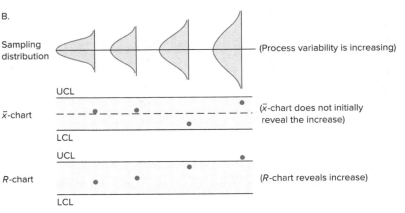

Once control charts have been set up, they can serve as a basis for deciding when to interrupt a process and search for assignable causes of variation. To determine initial control limits, one can use the following procedure:

1. Obtain 20 to 25 samples. Compute the appropriate sample statistic(s) for each sample (e.g., mean).
2. Establish preliminary control limits using the formulas.
3. Determine if any points fall outside the control limits.
4. Plot the data on the control chart and check for patterns.
5. If no out-of-control signals are found, assume that the process is in control. If any out-of-control signals are found, investigate and correct causes of variation. Then resume the process and collect another set of observations upon which control limits can be based.

Control Charts for Attributes

Control charts for attributes are used when the process characteristic is *counted* rather than measured. For example, the number of defective items in a sample is counted, whereas the length of each item is measured. There are two types of attribute control charts, one for the fraction of defective items in a sample (a *p*-chart) and one for the number of defects per unit (a *c*-chart). A *p*-chart is appropriate when the data consist of two categories of items. For instance, if glass bottles are inspected for chipping and cracking, both the good bottles and the defective ones can be counted. However, one can count the number of accidents that occur during a given period of time but *not* the number of accidents that did not occur. Similarly, one can count the number of scratches on a polished surface, the number of bacteria present in a water sample, and the number of crimes committed during the month of August, but one cannot count the number of non-occurrences. In such cases, a *c*-chart is appropriate. see Table 10.4.

p-**Chart.** A *p*-chart is used to monitor the proportion of defective items generated by a process. The theoretical basis for a *p*-chart is the binomial distribution, although for large sample sizes, the normal distribution provides a good approximation to it. Conceptually, a *p*-chart is constructed and used in much the same way as a mean chart.

p-**chart** Control chart for attributes, used to monitor the proportion of defective items in a process.

TABLE 10.4
p-chart or *c*-chart?

The following tips should help you select the type of control chart, a *p*-chart or a *c*-chart, that is appropriate for a particular application:

Use a *p*-chart:
1. When observations can be placed into one of *two* categories. Examples include items (observations) that can be classified as
   a. Good or bad
   b. Pass or fail
   c. Operate or don't operate
2. When the data consist of multiple samples of *n* observations each (e.g., 15 samples of $n = 20$ observations each).

Use a *c*-chart:
When only the number of occurrences per unit of measure can be counted; nonoccurrences cannot be counted. Examples of occurrences and units of measure include
a. Scratches, chips, dents, or errors per item
b. Cracks or faults per unit of distance (e.g., meters, miles)
c. Breaks or tears, per unit of area (e.g., square yard, square meter)
d. Bacteria or pollutants per unit of volume (e.g., gallon, cubic foot, cubic yard)
e. Calls, complaints, failures, equipment breakdowns, or crimes per unit of time (e.g., hour, day, month, year)

The centerline on a *p*-chart is the average fraction defective in the population, *p*. The standard deviation of the sampling distribution when *p* is known is

$$\sigma_p = \sqrt{\frac{p(1-p)}{n}}$$

Control limits are computed using the formulas

$$UCL_p = p + z\sigma_p$$
$$LCL_p = p - z\sigma_p$$

(10–4)

If *p* is unknown, which is generally the case, it can be estimated from samples. That estimate, $\bar{p}$, replaces *p* in the preceding formulas, and $\hat{\sigma}_p$ replaces σ_p as illustrated in Example 4.

Note: Because the formula is an approximation, it sometimes happens that the computed LCL is negative. In those instances, zero is used as the lower limit.

EXAMPLE 4

mhhe.com/stevenson13e

Computing Control Limits for the Fraction Defective

An inspector counted the number of defective monthly billing statements of a telephone company in each of 20 samples. Using the following information, construct a control chart that will describe 99.74 percent of the chance variation in the process when the process is in control. Each sample contained 100 statements.

Sample	Number of Defectives	Sample	Number of Defectives	Sample	Number of Defectives	Sample	Number of Defectives
1	7	6	11	11	8	16	10
2	10	7	10	12	12	17	8
3	12	8	18	13	9	18	12
4	4	9	13	14	10	19	10
5	9	10	10	15	16	20	21
							220

SOLUTION

To find *z*, divide .9974 by 2 to obtain .4987, and using that value, refer to Appendix B, Table A to find *z* = 3.00.

$$\bar{p} = \frac{\text{Total number of defectives}}{\text{Total number of observations}} = \frac{220}{20(100)} = .11$$

$$\hat{\sigma}_p = \sqrt{\frac{\bar{p}(1-\bar{p})}{n}} = \sqrt{\frac{.11(1-.11)}{100}} = 0.313$$

Control limits are

$$UCL_p = \bar{p} + z(\hat{\sigma}_p) = .11 + 3.00(0.313) = .2039$$

$$LCL_p = \bar{p} - z(\hat{\sigma}_p) = .11 - 3.00(0.313) = .0161$$

Plotting the control limits and the sample fraction defective, you can see that the last value is above the upper control limit. The process would be stopped at that point to find and correct the possible cause. Then new data would be collected to establish new control limits. If no cause is found, this could be due to chance. The new limits would remain, but future output would be monitored to assure the process remains in control.

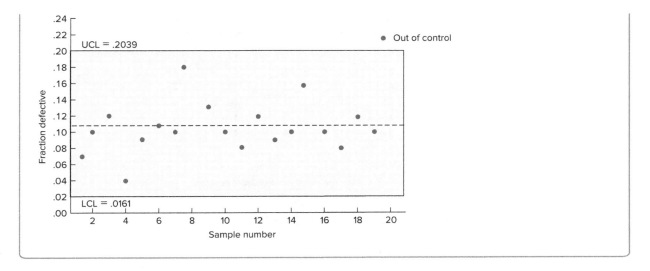

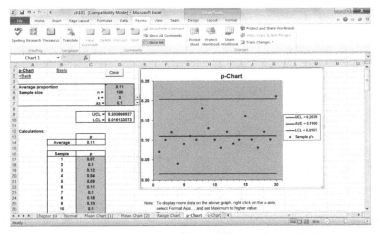

c-Chart. When the goal is to control the number of *occurrences* (e.g., defects) *per unit,* a *c*-chart is used. Units might be automobiles, hotel rooms, typed pages, or rolls of carpet. The underlying sampling distribution is the Poisson distribution. Use of the Poisson distribution assumes that defects occur over some *continuous* region and that the probability of more than one defect at any particular point is negligible. The mean number of defects per unit is c and the standard deviation is $\sqrt{c}$. For practical reasons, the normal approximation to the Poisson is used. The control limits are

c-chart Control chart for attributes, used to monitor the number of defects per unit.

$$UCL_c = c + z\sqrt{c}$$
$$LCL_c = c - z\sqrt{c}$$

(10–5)

If the value of c is unknown, as is generally the case, the sample estimate, $\bar{c}$, is used in place of c, using $\bar{c}$ = Number of defects ÷ Number of samples.

Computing Control Limits for the Number of Defects

Rolls of coiled wire are monitored using a *c*-chart. Eighteen rolls have been examined, and the number of defects per roll has been recorded in the following table. Is the process in control? Plot the values on a control chart using three standard deviation control limits.

EXAMPLE 5

mhhe.com/stevenson13e

Sample	Number of Defectives	Sample	Number of Defectives	Sample	Number of Defectives
1	3	7	4	13	2
2	2	8	1	14	4
3	4	9	2	15	2
4	5	10	1	16	1
5	1	11	3	17	3
6	2	12	4	18	1
					45

SOLUTION

$\bar{c} = 45/18 = 2.5 =$ Average number of defects per coil

$UCL_c = \bar{c} + 3\sqrt{\bar{c}} = 2.5 + 3\sqrt{2.5} = 7.24$

$LCL_c = \bar{c} - 3\sqrt{\bar{c}} = 2.5 - 3\sqrt{2.5} = -2.24 \rightarrow 0$

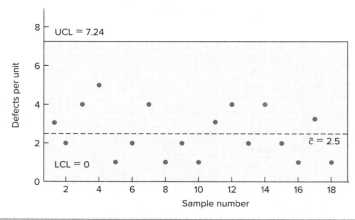

When the computed lower control limit is negative, the effective lower limit is zero. In such cases, if a control chart point is zero, it should not be deemed to be out of control. The calculation sometimes produces a negative lower limit due to the use of the normal distribution to approximate the Poisson distribution: The normal is symmetrical, whereas the Poisson is not symmetrical when c is close to zero.

Note that if an observation falls below the lower control limit on a p-chart or a c-chart, the cause should be investigated, just as it would be for a mean or range chart, even though such a point would imply that the process is exhibiting better than expected quality. It may turn out to be the result of an undesirable overuse of resources. On the other hand, it may lead to a discovery that can improve the quality of the process.

Managerial Considerations Concerning Control Charts

Using control charts adds to the cost and time needed to obtain output. Ideally a process is so good that the desired level of quality could be achieved without the use of any control charts. The best organizations strive to reach this level, but many are not yet there, so they employ control charts at various points in their processes. In those organizations, managers must make a number of important decisions about the use of control charts:

1. At what points in the process to use control charts
2. What size samples to take
3. What type of control chart to use (i.e., variables or attribute)
4. How often should samples be taken

The decision about where to use control charts should focus on those aspects of the process that (1) have a tendency to go out of control and (2) are critical to the successful operation of the product or service (i.e., variables that affect product or service characteristics).

Sample size is important for two reasons. One is that cost and time are functions of sample size; the greater the sample size, the greater the cost to inspect those items (and the greater the lost product if destructive testing is involved) and the longer the process must be held up while waiting for the results of sampling. The second reason is that smaller samples are more likely to reveal a change in the process than larger samples because a change is more likely to take place *within* the large sample, but *between* small samples. Consequently, a sample statistic such as the sample mean in the large sample could combine both "before-change" and "after-change" observations, whereas in two smaller samples, the first could contain "before" observations and the second "after" observations, making detection of the change more likely.

In some instances, a manager can choose between using a control chart for variables (a mean chart) and a control chart for attributes (a *p*-chart). If the manager is monitoring the diameter of a drive shaft, either the diameter could be measured and a mean chart used for control, or the shafts could be inspected using a *go, no-go gauge*—which simply indicates whether a particular shaft is within specification without giving its exact dimensions—and a *p*-chart could be used. Measuring is more costly and time-consuming per unit than the yes-no inspection using a go, no-go gauge, but because measuring supplies more information than merely counting items as good or bad, one needs a much smaller sample size for a mean chart than a *p*-chart. Hence, a manager must weigh the time and cost of sampling against the information provided.

Sampling frequency can be a function of the stability of a process and the cost to sample.

Run Tests

Control charts test for points that are too extreme to be considered random (e.g., points that are outside of the control limits). However, even if all points are within the control limits, the data may still not reflect a random process. In fact, any sort of pattern in the data would suggest a nonrandom process. Figure 10.11 illustrates some patterns that might be present.

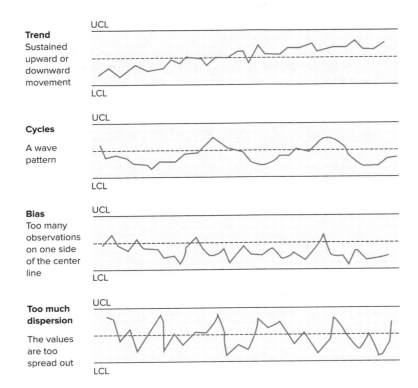

FIGURE 10.11

Some examples of nonrandom patterns in control chart plots

Run test A test for patterns in a sequence.

LO10.6 Perform run tests to check for nonrandomness in process output.

Run Sequence of observations with a certain characteristic.

Analysts often supplement control charts with a **run test**, which checks for patterns in a sequence of observations. This enables an analyst to do a better job of detecting abnormalities in a process and provides insights into correcting a process that is out of control. A variety of run tests are available; this section describes two that are widely used.

When a process is stable or in statistical control, the output it generates will exhibit random variability over a period of time. The presence of patterns, such as trends, cycles, or bias in the output indicates that assignable, or nonrandom, causes of variation exist. Hence, a process that produces output with such patterns is not in a state of statistical control. This is true even though all points on a control chart may be within the control limits. For this reason, it is usually prudent to subject control chart data to run tests to determine whether patterns can be detected.

A **run** is defined as a sequence of observations with a certain characteristic, followed by one or more observations with a different characteristic. The characteristic can be anything that is observable. For example, in the series A A A B, there are two runs: a run of three As followed by a run of one B. Underlining each run helps in counting them. In the series AA BBB A, the underlining indicates three runs.

Two useful run tests involve examination of the number of runs *up and down* and runs above and below the *median*.[2] In order to count these runs, the data are transformed into a series of Us and Ds (for *up* and *down*) and into a series of As and Bs (for *above* and *below* the median). Consider the following sequence, which has a median of 36.5. The first two values are below the median, the next two are above it, the next to last is below, and the last is above. Thus, there are four runs:

25	29	42	40	35	38
B	B	A	A	B	A

In terms of up and down, there are three runs in the same data. The second value is up from the first value, the third is up from the second, the fourth is down from the third, and so on:

25	29	42	40	35	38
—	U	U	D	D	U

(The first value does not receive either a U or a D because nothing precedes it.)

If a plot is available, the runs can be easily counted directly from the plot, as illustrated in Figures 10.12 and 10.13.

FIGURE 10.12
Counting above/below median runs

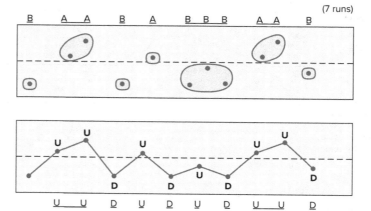

FIGURE 10.13
Counting up/down runs

To determine whether any patterns are present in control chart data, one must transform the data into both As and Bs and Us and Ds, and then count the number of runs in each case. These numbers must then be compared with the number of runs that would be expected in a completely random series. For both the median and the up/down run tests, the expected number of runs is a function of the number of observations in the series. The formulas are

$$E(r)_{med} = \frac{N}{2} + 1 \tag{10–6a}$$

$$E(r)_{uld} = \frac{2N - 1}{3} \tag{10–7a}$$

where N is the number of observations or data points, and $E(r)$ is the expected number of runs.

The actual number of runs in any given set of observations will vary from the expected number, due to chance and any patterns that might be present. Chance variability is measured by the standard deviation of runs. The formulas are

$$\sigma_{med} = \sqrt{\frac{N - 1}{4}} \tag{10–6b}$$

$$\sigma_{uld} = \sqrt{\frac{16N - 29}{90}} \tag{10–7b}$$

Distinguishing chance variability from patterns requires use of the sampling distributions for median runs and up/down runs. Both distributions are approximately normal. Thus, for example, 95.5 percent of the time a random process will produce an observed number of runs within two standard deviations of the expected number. If the observed number of runs falls in that range, there are probably no nonrandom patterns; for observed numbers of runs beyond such limits, we begin to suspect that patterns are present. Too few or too many runs can be an indication of nonrandomness.

In practice, it is often easiest to compute the number of standard deviations, z, by which an observed number of runs differs from the expected number. This z value would then be compared to the value ± 2 (z for 95.5 percent) or some other desired value (e.g., ± 1.96 for 95 percent, ± 2.33 for 98 percent). A test z that exceeds the desired limits indicates patterns are present. (See Figure 10.14.) The computation of z takes the form

$$z_{test} = \frac{\text{Observed number of runs} - \text{Expected number of runs}}{\text{Standard deviation of number of runs}}$$

For the median and up/down tests, one can find z using these formulas:

Median: $$z = \frac{r - [(N/2) + 1]}{\sqrt{(N - 1)/4}} \tag{10–8}$$

Up and down: $$z = \frac{r - [(2N - 1)/3]}{\sqrt{(16N - 29)/90}} \tag{10–9}$$

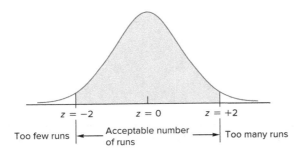

$z = -2 \qquad z = 0 \qquad z = +2$

Too few runs $\quad\longleftarrow$ Acceptable number $\longrightarrow\quad$ Too many runs
of runs

FIGURE 10.14

A sampling distribution for runs is used to distinguish chance variation from patterns

where

> N = Total number of observations
>
> r = Observed number of runs of either As and Bs or Us and Ds, depending on which test is involved.

It is desirable to apply both run tests to any given set of observations because each test is different in terms of the types of patterns it can detect. Sometimes both tests will pick up a certain pattern, but sometimes only one will detect nonrandomness. If either does, the implication is that some sort of nonrandomness is present in the data.

EXAMPLE 6

eXcel

mhhe.com/stevenson13e

Testing for Non-randomness using Run Tests

Twenty sample means have been taken from a process. The means are shown in the following table. Use median and up/down run tests with $z = 2$ to determine if assignable causes of variation are present. Assume the median is 11.0.

SOLUTION

The means are marked according to above/below the median and up/down. The solid lines represent the runs.

Sample	A/B	Mean	U/D	Sample	A/B	Mean	U/D
1	B	10.0	—	11	I	10.7	I
2	B	10.4	I	12	I	11.3	I
3	B	10.2	I	13	I	10.8	I
4	I	11.5	I U	14	A	11.8	I
5	I	10.8	I D	15	A	11.2	I
6	A	11.6	I U	16	A	11.6	I
7	A	11.1	I D	17	A	11.2	I D
8	A	11.2	I U	18	B	10.6	I D
9	B	10.6	I D	19	B	10.7	I U
10	B	10.9	I U	20	I	11.9	I U

A/B: 10 runs   U/D: 17 runs

The expected number of runs for each test is

$$E(r)_{med} = \frac{N}{2} + 1 = \frac{20}{2} + 1 = 11$$

$$E(r)_{uld} = \frac{2N - 1}{3} = \frac{2(20) - 1}{3} = 13$$

The standard deviations are

$$\sigma_{med} = \sqrt{\frac{N-1}{4}} = \sqrt{\frac{20-1}{4}} = 2.18$$

$$\sigma_{uld} = \sqrt{\frac{16N - 29}{90}} = \sqrt{\frac{16(20) - 29}{90}} = 1.80$$

The z_{test} values are

$$z_{med} \frac{10 - 11}{2.18} = -.46$$

$$z_{uld} \frac{17 - 13}{1.80} = +2.22$$

Although the median test does not reveal any pattern, because its z_{test} value is within the range ± 2, the up/down test does; its value exceeds $+2$. Consequently, nonrandom variations are probably present in the data and, hence, the process is not in control.

If ties occur in either test (e.g., a value equals the median or two values in a row are the same), assign A/B or U/D in such a manner that that z_{test} is as large as possible. If z_{test} still does not exceed ± 2 (± 1.96, etc.), you can be reasonably confident that a conclusion of randomness is justified.

Using Control Charts and Run Tests Together

Although for instructional purposes most of the examples, solved problems, and problems focus on either control charts or run tests, ideally both control charts and run tests should be used to analyze process output, along with a plot of the data. The procedure involves the following three steps:

1. Compute control limits for the process output.
   a. Determine which type of control chart is appropriate (see Figure 10.18 in the chapter summary).
   b. Compute control limits using the appropriate formulas. If no probability is given, use a value of $z = 2.00$ to compute the control limits.
   c. If any sample statistics fall outside of the control limits, the process is not in control. If all values are within the control limits, proceed to Step 2.

2. Conduct median and up/down run tests. Use $z = \pm 2.00$ for comparing the test scores. If either or both test scores are not within $z = \pm 2.00$, the output is probably not random. If both test scores are within $z = \pm 2.00$, proceed to Step 3.

3. *Note:* If you are at this point, there is no indication so far that the process output is nonrandom. Plot the sample data and visually check for patterns (e.g., cycling). If you see a pattern, the output is probably not random. Otherwise, conclude the output is random and that the process is in control.

What Happens When a Process Exhibits Possible Nonrandom Variation?

Nonrandom variation is indicated when a point is observed that is outside the control limits, or a run test produces a large z-value (e.g., greater than ± 1.96). Managers should have response plans in place to investigate the cause. It may be a false alarm (i.e., a Type I error), or it may be a real indication of the presence of an assignable cause of variation. If it appears to be a false alarm, resume the process but monitor it for a while to confirm this. If an assignable cause can be found, it needs to be addressed. If it is a good result (e.g., an observation below the lower control limit of a p-chart, a c-chart, or a range chart would indicate unusually good quality), it may be possible to change the process to achieve similar results on an ongoing basis. The more typical case is that there is a problem that needs to be corrected. Operators can be trained to handle simple problems, while teams may be needed to handle more complex problems. Problem solving often requires the use of various tools, described in Chapter 9, to find the root cause of the problem. Once the cause has been found, changes can be made to reduce the chance of recurrence.

10.4 PROCESS CAPABILITY

Once the stability of a process has been established (i.e., no nonrandom variations are present), it is necessary to determine if the process is capable of producing output that is within an acceptable range. The variability of a process becomes the focal point of the analysis.

Three commonly used terms refer to the variability of process output. Each term relates to a slightly different aspect of that variability, so it is important to differentiate these terms.

Specifications or *tolerances* are established by engineering design or customer requirements. They indicate a range of values in which individual units of output must fall in order to be acceptable.

Specifications A range of acceptable values established by engineering design or customer requirements.

To maximize production of a machine run in a paper mill, the machine's alignment must be correct. If not, performance and quality will be affected, which could result in machine downtime and expensive repairs. The on-board processor calculates the position of the paper in relationship to the machine datum. Two points are then measured on the roller. With the simple press of a button the operator is provided with any deviations on a display panel.

© Ken Hawkins/Alamy Stock Photo

Process variability Natural or inherent variability in a process.

Control limits are statistical limits that reflect the extent to which *sample statistics* such as means and ranges can vary due to randomness alone.

Process variability reflects the natural or inherent (i.e., random) variability in a process. It is measured in terms of the process standard deviation.

Control limits and process variability are directly related: Control limits are based on sampling variability, and sampling variability is a function of process variability. On the other hand, there is *no* direct link between specifications and either control limits or process variability. They are specified in terms of the output of a product or service, not in terms of the *process* by which the output is generated. Hence, in a given instance, the output of a process may or may not conform to specifications, even though the process may be statistically in control. That is why it is also necessary to take into account the *capability* of a process. The term **process capability** refers to the inherent variability of process output *relative to* the variation allowed by the design specifications. The following section describes capability analysis.

Process capability The inherent variability of process output relative to the variation allowed by the design specification.

Capability Analysis

Capability analysis is performed on a process that is in control (i.e., the process exhibits only random variation) for the purpose of determining if the range of variation is within design specifications that would make the output acceptable for its intended use. If it is within the specifications, the process is said to be "capable." If it is not, the manager must decide how to correct the situation.

Consider the three cases illustrated in Figure 10.15. In the first case, process capability and output specifications are well matched, so that nearly all of the process output can be expected to meet the specifications. In the second case, the process variability is much less than what is called for, so that virtually 100 percent of the output should be well within tolerance. In the third case, however, the specifications are tighter than what the process is capable of, so that even when the process is functioning as it should, a sizable percentage of the output will fail to meet the specifications. In other words, the process could be in control and still generate unacceptable output. Thus, we cannot automatically assume that a process that is in control will provide desired output. Instead, we must specifically check whether a process is *capable* of meeting specifications and not simply set up a control chart to monitor it. A process should

FIGURE 10.15 Process capability and specifications may or may not match

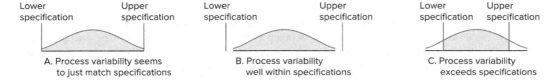

Lower specification	Upper specification	Lower specification	Upper specification	Lower specification	Upper specification
A. Process variability seems to just match specifications		B. Process variability well within specifications		C. Process variability exceeds specifications	

be both in control and within specifications *before* production begins—in essence, "Set the toaster correctly at the start. Don't burn the toast and then scrape it!"

In instances such as case C in Figure 10.15, a manager might consider a range of possible solutions: (1) redesign the process so that it can achieve the desired output, (2) use an alternative process that can achieve the desired output, (3) retain the current process but attempt to eliminate unacceptable output using 100 percent inspection, and (4) examine the specifications to see whether they are necessary or could be relaxed without adversely affecting customer satisfaction.

Obviously, process variability is the key factor in process capability. It is measured in terms of the process standard deviation. To determine whether the process is capable, compare ± 3 standard deviations (i.e., 6 standard deviations) of the process to the specifications for the process. For example, suppose the ideal length of time to perform a service is 10 minutes, and an acceptable range of variation around this time is ± 1 minute. If the process has a standard deviation of .5 minute, it would not be capable because ± 3 standard deviations would be ± 1.5 minutes, exceeding the specification of ± 1 minute.

Determining if a Process is Capable

EXAMPLE 7

A manager has the option of using any one of three machines for a job. The processes and their standard deviations are listed as follows. Determine which machines are capable if the specifications are 10.00 mm and 10.80 mm.

e**X**cel
mhhe.com/stevenson13e

Process	Standard Deviation (mm)
A	.13
B	.08
C	.16

SOLUTION

Determine the extent of process variability (the process width) of each process (i.e., six standard deviations) and compare that value to the specification *difference* of .80 mm.

Process	Standard Deviation (mm)	Process Width
A	.13	.78
B	.08	.48
C	.16	.96

C_p

To assess the capability of a machine or process, a **capability index** can be computed using the following formula:

$$\text{Process capability index, } C_p = \frac{\text{Specification width}}{\text{Process width}}$$

$$= \frac{\text{Upper specification} - \text{Lower specification}}{6\sigma \text{ of the process}}$$

(10–10)

capability index Used to assess the ability of a process to meet specifications.

LO10.7 Assess process capability.

For a process to be deemed to be capable, it must have a capability index of at least 1.00. However, an index of 1.00 would mean that the process is just barely capable. The current trend is to aim for an index of at least 1.33. An index of 1.33 allows some leeway. Consider driving a car into a garage that has a door opening that is 1 inch wider than the car versus driving into a garage where the door opening is 20 inches wider than the car, and you'll understand why this book and many companies use 1.33 as the standard for judging process capability instead of 1.00. So use 1.33 as the standard to achieve in judging process capability.

An index of 1.00 implies about 2,700 parts per million (ppm) can be expected to not be within the specifications, while an index of 1.33 implies only about 30 ppm won't be within specs. Moreover, the greater the capability index, the greater the probability that the output of a process will fall within design specifications.

EXAMPLE 8

Computing a Process Capability Index

Compute the process capability index for each process in Example 7.

SOLUTION

The specification width in Example 7 is .80 mm. Hence, to determine the capability index for each process, divide .80 by the process width (i.e., six standard deviations) of each machine. The results are shown in the following table.

Process	Standard Deviation (mm)	Process Capability	C_P
A	.13	.78	.80/.78 = 1.03
B	.08	.48	.80/.48 = 1.67
C	.16	.96	.80/.96 = 0.83

We can see that only process B is capable because its index is not less than 1.33. (See Figure 10.15 for a visual portrayal of these results.)

For processes that are not capable, several options might be considered, such as performing 100 percent inspection to weed out unacceptable items, improving the process to reduce variability, switching to a capable process, outsourcing, etc.

The Motorola Corporation is well known for its use of the term *Six Sigma,* which refers to its goal of achieving a process variability so small that the design specifications represent six standard deviations above *and* below the process mean. That means a process capability index equal to 2.00, resulting in an extremely small probability of getting any output not within the design specifications. This is illustrated in Figure 10.16.

To get an idea of how a capability index of 2.00 compares to an index of, say, 1.00 in terms of defective items, consider that if the U.S. Postal Service had a capability index of 1.00 for delivery errors of first-class mail, this would translate into about 10,000 misdelivered pieces per day; if the capability index was 2.00, that number would drop to about 1,000 pieces a day.

Care must be taken when interpreting the C_p index, because its computation does not involve the process mean. Unless the target value (i.e., process mean) is *centered* between

FIGURE 10.16   Three-sigma versus Six-Sigma capability

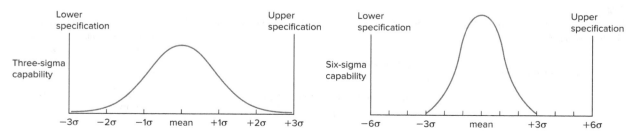

the upper and lower specifications, the C_p index can be misleading. For example, suppose the specifications are 10 and 11, and the standard deviation of the process is equal to .10. The C_p would seem to be very favorable:

$$\frac{11 - 10}{6(.10)} = 1.67$$

However, suppose that the process mean is 12, with a standard deviation of .10; $\pm$ 3 standard deviations would be 11.70 to 12.30, so it is very unlikely that *any* of the output would be within the specifications of 10 to 11!

There are situations in which the target value is not centered between the specifications, either intentionally or unavoidably. In such instances, a more appropriate measure of process capability is the C_{pk} index, because it does take the process mean into account.

C_{pk}

If a process is not centered, a slightly different measure is used to compute its capability. This index is represented by the symbol C_{pk}. It is computed by finding the difference between each of the specification limits and the mean, identifying the smaller difference, and dividing that difference by three standard deviations of the process. Thus, C_{pk} is equal to the *smaller* of

$$\frac{\text{Upper specification} - \text{Process mean}}{3\sigma} \qquad (10\text{--}11)$$

and

$$\frac{\text{Process mean} - \text{Lower specification}}{3\sigma}$$

Computing C_{pk}

EXAMPLE 9

mhhe.com/stevenson13e

A process has a mean of 9.20 grams and a standard deviation of .30 gram. The lower specification limit is 7.50 grams and the upper specification limit is 10.50 grams. Compute C_{pk}.

SOLUTION

1. Compute the index for the lower specification:

$$\frac{\text{Process mean} - \text{Lower specification}}{3\sigma} = \frac{9.20 - 7.50}{3(.30)} = \frac{1.70}{.90} = 1.89$$

2. Compute the index for the upper specification:

$$\frac{\text{Upper specification} - \text{Process mean}}{3\sigma} = \frac{10.50 - 9.20}{3(.30)} = \frac{1.30}{.90} = 1.44$$

The *smaller* of the two indexes is 1.44, so this is the C_{pk}. Because the C_{pk} is more than 1.33, the process is capable.

You might be wondering why a process wouldn't be centered as a matter of course. One reason is that only a range of acceptable values, not a target value, may be specified. A more compelling reason is that the cost of nonconformance is greater for one specification limit than it is for nonconformance for the other specification limit. In that case, it would make sense to have the target value be closer to the spec that has the lower cost of nonconformance. This would result in a noncentered process.

Improving Process Capability

Improving process capability requires changing the process target value and/or reducing the process variability that is inherent in a process. This might involve simplifying, standardizing, making the process mistake-proof, upgrading equipment, or automating. See Table 10.5 for examples.

TABLE 10.5
Process capability improvement

Method	Examples
Simplify	Eliminate steps, reduce the number of parts, use modular design
Standardize	Use standard parts, standard procedures
Make mistake-proof	Design parts that can only be assembled the correct way; have simple checks to verify a procedure has been performed correctly
Upgrade equipment	Replace worn-out equipment; take advantage of technological improvements
Automate	Substitute automated processing for manual processing

Improved process capability means less need for inspection, lower warranty costs, fewer complaints about service, and higher productivity. For process control purposes, it means narrower control limits.

Taguchi Loss Function

Genichi Taguchi, a Japanese quality expert, holds a nontraditional view of what constitutes poor quality, and hence the cost of poor quality. The traditional view is that as long as output is within specifications, there is no cost. Taguchi believes that any deviation from the target value represents poor quality, and that the farther away from target a deviation is, the greater the cost. Figure 10.17 illustrates the two views. The implication for Taguchi is that reducing the variation inherent in a process (i.e., increasing its capability ratio) will result in lowering the cost of poor quality, and consequently, the loss to society.

Limitations of Capability Indexes

There are several risks of using a capability index:

1. The process may not be stable, in which case a capability index is meaningless.
2. The process output may not be normally distributed, in which case inferences about the fraction of output that isn't acceptable will be incorrect.
3. The process is not centered but the C_p index is used, giving a misleading result.

10.5 OPERATIONS STRATEGY

Quality is a major consideration for virtually all customers, so achieving and maintaining quality standards is of strategic importance to all business organizations. Quality assurance and product and service design are two vital links in the process. Organizations should continually seek to increase the capability of the processes they use, so that they can move from

FIGURE 10.17
Taguchi and traditional views of the cost of poor quality

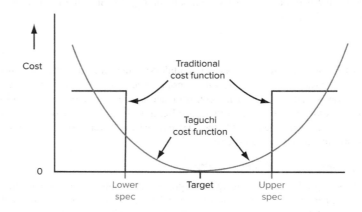

READING

BAR CODES MIGHT CUT DRUG ERRORS IN HOSPITALS

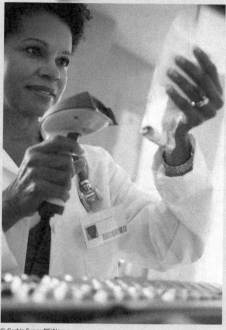

© Corbis Super RF/Alamy

It's estimated that more than 7,000 hospital patients die each year because of drug errors, and many others suffer ill effects from being given the wrong drug or the wrong dosage. Some hospitals are using bar codes attached to patients' wristbands that allow hospital personnel who administer drugs to patients to electronically check to make sure the drug and dosage are appropriate. Before administering a drug, the doctor or nurse scans the bar code attached to the patient to see what drug is needed and when, and then the drug's bar code is scanned to verify that the medication is correct.

But bar codes are not foolproof, as a recent study of hospitals showed. Nurses may develop a workaround that involves using photo copies of a group of patients' bar codes which are then used to obtain drugs for the entire group. The nurse would then have a tray that may contain drugs of different dosages intended for different patients. At that point, the bar code protection has been circumvented.

Questions

1. Why are bar codes being used in hospitals?
2. What action would you suggest to avoid the problem of workarounds?

Source: Based on "Bar Codes Might Cut Drug Errors," *Rochester Democrat and Chronicle*, March 14, 2003, p. 9A; and "Bar Codes Are Not Foolproof in Hospitals, says Study," *Rochester Democrat and Chronicle*, July 3, 2008, p. 3A.

---

a position of using inspection or extensive use of control charts to achieve desired levels of quality to one where quality is built into products and processes, so that little or no effort is needed to assure quality. Processes that exhibit evidence of nonrandomness, or processes that are deemed to not be capable, should be viewed as opportunities for continuous process improvement.

SUMMARY

This chapter describes inspection and statistical process control. Inspection means examining the output of a process to determine whether it is acceptable. Key issues in inspection include where to inspect in the process, how often to inspect, and whether to inspect on-site or in a laboratory.

Statistical process control focuses on detecting departures from randomness in a process. Two basic tools of process control are control charts and run tests. Figure 10.18 gives an overview of quality control. The general theory of control charts is discussed, and four types of control charts—two for variables and two for attributes—and two types of run tests are described in the chapter. The chapter ends with a discussion of process capability. Process capability studies are used to determine if the output of a process will satisfy specifications. They can provide valuable information for managers in terms of reducing costs and avoiding problems created by generating output that is not within specifications. Table 10.6 provides a summary of formulas.

KEY POINTS

1. All processes exhibit random variation. Quality control's purpose is to identify a process that also exhibits nonrandom (correctable) variation on the basis of sample statistics (e.g., sample means) obtained from the process.

2. Control charts and run tests can be used to detect nonrandom variation in sample statistics. It is also advisable to plot the data to visually check for patterns.

3. If a process does not exhibit nonrandom variation, its capability to produce output that meets specifications can be assessed.

FIGURE 10.18
Overview of quality control

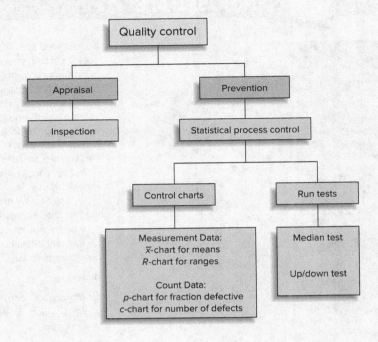

TABLE 10.6
Summary of formulas

CONTROL CHARTS		
Name	**Usage**	**Control Limits**
Mean, x–bar chart	Measurement data. Use for average.	$\bar{\bar{x}} \pm \frac{z\sigma}{\sqrt{n}}$ or $\bar{\bar{x}} \pm A_2\bar{R}$ n = sample size
Range, R chart	Measurement data. Use for range or dispersion.	$UCL = D_4\bar{R}$, $LCL = D_3\bar{R}$
Fraction defective, p-chart	Count data. Use when both the "good" and "bad" can be counted.	$\bar{p} \pm z\sqrt{\dfrac{\bar{p}(1-\bar{p})}{n}}$ n = samplesize
Number of defects, c-chart	Count data. Use when only the "occurrences" can be counted.	$\bar{c} \pm z\sqrt{\bar{c}}$

RUN TESTS				
	NUMBER OF RUNS			
Name	**Observed**	**Expected**	**Standard Deviation**	**z**
Median	r	$\dfrac{N}{2}+1$	$\sqrt{\dfrac{N-1}{4}}$	$\dfrac{r-[(N/2)+1]}{\sqrt{(N-1)/4}}$
Up/down	r	$\dfrac{2N-1}{3}$	$\sqrt{\dfrac{16N-29}{90}}$	$\dfrac{r-[(2N-1)/3]}{\sqrt{(16N-29)/90}}$

N = number of observations

(continued)

PROCESS CAPABILITY			TABLE 10.6
Name	**Symbol**	**Formula**	(*concluded*)
Capability index for a centered process	C_p	$\dfrac{\text{Specification width}}{6\sigma \text{ of process}}$	
Capability index for a noncentered process	C_{pk}	Smaller of $\begin{cases} \dfrac{\text{Mean} - \text{Lower specification}}{3\sigma} \\ \dfrac{\text{Upper specification} - \text{Mean}}{3\sigma} \end{cases}$	

KEY TERMS

assignable variation 424
attributes 428
capability index 443
c-chart 435
central limit theorem 424
control chart 426
control limits 427
inspection 418

mean control chart 428
p-chart 433
process capability 442
process variability 442
quality control 417
quality of conformance 423
random variation 423
range control chart 430

run 438
run test 438
sampling distribution 424
specifications 441
statistical process control (SPC) 423
Type I error 427
Type II error 427
variables 428

SOLVED PROBLEMS

Problem 1

Process distribution and sampling distribution. An industrial process that makes 3-foot sections of plastic pipe produces pipe with an average inside diameter of 1 inch and a standard deviation of .05 inch.

a. If you randomly select one piece of pipe, what is the probability that its inside diameter will exceed 1.02 inches, assuming the population is normal?

b. If you select a random sample of 25 pieces of pipe, what is the probability that the sample mean will exceed 1.02 inches?

$\mu = 1.00, \sigma = .05$

Solution

a. $z = \dfrac{x - \mu}{\sigma} = \dfrac{1.02 - 1.00}{.05} = .40$

Using Appendix B, Table A, $P(z > .4) = .5000 - .1554 = .3446$

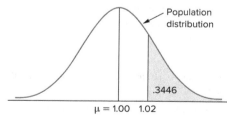

b. $z = \dfrac{\bar{x} - \mu}{\sigma / \sqrt{n}} = \dfrac{1.02 - 1.00}{.05 / \sqrt{25}} = 2.00$

Using Appendix B, Table A, $P(z > 2.00) = .5000 - .4772 = .0228$

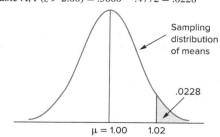

Problem 2

Control charts for means and ranges. Processing times for new accounts at a bank are shown in the following table. Five samples of four observations each have been taken. Use the sample data in conjunction with Table 10.3 to construct upper and lower control limits for both a mean chart and a range chart. Do the results suggest that the process is in control?

	Sample 1	Sample 2	Sample 3	Sample 4	Sample 5
	10.2	10.3	9.7	9.9	9.8
	9.9	9.8	9.9	10.3	10.2
	9.8	9.9	9.9	10.1	10.3
	10.1	10.4	10.1	10.5	9.7
Totals	40.0	40.4	39.6	40.8	40.0

Solution

a. Determine the mean and range of each sample.

$$\bar{x} = \frac{\sum x}{n}, \text{Range} = \text{Largest} - \text{Smallest}$$

Sample	Mean	Range
1	40.0/4 = 10.0	10.2 − 9.8 = .4
2	40.4/4 = 10.1	10.4 − 9.8 = .6
3	39.6/4 = 9.9	10.1 − 9.7 = .4
4	40.8/4 = 10.2	10.5 − 9.9 = .6
5	40.0/4 = 10.0	10.3 − 9.7 = .6

b. Compute the average mean and average range:

$$\bar{\bar{x}} = \frac{10.0 + 10.1 + 9.9 + 10.2 + 10.0}{5} = \frac{50.2}{5} = 10.04$$

$$\bar{R} = \frac{.4 + .6 + .4 + .6 + .6}{5} = \frac{2.6}{5} = .52$$

c. Obtain factors A_2, D_4, and D_3 from Table 10.3 for $n = 4$: $A_2 = .73$, $D_4 = 2.28$, $D_3 = 0$.

d. Compute upper and lower limits:

$$\text{UCL}_{\bar{x}} = \bar{\bar{x}} + A_2\bar{R} = 10.04 + .73(.52) = 10.42$$
$$\text{LCL}_{\bar{x}} = \bar{\bar{x}} - A_2\bar{R} = 10.04 - .73(.52) = 9.66$$
$$\text{UCL}_R = D_4\bar{R} = 2.28(.52) = 1.19$$
$$\text{LCL}_R = D_3\bar{R} = 0(.52) = 0$$

e. Verify that points are within limits. (If they were not, the process would be investigated to correct assignable causes of variation.)

The smallest sample mean is 9.9, and the largest is 10.2. Both are well within the control limits. Similarly, the largest sample range is .6, which is also within the control limits. Hence, the results suggest that the process is in control. Note, however, that for illustrative purposes, the number of samples is deliberately small; 20 or more samples would give a clearer indication of control limits and whether the process is in control.

Problem 3

Type I error (alpha risk). After several investigations of points outside control limits revealed nothing, a manager began to wonder about the probability of a Type I error for the control limits used ($z = 1.90$).

a. Determine the alpha risk (i.e., P [Type I error]) for this value of z.

b. What z would provide an alpha risk of about 2 percent?

a. Using Appendix B, Table A, find that the area under the curve between $z = 0$ and $z = +1.90$ is .4713. Therefore, the area (probability) of values *within* -1.90 to $+1.90$ is 2 (.4713) = .9426, and the area *beyond* these values is $1 - .9426 = .0574$. Hence, the alpha risk is 5.74 percent.

b. The alpha risk (Type I error probability) is always specified as an *area* in the tail(s) of a distribution. With control charts, you use two-sided control limits. Consequently, half of the risk lies in each tail. Hence, the area in the right tail is 1 percent, or .0100. This means that .4900 should be the area under the curve between $z = 0$ and the value of z you are looking for. The closest value is .4901 for $z = 2.33$. Thus, control limits based on $z = \pm 2.33$ provide an alpha risk of about 2 percent.

p-chart and *c-chart*. Using the appropriate control chart, determine two-sigma control limits for each case:

a. An inspector found an average of 3.9 scratches in the exterior paint of each of the automobiles being prepared for shipment to dealers.

b. Before shipping lawn mowers to dealers, an inspector attempts to start each mower and notes any that do not start on the first try. The lot size is 100 mowers, and an average of 4 did not start (4 percent).

The choice between these two types of control charts relates to whether *two* types of results can be counted (*p*-chart) or whether *only occurrences* can be counted (*c*-chart).

a. The inspector can only count the scratches that occurred, not the ones that did not occur. Consequently, a *c*-chart is appropriate. The sample average is 3.9 scratches per car. Two-sigma control limits are found using the formulas

$$UCL = \bar{c} + z\sqrt{\bar{c}}$$
$$LCL = \bar{c} - z\sqrt{\bar{c}}$$

where $\bar{c} = 3.9$ and $z = 2$. Thus,

$$UCL = 3.9 + 2\sqrt{3.9} = 7.85 \text{ scratches}$$
$$LCL = 3.9 - 2\sqrt{3.9} = -.05, \text{ so the lower limit is 0 scratches}$$

(Note: Round to zero only if the computed lower limit is negative.)

b. The inspector can count both the lawn mowers that started and those that did not start. Consequently, a *p*-chart is appropriate. Two-sigma control limits can be computed using the following:

$$UCL = \bar{p} + z\sqrt{\frac{\bar{p}(1 - \bar{p})}{n}}$$

$$LCL = \bar{p} - z\sqrt{\frac{\bar{p}(1 - \bar{p})}{n}}$$

where

$\bar{p} = .04$
$n = 100$
$z = 2$

Thus,

$$UCL = .04 + 2\sqrt{\frac{.04(.96)}{100}} = .079$$

$$LCL = .04 - 2\sqrt{\frac{.04(.96)}{100}} = .001$$

Problem 5

Run tests. The number of defective items per sample for 11 samples is shown below. Determine if nonrandom patterns are present in the sequence.

	SAMPLE										
	1	**2**	**3**	**4**	**5**	**6**	**7**	**8**	**9**	**10**	**11**
Number of defectives	22	17	19	25	18	20	21	17	23	23	24

Solution

Since the median isn't given, it must be estimated from the sample data. To do this, array the data from low to high; the median is the middle value. (In this case, there is an odd number of values. For an even number of values, average the middle two to obtain the median.) Thus,

17 17   18   19 20   21   22 23 23   24 25
     (5 below)   ↑   (5 above)
                            median

The median is 21.

Next, code the observations using A/B and U/D:

Sample	A/B	Number of Defectives	U/D
1	IA	22	—
2	IB	17	ID
3	IB	19	IU
4	IA	25	IU
5	IB	18	ID
6	IB	20	IU
7	tie	21	IU
8	IB	17	ID
9	IA	23	IU
10	IA	23	tie
11	IA	24	IU

Note that each test has tied values. How these are resolved can affect the number of observed runs. Suppose that you adhere to this rule: Assign letter (A or B, U or D) so that the resulting difference between the observed and expected number of runs is as large as possible. To accomplish this, it is necessary to initially ignore ties and count the runs to see whether there are too many or too few. Then return to the ties and make the assignments. The rationale for this rule is that it is a conservative method for retaining data; if you conclude that the data are random using this approach, you can be reasonably confident that the method has not "created" randomness. With this in mind, assign a B to sample 7 since the expected number of runs is

$$E(r)_{med} = N/2 + 1 = 11/2 + 1 = 6.5$$

and the difference between the resulting number of runs, 5, and 6.5 is greater than between 6.5 and 7 (which occurs if A is used instead of B). Similarly, in the up/down test, a U for sample 10 produces six runs, whereas a D produces eight runs. Since the expected number of runs is

$$E(r)_{u/d} = (2N - 1) \div 3 = (22 - 1) \div 3 = 7$$

it makes no difference which one is used: both yield a difference of 1. For the sake of illustration, a D is assigned.

The computations for the two tests are summarized as follows. Each test has a z-value that is within the range of ± 2.00. Because neither test reveals nonrandomness, you may conclude that the data are random.

	Runs Observed	*Expected*	σ_r	**z**	**Conclude**
Median	5	6.5	1.58	−.95	Random
Up/down	8	7.0	1.28	.78	Random

Process capability. Determine which of these three processes are capable: **Problem 6**

Process	Mean	Standard Deviation	Lower Spec	Upper Spec
1	7.5	.10	7.0	8.0
2	4.6	.12	4.3	4.9
3	6.0	.14	5.5	6.7

Notice that the means of the first two processes are exactly in the center of their upper and lower specs. Hence, the C_p index (Formula 10–10) is appropriate. However, the third process is not centered, so C_{pk} (Formula 10–11) is appropriate.   **Solution**

For Processes 1 and 2: $C_p = \dfrac{\text{Upper spec} - \text{Lower spec}}{6\sigma}$

In order to be capable, C_p must be at least 1.33.

Process 1: $C_p = \dfrac{8.0 - 7.0}{6(.10)} = 1.67$ (capable)

Process 2: $C_p = \dfrac{4.9 - 4.3}{6(.12)} = .83$ (not capable)

For Process 3, C_{pk} must be at least 1.33. It is the lesser of these two:

$\dfrac{\text{Upper spec} - \text{Mean}}{3\sigma} = \dfrac{6.7 - 6.0}{3(.14)} = 1.67$

$\dfrac{\text{Mean} - \text{Lower spec}}{3\sigma} = \dfrac{6.0 - 5.5}{3(.14)} = 1.19$ (not capable)

DISCUSSION AND REVIEW QUESTIONS

1. List the steps in the control process.
2. What are the key concepts that underlie the construction and interpretation of control charts?
3. What is the purpose of a control chart?
4. Why is order of observation important in process control?
5. Briefly explain the purpose of each of these control charts:
   a. *x*-bar
   b. Range
   c. *p*-chart
   d. *c*-chart
6. What is a run? How are run charts useful in process control?
7. If all observations are within control limits, does that guarantee that the process is random? Explain.
8. Why is it usually desirable to use both a median run test and an up/down run test on the same data?
9. If both run tests are used, and neither reveals nonrandomness, does that prove that the process is random? Explain.
10. Define and contrast control limits, specifications, and process variability.
11. A customer has recently tightened the specs for a part your company supplies. The specs are now much tighter than the machine being used for the job is capable of. Briefly identify alternatives you might consider to resolve this problem. (See Figure 10.15C.)
12. A new order has come into your department. The capability of the process used for this type of work will enable virtually all of the output to be well within the specs. (See Figure 10.15B.)
    a. What benefits might be derived from this situation?
    b. What alternatives might be considered by the manager?

13. Answer these questions about inspection:
    a. What level of inspection is optimal?
    b. What factors guide the decision of how much to inspect?
    c. What are the main considerations in choosing between centralized inspection and on-site inspection?
    d. What points are potential candidates for inspection?

14. What two basic assumptions must be satisfied in order to use a process capability index?

15. How important is it for managers to maintain and promote ethical behavior in dealing with quality issues? Does your answer depend on the product or service involved?

16. Classify each of the following as either a Type I error or a Type II error:
    a. Putting an innocent person in jail
    b. Releasing a guilty person from jail
    c. Eating (or not eating) a cookie that fell on the floor
    d. Not seeing a doctor as soon as possible after ingesting poison

TAKING STOCK

1. What trade-offs are involved in each of these decisions?
    a. Deciding whether to use two-sigma or three-sigma control limits.
    b. Choosing between a large sample size and a smaller sample size.
    c. Trying to increase the capability of a process that is barely capable.

2. Who needs to be involved in setting quality standards?

3. Name several ways that technology has had an impact on quality control.

CRITICAL THINKING EXERCISES

1. Analysis of the output of a process has suggested that the variability is nonrandom on several occasions recently. However, each time an investigation has not revealed any assignable causes. What are some of the possible explanations for not finding any causes? What should the manager do?

2. Many organizations use the same process capability standard for all their products or services (e.g., 1.33), but some companies use multiple standards: different standards for different products or services (e.g., 1.00, 1.20, 1.33, and 1.40). What reasons might there be for using a single measure, and what reasons might there be for using multiple standards?

3. Give two examples of unethical behavior for each of these areas: inspection, process control, process capability. For each, name the relevant ethical principle (see Chapter 1).

4. In repetitive operations it is often possible to automatically check for quality and then reject parts that are unacceptable. In those situations, does that mean that control charts arent needed? Explain.

PROBLEMS

1. Specifications for a part for a DVD player state that the part should weigh between 24 and 25 ounces. The process that produces the parts has a mean of 24.5 ounces and a standard deviation of .2 ounce. The distribution of output is normal.
    a. What percentage of parts will not meet the weight specs?
    b. Within what values will 95.44 percent of sample means of this process fall, if samples of $n = 16$ are taken and the process is in control (random)?

2. An automatic filling machine is used to fill 1-liter bottles of cola. The machine's output is approximately normal with a mean of 1.0 liter and a standard deviation of .01 liter. Output is monitored using means of samples of 25 observations.
    a. Determine upper and lower control limits that will include roughly 97 percent of the sample means when the process is in control.
    b. Given these sample means: 1.005, 1.001, .998, 1.002, .995, and .999, is the process in control?

3. The time to replace vehicle wiper blades at a service center was monitored using a mean and a range chart. Six samples of $n = 20$ observations were obtained and the sample means and ranges computed:

Sample	Mean	Range	Sample	Mean	Range
1	3.06	.42	4	3.13	.46
2	3.15	.50	5	3.06	.46
3	3.11	.41	6	3.09	.45

a. Using the factors in Table 10.3, determine upper and lower limits for mean and range charts.

b. Is the process in control?

4. Computer upgrade times (in minutes) are being evaluated. Samples of five observations each have been taken, and the results are as listed. Using factors from Table 10.3, determine upper and lower control limits for mean and range charts, and decide if the process is in control.

		SAMPLE			
1	**2**	**3**	**4**	**5**	**6**
79.2	80.5	79.6	78.9	80.5	79.7
78.8	78.7	79.6	79.4	79.6	80.6
80.0	81.0	80.4	79.7	80.4	80.5
78.4	80.4	80.3	79.4	80.8	80.0
81.0	80.1	80.8	80.6	78.8	81.1

5. Using samples of 200 credit card statements, an auditor found the following:

Sample	1	2	3	4
Number with errors	4	2	5	9

a. Determine the fraction defective in each sample.

b. If the true fraction defective for this process is unknown, what is your estimate of it?

c. What is your estimate of the mean and standard deviation of the sampling distribution of fractions defective for samples of this size?

d. What control limits would give an alpha risk of .03 for this process?

e. What alpha risk would control limits of .047 and .003 provide?

f. Using control limits of .047 and .003, is the process in control?

g. Suppose that the long-term fraction defective of the process is known to be 2 percent. What are the values of the mean and standard deviation of the sampling distribution?

h. Construct a control chart for the process, assuming a fraction defective of 2 percent, using two-sigma control limits. Is the process in control?

6. A medical facility does MRIs for sports injuries. Occasionally a test yields inconclusive results and must be repeated. Using the following sample data and $n = 200$, determine the upper and lower control limits for the fraction of retests using two-sigma limits. Is the process in control?

						SAMPLE							
	1	**2**	**3**	**4**	**5**	**6**	**7**	**8**	**9**	**10**	**11**	**12**	**13**
Number of retests	1	2	2	0	2	1	2	0	2	7	3	2	1

7. The postmaster of a small western town receives a certain number of complaints each day about mail delivery. Determine three-sigma control limits using the following data. Is the process in control?

							DAY							
	1	**2**	**3**	**4**	**5**	**6**	**7**	**8**	**9**	**10**	**11**	**12**	**13**	**14**
Number of complaints	4	10	14	8	9	6	5	12	13	7	6	4	2	10

8. Given the following data for the number of defects per spool of cable, using three-sigma limits, is the process in control?

							OBSERVATION							
	1	**2**	**3**	**4**	**5**	**6**	**7**	**8**	**9**	**10**	**11**	**12**	**13**	**14**
Number of defects	2	3	1	0	1	3	2	0	2	1	3	1	2	0

456   **Chapter Ten**   Quality Control

9. After a number of complaints about its directory assistance, a telephone company examined samples of calls to determine the frequency of wrong numbers given to callers. Each sample consisted of 100 calls. Determine 95 percent limits. Is the process stable (i.e., in control)? Explain.

	SAMPLE															
	1	2	3	4	5	6	7	8	9	10	11	12	13	14	15	16
Number of errors	5	3	5	7	4	6	8	4	5	9	3	4	5	6	6	7

10. Specifications for a metal shaft are much wider than the machine used to make the shafts is capable of. Consequently, the decision has been made to allow the cutting tool to wear a certain amount before replacement. The tool wears at the rate of .004 centimeter per piece. The process has a natural variation, σ, of .02 centimeter and is normally distributed. Specifications are 15.0 to 15.2 centimeters. A three-sigma cushion is set at each end to minimize the risk of output outside of the specifications. How many shafts can the process turn out before tool replacement becomes necessary? (See diagram.)

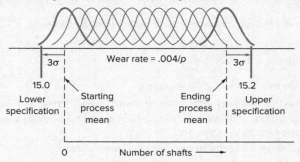

11. The lower and upper specifications for the computer upgrades in Problem 4 are 78 minutes and 81 minutes. Based on the data in the problem, would you say that the specifications are being met? Estimate the percentage of process output that can be expected to fall within the specifications.

12. The time needed for checking in at a hotel is to be investigated. Historically, the process has had a standard deviation equal to .146. The means of 39 samples of $n = 14$ are

Sample	Mean	Sample	Mean	Sample	Mean	Sample	Mean
1	3.86	11	3.88	21	3.84	31	3.88
2	3.90	12	3.86	22	3.82	32	3.76
3	3.83	13	3.88	23	3.89	33	3.83
4	3.81	14	3.81	24	3.86	34	3.77
5	3.84	15	3.83	25	3.88	35	3.86
6	3.83	16	3.86	26	3.90	36	3.80
7	3.87	17	3.82	27	3.81	37	3.84
8	3.88	18	3.86	28	3.86	38	3.79
9	3.84	19	3.84	29	3.98	39	3.85
10	3.80	20	3.87	30	3.96		

a. Construct an $\bar{x}$-chart for this process with three-sigma limits. Is the process in control?

b. Analyze the data using a median run test and an up/down run test. What can you conclude?

13. For each of the accompanying control charts, analyze the data using both median and up/down run tests with $z = \pm 1.96$ limits. Are nonrandom variations present? Assume the center line is the long-term median.

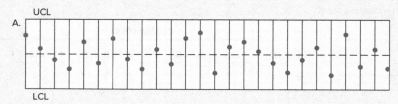

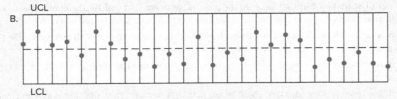

14. Analyze the data in the following problems using median and up/down run tests with $z = \pm 2$.

    a. Given the following run test results of process output, what do the results of the run tests suggest about the process?

Test	z–score
Median	+ 1.37
Up/Down	+ 1.05

    b. Twenty means were plotted on a control chart. An analyst counted 14 runs above/below the median, and 8 up/down runs. What do the results suggest about the process?

    c. Problem 8.

    d. Problem 7.

15. Use both types of run tests to analyze the daily expense voucher listed. Assume a median of $31.

Day	Amount	Day	Amount	Day	Amount	Day	Amount
1	$27.69	16	$29.65	31	$40.54	46	$25.16
2	28.13	17	31.08	32	36.31	47	26.11
3	33.02	18	33.03	33	27.14	48	29.84
4	30.31	19	29.10	34	30.38	49	31.75
5	31.59	20	25.19	35	31.96	50	29.14
6	33.64	21	28.60	36	32.03	51	37.78
7	34.73	22	20.02	37	34.40	52	34.16
8	35.09	23	26.67	38	25.67	53	38.28
9	33.39	24	36.40	39	35.80	54	29.49
10	32.51	25	32.07	40	32.23	55	30.81
11	27.98	26	44.10	41	26.76	56	30.60
12	31.25	27	41.44	42	30.51	57	34.46
13	33.98	28	29.62	43	29.35	58	35.10
14	25.56	29	30.12	44	24.09	59	31.76
15	24.46	30	26.39	45	22.45	60	34.90

16. A company has just negotiated a contract to produce a part for another firm. In the process of manufacturing the part, the inside diameter of successive parts becomes smaller and smaller as the cutting tool wears. However, the specs are so wide relative to machine capabilities that it is possible to set the diameter initially at a large value and let the process run for a while before replacing the cutting tool.

    The inside diameter decreases at an average rate of .001 cm per part, and the process has a standard deviation of .05 cm. The variability is approximately normal. Assuming a three-sigma buffer at each end, how frequently must the tool be replaced if the process specs are 3 cm and 3.5 cm?

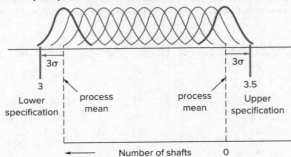

17. (Refer to Solved Problem 2.) Suppose the process specs are 9.65 and 10.35 minutes. Based on the data given, does it appear that the specs are being met? If not, what should one look for?

18. A production process consists of a three-step operation. The scrap rate is 10 percent for the first step and 6 percent for the other two steps.

    a. If the desired daily output is 450 units, how many units must be started to allow for loss due to scrap?

    b. If the scrap rate for each step could be cut in half, how many units would this save in terms of the scrap allowance?

    c. If the scrap represents a cost of $10 per unit, how much is it costing the company per day for the original scrap rate?

19. (Refer to the data in Example 5.) Two additional observations have been taken. The first resulted in three defects, and the second had four defects. Using the set of 20 observations, perform run tests on the data. What can you conclude about the data?

20. A teller at a drive-up window at a bank had the following service times (in minutes) for 20 randomly selected customers.

SAMPLE			
1	**2**	**3**	**4**
4.5	4.6	4.5	4.7
4.2	4.5	4.6	4.6
4.2	4.4	4.4	4.8
4.3	4.7	4.4	4.5
4.3	4.3	4.6	4.9

    a. Determine the mean of each sample.

    b. If the process parameters are unknown, estimate its mean and standard deviation.

    c. Estimate the mean and standard deviation of the sampling distribution.

    d. What would three-sigma control limits for the process be? What alpha risk would they provide?

    e. What alpha risk would control limits of 4.14 and 4.86 provide?

    f. Using limits of 4.14 and 4.86, are any sample means beyond the control limits? If so, which one(s)?

    g. Construct control charts for means and ranges using Table 10.3. Are any samples beyond the control limits? If so, which one(s)?

    h. Explain why the control limits are different for means in parts d and g.

    i. If the process has a known mean of 4.4 and a known standard deviation of .18, what would three-sigma control limits be for a mean chart? Are any sample means beyond the control limits? If so, which one(s)?

21. A process that produces computer chips has a mean of .04 defective chip and a standard deviation of .003 chip. The allowable variation is from .03 to .05 defective.

    a. Compute the capability index for the process.

    b. Is the process capable?

22. Given the following list of processes, the standard deviation for each, and specifications for a job that may be processed on that machine, determine which machines are capable of performing the given jobs.

Process	Standard Deviation (in.)	Job Specification (± in.)
001	.02	.05
002	.04	.07
003	.10	.18
004	.05	.15
005	.01	.04

23. Suppose your manager presents you with the following information about machines that could be used for a job, and wants your recommendation on which one to choose. The specification width is .48 mm. In this instance, you can narrow the set of choices, but you probably wouldn't make a recommendation without an additional piece of information. Explain the logic of the last statement.

Machine	Cost per Unit ($)	Standard Deviation (mm)
A	20	.059
B	12	.060
C	11	.063
D	10	.061

24. Each of the processes listed is noncentered with respect to the specifications for that process. Compute the appropriate capability index for each, and decide if the process is capable.

Process	Mean	Standard Deviation	Lower Spec	Upper Spec
H	15.0	0.32	14.1	16.0
K	33.0	1.00	30.0	36.5
T	18.5	0.40	16.5	20.1

25. An appliance manufacturer wants to contract with a repair shop to handle authorized repairs in Indianapolis. The company has set an acceptable range of repair time of 50 minutes to 90 minutes. Two firms have submitted bids for the work. In test trials, one firm had a mean repair time of 74 minutes with a standard deviation of 4.0 minutes and the other firm had a mean repair time of 72 minutes with a standard deviation of 5.1 minutes. Which firm would you choose? Why?

26. As part of an insurance company's training program, participants learn how to conduct an analysis of clients' insurability. The goal is to have participants achieve a time in the range of 30 to 45 minutes. Test results for three participants were: Armand, a mean of 38 minutes and a standard deviation of 3 minutes; Jerry, a mean of 37 minutes and a standard deviation of 2.5 minutes; and Melissa, a mean of 37.5 minutes and a standard deviation of 1.8 minutes.

   a. Which of the participants would you judge to be capable? Explain.

   b. Can the value of the C_{pk} exceed the value of C_p for a given participant? Explain.

27. The Good Chocolate Company makes a variety of chocolate candies, including a 12-ounce chocolate bar (340 grams) and a box of six 1-ounce chocolate bars (170 grams).

   a. Specifications for the 12-ounce bar are 330 grams to 350 grams. What is the largest standard deviation (in grams) that the machine that fills the bar molds can have and still be considered capable if the average fill is 340 grams?

   b. The machine that fills the bar molds for the 6-ounce bars has a standard deviation of .80 gram. The filling machine is set to deliver an average of 1.01 ounces per bar. Specifications for the six-bar box are 160 to 180 grams. Is the process capable? *Hint:* The *variance* for the box is equal to six times the bar *variance*.

   c. What is the *lowest* setting in ounces for the filling machine that will provide capability in terms of the six-bar box?

28. The following is a control chart for the average number of minor errors in 22 service reports. What can you conclude from these data? Explain how you reached your conclusion.

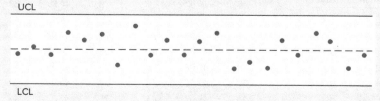

29. Use the three-step process described in the previous section on Using Control Charts and Runs Tests Together to decide if the following observations represent a process that is in control.

Observation	1	2	3	4	5	6	7	8	9	10	11	12
No. of errors	1	0	3	2	0	1	3	2	1	0	2	3

CASE   TOYS, INC.

Toys, Inc., is a 20-year-old company engaged in the manufacture and sale of toys and board games. The company has built a reputation on quality and innovation. Although the company is one of the leaders in its field, sales have leveled off in recent years. For the most recent six-month period, sales actually declined compared with the same period last year. The production manager, Ed Murphy, attributed the lack of sales growth to "the economy." He was prompted to undertake a number of belt-tightening moves that included cuts in production costs and layoffs in the design and product development departments. Although profits are still flat, he believes that within the next six months, the results of his decisions will be reflected in increased profits.

The vice president of sales, Joe Martin, has been concerned with customer complaints about the company's realistic line of working-model factories, farms, and service stations. The moving parts on certain models have become disengaged and fail to operate or operate erratically. His assistant, Keith McNally, has

proposed a trade-in program by which customers could replace malfunctioning models with new ones. McNally believes that this will demonstrate goodwill and appease dissatisfied customers. He also proposes rebuilding the trade-ins and selling them at discounted prices in the company's retail outlet store. He doesn't think that this will take away from sales of new models. Under McNally's program, no new staff would be needed. Regular workers would perform needed repairs during periods of seasonal slowdowns, thus keeping production level.

When Steve Bukowski, a production assistant, heard Keith's proposal, he said that a better option would be to increase inspection of finished models before they were shipped. "With 100 percent inspection, we can weed out any defective models and avoid the problem entirely."

Take the role of a consultant who has been called in for advice by the company president, Marybeth Corbella. What do you recommend?

CASE   TIGER TOOLS

Tiger Tools, a division of Drillmore Industries, was about to launch a new product. Production Manager Michelle York asked her assistant, Jim Peterson, to check the capability of the oven used in the process. Jim obtained 18 random samples of 20 pieces each. The results of those samples are shown in the following table. After he analyzed the data, he concluded that the process was not capable based on a specification width of 1.44 cm.

Michelle was quite disappointed when she heard this. She had hoped that with the introduction of the new product her operation could run close to full capacity and regain some of its lost luster. The company had a freeze on capital expenditures of more than $10,000, and a replacement oven would cost many times that amount. Jim Peterson worked with the oven crew to see if

perhaps different settings could produce the desired results, but they were unable to achieve any meaningful improvements.

Still not ready to concede, Michelle contacted one of her former professors and explained the problem. The professor suggested obtaining another set of samples, this time using a smaller sample size and taking more samples. Michelle then conferred with Jim and they agreed that he would take 27 samples of five observations each. The results are shown in the following table.

Sample	Mean	Range	Sample	Mean	Range
1	44.96	.42	15	45.00	.39
2	44.98	.39	16	44.95	.41
3	44.96	.41	17	44.94	.43
4	44.97	.37	18	44.94	.40
5	45.02	.39	19	44.87	.38
6	45.03	.40	20	44.95	.41
7	45.04	.39	21	44.93	.39
8	45.02	.42	22	44.96	.41
9	45.08	.38	23	44.99	.40
10	45.12	.40	24	45.00	.44
11	45.07	.41	25	45.03	.42
12	45.02	.38	26	45.04	.38
13	45.01	.41	27	45.03	.40
14	44.98	.40			

Sample	Mean	Range	Sample	Mean	Range
1	45.01	.85	10	44.97	.91
2	44.99	.89	11	45.11	.84
3	45.02	.86	12	44.96	.87
4	45.00	.91	13	45.00	.86
5	45.04	.87	14	44.92	.89
6	44.98	.90	15	45.06	.87
7	44.91	.86	16	44.94	.86
8	45.04	.89	17	45.00	.85
9	45.00	.85	18	45.03	.88

(continued)

(*concluded*)

Questions

Consider the following questions, and then write a brief report to Michelle summarizing your findings.

1. How did Jim conclude that the process was not capable based on his first set of samples? (*Hint:* Estimate the process standard deviation, σ, using $A_2\overline{R} \approx 3\frac{\sigma}{\sqrt{n}}$.)

2. Does the second set of samples show anything that the first set did not? Explain what and why.

3. Assuming the problem can be found and corrected, what impact do you think this would have on the capability of the process? Compute the potential process capability using the second data set.

4. If small samples can reveal something that large samples might not, why not just take small samples in every situation?

Besterfield, Dale H. *Quality Control.* Upper Saddle River, NJ: Prentice Hall, 2009.

Mitra, Amitava. *Fundamentals of Quality Control and Improvement,* 3rd ed. Hoboken, NJ: John Wiley & Sons, 2008.

Montgomery, Douglas C. *Introduction to Statistical Quality Control,* 6th ed. New York: John Wiley and Sons, 2009.

Quality Management Journal. ASQ. asq.org

Quality Progress. QP. www.qualityprogress.com

Summers, Donna. *Quality,* 5th ed. Upper Saddle River, NJ: Prentice Hall, 2009.

SELECTED BIBLIOGRAPHY AND FURTHER READINGS

11 Aggregate Planning and Master Scheduling

LEARNING OBJECTIVES

After completing this chapter, you should be able to:

LO11.1   Explain what aggregate planning is and how it is useful.

LO11.2   Identify the variables decision makers have to work with in aggregate planning.

LO11.3   Describe some of the strategies that can be used for meeting uneven demand.

LO11.4   Describe some of the graphical and quantitative techniques planners use.

LO11.5   Prepare aggregate plans and compute their costs.

LO11.6   Discuss aggregate planning in services.

LO11.7   Disaggregate an aggregate plan.

LO11.8   Describe the master scheduling process and explain its importance.

CHAPTER OUTLINE

11.1 Introduction *464*
Intermediate Planning in
Perspective *464*
The Concept of Aggregation *465*
Dealing with Variations *466*
An Overview of Aggregate
Planning *466*
Aggregate Planning and the
Supply Chain *467*
Demand and Supply Options *467*

**11.2 Basic Strategies for Meeting
Uneven Demand** *471*
Choosing a Strategy *473*

**11.3 Techniques for Aggregate
Planning** *474*
Trial-and-Error Techniques Using
Graphs and Spreadsheets *474*
Mathematical Techniques *478*

**11.4 Aggregate Planning in
Services** *481*

**11.5 Disaggregating the
Aggregate Plan** *483*

11.6 Master Scheduling *483*
The Master Scheduler *484*

**11.7 The Master Scheduling
Process** *484*
Time Fences *485*
Inputs *486*
Outputs *486*
Case: Eight Glasses a Day (EGAD) *498*

Courtesy of Nikon Inc., Melville, New York.

Aggregate planning is intermediate-range capacity planning that typically covers a time horizon of 2 to 12 months, although in some companies it may extend to as much as 18 months. It is particularly useful for organizations that experience seasonal or other fluctuations in demand or capacity. The goal of aggregate planning is to achieve a production plan that will effectively utilize the organization's resources to match expected demand. Planners must make decisions on output rates, employment levels and changes, inventory levels and changes, back orders, and subcontracting in or out. They do this for products that are grouped (i.e., aggregated) into categories rather than for individual products. For instance, a company that makes lawn mowers might have multiple models of push mowers, self-propelled mowers, and riding mowers. The company would aggregate along those three lines. For example,

LO11.1 Explain what aggregate planning is and how it is useful.

Aggregate planning
Intermediate-range capacity planning, usually covering 2 to 12 months.

Sales and operations planning
Intermediate-range decisions to balance supply and demand, integrating financial and operations planning.

Category	Models
Push	2
Self-propelled	6
Riding	3

Seasonal variations in demand are quite common in many industries and public services, such as air-conditioning, fuel, public utilities, police and fire protection, and travel. And these are just a few examples of industries and public services that have to deal with uneven demands. Generally speaking, organizations cannot predict exactly the quantity and timing of demands for specific products or services months in advance under these conditions. Even so, they typically must assess their capacity needs (e.g., labor, inventories) and costs months in advance in order to be able to handle demand.

Some organizations use the term "sales and operations planning" instead of aggregate planning for intermediate-range planning. Similarly, **sales and operations planning** is defined as making intermediate-range decisions to balance supply and demand, integrating financial and operations planning. Because the plan affects functions throughout the organization, it is typically prepared with inputs from sales (demand forecasts), finance (financial constraints), and operations (capacity constraints). Note that the sales and operations plan is important planning information that will have impacts throughout the supply chain, and it should be shared with supply chain partners, who might also have valuable inputs.

11.1 INTRODUCTION

Intermediate Planning in Perspective

Organizations make capacity decisions on three levels: long term, intermediate term, and short term. Long-term decisions relate to product and service selection (i.e., determining which products or services to offer), facility size and location, equipment decisions, and layout of facilities. These long-term decisions essentially establish the capacity constraints within which intermediate planning must function. Intermediate decisions, as noted previously, relate to general levels of employment, output, and inventories, which in turn establish boundaries within which short-range capacity decisions must be made. Thus, short-term decisions essentially consist of deciding the best way to achieve desired results within the constraints resulting from long-term and intermediate-term decisions. Short-term decisions involve scheduling jobs, workers and equipment, and the like. The three levels of capacity decisions are depicted in Table 11.1. Long-term capacity decisions were covered in Chapter 5, and scheduling and related matters are covered in Chapter 16. This chapter covers intermediate capacity decisions.

Many business organizations develop a *business plan* that encompasses both long-term and intermediate-term planning. The business plan establishes guidelines for the organization,

Even though Toyota cars have a variety of makes and models, they often share the same chassis and the same parts. How does this add to the company's efficiencies as a top automaker?

© Matt Cardy/Getty Images News

TABLE 11.1
Overview of planning levels (chapter numbers are shown)

Long-Range Plans	Intermediate Plans	Short-Range Plans
Long-term capacity }5	(This chapter)	Detailed plans:
Location }8	General levels of:	Production lot size }13
Layout }6	Employment	Order quantities }13
Product design }4	Output	Machine loading }16
Work system design }7	Finished-goods	Job assignments }16
	inventories	Job sequencing }16
	Subcontracting	Work schedules }16
	Back orders	

taking into account the organization's strategies and policies; forecasts of demand for the organization's products or services; and economic, competitive, and political conditions. A key objective in business planning is to coordinate the intermediate plans of various organization functions, such as marketing, operations, and finance. In manufacturing companies, coordination also includes engineering and materials management. Consequently, all of these functional areas must work together to formulate the aggregate plan. Aggregate planning decisions are strategic decisions that define the framework within which operating decisions will be made. They are the starting point for scheduling and production control systems. They provide input for financial plans; they involve forecasting input and demand management, and they may require changes in employment levels. And if the organization is involved in *time-based competition,* it will be important to incorporate some flexibility in the aggregate plan to be able to handle changing requirements promptly. As noted, the plans must fit into the framework established by the organization's long-term goals and strategies, and the limitations established by long-term facility and capital budget decisions. The aggregate plan will guide the more detailed planning that eventually leads to a *master schedule.* Figure 11.1 illustrates the planning sequence.

Aggregate planning also can serve as an important input to other strategic decisions; for example, management may decide to add capacity when aggregate planning alternatives for temporarily increasing capacity, such as working overtime and subcontracting, are too costly.

The Concept of Aggregation

Aggregate planning is essentially a "big-picture" approach to planning. Planners usually try to avoid focusing on individual products or services—unless the organization has only one major product or service. Instead, they focus on a group of similar products or services, or sometimes an entire product or service line. For example, planners in a company producing high-definition television sets would not concern themselves with 40-inch sets versus 46-inch or 55-inch sets. Instead, planners would lump all models together and deal with them as though they were a single product, hence the term *aggregate* planning. Thus, when fast-food companies such as McDonald's, Burger King, or Wendy's plan employment and output levels, they don't try to determine how demand will be broken down into the various menu options they offer; they focus on overall demand and the overall capacity they want to provide.

Now consider how aggregate planning might work in a large department store. Space allocation is often an aggregate decision. That is, a manager might decide to allocate 20 percent of

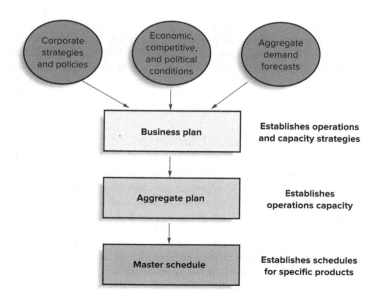

FIGURE 11.1
Planning sequence

the available space in the clothing department to women's sportswear, 30 percent to juniors, and so on, without regard for what brand names will be offered or how much of juniors will be jeans. The aggregate measure might be square feet of space or racks of clothing.

For purposes of aggregate planning, it is often convenient to think of capacity in terms of labor hours or machine hours per period, or output rates (barrels per period, units per period), without worrying about how much of a particular item will actually be involved. This approach frees planners to make general decisions about the use of resources without having to get into the complexities of individual product or service requirements. Product groupings make the problem of obtaining an acceptable unit of aggregation easier because product groupings may lend themselves to the same aggregate measures.

Why do organizations need to do aggregate planning? The answer is twofold. One part is related to *planning:* It takes time to implement plans. For instance, if plans call for hiring (and training) new workers, that will take time. The second part is strategic: *Aggregation* is important because it is not possible to predict with any degree of accuracy the timing and volume of demand for individual items. So if an organization were to "lock in" on individual items, it would lose the flexibility to respond to the market.

Generally speaking, aggregate planning is connected to the budgeting process. Most organizations plan their financial requirements annually on a department-by-department basis.

Finally, aggregate planning is important because it can help synchronize flow throughout the supply chain; it affects costs, equipment utilization, employment levels, and customer satisfaction.

A key issue in aggregate planning is how to handle variations.

Dealing with Variations

As in other areas of business management, variations in either supply or demand can occur. Minor variations are usually not a problem, but large variations generally have a major impact on the ability to match supply and demand, so they must be dealt with. Most organizations use rolling 3-, 6-, 9-, and 12-month forecasts—forecasts that are updated periodically—rather than relying on a once-a-year forecast. This allows planners to take into account any changes in either expected demand or expected supply and to develop revised plans.

Some businesses tend to exhibit a fair degree of stability, whereas in others, variations are more the norm. In those instances, a number of strategies are used to counter variations. One is to maintain a certain amount of excess capacity to handle increases in demand. This strategy makes sense when the opportunity cost of lost revenue greatly exceeds the cost of maintaining excess capacity. Another strategy is to maintain a degree of flexibility in dealing with changes. That might involve hiring temporary workers and/or working overtime when needed. Organizations that experience seasonal demands typically use this approach. Some of the design strategies mentioned in Chapter 4, such as delayed differentiation and modular design, may also be options. Still another strategy is to wait as long as possible before committing to a certain level of supply capability. This might involve scheduling products or services with known demands first, which allows some time to pass, shortening the time horizon, and perhaps enabling demands for the remaining products or services to become less uncertain.

An Overview of Aggregate Planning

Aggregate planning begins with a forecast of aggregate demand for the intermediate range. This is followed by a general plan to meet demand requirements by setting output, employment, and finished-goods inventory levels or service capacities. Managers might consider a number of plans, each of which must be examined in light of feasibility and cost. If a plan is reasonably good but has minor difficulties, it may be reworked. Conversely, a poor plan should be discarded and alternative plans considered until an acceptable one is uncovered. An aggregate production plan is essentially the output of aggregate planning.

Aggregate plans are updated periodically, often monthly, to take into account updated forecasts and other changes. This results in a *rolling planning horizon* (i.e., the aggregate plan always covers the next 12 to 18 months).

Demand and Supply. Aggregate planners are concerned with the *quantity* and the *timing* of expected demand. If total expected demand for the planning period is much different from available capacity over that same period, the major approach of planners will be to try to achieve a balance by altering capacity, demand, or both. On the other hand, even if capacity and demand are approximately equal for the planning horizon as a whole, planners may still be faced with the problem of dealing with uneven demand *within* the planning interval. In some periods, expected demand may exceed projected capacity, in others expected demand may be less than projected capacity, and in some periods the two may be equal. The task of aggregate planners is to achieve rough equality of demand and capacity over the entire planning horizon. Moreover, planners are usually concerned with minimizing the cost of the aggregate plan, although cost is not the only consideration.

Inputs to Aggregate Planning. Effective aggregate planning requires good *information*. First, the available resources over the planning period must be known. Then, a forecast of expected demand must be available. Finally, planners must take into account any policies regarding changes in employment levels (e.g., some organizations view layoffs as extremely undesirable, so they would use that only as a last resort).

Table 11.2 lists the major inputs to aggregate planning.

Companies in the travel industry and some other industries often experience duplicate orders from customers who make multiple reservations but only intend to keep at most one of them. This makes capacity planning all the more difficult.

Aggregate Planning and the Supply Chain

It is essential to take supply chain capabilities into account when doing aggregate planning, to assure that there are no quantity or timing issues that need to be resolved. While this is particularly true if new or changed goods or services are involved, it is also true even when no changes are planned. Supply chain partners should be consulted during the planning stage so that any issues or advice they may have can be taken into account, and they should be informed when plans have been finalized.

Demand and Supply Options

Aggregate planning strategies can pertain to demand, capacity, or both. Demand strategies are intended to alter demand so that it matches capacity. Capacity strategies involve altering capacity so that it matches demand. *Mixed* strategies involve both of these approaches.

Inputs	Outputs
Resources	Total cost of a plan
Workforce/production rates	Projected levels of
Facilities and equipment	Inventory
Demand forecast	Output
Policies on workforce changes	Employment
Subcontracting	Subcontracting
Overtime	Backordering
Inventory levels/changes	
Back orders	
Costs	
Inventory carrying cost	
Back orders	
Hiring/firing	
Overtime	
Inventory changes	
Subcontracting	

TABLE 11.2
Aggregate planning inputs and outputs

READING　DUPLICATE ORDERS CAN LEAD TO EXCESS CAPACITY

We've all heard about someone who booked seats on two airlines, or reserved two hotel rooms, usually because travel plans weren't firmed up, but the person didn't want to miss out on the trip. Later, the person canceled one set of reservations. This sort of duplicate ordering isn't just limited to the travel industry. The trouble is, companies base their capacity planning on demand estimates, and when there are numerous duplicate orders, it is easy to overestimate demand and end up with excess capacity. In some instances, this has led companies to expand at a time when demand was actually leveling off or even decreasing! The problem is further compounded if companies conclude that canceled orders reflect customers' reluctance to wait, and respond by *adding* capacity when, in fact, order cancellation may actually reflect duplicate ordering.

Some semiconductor companies downplay data on bookings because it is too difficult to distinguish between duplicate orders and actual demand.

Yet it is important to account for double orders. Otherwise, by counting duplicate orders as true demand, you overestimate the demand rate, and by counting the cancellations of duplicate orders as lost sales, you overestimate customers' sensitivity to delay, and then you wind up with excess capacity.

"The optimal level of capacity increases with customers' sensitivity to delay, so estimating customers' sensitivity to delay is a very important part of the puzzle."

Duplicate orders can make capacity planning very difficult. The key is to carefully estimate both the rate of duplicate ordering and the degree of order cancellation that can be attributed to duplicate ordering.

Source: Based on Mor Armony and Erica L. Plambeck, "The Impact of Duplicate Orders on Demand Estimation and Capacity Investment," GSB Research Paper #1740, Graduate School of Business, Stanford University, June 2002.

LO11.2 Identify the variables decision makers have to work with in aggregate planning.

Demand Options. Demand options include pricing, promotions, using back orders (delaying order filling), and creating new demand.

1. **Pricing.** Pricing differentials are commonly used to shift demand from peak periods to off-peak periods. Some hotels, for example, offer lower rates for weekend stays, and some airlines offer lower fares for night travel. Movie theaters may offer reduced rates for matinees, and some restaurants offer "early bird specials" in an attempt to shift some of the heavier dinner demand to an earlier time that traditionally has less traffic. Some restaurants also offer smaller portions at reduced rates, and most have smaller portions and prices for children. To the extent that pricing is effective, demand will be shifted so that it corresponds more closely to capacity, albeit for an *opportunity cost* that represents the lost profit stemming from capacity insufficient to meet demand during certain periods.

   An important factor to consider is the *degree* of price elasticity for the product or service: The more the elasticity, the more effective pricing will be in influencing demand patterns.

2. **Promotion.** Advertising and other forms of promotion, such as displays and direct marketing, can sometimes be very effective in shifting demand so that it conforms more closely to capacity. Obviously, timing of these efforts and knowledge of response rates and response patterns will be needed to achieve the desired results. Unlike pricing policy, there is much less control over the timing of demand, so there is the risk that promotion can worsen the condition it was intended to improve, by bringing in demand at the wrong time, further stressing capacity.

3. **Back orders.** An organization can shift demand fulfillment to other periods by allowing back orders. That is, orders are taken in one period and deliveries promised for a later period. The success of this approach depends on how willing customers are to wait for delivery. Moreover, the costs associated with back orders can be difficult to pin down since they would include lost sales, annoyed or disappointed customers, and perhaps additional paperwork.

4. **New demand.** Many organizations are faced with the problem of having to provide products or services for peak demand in situations where demand is very uneven. For instance, demand for bus transportation tends to be more intense during the morning and late afternoon rush hours but much lighter at other times. Creating new demand for buses at other times (e.g., trips by schools, clubs, and senior citizen groups) would make use of the excess capacity during those slack times. Similarly, many fast-food restaurants are open for breakfast to use their capacities more fully, and some landscaping firms in northern climates use their equipment during the winter months for snow removal. Manufacturing firms that experience seasonal demands for certain products (e.g., snowblowers) are sometimes able to develop a demand for a complementary product (e.g., lawn mowers, garden equipment) that makes use of the same production processes. They thereby achieve a more consistent use of labor, equipment, and facilities. Another option may be "insourcing" work from another organization.

Supply Options. Supply options include hiring/laying off workers, overtime/slack time, part-time or temporary workers, inventories, and subcontractors.

1. **Hire and lay off workers.** The extent to which operations are labor intensive determines the impact that changes in the workforce level will have on capacity. The resource requirements of each worker also can be a factor. For instance, if a supermarket usually has 10 of 14 checkout lines operating, an additional four checkout workers could be added. Hence, the ability to add workers is constrained at some point by other resources needed to support the workers. Conversely, there may be a lower limit on the number of workers needed to maintain a viable operation (e.g., a skeleton crew).

    Union contracts may restrict the amount of hiring and laying off a company can do. Moreover, because laying off can present serious problems for workers, some firms have policies that either prohibit or limit downward adjustments to a workforce. On the other hand, hiring presumes an available supply of workers. This may change from time to time and, at times of low supply, have an impact on the ability of an organization to pursue this approach.

    Another consideration is the skill level of workers. Highly skilled workers are generally more difficult to find than lower-skilled workers, and recruiting them involves greater costs. So the usefulness of this option may be limited by the need for highly skilled workers.

    The use of hiring and laying off entails certain costs. Hiring costs include recruitment, screening, and training to bring new workers "up to speed." And quality may suffer. Some savings may occur if workers who have recently been laid off are rehired. Layoff costs include severance pay, the cost of realigning the remaining workforce, potential bad feelings toward the firm on the part of workers who have been laid off, and some loss of morale for workers who are retained (i.e., in spite of company assurances, some workers will believe that in time they too will be laid off).

    An increasing number of organizations view workers as assets rather than as variable costs, and would not consider this approach. Instead, they might use slack time for other purposes.

2. **Overtime/slack time.** Use of overtime or slack time is a less severe method for changing capacity than hiring and laying off workers, and it can be used across the board or selectively as needed. It also can be implemented more quickly than hiring and laying off and allows the firm to maintain a steady base of employees. The use of overtime can be especially attractive in dealing with seasonal demand peaks by reducing the need to hire and train people who will have to be laid off during the off-season. Overtime also permits the company to maintain a skilled workforce and employees to increase earnings, and companies may save money because fringe and other benefits are generally fixed. Moreover, in situations with crews, it is often necessary to use a full crew rather than to hire one or two additional people. Thus, having the entire crew work overtime would be preferable to hiring extra people.

It should be noted that some union contracts allow workers to refuse overtime. In those cases, it may be difficult to muster a full crew to work overtime or to get an entire production line into operation after regular hours. Although workers often like the additional income overtime can generate, they may not appreciate having to work on short notice or the fluctuations in income that result. Still other considerations relate to the fact that overtime often results in lower productivity, poorer quality, more accidents, and increased payroll costs, whereas idle time results in less efficient use of machines and other fixed assets.

The use of slack when demand is less than capacity can be an important consideration. Some organizations use this time for training. It also can give workers time for problem solving and process improvement, while retraining skilled workers.

3. **Part-time workers.** In certain instances, the use of part-time workers is a viable option—much depends on the nature of the work, training and skills needed, and union agreements. Seasonal work requiring low-to-moderate job skills lends itself to part-time workers, who generally cost less than regular workers in hourly wages and fringe benefits. However, unions may regard such workers unfavorably because they typically do not pay union dues and may lessen the power of unions. Department stores, restaurants, and supermarkets make use of part-time workers. So do parks and recreation departments, resorts, travel agencies, hotels, and other service organizations with seasonal demands. In order to be successful, these organizations must be able to hire part-time employees when they are needed.

    Some companies use contract workers, also called *independent contractors,* to fill certain needs. Although they are not regular employees, often they work alongside regular workers. In addition to having different pay scales and no benefits, they can be added or subtracted from the workforce with greater ease than regular workers, giving companies great flexibility in adjusting the size of the workforce.

4. **Inventories.** The use of finished-goods inventories allows firms to produce goods in one period and sell or ship them in another period, although this involves holding or carrying those goods as inventory until they are needed. The cost includes not only storage costs and the cost of money tied up that could be invested elsewhere, but also the cost of insurance, obsolescence, deterioration, spoilage, breakage, and so on. In essence, inventories can be built up during periods when production capacity exceeds demand and drawn down in periods when demand exceeds production capacity.

Amazon is very aggressive about managing its inventory levels. This may mean that rarely ordered items are not kept in inventory and may require time to source from a supplier. It also means that Amazon tries to move inventory out to customers as quickly as possible.

© Scott Sady/AP Images

This method is more amenable to manufacturing than to service industries since manufactured goods can be stored whereas services generally cannot. However, an analogous approach used by services is to make efforts to streamline services (e.g., standard forms) or otherwise do a portion of the service during slack periods (e.g., organize the workplace). In spite of these possibilities, services tend not to make much use of inventories to alter capacity requirements.

5. **Subcontracting.** Subcontracting enables planners to acquire temporary capacity, although it affords less control over the output and may lead to higher costs and quality problems. The question of whether to make or buy (i.e., in manufacturing) or to perform a service or hire someone else to do the work generally depends on factors such as available capacity, relative expertise, quality considerations, cost, and the amount and stability of demand.

   Conversely, in periods of excess capacity, an organization may subcontract *in,* that is, conduct work for another organization. As an alternative to subcontracting, an organization might consider *outsourcing:* contracting with another organization to supply some portion of the goods or services on a regular basis.

11.2 BASIC STRATEGIES FOR MEETING UNEVEN DEMAND

As you see, managers have a wide range of decision options they can consider for achieving a balance of demand and capacity in aggregate planning. Since the options that are most suited to influencing demand fall more in the realm of marketing than in operations (with the exception of backlogging), we shall concentrate on the capacity options, which are in the realm of operations but include the use of back orders.

Aggregate planners might adopt a number of strategies. Some of the more prominent ones are the following:

1. Maintain a level workforce (level capacity)
2. Maintain a steady output rate (level capacity)
3. Match demand period by period (chase demand)
4. Use a combination of decision variables

While other strategies might be considered, these will suffice to give you a sense of how aggregate planning operates in a vast number of organizations. The first three strategies are "pure" strategies because each has a single focal point; the last strategy is "mixed" because it lacks the single focus. Under a **level capacity strategy**, variations in demand are met by using some combination of inventories, overtime, part-time workers, subcontracting, and back orders while maintaining a steady rate of output. Matching capacity to demand implies a **chase demand strategy**; the planned output for any period would be equal to expected demand for that period.

Many organizations regard a level workforce as very appealing. Since workforce changes through hiring and laying off can have a major impact on the lives and morale of employees and can be disruptive for managers, organizations often prefer to handle uneven demand in other ways. Moreover, changes in workforce size can be very costly, and there is always the risk that there will not be a sufficient pool of workers with the appropriate skills when needed. Aside from these considerations, such changes can involve a significant amount of paperwork. Unions tend to favor a level workforce because the freedom to hire and lay off workers diminishes union strengths.

To maintain a constant level of output and still satisfy varying demand, an organization must resort to some combination of subcontracting, backlogging, and use of inventories to absorb fluctuations. Subcontracting requires an investment in evaluating sources of supply as well as possible increased costs, less control over output, and perhaps quality considerations.

SCREENCAM TUTORIAL

LO11.3 Describe some of the strategies that can be used for meeting uneven demand.

Level capacity strategy
Maintaining a steady rate of regular-time output while meeting variations in demand by a combination of options.

Chase demand strategy
Matching capacity to demand; the planned output for a period is set at the expected demand for that period.

472   **Chapter Eleven**   Aggregate Planning and Master Scheduling

Backlogs can lead to lost sales, increased record keeping, and lower levels of customer service. Allowing inventories to absorb fluctuations can entail substantial costs by having money tied up in inventories, having to maintain relatively large storage facilities, and incurring other costs related to inventories. Furthermore, inventories are not usually an alternative for service-oriented organizations. However, there are certain advantages, such as minimum costs of recruitment and training, minimum overtime and idle-time costs, fewer morale problems, and stable use of equipment and facilities.

A chase demand strategy presupposes a great deal of ability and willingness on the part of managers to be flexible in adjusting to demand. A major advantage of this approach is that inventories can be kept relatively low, which can yield substantial savings for an organization. A major disadvantage is the lack of stability in operations—the atmosphere is one of dancing to demand's tune. Also, when forecast and reality differ, morale can suffer, since it quickly becomes obvious to workers and managers that efforts have been wasted. Figure 11.2

FIGURE 11.2   A varying demand pattern and a comparison of a chase demand strategy versus a level strategy

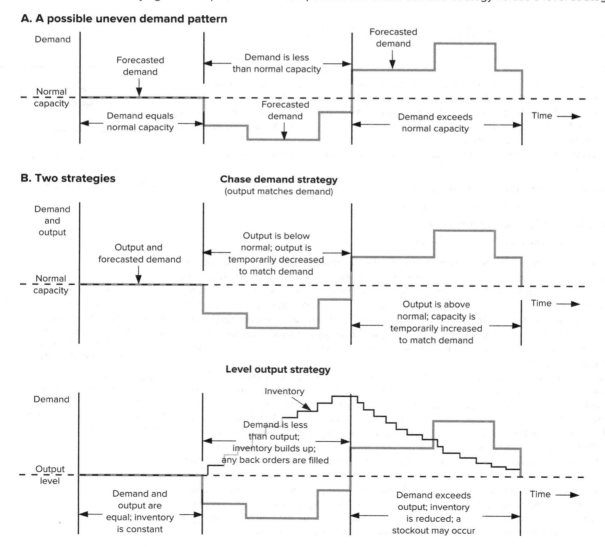

provides a comparison of the two strategies, using a varying demand pattern to highlight the differences in the two approaches. The same demand pattern is used for each approach. In the upper portion of the figure the pattern is shown. Notice that there are three situations: (1) demand and capacity are equal; (2) demand is less than capacity; and (3) demand exceeds capacity.

The middle portion of the figure illustrates what happens with a chase approach. When normal capacity would exceed demand, capacity is cut back to match demand. Then, when demand exceeds normal capacity, the chase approach is to temporarily increase capacity to match demand.

The bottom portion of the figure illustrates the level-output strategy. When demand is less than capacity, output continues at normal capacity, and the excess output is put into inventory in anticipation of the time when demand exceeds capacity. When demand exceeds capacity, inventory is used to offset the shortfall in output.

Organizations may opt for a strategy that involves some combination of the pure strategies. This allows managers greater flexibility in dealing with uneven demand and perhaps in experimenting with a wide variety of approaches. However, the absence of a clear focus may lead to an erratic approach and confusion on the part of employees.

Choosing a Strategy

Whatever strategy an organization is considering, three important factors are *company policy, flexibility,* and *costs*. Company policy may set constraints on the available options or the extent to which they can be used. For instance, company policy may discourage layoffs except under extreme conditions. Subcontracting may not be a viable alternative due to the desire to maintain secrecy about some aspect of the manufacturing of the product (e.g., a secret formula or blending process). Union agreements often impose restrictions. For example, a union contract may specify both minimum and maximum numbers of hours part-time workers can be used. The degree of flexibility needed to use the chase approach may not be present for companies designed for high, steady output, such as refineries and auto assembly plants.

As a rule, aggregate planners seek to match supply and demand within the constraints imposed on them by policies or agreements and at minimum cost. They usually evaluate alternatives in terms of their overall costs. Table 11.3 compares reactive strategies. In the next section, a number of techniques for aggregate planning are described and presented with some examples of cost evaluation of alternative plans.

TABLE 11.3
Comparison of reactive strategies

Chase approach

Capacities (workforce levels, output rates, etc.) are adjusted to match demand requirements over the planning horizon. A chase strategy works best when inventory carrying costs are high and costs of changing capacity are low.

Advantages:

  Investment in inventory is low.

  Labor utilization is kept high.

Disadvantage:

  The cost of adjusting output rates and/or workforce levels.

Level approach

Capacities (workforce levels, output rates, etc.) are kept constant over the planning horizon. A level strategy works best when inventory carrying costs and backlog costs are relatively low.

Advantage:

  Stable output rates and workforce levels.

Disadvantages:

  Greater inventory costs.

  Increased overtime and idle time.

  Resource utilizations that vary over time.

11.3 TECHNIQUES FOR AGGREGATE PLANNING

LO11.4 Describe some of the graphical and quantitative techniques planners use.

Numerous techniques are available to help with the task of aggregate planning. Generally, they fall into one of two categories: Informal trial-and-error techniques and mathematical techniques. In practice, informal techniques are more frequently used. However, a considerable amount of research has been devoted to mathematical techniques, and even though they are not as widely used, they often serve as a basis for comparing the effectiveness of alternative techniques for aggregate planning. Thus, it will be instructive to briefly examine them as well as the informal techniques.

A general procedure for aggregate planning consists of the following steps:

1. Determine demand for each period.
2. Determine capacities (regular time, overtime, subcontracting) for each period.
3. Identify company or departmental policies that are pertinent (e.g., maintain a safety stock of 5 percent of demand, maintain a reasonably stable workforce).
4. Determine unit costs for regular time, overtime, subcontracting, holding inventories, back orders, layoffs, and other relevant costs.
5. Develop alternative plans and compute the cost for each.
6. If satisfactory plans emerge, select the one that best satisfies objectives. Otherwise, return to step 5.

It can be helpful to use a worksheet or spreadsheet, such as the one illustrated in Table 11.4, to summarize demand, capacity, and cost for each plan. In addition, graphs can be used to guide the development of alternatives.

Trial-and-Error Techniques Using Graphs and Spreadsheets

Trial-and-error approaches consist of developing simple tables or graphs that enable planners to visually compare projected demand requirements with existing capacity. Alternatives are usually evaluated in terms of their overall costs. The chief disadvantage of such techniques is that they do not necessarily result in the optimal aggregate plan.

Two examples illustrate the development and comparison of aggregate plans. In the first example, regular output is held steady, with inventory absorbing demand variations. In the second example, a lower rate of regular output is used, supplemented by the use of overtime. In both examples, some backlogs are allowed to build up.

These examples and other examples and problems in this chapter are based on the following assumptions:

1. The regular output capacity is the same in all periods. No allowance is made for holidays, different numbers of workdays in different months, and so on. This assumption simplifies computations.
2. Cost (back order, inventory, subcontracting, etc.) is a linear function composed of unit cost and number of units. This often has a reasonable approximation to reality, although there may be only narrow ranges over which this is true. Cost is sometimes more of a step function.
3. Plans are feasible; that is, sufficient inventory capacity exists to accommodate a plan, subcontractors with appropriate quality and capacity are standing by, and changes in output can be made as needed.
4. All costs associated with a decision option can be represented by a lump sum or by unit costs that are independent of the quantity involved. Again, a step function may be more realistic; but for purposes of illustration and simplicity, this assumption is appropriate.
5. Cost figures can be reasonably estimated and are constant for the planning horizon.

Period	1	2	3	4	5		Total
Forecast							
Output							
Regular time							
Overtime							
Subcontract							
Output – Forecast							
Inventory							
Beginning							
Ending							
Average							
Backlog							
Costs							
Output							
Regular							
Overtime							
Subcontract							
Hire/Lay off							
Inventory							
Back orders							
Total							

TABLE 11.4
Worksheet/spreadsheet

6. Inventories are built up and drawn down at a uniform rate, and output occurs at a uniform rate throughout each period. However, backlogs are treated as if they exist for an entire period, even though in periods where they initially appear, they would tend to build up toward the end of the period. Hence, this assumption is a bit unrealistic for some periods, but it simplifies computations.

In the examples and problems in this chapter, we use the following relationships to determine the number of workers, the amount of inventory, and the cost of a particular plan.

The number of workers available in any period is calculated as follows:

$$
\begin{array}{c}
\text{Number of} \\
\text{workers in} \\
\text{a period}
\end{array}
=
\begin{array}{c}
\text{Number of} \\
\text{workers at end of} \\
\text{the previous period}
\end{array}
+
\begin{array}{c}
\text{Number of new} \\
\text{workers at start of} \\
\text{the period}
\end{array}
-
\begin{array}{c}
\text{Number of laid-off} \\
\text{workers at start of} \\
\text{the period}
\end{array}
$$

Note: An organization would not hire and lay off simultaneously, so at least one of the last two terms will equal zero.

The amount of inventory at the end of a given period is calculated as follows:

$$
\begin{array}{c}
\text{Inventory} \\
\text{at the end of} \\
\text{a period}
\end{array}
=
\begin{array}{c}
\text{Inventory} \\
\text{at end of the} \\
\text{previous period}
\end{array}
+
\begin{array}{c}
\text{Production} \\
\text{in the} \\
\text{current period}
\end{array}
-
\begin{array}{c}
\text{Amount used to} \\
\text{satisfy demand in the} \\
\text{current period}
\end{array}
$$

The average inventory for a period is equal to

$$
\frac{\text{Beginning inventory} + \text{Ending inventory}}{2}
$$

The cost of a particular plan for a given period can be determined by summing the appropriate costs:

$$
\begin{array}{c}
\text{Cost for} \\
\text{a period}
\end{array}
=
\begin{array}{c}
\text{Output cost} \\
\text{(Reg + OT + Subcontract)}
\end{array}
=
\begin{array}{c}
\text{Hire/lay-off} \\
\text{cost}
\end{array}
+
\begin{array}{c}
\text{Inventory} \\
\text{cost}
\end{array}
+
\begin{array}{c}
\text{Backorder} \\
\text{cost}
\end{array}
$$

LO11.5 Prepare aggre-gate plans and compute their costs.

The appropriate costs are calculated as follows:

Type of Cost	How to Calculate
Output	
Regular	Regular cost per unit × Quantity of regular output
Overtime	Overtime cost per unit × Overtime quantity
Subcontract	Subcontract cost per unit × Subcontract quantity
Hire/layoff	
Hire	Cost per hire × Number hired
Layoff	Cost per layoff × Number laid off
Inventory	Carrying cost per unit × Average inventory
Back order	Backorder cost per unit × Number of backorder units

The following examples are only two of many possible options that could be tried. Perhaps some of the others would result in a lower cost. With trial and error, you can never be completely sure you have identified the lowest-cost alternative unless every possible alternative is evaluated. Of course, the purpose of these examples is to illustrate the process of developing and evaluating an aggregate plan rather than to find the lowest-cost plan. Problems at the end of the chapter cover still other alternatives.

In practice, successful achievement of a good plan depends on the resourcefulness and persistence of the planner. Computer software such as the Excel templates that accompany this book can eliminate the computational burden of trial-and-error techniques.

EXAMPLE 1

mhhe.com/stevenson13e

Preparing an Aggregate Plan

Planners for a company that makes several models of skateboards are about to prepare the aggregate plan that will cover six periods. They have assembled the following information.

Period	1	2	3	4	5	6	Total
Forecast	200	200	300	400	500	200	1,800

Costs
- Output
  - Regular time = $2 per skateboard
  - Overtime = $3 per skateboard
  - Subcontract = $6 per skateboard
- Inventory = $1 per skateboard per period on average inventory
- Back orders = $5 per skateboard per period

They now want to evaluate a plan that calls for a steady rate of regular-time output, mainly using inventory to absorb the uneven demand but allowing some backlog. Overtime and subcontracting are not used because they want steady output. They intend to start with zero inventory on hand in the first period. Prepare an aggregate plan and determine its cost using the preceding information. Assume a level output rate of 300 units (skateboards) per period with regular time (i.e., 1,800/6 = 300). Note that the planned ending inventory is zero. There are 15 workers, and each can produce 20 skateboards per period.

SOLUTION

Period	1	2	3	4	5	6	Total
Forecast	200	200	300	400	500	200	1,800
Output							
Regular	300	300	300	300	300	300	1,800
Overtime	—	—	—	—	—	—	
Subcontract	—	—	—	—	—	—	
Output 2 Forecast	100	100	0	(100)	(200)	100	0
Inventory							
Beginning	0	100	200	200	100	0	
Ending	100	200	200	100	0	0	
Average	50	150	200	150	50	0	600
Backlog	0	0	0	0	100	0	100

Period	1	2	3	4	5	6	Total
Costs							
Output							
Regular	$600	600	600	600	600	600	$3,600
Overtime	—	—	—	—	—	—	
Subcontract	—	—	—	—	—	—	
Hire/Lay off	—	—	—	—	—	—	
Inventory	$ 50	150	200	150	50	0	$ 600
Back orders	$ 0	0	0	0	500	0	$ 500
Total	$650	750	800	750	1,150	600	$4,700

Note that the total regular-time output of 1,800 units equals the total expected demand. Ending inventory equals beginning inventory plus or minus the quantity Output – Forecast. If Output – Forecast is negative, inventory is decreased in that period by that amount. If insufficient inventory exists, a backlog equal to the shortage amount appears, as in period 5. This is taken care of using the excess output in period 6.

The costs were computed as follows: Regular cost in each period equals 300 units × $2 per unit or $600. Inventory cost equals average inventory × $1 per unit. Backorder cost is $5 per unit. The total cost for this plan is $4,700.

Note that the first two quantities in each column are givens. The remaining quantities in the upper portion of the table were determined working down each column, beginning with the first column. The costs were then computed based on the quantities in the upper part of the table.

Very often, graphs can be used to guide the development of alternatives. Some planners prefer cumulative graphs while others prefer to see a period-by-period breakdown of a plan. For instance, Figure 11.3 shows a cumulative graph for a plan with steady output (the slope of the dashed line represents the production rate) and inventory absorption of demand variations. Figure 11.2 is an example of a period-by-period graph. The obvious advantage of a graph is that it provides a visual portrayal of a plan. The preference of the planner determines which of these two types of graphs is chosen.

Developing and Comparing Aggregate Plans

EXAMPLE 2

After reviewing the plan developed in the preceding example, planners have decided to develop an alternative plan. They have learned that one person is about to retire from the company. Rather than replace that person, they would like to stay with the smaller workforce and use overtime to make up for the lost output. The reduced regular-time output is 280 units per period. The maximum amount of overtime output per period is 40 units. Develop a plan and compare it to the previous one.

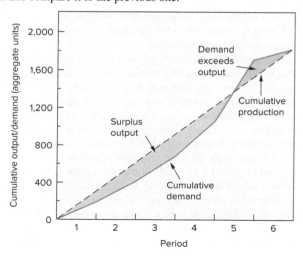

FIGURE 11.3
A cumulative graph

SOLUTION

Period	1	2	3	4	5	6	Total
Forecast	200	200	300	400	500	200	1,800
Output							
Regular	280	280	280	280	280	280	1,680
Overtime	0	0	40	40	40	0	120
Subcontract	—	—	—	—	—	—	
Output – Forecast	80	80	20	(80)	(180)	80	0
Inventory							
Beginning	0	80	160	180	100	0	
Ending	80	160	180	100	0	0	
Average	40	120	170	140	50	0	520
Backlog	0	0	0	0	80	0	80
Costs							
Output							
Regular	$560	560	560	560	560	560	$3,360
Overtime	0	0	120	120	120	0	$ 360
Subcontract	—	—	—	—	—	—	
Hire/Lay off	—	—	—	—	—	—	
Inventory	40	120	170	140	50	0	$ 520
Back orders	$ 0	0	0	0	400	0	$ 400
Total	$600	680	850	820	1,130	560	$4,640

The amount of overtime that must be scheduled has to make up for lost output of 20 units per period for six periods, which is 120. This is scheduled toward the center of the planning horizon because that is where the bulk of demand occurs. Although other amounts and time periods could be used as long as the total equals 120, scheduling it earlier would increase inventory carrying costs; scheduling it later would increase the backlog cost.

Overall, the total cost for this plan is $4,640, which is $60 less than the previous plan. Regular-time production cost and inventory cost are down, but there is overtime cost. However, this plan achieves savings in backorder cost, making it somewhat less costly overall than the plan in Example 1.

SCREENCAM TUTORIAL

Mathematical Techniques

A number of mathematical techniques have been developed to handle aggregate planning. They range from mathematical programming models to heuristic and computer search models. This section briefly describes some of the better-known techniques.

Linear Programming. Linear programming (LP) models are methods for obtaining optimal solutions to problems involving the allocation of scarce resources in terms of cost minimization or profit maximization. With aggregate planning, the goal is usually to minimize the sum of costs related to regular labor time, overtime, subcontracting, carrying inventory, and costs associated with changing the size of the workforce. Constraints involve the capacities of the workforce, inventories, and subcontracting.

The problem can be formulated as a transportation-type programming model as a way to obtain aggregate plans that would match capacities with demand requirements and minimize costs. In order to use this approach, planners must identify capacity (supply) of regular time, overtime, subcontracting, and inventory on a period-by-period basis, as well as related costs of each variable.

Table 11.5 shows the notation and setup of a transportation table. Note the systematic way that costs change as you move across a row from left to right. Regular cost, overtime cost, and subcontracting cost are at their lowest when the output is consumed (i.e., delivered, etc.) in the same period it is produced (at the intersection of period 1 row and column for regular cost, at the intersection of period 2 row and column for regular cost, and so on). If goods are made available in one period but carried over to later periods (i.e., moving across a row), holding costs are incurred at the rate of h per period. Thus, holding goods for two periods results in a unit cost of $2h$, whether or not the goods came from regular production, overtime, or subcontracting. Conversely, with back orders, the unit cost increases as you move across a row from right to left, beginning at the intersection of a row and column for the same period

TABLE 11.5   Transportation notation for aggregate planning

		Period 1	Period 2	Period 3	. . .	Ending inventory period n	Unused capacity	Capacity
Period	Beginning inventory	0	h	2h	. . .	(n−1)h	0	I_0
1	Regular time	r	r + h	r + 2h	. . .	r + (n−1)h	0	R_1
	Overtime	t	t + h	t + 2h	. . .	t + (n−1)h	0	O_1
	Subcontract	s	s + h	s + 2h	. . .	s + (n−1)h	0	S_1
2	Regular time	r + b	r	r + h	. . .	r + (n−2)h	0	R_2
	Overtime	t + b	t	t + h	. . .	t + (n−2)h	0	O_2
	Subcontract	s + b	s	s + h	. . .	s + (n−2)h	0	S_2
3	Regular time	r + 2b	r + b	r	. . .	r + (n−3)h	0	R_3
	Overtime	t + 2b	t + b	t	. . .	t + (n−3)h	0	O_3
	Subcontract	s + 2b	s + b	s	. . .	s + (n−3)h	0	S_3
	Demand				. . .			Total

r = Regular production cost per unit
f = Overtime cost per unit
s = Subcontracting cost per unit
h = Holding cost per unit period
b = Backorder cost per unit per period
n = Number of periods in planning horizon

(e.g., period 3). For instance, if some goods are produced in period 3 to satisfy back orders from period 2, a unit backorder cost of b is incurred. And if goods in period 3 are used to satisfy back orders two periods earlier (e.g., from period 1), a unit cost of $2b$ is incurred. Unused capacity is generally given a unit cost of 0, although it is certainly possible to insert an actual cost if that is relevant. Finally, beginning inventory is given a unit cost of 0 if it is used to satisfy demand in period 1. However, if it is held over for use in later periods, a holding cost of h per unit is added for each period. If the inventory is to be held for the entire planning horizon, a total unit cost of h times the number of periods, n, will be incurred.

Example 3 illustrates the setup and final solution of a transportation model of an aggregate planning problem.

Setting Up and Solving a Transportation Table

Given the following information, set up the problem in a transportation table (see Table 11.6) and solve for the minimum-cost plan.

	PERIOD		
	1	2	3
Demand	550	700	750
Capacity			
Regular	500	500	500
Overtime	50	50	50
Subcontract	120	120	100
Beginning inventory	100		
Costs			
Regular time	$60 per unit		
Overtime	$80 per unit		
Subcontract	$90 per unit		
Inventory carrying cost	$1 per unit per month		
Backorder cost	$3 per unit per month		

EXAMPLE 3

SOLUTION

The transportation table and solution are shown in Table 11.6. Some of the entries require additional explanation:

a. In this example, inventory carrying costs are $1 per unit per period (costs are shown in the upper right-hand corner of each cell in the table). Hence, units produced in one period and carried over to a later period will incur a holding cost that is a linear function of the length of time held.

b. Linear programming models of this type require that supply (capacity) and demand be equal. A dummy column has been added (nonexistent capacity) to satisfy that requirement. Since it does not "cost" anything extra to not use capacity that doesnt actually exist, cell costs of $0 have been assigned.

c. No backlogs were needed in this example.

d. The quantities (e.g., 100 and 450 in column 1) are the amounts of output or inventory that will be used to meet demand requirements. Thus, the demand of 550 units in period 1 will be met using 100 units from inventory and 450 obtained from regular-time output.

Where backlogs are not permitted, the cell costs for the backlog positions can be made prohibitively high so that no backlogs will appear in the solution.

The main limitations of LP models are the assumptions of linear relationships among variables, the inability to continuously adjust output rates, and the need to specify a single objective (e.g., minimize costs) instead of using multiple objectives (e.g., minimize cost while stabilizing the workforce).

TABLE 11.6
Transportation solution

Supply from		Demand for				Total capacity available (supply)
		Period 1	Period 2	Period 3	Unused capacity (dummy)	
Period	Beginning inventory	0 / 100	1	2	0	100
1	Regular time	60 / 450	61 / 50	62	0	500
	Overtime	80	81 / 50	82	0	50
	Subcontract	90	91 / 30	92	0 / 90	120
2	Regular time	63	60 / 500	61	0	500
	Overtime	83	80 / 50	81	0	50
	Subcontract	93	90 / 20	91 / 100	0	120
3	Regular time	66	63	60 / 500	0	500
	Overtime	86	83	80 / 50	0	50
	Subcontract	96	93	90 / 100	0	100
Demand		550	700	750	90	2,090

Technique	Solution Approach	Characteristics
Spreadsheet	Heuristic (trial and error)	Intuitively appealing, easy to understand; solution not necessarily optimal
Linear programming	Optimizing	Computerized; linear assumptions not always valid
Simulation	Heuristic (trial and error)	Computerized models can be examined under a variety of conditions

TABLE 11.7
Summary of planning techniques

Simulation Models. A number of **simulation models** have been developed for aggregate planning. (An introduction to simulation is available on the textbook website.) The essence of simulation is the development of computerized models that can be tested under a variety of conditions in an attempt to identify reasonably acceptable (although not always optimal) solutions to problems.

Simulation models
Computerized models that can be tested under different scenarios to identify acceptable solutions to problems.

Table 11.7 summarizes planning techniques.

Aggregate planning techniques other than trial and error do not appear to be widely used. Instead, in the majority of organizations, aggregate planning seems to be accomplished more on the basis of experience along with trial-and-error methods. It is difficult to say exactly why some of the mathematical techniques mentioned are not used to any great extent. Perhaps the level of mathematical sophistication discourages greater use, or the assumptions required in certain models appear unrealistic, or the models may be too narrow in scope. Whatever the reasons, none of the techniques to date have captured the attention of aggregate planners on a broad scale. Simulation is one technique that seems to be gaining favor. Research on improved approaches to aggregate planning is continuing.

11.4 AGGREGATE PLANNING IN SERVICES

LO11.6 Discuss aggregate planning in services.

Aggregate planning for services takes into account projected customer demands, equipment capacities, and labor capabilities. The resulting plan is a time-phased projection of service staff requirements.

The following are examples of service organizations that use aggregate planning.

Hospitals: Hospitals use aggregate planning to allocate funds, staff, and supplies to meet the demands of patients for their medical services. For example, plans for bed capacity, medications, surgical supplies, and personnel needs are based on patient load forecasts.

Airlines: Aggregate planning in the airline industry is fairly complex due to the need to take into account a wide range of factors (planes, flight personnel, ground personnel) and multiple routes and landing/departure sites. Also, capacity decisions must take into account the percentage of seats to be allocated to various fare classes in order to maximize profit or yield.

Restaurants: Aggregate planning in the case of a high-volume product output business such as a restaurant is directed toward smoothing the service rate, determining the size of the workforce, and managing demand to match a fixed kitchen and eating capacity. The general approach usually involves adjusting the number of staff according to the time of day and the day of the week.

Other services: Financial, hospitality, transportation, and recreation services provide a high-volume, intangible output. Aggregate planning for these and similar services involves managing demand and planning for human resource requirements. The main goals are to accommodate peak demand and to find ways to effectively use labor resources during periods of low demand.

Lunchtime line of people at Chacarero, a popular fast-food Chilean restaurant at Downtown Crossing, Boston, Massachussetts. Predicting steady demand from nearby office workers makes it much easier to provide staffing and prompt food service.

© Chuck Pefley/Alamy

Aggregate planning for manufacturing and aggregate planning for services share similarities in some respects, but there are some important differences—related in general to the differences between manufacturing and services:

1. **Demand for service can be difficult to predict.** The volume of demand for services is often quite variable. In some situations, customers may *need* prompt service (e.g., police, fire, medical emergency), while in others, they simply *want* prompt service and may be willing to go elsewhere if their wants are not met. These factors place a greater burden on service providers to anticipate demand. Consequently, service providers must pay careful attention to planned capacity levels.

2. **Capacity availability can be difficult to predict.** Processing requirements for services can sometimes be quite variable, similar to the variability of work in a job shop setting. Moreover, the variety of tasks required of servers can be great, again similar to the variety of tasks in a job shop. However, in services, the types of variety are more pervasive than they are in manufacturing. This makes it more difficult to establish simple measures of capacity. For example, what would be the capacity of a person who paints interiors of houses? The number of rooms per day or the number of square feet per hour are possible measures, but rooms come in many different sizes, and because the level of detail (and, thus, the painting implements that can be used) vary tremendously, a suitable measure for planning purposes can be quite difficult to arrive at. Similarly, bank tellers are called upon to handle a wide variety of transactions and requests for information, again making it difficult to establish a suitable measure of their capacity.

3. **Labor flexibility can be an advantage in services.** Labor often comprises a significant portion of service compared to manufacturing. That, coupled with the fact that service providers are often able to handle a fairly wide variety of service requirements, means that to some extent, planning is easier than it is in manufacturing. Of course, manufacturers recognize this advantage, and many are cross-training their employees to achieve the same flexibility. Moreover, in both manufacturing and service systems, the use of part-time workers can be an important option. Note that in self-service systems, the (customer) labor automatically adjusts to changes in demand!

4. **Services occur when they are rendered.** Unlike manufacturing output, most services cant be inventoried. Services such as financial planning, tax counseling, and oil changes cant be stockpiled. This removes the option of building up inventories during a slow period in anticipation of future demand. Moreover, service capacity that goes unused is essentially wasted. Consequently, it becomes even more important to be able to match capacity and demand.

Because service capacity is perishable (e.g., an empty seat on an airplane flight can't be saved for use on another flight), aggregate planners need to take that into account when deciding how to match supply and demand. **Yield management** is an approach that seeks to maximize revenue by using a strategy of variable pricing; prices are set relative to capacity availability. Thus, during periods of low demand, price discounts are offered to attract a wider population. Conversely, during peak periods, higher prices are posted to take advantage of limited supply relative to demand. Users of yield management include airlines, restaurants, theaters, hotels, resorts, cruise lines, and parking lots.

Yield management The application of pricing strategies to allocate capacity among various categories of demand.

11.5 DISAGGREGATING THE AGGREGATE PLAN

LO11.7 Disaggregate an aggregate plan.

For the production plan to be translated into meaningful terms for production, it is necessary to *disaggregate* the aggregate plan. This means breaking down the aggregate plan into specific product requirements in order to determine labor requirements (skills, size of workforce), materials, and inventory requirements.

Working with aggregate units facilitates intermediate planning. However, to put the production plan into operation, one must convert, or disaggregate, those aggregate units into units of actual products or services that are to be produced or offered. For example, a lawn mower manufacturer may have an aggregate plan that calls for 200 riding mowers in January, 300 in February, and 400 in March. That company may produce three different models of riding mowers. Although all the mowers probably contain some of the same parts and involve some similar or identical operations for fabrication and assembly, there would be some differences in the materials, parts, and operations that each type requires. Hence, the 200, 300, and 400 aggregate lawn mowers that are to be produced during those three months must be translated into specific numbers of mowers of each model prior to actually purchasing the appropriate materials and parts, scheduling operations, and planning inventory requirements.

The result of disaggregating the aggregate plan is a **master production schedule (MPS)**, or simply master schedule, showing the quantity and timing of *specific* end items for a scheduled horizon, which often covers about six to eight weeks ahead. A master schedule shows the planned output for individual products rather than an entire product group, along with the timing of production. The master schedule contains important information for marketing as well as for production. It reveals when orders are scheduled for production and when completed orders are to be shipped.

Figure 11.4 shows an overview of the context of disaggregation.

Figure 11.5 illustrates disaggregating the aggregate plan. The illustration makes a simple assumption in order to clearly show the concept of disaggregation: The totals of the aggregate and the disaggregated units are equal. In reality, that is not always true. As a consequence, disaggregating the aggregate plan may require considerable effort.

Figure 11.5 shows the aggregate plan broken down by units. However, it also can be useful to show the breakdown in *percentages* for different products or product families.

Master production schedule (MPS) This schedule indicates the quantity and timing of planned completed production.

FIGURE 11.4

Moving from the aggregate plan to a master production schedule

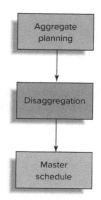

11.6 MASTER SCHEDULING

The master schedule is the heart of production planning and control. It determines the quantities needed to meet demand from all sources, and that governs key decisions and activities throughout the organization.

FIGURE 11.5
Disaggregating the
aggregate plan

Aggregate plan	*Month Planned output**	Jan.	Feb.	Mar.
		200	300	400

*Aggregate units

Master schedule	*Month Planned output**	Jan.	Feb.	Mar.
	RMa	100	100	100
	RMb	75	150	200
	RMc	25	50	100
	Total	200	300	400

*Actual units

The master schedule interfaces with marketing, capacity planning, production planning, and distribution planning: It enables marketing to make valid delivery commitments to warehouses and final customers; it enables production to evaluate capacity requirements; it provides the necessary information for production and marketing to negotiate when customer requests cannot be met by normal capacity; and it provides senior management with the opportunity to determine whether the business plan and its strategic objectives will be achieved. The master schedule also drives the material requirements planning (MRP) system that will be discussed in the next chapter.

The capacities used for master scheduling are based on decisions made during aggregate planning. Note that there is a time lapse between the time the aggregate plan is made and the development of a master schedule. Consequently, the outputs shown in a master schedule will not necessarily be identical to those of the aggregate plan for the simple reason that more up-to-date demand information might be available, which the master schedule would take into account.

The central person in the master scheduling process is the master scheduler.

The Master Scheduler

Most manufacturing organizations have (or should have) a master scheduler. The duties of the master scheduler generally include:

1. Evaluating the impact of new orders
2. Providing delivery dates for orders
3. Dealing with problems:
    a. Evaluating the impact of production delays or late deliveries of purchased goods
    b. Revising the master schedule when necessary because of insufficient supplies or capacity
    c. Bringing instances of insufficient capacity to the attention of production and marketing personnel so that they can participate in resolving conflicts

11.7 THE MASTER SCHEDULING PROCESS

LO11.8 Describe the
master scheduling process
and explain its importance.

A master schedule indicates the quantity and timing (i.e., delivery times) for a product, or a group of products, but it does not show planned *production*. For instance, a master schedule may call for delivery of 50 cases of cranberry-apple juice to be delivered on May 1. But this may not require any production; there may be 200 cases in inventory. Or it may require *some* production: If there were 40 cases in inventory, an additional 10 cases would be needed to achieve the specified delivery amount. Or it may involve production of 50 or more cases: In some instances, it is more economical to produce large amounts rather than small amounts, with the excess temporarily placed in inventory until needed. Thus, the *production lot size* might be 70 cases, so if additional cases were needed (e.g., 50 cases), a run of 70 cases would be made.

The master production schedule is one of the primary outputs of the master scheduling process, as illustrated in Figure 11.6.

Inputs   Outputs

Beginning inventory ──────┐   ┌────→ Projected inventory of finished goods
                          │   Master   │
Forecast ─────────────────┼─→ scheduling ──────────┼────→ Master production schedule
                          │   │
Customer orders ──────────┘   └────→ Uncommitted inventory

FIGURE 11.6
The master scheduling process

Once a *tentative* master schedule has been developed, it must be validated. This is an extremely important step. Validation is referred to as **rough-cut capacity planning (RCCP).** It involves testing the feasibility of a proposed master schedule relative to available capacities, to assure that no obvious capacity constraints exist. This means checking capacities of production and warehouse facilities, labor, and vendors to ensure that no gross deficiencies exist that will render the master schedule unworkable. The master production schedule then serves as the basis for *short-range* planning. It should be noted that whereas the aggregate plan covers an interval of, say, 12 months, the master schedule covers only a portion of this. In other words, the aggregate plan is disaggregated in stages, or phases, that may cover a few weeks to two or three months. Moreover, the master schedule may be updated monthly, even though it covers two or three months. For instance, the lawn mower master schedule would probably be updated at the end of January to include any revisions in planned output for February and March as well as new information on planned output for April.

Rough-cut capacity planning (RCCP) Approximate balancing of capacity and demand to test the feasibility of a master schedule.

Time Fences

Changes to a master schedule can be disruptive, particularly changes to the early, or near, portions of the schedule. Typically, the further out in the future a change is, the less the tendency to cause problems.

High-performance organizations have an effective master scheduling process. A key component of effective scheduling is the use of *time fences* to facilitate order promising and the entry of orders into the system. **Time fences** divide a scheduling time horizon into three sections or phases, sometimes referred to as *frozen, slushy,* and *liquid,* in reference to the firmness of the schedule (see Figure 11.7).

Frozen is the near-term phase that is so soon that delivery of a new order would be impossible, or only possible using very costly or extraordinary options such as delaying another order. Authority for new-order entry in this phase usually lies with the VP of manufacturing. The length of the frozen phase is often a function of the total time needed to produce a product, from procuring materials to shipping the order. There is a high degree of confidence in order-promise dates.

Slushy is the next phase, and its time fence is usually a few periods beyond the frozen phase. Order entry in this phase necessitates trade-offs, but is less costly or disruptive than in the frozen phase. Authority for order entry usually lies with the master scheduler. There is relative confidence in order-promise dates, and capacity planning becomes very specific.

Liquid is the farthest out on the time horizon. New orders or cancellations can be entered with ease. Order promise dates are tentative, and will be firmed up with the passage of time when orders are in the firm phase of the schedule horizon.

A key element in the success of the master scheduling process is strict adherence to time fence policies and rules. It is essential that they be adhered to and communicated throughout the organization.

Time fences Points in time that separate phases of a master schedule planning horizon.

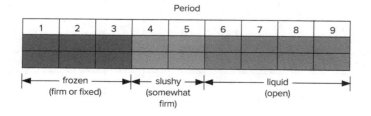

FIGURE 11.7
Time fences in an MPS

Inputs

The master schedule has three inputs: the beginning inventory, which is the actual quantity on hand from the preceding period; forecasts for each period of the schedule; and customer orders, which are quantities already *committed* to customers. Other factors that might need to be taken into consideration include any hiring or firing restrictions imposed by HR, skill levels, limits on inventory such as available space, whether items are perishable, and whether there are some market lifetime (e.g., seasonal or obsolescence) considerations.

Outputs

Available-to-promise (ATP) inventory Uncommitted inventory.

The master scheduling process uses this information on a period-by-period basis to determine the projected inventory, production requirements, and the resulting uncommitted inventory, which is referred to as **available-to-promise (ATP) inventory**. Knowledge of the uncommitted inventory can enable marketing to make realistic promises to customers about deliveries of new orders.

The master scheduling process begins with a preliminary calculation of projected on-hand inventory. This reveals when additional inventory (i.e., production) will be needed. Consider this example. A company that makes industrial pumps wants to prepare a master production schedule for June and July. Marketing has forecasted demand of 120 pumps for June and 160 pumps for July. These have been evenly distributed over the four weeks in each month: 30 per week in June and 40 per week in July, as illustrated in Figure 11.8A.

Now, suppose that there are currently 64 pumps in inventory (i.e., beginning inventory is 64 pumps), and that there are customer orders that have been committed (booked) and must be filled (see Figure 11.8B).

Figure 11.8B contains the three primary inputs to the master scheduling process: the beginning inventory, the forecast, and the customer orders that have been booked or committed. This information is necessary to determine three quantities: the projected on-hand inventory, the master production schedule, and the uncommitted (ATP) inventory. The first step is to calculate the projected on-hand inventory, one week at a time, until it falls below a specified limit. In this example, the specified limit will be zero. Hence, we will continue until the projected on-hand ending inventory becomes negative.

The projected on-hand inventory is calculated as follows:

$$\text{Projected on-hand inventory} = \text{Inventory from previous week} - \text{Current week's requirements} \qquad (11\text{--}1)$$

where the current week's requirements are the *larger* of forecast and customer orders (committed).

FIGURE 11.8A
Weekly forecast requirements for industrial pumps

	June				July			
	1	2	3	4	5	6	7	8
Forecast	30	30	30	30	40	40	40	40

FIGURE 11.8B
Eight-week schedule showing forecasts, customer orders, and beginning inventory

Beginning inventory 64	June				July			
	1	2	3	4	5	6	7	8
Forecast	30	30	30	30	40	40	40	40
Customer orders (committed)	33	20	10	4	2			

Chapter Eleven   Aggregate Planning and Master Scheduling   **487**

For the first week, projected on-hand inventory equals beginning inventory minus the larger of forecast and customer orders. Because customer orders (33) are larger than the forecast (30), the customer orders amount is used. Thus, for the first week, we obtain

Projected on-hand inventory = 64 − 33 = 31

Projected on-hand inventories are shown in Figure 11.9 for the first three weeks (i.e., until the projected on-hand amount becomes negative).

When the projected on-hand inventory becomes negative, this is a signal that production will be needed to replenish inventory. Hence, a negative projected on-hand inventory will require planned production. Suppose that a production lot size of 70 pumps is used, so that whenever production is called for, 70 pumps will be produced. (The determination of lot size is described in Chapter 13.) Hence, the negative projected on-hand inventory in the third week will require production of 70 pumps, which will meet the projected shortfall of 29 pumps and leave 41 (i.e., 70 − 29 = 41) pumps for future demand.

These calculations continue for the entire schedule. Every time projected inventory becomes negative, another production lot of 70 pumps is added to the schedule. Figure 11.10 illustrates the calculations. The result is the master schedule and projected on-hand inventory for each week of the schedule. These can now be added to the master schedule (see Figure 11.11).

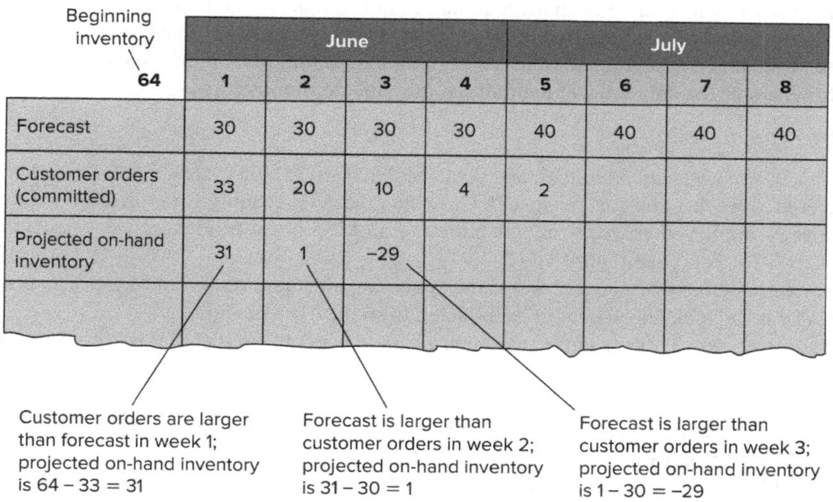

FIGURE 11.9
Projected on-hand inventory is computed week by week until it becomes negative

FIGURE 11.10
Determining the MPS and projected on-hand inventory

Week	Inventory from Previous Week	Requirements*	Net Inventory before MPS	(70) MPS			Projected Inventory
1	64	33	31				31
2	31	30	1				1
3	1	30	−29	+	70	=	41
4	41	30	11				11
5	11	40	−29	+	70	=	41
6	41	40	1				1
7	1	40	−39	+	70	=	31
8	31	40	−9	+	70	=	61

*Requirements equals the larger of forecast and customer orders in each week.

FIGURE 11.11
Projected on-hand inventory and MPS are added to the master schedule

		June				July			
64	1	2	3	4	5	6	7	8
Forecast	30	30	30	30	40	40	40	40
Customer orders (committed)	33	20	10	4	2			
Projected on-hand inventory	31	1	41	11	41	1	31	61
MPS			70		70		70	70

It is now possible to determine the amount of inventory that is uncommitted and, hence, available to promise. Several methods are used in practice. The one we will employ involves a "look-ahead" procedure: Sum booked customer orders week by week until (but not including) a week in which there is an MPS amount. For example, in the first week, this procedure results in summing customer orders of 33 (week 1) and 20 (week 2) to obtain 53. In the first week, this amount is subtracted from the beginning inventory of 64 pumps plus the MPS (zero in this example) to obtain the amount that is available to promise. Thus,

$$64 + 0 - (33 + 20) = 11$$

This inventory is uncommitted, and it can be delivered in either week 1 or 2, or part can be delivered in week 1 and part in week 2. (Note that the ATP quantity is only calculated for the first week and for other weeks in which there is an MPS quantity. Hence, it is calculated for weeks 1, 3, 5, 7, 8.) See Figure 11.12.

For weeks other than the first week, the beginning inventory drops out of the computation, and ATP is the look-ahead quantity subtracted from the MPS quantity.

Thus, for week 3, the promised amounts are $10 + 4 = 14$, and the ATP is $70 - 14 = 56$.

For week 5, customer orders are 2 (future orders have not yet been booked). The ATP is $70 - 2 = 68$.

For weeks 7 and 8, there are no customer orders, so for the present, all of the MPS amount is available to promise.

As additional orders are booked, these would be entered in the schedule, and the ATP amounts would be updated to reflect those orders. Marketing can use the ATP amounts to provide realistic delivery dates to customers.

FIGURE 11.12
The available-to-promise inventory quantities have been added to the master schedule

		June				July			
64	1	2	3	4	5	6	7	8
Forecast	30	30	30	30	40	40	40	40
Customer orders (committed)	33	20	10	4	2			
Projected on-hand inventory	31	1	41	11	41	1	31	61
MPS			70		70		70	70
Available-to-promise inventory (uncommitted)	11		56		68		70	70

Aggregate planning establishes general levels of employment, output, and inventories for periods of 2 to 12 months. In the spectrum of planning, it falls between the broad decisions of long-range planning and the very specific and detailed short-range planning decisions. It begins with an overall forecast for the planning horizon and ends with preparations for applying the plans to specific products and services.

The essence of aggregate planning is the aggregation of products or services into one "product" or "service." This permits planners to consider overall levels of employment and inventories without having to become involved with specific details that are better left to short-range planning. Planners often use informal graphic and charting techniques to develop plans, although various mathematical techniques have been suggested. It appears that the complexity and the restrictive assumptions of these techniques limit their widespread use in practice.

After the aggregate plan has been developed, it is disaggregated or broken down into specific product requirements. This leads to a master schedule, which indicates the planned quantities and timing of specific outputs. Inputs to the master schedule are on-hand inventory amounts, forecasts of demand, and customer orders. The outputs are projected production and inventory requirements, and the projected uncommitted inventory, which is referred to as available-to-promise (ATP) inventory.

SUMMARY

1. An aggregate plan is an intermediate-range plan for a collection of similar products or services that sets the stage for shorter-range plans. See Table 11.8 for a convenient summary of aggregate planning.

2. Master scheduling breaks an aggregate plan into specific shorter-range output quantity and timing requirements.

KEY POINTS

Purpose

Decide on the combination of

   Output rates

   Employment levels

   On-hand inventory levels

Objectives

   Minimize cost

   Others, may include

      Maintain a desirable level of customer service

      Minimize workforce fluctuations

Possible Strategies

A. Supply Management (reactive)

Level Production

Allow inventory to absorb variations in demand

Use back ordering during periods of high demand

Chase Production

Vary output by varying the number of workers by hiring or layoffs to track demand

Vary output throughout the use of overtime or idle time

Vary output using part-time workers

Use subcontracting to supplement output

Mixed Strategy

Use a combination of level and chase approaches

B. Demand Management (proactive)

Influence demand through promotion, pricing, etc.

Produce goods or services that have complementary demand patterns

Managerial Importance of Aggregate Planning

Has an effect on

   Costs

   Equipment utilization

   Customer satisfaction

   Employment levels

   Synchronization of flow throughout the supply chain

TABLE 11.8
Summary of aggregate planning

490   **Chapter Eleven**   Aggregate Planning and Master Scheduling

    a. Rough-cut capacity planning tests the feasibility of a tentative master plan in terms of capacity.

    b. Time fences describe the various time periods in terms of the degree to which the master schedule is firm or flexible. Early periods do not generally allow changes, while later periods have more flexibility.

3. It is essential to include the entire supply chain when developing the aggregate plan.

KEY TERMS			

aggregate planning, 463
available-to-promise (ATP)
  inventory, 486
chase demand
  strategy, 471

level capacity strategy, 471
master production schedule
  (MPS), 483
rough-cut capacity planning
  (RCCP), 485

sales and operations
  planning, 463
simulation models, 481
time fences, 485
yield management, 483

SOLVED PROBLEMS

Problem 1   A manager is attempting to put together an aggregate plan for the coming nine months. She has obtained a forecast of expected demand for the planning horizon. The plan must deal with highly seasonal demand; demand is relatively high in periods 3 and 4 and again in period 8, as can be seen from the following forecasts.

Period	1	2	3	4	5	6	7	8	9	Total
Forecast	190	230	260	280	210	170	160	260	180	1,940

The department now has 20 full-time employees, each of whom produces 10 units of output per period at a cost of $6 per unit. Beginning inventory for period 1 is zero. Inventory carrying cost is $5 per unit per period, and backlog cost is $10 per unit per period.

    a. Will the current work force be able to handle the forecast demand?

    b. Determine the total cost of the plan, including production, inventory, and backorder costs.

Solution   a. With the current workforce of 20 people each producing 10 units per period, regular capacity is 1,800 units for the 9-month period. That is 140 units less than expected demand. So there will be a backlog of unfilled demand if actual demand equals the forecast.

    b. The production plan is:

Period	1	2	3	4	5	6	7	8	9	Total
Forecast	190	230	260	280	210	170	160	260	180	1,940
Output										
Regular	200	200	200	200	200	200	200	200	200	1,800
Overtime	—	—	—	—	—	—	—	—	—	—
Subcontract	—	—	—	—	—	—	—	—	—	—
Output — Forecast	10	(30)	(60)	(80)	(10)	30	40	(60)	20	(140)
Inventory										
Beginning	0	10	0	0	0	0	0	20	0	
Ending	10	0	0	0	0	0	20	0	0	
Average	5	5	10	0	0	0	10	10	0	10
Backlog	0	20	80	160	170	140	100	160	140	970
Costs										
Output										
Regular @ $6	1,200	1,200	1,200	1,200	1,200	1,200	1,200	1,200	1,200	$10,800
Overtime										
Subcontract										
Inventory @ $5	$ 25	$ 25	0	0	0	0	0	0	0	$ 50
Back order @ $10	0	$ 200	800	1,600	1,700	1,400	1,000	1,600	1,400	$ 9,700
Total	$1,225	1,425	2,000	2,800	2,900	2,600	2,200	2,800	2,600	$20,550

The total cost for this plan is $20,550. This plan may or may not be good. The manager would need information on other costs and options before settling on one plan.

Although the calculations are relatively straightforward, the backlogs can sometimes seem difficult to obtain. Consider these rules for computing the backlog:

1. Start with the Output – Forecast value. If this is positive and there was a backlog in the preceding period, reduce the backlog by this amount. If the amount exceeds the backlog, the difference becomes the ending inventory for the period. If they are exactly equal, the backlog and the ending inventory will both be equal to zero.

2. If Output – Forecast is negative, subtract it from the beginning inventory. If this produces a negative value, that value becomes the backlog for that period.

You also can use the Excel template Aggregate Planning (B) to obtain the solution:

Period		1	2	3	4	5	6	7	8	9	Total
Forecast		190	230	260	280	210	170	160	260	180	1,940
Output											
Regular Part		200	200	200	200	200	200	200	200	200	1,800
Time											0
Overtime											0
Subcontract											0
Output — Forecast		10	−30	−60	−80	−10	30	40	−60	20	−140
Inventory											
Beginning		0	10	0	0	0	0	0	0	0	10
Ending		10	0	0	0	0	0	0	0	0	
Average		5	5	0	0	0	0	0.0	0.0	0.0	
Backlog		0	20	80	160	170	140	100	160	140	970
Costs											
Regular	@ 6	$1,200	$1,200	$1,200	$1,200	$1,200	$1,200	$1,200	$1,200	$1,200	$10,800
Part Time	@ $	0 $	0 $	0 $	0 $	0 $	0 $	0 $	0 $	0 $	0
Overtime	@ $	0 $	0 $	0 $	0 $	0 $	0 $	0 $	0 $	0 $	0
Subcontract	@ $	0 $	0 $	0 $	0 $	0 $	0 $	0 $	0 $	0 $	0
Hire/Layoff										$	0
Inventory	@ 5 $	25 $	25 $	0 $	0 $	0 $	0 $	0 $	0 $	0 $	50
Back orders	@ 10 $	0 $	200 $	800 $	1,600 $	1,700 $	1,400	$1,000	$1,600	$1,400	$ 9,700
Total		$1,225	$1,425	$2,000	$2,800	$2,900	$2,600	$2,200	$2,800	$2,600	$20,550

Spring and Summer Fashions, a clothing producer, has generated a forecast for the next eight weeks. Demand is expected to be fairly steady, except for periods 3 and 4, which have higher demands.

Problem 2

Period	1	2	3	4	5	6	7	8	Total
Forecast	1,200	1,200	1,400	3,000	1,200	1,200	1,200	1,200	11,600

The company typically hires seasonal workers to handle the extra workload in periods 3 and 4. The cost for hiring and training a seasonal worker is $50 per worker, and the company plans to hire two additional workers and train them in period 3, for work in period 4, and then lay them off (no cost for layoff). Develop an aggregate plan that uses steady output from regular workers with added output from the two seasonal workers in period 4. The output rate for the seasonal workers is slightly less than that of regular workers, so their cost per unit is higher. The cost per unit for regular workers is $4 per unit, while cost per unit for the seasonal workers is $5 per unit. Backlog cost is $1 per unit per period.

Solution

Period			1	2	3	4	5	6	7	8	Total
Forecast			1,200	1,200	1,400	3,000	1,200	1,200	1,200	1,200	11,600
Output											
Regular			1,200	1,200	1,200	1,200	1,200	1,200	1,200	1,200	9,600
Part Time						2,000					2,000
Overtime											0
Subcontract											0
Output – Forecast			0	0	–200	200	0	0	0	0	0
Inventory											
Beginning			0	0	0	0	0	0	0	0	
Ending			0	0	0	0	0	0	0	0	
Average			0.0	0.0	0.0	0.0	0.0	0.0	0.0	0.0	0
Backlog			0	0	200	0	0	0	0	0	200
Costs :											
Regular	@	4	4,800	4,800	4,800	4,800	4,800	4,800	4,800	4,800	38,400
Part Time	@	5	0	0	0	10,000	0	0	0	0	10,000
OverTime	@		0	0	0	0	0	0	0	0	0
Subcontract	@		0	0	0	0	0	0	0	0	0
Hire/Layoff		50			100						100
Inventory	@		0.0	0.0	0.0	0.0	0.0	0.0	0.0	0.0	0.0
Back orders	@	1	0	0	200	0	0	0	0	0	200
Total			4,800	4,800	5,100	14,800	4,800	4,800	4,800	4,800	48,700

Problem 3

Prepare a schedule like that shown in Figure 11.12 for the following situation: The forecast for each period is 70 units. The starting inventory is zero. The MPS rule is to schedule production if the projected inventory on hand is negative. The production lot size is 100 units. The following table shows committed orders.

Period	Customer Orders
1	80
2	50
3	30
4	10

Solution

Period	(A) Projected Inventory from Previous Period	(B) Requirements*	(C = A – B) Net Inventory before MPS	MPS	(MPS + C) Projected On-Hand Inventory
1	0	80	(80)	100	20
2	20	70	(50)	100	50
3	50	70	(20)	100	80
4	80	70	10	0	10

*Requirements equal the larger of forecast and customer orders in each period.

Starting Inv. = 0	1	2	3	4
Forecast	70	70	70	70
Customer orders	80	50	30	10
Projected on-hand inventory	20	50	80	10
MPS	100	100	100	0
ATP	20	50	60	0

You could also obtain the same solution using the Excel template for master scheduling.

Week	0	1	2	3	4	5	6	7	8
Forecast		70	70	70	70				
Customer orders (committed)		80	50	30	10				
Projected on-hand inventory		20	50	80	10	10	10	10	10
MPS		100	100	100					
ATP		20	50	60					

Chapter Eleven   Aggregate Planning and Master Scheduling   493

1. What three levels of planning involve operations managers? What kinds of decisions are made at the various levels?
2. What are the three phases of intermediate planning?
3. What is aggregate planning? What is its purpose?
4. Why is there a need for aggregate planning?
5. What are the most common decision variables for aggregate planning in a manufacturing setting? In a service setting?
6. What aggregate planning difficulty that might confront an organization offering a variety of products and/or services would not confront an organization offering one or a few similar products or services?
7. Briefly discuss the advantages and disadvantages of each of these planning strategies:
   a. Maintain a level rate of output and let inventories absorb fluctuations in demand.
   b. Vary the size of the workforce to correspond to predicted changes in demand requirements.
   c. Maintain a constant workforce size, but vary hours worked to correspond to predicted demand requirements.
8. What are the primary advantages and limitations of informal graphic and charting techniques for aggregate planning?
9. Briefly describe the planning techniques listed as follows, and give an advantage and disadvantage for each:
   a. Spreadsheet
   b. Linear programming
   c. Simulation
10. What are the inputs to master scheduling? What are the outputs?
11. Explain the managerial significance of aggregate planning.

1. What general trade-offs are involved in master scheduling in terms of the frozen portion of the schedule?
2. Who needs to interface with the master schedule and why?
3. How has technology had an impact on master scheduling?

1. Service operations often face more difficulty in planning than their manufacturing counterparts. However, service does have certain advantages that manufacturing often does not. Explain service planning difficulty, and the advantages and disadvantages.
2. Name several behaviors related to aggregate planning or master scheduling that you believe would be unethical, and the ethical principle that would be violated for each.

1. Compute the total cost for each aggregate plan using these unit costs:
   Regular output = $40
   Overtime = $50
   Subcontract = $60
   Average Balance Inventory = $10

a. Month	Jan	Feb	Mar	Apr	May	Jun
Forecast Output	300	320	320	340	320	320
Regular	300	300	300	300	300	300
Overtime	20	20	20	20	20	20
Subcontract	0	0	0	0	0	0
Output—Forecast						
Inventory						
Beginning						
Ending						
Average						

b.

Month	Jul	Aug	Sep	Oct	Nov	Dec
Forecast	320	340	360	380	400	400
Output						
Regular	300	300	300	300	300	300
Overtime	20	20	20	20	30	30
Subcontract	20	30	40	40	60	70
Output—Forecast						
Inventory						
Beginning						
Ending						
Average						

c. (Refer to part *b.*) After complaints from some workers about working overtime every month during the first half of the year, the manager is now considering adding some temporary workers for the second half of the year, which would increase regular output to a steady 350 units a month, not using any overtime, and using subcontracting to make up needed output. Determine the total cost of that plan.

2. A manager would like to know the total cost of a chase strategy that matches the forecast below using a steady regular production rate of 200 units a month, a maximum of 20 units per month of overtime, and subcontracting as needed to make up any shortages. The unit costs are:

Regular production = $35

Overtime = $70

Subcontracting = $80

Month	1	2	3	4	5	6
Forecast	230	200	240	240	250	240

3. Determine the total cost for this plan given the following forecast:

Month	1	2	3	4	5	6
Forecast	380	400	420	440	460	480

Use steady regular output of 400 units per month, use overtime as needed for up to 40 units per month, and use subcontracting to make up any needed output to match the forecast. Unit costs are:

Regular output = $25

Overtime = $40

Subcontract = $60

Average Balance Inventory = $15

4. a. Given the following forecast and steady regular output of 550 every month, what total cost would result if overtime is limited to a maximum of 40 units a month, and subcontracting is limited to a maximum of 10 units a month? Unit costs are:

Regular output = $20

Overtime = $30

Subcontract = $25

Average Inventory = $10

Backlog = $18

Month	1	2	3	4	5	6
Forecast	540	540	570	590	600	580

b. Suppose now that backlogs are not allowed. Modify your plan from part *a* to accommodate that new condition as economically as possible. The limits on overtime and subcontracting remain the same.

5. Manager T. C. Downs of Plum Engines, a producer of lawn mowers and leaf blowers, must develop an aggregate plan given the forecast for engine demand shown in the table. The department has a regular output capacity of 130 engines per month. Regular output has a cost of $60 per engine. The beginning inventory is zero engines. Overtime has a cost of $90 per engine.

a. Develop a chase plan that matches the forecast and compute the total cost of your plan. Regular production can be less than regular capacity.

b. Compare the costs to a level plan that uses inventory to absorb fluctuations. Inventory carrying cost is $2 per engine per month. Backlog cost is $90 per engine per month. There should not be a backlog in the last month.

	MONTH								
	1	**2**	**3**	**4**	**5**	**6**	**7**	**8**	**Total**
Forecast	120	135	140	120	125	125	140	135	1,040

6. Manager Chris Channing of Fabric Mills, Inc., has developed the forecast shown in the table for bolts of cloth. The figures are in hundreds of bolts. The department has a regular output capacity of 275(00) bolts per month, except for the seventh month, when capacity will be 250(00) bolts. Regular output has a cost of $40 per hundred bolts. Workers can be assigned to other jobs if production is less than regular. The beginning inventory is zero bolts.

a. Develop a chase plan that matches the forecast and compute the total cost of your plan. Overtime is $60 per hundred bolts. Regular production can be less than regular capacity.

b. Would the total cost be less with regular production with no overtime, but using a subcontractor to handle the excess above regular capacity at a cost of $50 per hundred bolts? Backlogs are not allowed. The inventory carrying cost is $2 per hundred bolts.

Month	**1**	**2**	**3**	**4**	**5**	**6**	**7**	**Total**
Forecast	250	300	250	300	280	275	270	1,925

7. SummerFun, Inc., produces a variety of recreation and leisure products. The production manager has developed an aggregate forecast:

Month	**Mar**	**Apr**	**May**	**Jun**	**Jul**	**Aug**	**Sep**	**Total**
Forecast	50	44	55	60	50	40	51	350

Use the following information to develop aggregate plans.

Regular production cost	$80 per unit	Backorder cost	$20 per unit
Overtime production cost	$120 per unit	Beginning inventory	0 units
Regular capacity	40 units per month		
Overtime capacity	8 units per month		
Subcontracting cost	$140 per unit		
Subcontracting capacity	12 units per month		
Holding cost	$10 per unit per month		

Develop an aggregate plan using each of the following guidelines and compute the total cost for each plan. *Hint:* You will need extra output in April and August to accommodate demand in the following months.

a. Use regular production. Supplement using inventory, overtime, and subcontracting as needed. No backlogs allowed.

b. Use a level strategy. Use a combination of backlogs, subcontracting, and inventory to handle variations in demand. There should not be a backlog in the final period.

8. Nowjuice, Inc., produces Shakewell® fruit juice. A planner has developed an aggregate forecast for demand (in cases) for the next six months.

Month	**May**	**Jun**	**Jul**	**Aug**	**Sep**	**Oct**
Forecast	4,000	4,800	5,600	7,200	6,400	5,000

Use the following information to develop aggregate plans.

Regular production cost	$10 per case
Regular production capacity	5,000 cases
Overtime production cost	$16 per case
Subcontracting cost	$20 per case
Holding cost	$1 per case per month
Beginning inventory	0

Develop an aggregate plan using each of the following guidelines and compute the total cost for each plan. Which plan has the lowest total cost? Note: Backlogs are not allowed.

a. Use level production. Supplement using overtime as needed.

b. Use a combination of overtime (500 cases per period maximum), inventory, and subcontracting (500 cases per period maximum) to handle variations in demand.

c. Use overtime up to 750 cases per period and inventory to handle variations in demand.

9. Wormwood, Ltd., produces a variety of furniture products. The planning committee wants to prepare an aggregate plan for the next six months using the following information.

	Month							Cost Per Unit	
	1	**2**	**3**	**4**	**5**	**6**		Regular time	$50
Demand	160	150	160	180	170	140		Overtime	75
Capacity								Subcontract	80
Regular	150	150	150	150	160	160		Inventory holding, per month	4
Overtime	10	10	0	10	10	10			

Subcontracting can handle a maximum of 10 units per month. Beginning inventory is zero. Develop a plan that minimizes total cost. No back orders are allowed. Regular capacity = Regular production.

10. Refer to Solved Problem 1. Prepare two additional aggregate plans. Call the one in the solved problem plan A. For plan B, hire one more worker at a cost of $200. Make up any shortfall using subcontracting at $8 per unit, with a maximum of 20 units per period (i.e., use subcontracting to reduce back orders when the forecast exceeds regular output). Note that the ending inventory in period 9 should be zero. Therefore, Total forecast −Total output = Quantity subcontracted. An additional constraint is that back orders cannot exceed 80 units in any period. For plan C, assume no workers are hired (so regular output is 200 units per period instead of 210 as in plan B). Use subcontracting as needed, but no more than 20 units per period. Compute the total cost of each plan. Which plan has the lowest cost? Assume regular monthly production = regular capacity.

11. Refer to Solved Problem 1. Suppose another option is to use part-time workers to assist during seasonal peaks. The cost per unit, including hiring and training, is $11. The output rate is 10 units per worker per period for all workers. A maximum of 10 part-time workers can be used, and the same number of part-time workers must be used in all periods that have part-time workers. The ending inventory in period 9 should be 10 units. The limit on backlogs is 20 units per period. Try to make up backlogs as soon as possible. Compute the total cost for this plan, and compare it to the cost of the plan used in the solved problem. Assume 20 full-time workers and regular monthly production = regular capacity.

12. Refer to Solved Problem 1. Prepare an aggregate plan that uses overtime ($9 per unit, maximum output 25 units per period) and inventory variation. Try to minimize backlogs. The ending inventory in period 9 should be zero, and the limit on backlogs is 60 units per period. Compute the total cost of your plan, and compare it to the total cost of the plan used in the solved problem. Assume 20 full-time workers.

13. Refer to Example 2. Determine if a plan to use subcontracting at a maximum rate of 50 units per period as needed with no overtime would achieve a lower total cost than the plan shown in Example 2. Again, plan for a zero inventory balance at the end of period 6. Regular production can be less than regular capacity.

14. Verify the transportation solution shown in Example 3.

15. Refer to Example 3. Suppose that an increase in warehousing costs and other costs brings inventory carrying costs to $2 per unit per month. All other costs and quantities remain the same. Determine a revised solution to this transportation problem. Solve by modifying Table 11.6.

16. Refer to Example 3. Suppose that regular-time capacity will be reduced to 440 units in period 3 to accommodate a companywide safety inspection of equipment. What will the additional cost of the optimal plan be as compared to the one shown in Example 3? Assume all costs and quantities are the same as given in Example 3 except for the regular-time output in period 3. Solve by modifying Table 11.6.

17. Solve Problem 16 using an inventory carrying cost of $2 per unit per period.

18. Dundas Bike Components Inc. of Wheelville, Illinois, manufactures bicycle wheels in two different sizes for the Big Bike Co. assembly plant located across town. David Dundas, the firm's owner-manager, has just received Big Bike's order for the next six months.

Chapter Eleven Aggregate Planning and Master Scheduling   497

	Nov.	Dec.	Jan.	Feb.	Mar.	Apr.
20-Inch Wheels	1,000 units	900	600	700	1,100	1,100
24-Inch Wheels	500 units	500	300	500	400	600

a. Under what circumstances will it be possible to develop just one aggregate plan rather than two (one for each size wheel)? Explain in two to three sentences without calculations.

b. Currently Dundas employs 28 full-time, highly skilled employees, each of whom can produce 50 wheels per month. Because skilled labor is in short supply in the Wheelville area, David would like to develop one pure level-output plan. There is no inventory of finished wheels on hand at present, but David would like to have 300 on hand at the end of April. Big Bike will tolerate back orders of up to 200 units per month. Show your level plan in tabular form. The amount produced using overtime should be the same except for the last month.

c. Calculate the total annual cost of your plan using these costs:

Regular	$5.00	Hiring	$300
Overtime	$7.50	Layoff	$400
Part-time	NA	Inventory	$1.00
Subcontract	NA	Back order	$6.00

19. Prepare a master production schedule for industrial pumps in the manner of Figure 11.11 in the chapter. Use the same inputs as the example, and lot sizes of 70, but change the MPS rule from "schedule production when the projected on-hand inventory would be negative without production" to "schedule production when the projected on-hand inventory would be less than 10 without production."

20. Update the master schedule shown in Figure 11.11 given these updated inputs: It is now the end of week 1; customer orders are 25 for week 2, 16 for week 3, 11 for week 4, 8 for week 5, and 3 for week 6. Use the MPS rule of ordering production when projected on-hand inventory would be negative without production. Prepare the master schedule for weeks 2 through 8.

21. Prepare a master schedule like that shown in Figure 11.11 given this information: The forecast for each week of an eight-week schedule is 50 units. The MPS rule is to schedule production if the projected on-hand inventory would be negative without it. Customer orders (committed) are as follows.

Week	Customer Orders
1	52
2	35
3	20
4	12

Use a production lot size of 75 units and no beginning inventory.

22. Determine the available-to-promise (ATP) quantities for each period for Problem 21.

23. Prepare a schedule like that shown in Figure 11.12 for the following situation: The forecast is 80 units for each of the first two periods and 60 units for each of the next three periods. The starting inventory is 20 units. The company uses a chase strategy for determining the production lot size, except there is an upper limit on the lot size of 70 units. Also, the desired safety stock is 10 units. *Note:* The ATP quantities are based on maximum allowable production. *Note:* A negative projected on-hand can occur.

Committed orders are as follows.

Period	Customer Orders
1	82
2	80
3	60
4	40
5	20

CASE   EIGHT GLASSES A DAY (EGAD)

The EGAD Bottling Company has decided to introduce a new line of premium bottled water that will include several "designer" flavors. Marketing manager Georgianna Mercer is predicting an upturn in demand based on the new offerings and the increased public awareness of the health benefits of drinking more water. She has prepared aggregate forecasts for the next six months, as shown in the following table (quantities are in tankloads).

Month	May	Jun	Jul	Aug	Sept	Oct	Total
Forecast	50	60	70	90	80	70	420

Production manager Mark Mercer (no relation to Georgianna) has developed the following information. (Costs are in thousands of dollars.)

Regular production cost	$1 per tankload
Regular production capacity	60 tankloads
Overtime production cost	$1.6 per tankload
Subcontracting cost	$1.8 per tankload
Holding cost	$2 per tankload per month
Backordering cost	Backlogs are not allowed
Beginning inventory	0 tankloads

Among the strategies being considered are the following:

1. Level production supplemented by up to 10 tankloads a month from overtime.
2. A combination of overtime, inventory, and subcontracting. Regular production should be the same each month.
3. Using overtime for up to 15 tankloads a month, along with inventory to handle variations. Regular production should be the same each month.

Question

1. The objective is to choose the plan that has the lowest cost. Which plan would you recommend?
2. Presumably, information about the new line has been shared with supply chain partners. Explain what information should be shared with various partners, and why sharing that information is important.

SELECTED BIBLIOGRAPHY AND FURTHER READINGS

Burrows, Robert P., Lora Cecere, and Gregory P. Hackett. *The Market-Driven Supply Chain: A Revolutionary Model for Sales and Operations Planning in the New On-Demand Economy.* Miama, FL: The Hackett Group, 2012.

Jacobs, F. Robert, William L. Berry, D. Clay Whybark, and Thomas Vollman. *Manufacturing Planning and Control for Supply Chain Management,* 6th ed. Burr Ridge, IL: McGraw-Hill/Irwin, 2011.

Wallace, Thomas F. and Robert A. Stahl. *Sales and Operations Planning: The How-to Handbook,* 3rd ed. T. F. Wallace and Company, 2008.

12 MRP and ERP

LEARNING OBJECTIVES

After completing this chapter, you should be able to:

LO12.1   Describe the conditions under which MRP is most appropriate.

LO12.2   Describe the inputs, outputs, and nature of MRP processing.

LO12.3   Explain how requirements in a master production schedule are translated into material requirements for lower-level items.

LO12.4   Discuss the benefits and requirements of MRP.

LO12.5   Describe some of the difficulties users have encountered with MRP.

LO12.6   Describe MRP II and its benefits.

LO12.7   Explain how an MRP system is useful in capacity requirements planning.

LO12.8   Describe ERP, what it provides, and its hidden costs.

CHAPTER OUTLINE

12.1   **Introduction** 501
12.2   **An Overview of MRP** 501
12.3   **MRP Inputs** 502
          The Master Schedule 502
          The Bill of Materials 503
          The Inventory Records 506
12.4   **MRP Processing** 506
          Updating the System 511
12.5   **MRP Outputs** 513
12.6   **Other Considerations** 514

Safety Stock 514
Lot Sizing 515
12.7   **MRP in Services** 516
12.8   **Benefits and Requirements of MRP** 516
          Benefits 516
          Requirements 517
12.9   **MRP II** 517
          Closed–Loop MRP 518
12.10 **Capacity Requirements Planning** 519

Distribution Resource Planning for the Supply Chain 520
12.11 **ERP** 521
          ERP in Services 527
12.12 **Operations Strategy** 529
          Cases: Promotional Novelties 545
          DMD Enterprises 546
          Operations Tour: Stickley Furniture 546

©Monty Rakusen/Cultura/Getty Images

This chapter describes material requirements planning (MRP) and enterprise resource planning (ERP). MRP is a planning and scheduling technique used for batch production of assembled items. The first portion of the chapter is devoted to MRP. The remainder of the chapter is devoted to ERP, which involves the use of extensive software to integrate record keeping and information sharing throughout an organization and portions of its supply chain.

12.1 INTRODUCTION

LO12.1 Describe the conditions under which MRP is most appropriate.

A major distinction in the way inventories are managed results from the nature of demand for those items. When demand for items is derived from plans to make certain products, as it is with raw materials, parts, and assemblies used in producing a finished product, those items are said to have **dependent demand**. The parts and materials that go into the production of cars are examples of dependent demand because the total quantity of parts and raw materials needed during any time period depends on the number of cars that will be produced. Conversely, demand for the *finished* cars is independent—a car is not a component of another item.

dependent demand Demand for items that are subassemblies or component parts to be used in the production of finished goods.

12.2 AN OVERVIEW OF MRP

Material requirements planning (MRP) is a methodology used for planning the production of assembled products such as smartphones, automobiles, kitchen tables, and a whole host of other products that are assembled. Some items are produced repetitively while others are produced in batches. The process begins with a master schedule. The master schedule designates the quantity and completion time of an assembled product, often referred to as the end item. Materials requirements planning then generates a production plan for the end item that indicates the quantities and timing of the subassemblies, component parts, and raw materials required for assembly of that end item. This sequence is depicted in Figure 12-1.

material requirements planning (MRP) A methodology that translates master schedule requirements for end items into time-phased requirements for subassemblies, components, and raw materials.

502   **Chapter Twelve**   MRP and ERP

FIGURE 12.1
A material requirements
plan indicates quantity
and timing details needed
to achieve the master
schedule

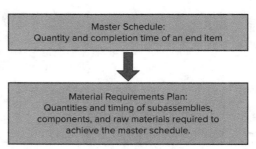

FIGURE 12.2
MRP inputs, processing,
and outputs

LO12.2 Describe the
inputs, outputs, and nature
of MRP processing.

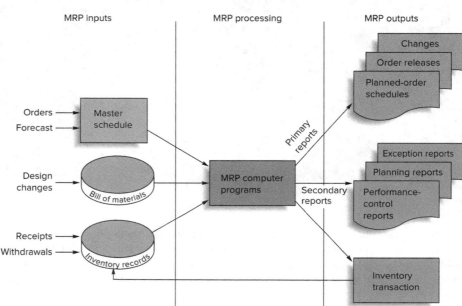

MRP is designed to answer three questions: *What* is needed? *How much* is needed? and *When* is it needed?

The primary inputs of MRP are a bill of materials, which tells the composition of a finished product; a master schedule, which tells how much finished product is desired and when; and an inventory records file, which tells how much inventory is on hand or on order. The planner processes this information to determine the *net* requirements for each period of the planning horizon.

Outputs from the process include planned-order schedules, order releases, changes, performance-control reports, planning reports, and exception reports. These topics are discussed in more detail in subsequent sections. (See Figure 12.2.)

12.3 MRP INPUTS

An MRP system has three major sources of information: a master schedule, a bill-of-materials file, and an inventory records file (see Figure 12.2). Let's consider each of these inputs.

The Master Schedule

master schedule One of
three primary inputs in MRP;
states which end items are to
be produced, when these are
needed, and in what quantities.

The **master schedule**, also referred to as the *master production schedule,* states which end items are to be produced, when they are needed, and in what quantities. Figure 12.3 illustrates a portion of a master schedule that shows planned output for end item X for the planning horizon. The schedule indicates that 100 units of X will be needed (e.g., for shipments to customers) at the *start* of week 4 and that another 150 units will be needed at the *start* of week 8.

Chapter Twelve   MRP and ERP   **503**

Week number

Item: X	1	2	3	4	5	6	7	8
Quantity				100				150

FIGURE 12.3
A master schedule for end item X

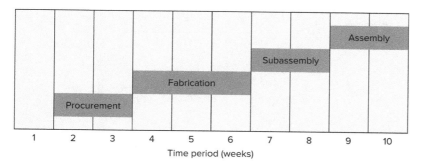

FIGURE 12.4
The planning horizon must cover the cumulative lead time

The quantities in a master schedule come from a number of different sources, including customer orders, forecasts, and orders from warehouses to build up seasonal inventories.

The master schedule separates the planning horizon into a series of time periods or time *buckets,* which are often expressed in weeks. However, the time buckets need not be of equal length. In fact, the near-term portion of a master schedule may be in weeks, but later portions may be in months or quarters. Usually, plans for those more distant time periods are more tentative than near-term requirements.

Although a master production schedule has no set time period that it must cover, most managers like to plan far enough into the future so they have some general idea of probable upcoming demands for the near term. It is important, though, that the master schedule cover the *stacked* or **cumulative lead time** necessary to produce the end items. This amounts to the sum of the lead times that sequential phases of the production or assembly process require, as illustrated in Figure 12.4, where a total of nine weeks of lead time is needed from ordering parts and raw materials until final assembly is completed. Note that lead times include move and wait times in addition to setup and run times.

cumulative lead time The sum of the lead times that sequential phases of a process require, from ordering of parts or raw materials to completion of final assembly.

The Bill of Materials

A **bill of materials (BOM)** contains a listing of all of the assemblies, subassemblies, parts, part costs, and raw materials that are needed to produce *one* unit of a finished product. Thus, each finished product has its own bill of materials.

The listing in the bill of materials is hierarchical; it shows the quantity of each item needed to complete one unit of its parent item. The nature of this aspect of a bill of materials is clear when you consider a **product structure tree**, which provides a visual depiction of the subassemblies and components needed to assemble a product. Figure 12.5 shows an *assembly diagram* for a chair and a simple product structure tree for the chair. The end item (in this case, the chair, the finished product) is shown at the top of the tree. Just beneath it are the subassemblies, or major components, that must be put together to make up the end item. Beneath each major component are the necessary lesser components. At each stage moving down the tree are the components (parts, materials) needed to make one unit of the next higher item in the tree.

A product structure tree is useful in illustrating how the bill of materials is used to determine the quantities of each of the ingredients (requirements) needed to obtain a desired number of end items. Items at the lowest levels of a tree often are raw materials or purchased parts, while items at higher levels are typically assemblies or subassemblies. Product-structure trees for items at the lowest levels are the concerns of suppliers.

Let's consider the product structure tree shown in Figure 12.6. End item X is composed of two Bs and one C. Moreover, each B requires three Ds and one E, and each D requires four Es. Similarly, each C is made up of two Es and two Fs. These *requirements* are listed by *level,*

bill of materials (BOM) One of the three primary inputs of MRP; a listing of all of the raw materials, parts, subassemblies, and assemblies needed to produce one unit of a product.

product structure tree A visual depiction of the requirements in a bill of materials, where all components are listed by levels.

504   **Chapter Twelve** MRP and ERP

FIGURE 12.5
Assembly diagram and product structure tree for chair assembly

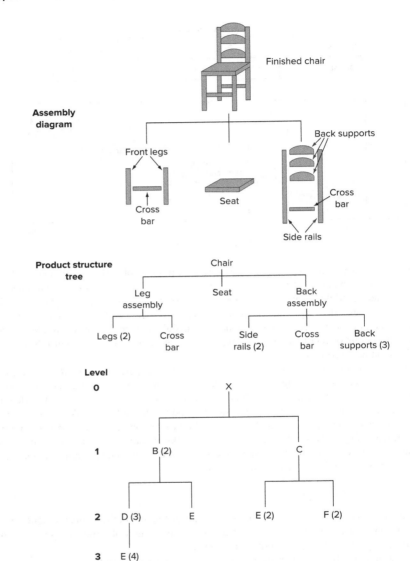

Bill of Materials		
Level		Quantity
0	Chair	1
1	Leg assembly	1
2	Legs	2
2	Cross bar	1
1	Seat	1
1	Back assemby	1
2	Side rails	2
2	Cross bar	1
2	Back supports	3

FIGURE 12.6
A product structure tree for end item X

beginning with 0 for the end item, then 1 for the next level, and so on. The items at each level are *components* of the next level up and, as in a family tree, are *parents* of their respective components. Note that the quantities of each item in the product structure tree refer only to the amounts needed to complete the assembly at the next higher level.

EXAMPLE 1

mhhe.com/stevenson13e

Determining How much of Each Component will be needed for Assembly

Use the information presented in Figure 12.6 to do the following:

a. Determine the quantities of B, C, D, E, and F needed to assemble one X.

b. Determine the quantities of these components that will be required to assemble 10 Xs, taking into account the quantities on hand (i.e., in inventory) of various components:

Component	On Hand
B	4
C	10
D	8
E	60

a.

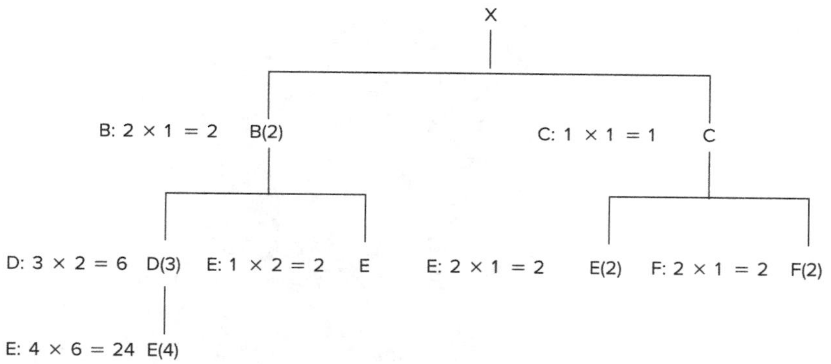

Thus, one X will require

B:	2
C:	1
D:	6
E:	28 (Note that E occurs in three places, with requirements of 24 + 2 + 2 = 28)
F:	2

b.

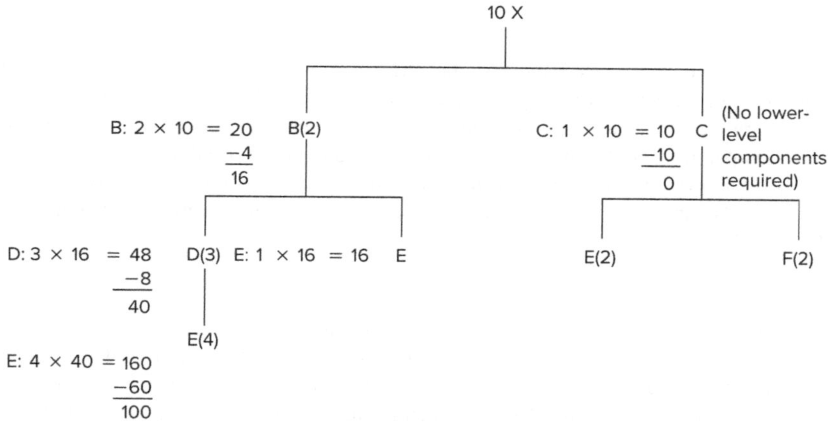

Thus, given the amounts of on-hand inventory, 10 Xs will require

B:	16
C:	0
D:	40
E:	116
F:	0

SOLUTION

Determining total requirements is usually more complicated than Example 1 might suggest. For one thing, many products have considerably more components. For another, the issue of *timing* is essential (i.e., when must the components be ordered or made) and must be included in the analysis. Finally, for a variety of reasons, some of the components/subassemblies may be on hand (i.e., currently in inventory). Consequently, in determining total requirements, the amounts on hand must be *netted out* (i.e., subtracted from the apparent requirements) to determine the true requirements as illustrated in Example 1.

VX Corporation's CAD/CAM software can be used not only for design specification but also to prepare parts lists. This screen shows a parts list for a bass drum pedal along with a three-dimensional view of the product subassemblies.

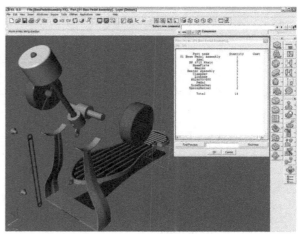

Courtesy of VX Corporation

low-level coding Restructuring the bill of materials so that multiple occurrences of a component all coincide with the lowest level at which the component occurs.

When an MRP system calculates requirements, the computer scans a bill of materials by level. When a component such as E in Figure 12.6 appears on more than one level, **low-level coding** is used so that all occurrences of that component appear on the lowest level at which the component appears. In Figure 12.6, conceptually that would be equivalent to lengthening the vertical line for the two appearances of E at level 2 so that all three occurrences line up at level 3 in the tree.

Comment It is extremely important that the bill of materials accurately reflects the composition of a product, particularly since errors at one level become magnified by the multiplication process used to determine quantity requirements. As obvious as this might seem, many companies find themselves with incorrect bill-of-material records. These make it impossible to effectively determine material requirements; moreover, the task of correcting these records can be complex and time-consuming. Accurate records are a prerequisite for effective MRP.

The Inventory Records

inventory records One of the three primary inputs in MRP; includes information on the status of each item by time period.

Inventory records refer to stored information on the status of each item by time period, called *time buckets*. This includes quantities on hand quantities ordered. It also includes other details for each item, such as supplier, lead time, and lot size policy. Changes due to stock receipts and withdrawals, canceled orders, and similar events also are recorded in this file.

Like the bill of materials, inventory records must be accurate. Erroneous information on requirements or lead times can have a detrimental impact on MRP and create turmoil when incorrect quantities are on hand or expected delivery times are not met.

12.4 MRP PROCESSING

LO12.3 Explain how requirements in a master production schedule are translated into material requirements for lower-level items.

MRP processing takes the end item requirements specified by the master schedule and "explodes" them into *time-phased* requirements for assemblies, parts, and raw materials using the bill of materials offset by lead times. You can see the time-phasing of requirements in the assembly time chart in Figure 12.7. For example, raw materials D, F, and I must be ordered at the start of week 2; part C at the start of week 4; and part H at the start of week 5 in order to be available for delivery as planned.

MRP processing combines the time phasing and "explosion" into a sequence of spreadsheet sections, where each section has the following format:

Chapter Twelve   MRP and ERP   **507**

Week Number	Beg. Inv.	1	2	3	4	5	6	7	8
Item:									
Gross requirements									
Scheduled receipts									
Projected on hand									
Net requirements									
Planned-order receipts									
Planned-order releases									

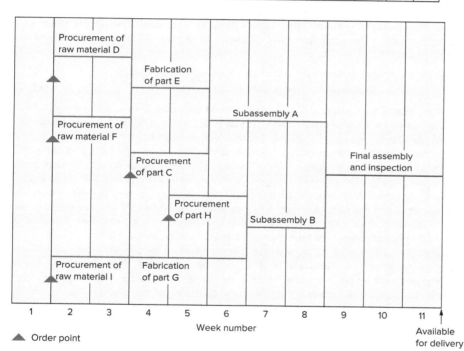

▲ Order point

FIGURE 12.7
Assembly time chart showing material order points needed to meet scheduled availability of the end item

The terms in the spreadsheet are defined as follows.

Gross requirements: The total expected demand for an item or raw material *during* each time period without regard to the amount on hand. For end items, these quantities are shown in the master schedule; for components, these quantities are derived from the planned-order releases of their immediate "parents."

Scheduled receipts: Open orders (orders that have been placed and are scheduled to arrive from vendors or elsewhere in the pipeline by the *beginning* of a period). Note that the ending inventory for a period becomes the beginning inventory for the following period.

Projected on hand: The expected amount of inventory that will be on hand at the *beginning* of each time period: scheduled receipts plus available inventory from last period.

Net requirements: The actual amount needed in each time period.

Planned-order receipts: The quantity expected to be received by the *beginning* of the period in which it is shown. Under lot-for-lot ordering, this quantity will equal net requirements. Under lot-size ordering, this quantity may exceed net requirements.

gross requirements Total expected demand for an item or raw material in a time period.

scheduled receipts Open orders scheduled to arrive from vendors or elsewhere in the pipeline.

projected on hand Expected amount of inventory that will be on hand at the beginning of each time period.

net requirements The actual amount needed in each time period.

planned-order receipts Quantity expected to be received by the beginning of the period in which it is shown.

Any excess is added to available inventory in the *next* time period for simplicity, although in reality, it would be available in that period.

Planned-order releases: Indicates a *planned* amount to order in each time period; equals planned-order receipts offset by lead time. This amount generates gross requirements at the next level in the assembly or production chain. When an order is executed, it is removed from "planned-order releases" and entered under "scheduled receipts."

The quantities that are generated by exploding the bill of materials are *gross requirements;* they do not take into account any inventory that is currently on hand or due to be received.

$$\begin{aligned} \text{Project inventory on-hand for current period} = \text{Planned receipts} \\ \text{for previous period} - \text{Net requirements for previous period} \\ + \text{Scheduled receipts for current period} \end{aligned} \qquad (12-1)$$

The materials that a firm must actually acquire to meet the demand generated by the master schedule are the *net material requirements.*

The determination of the net requirements *(netting)* is the core of MRP processing. One accomplishes it by subtracting from gross requirements the sum of inventory on hand and any scheduled receipts.

$$\begin{aligned} \text{Net requirements for current period} = \text{Gross requirements for current} \\ \text{period} - \text{Projected on-hand inventory for current period} \end{aligned} \qquad (12-2)$$

(Negative results for equations 12–1 or 12–2 should be rounded up to zero.) Projected on-hand inventory includes scheduled receipts, which are executed orders for components that are scheduled to be completed in-house or received from suppliers.

The timing and sizes of orders (i.e., materials ordered from suppliers or work started within the firm) are determined by *planned-order releases.* The timing of the receipts of these quantities is indicated by *planned-order receipts.* Depending on ordering policy, the planned-order releases may be multiples of a specified quantity (e.g., 50 units), or they may be equal to the quantity needed at that time. Although there are other possibilities, these two seem to be the most widely used. Example 2 illustrates the difference between these two ordering policies as well as the general concepts of time-phasing material requirements in MRP.

Development of a material requirements plan is based on the product structure tree diagram. Requirements are determined level by level, beginning with the end item (the top of the tree) and working down the tree, because the timing and quantity of each "parent" item become the basis for determining the timing and quantities of the "children" items directly below it. The children items then become the parent items for the next level, and so on.

EXAMPLE 2

Preparing a Material Requirements Plan for Lot-for-Lot Ordering and for Lot-Size Ordering

A firm that produces wood shutters and bookcases has received two orders for shutters: one for 100 shutters and one for 150 shutters. The 100-unit order is due for delivery at the start of week 4 of the current schedule, and the 150-unit order is due for delivery at the start of week 8. Each shutter consists of two frames and four slatted wood sections. The wood sections are made by the firm, and fabrication takes one week. The frames are ordered, and lead time is two weeks. Assembly of the shutters requires one week. There is a scheduled receipt of 70 wood sections in (i.e., at the beginning of) week 1. Determine the size and timing of planned-order releases necessary to meet delivery requirements under each of these conditions:

1. Lot-for-lot ordering (i.e., planned-order release equal to net requirements).

2. Lot-size ordering with a lot size of 320 units for frames and 70 units for wood sections.

Chapter Twelve   MRP and ERP   **509**

a. Develop a master schedule:

Week number	1	2	3	4	5	6	7	8
Quantity				100				150

b. Develop a product structure tree:

Shutter
Frames (2)   Wood sections (4)

c. Using the master schedule, determine gross requirements for shutters. Next, compute net requirements. Using *lot-for-lot ordering,* determine planned-order receipt quantities and the planned-order release timing to satisfy the master schedule (see Figure 12.8).

The master schedule calls for 100 shutters to be ready for delivery, and no shutters are projected to be on hand at the start of week 4, so the net requirements are also 100 shutters.

FIGURE 12.8   MRP schedule with lot-for-lot ordering

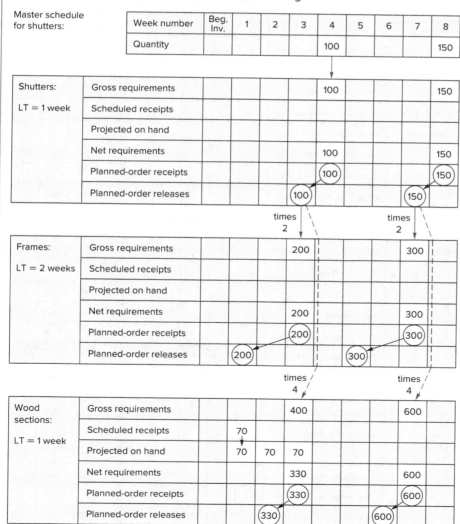

Therefore, planned receipts for week 4 equal 100 shutters. Because shutter assembly requires one week, this means a planned-order release at the start of week 3. Using the same logic, 150 shutters must be assembled during week 7 in order to be available for delivery at the start of week 8.

The planned-order release of 100 shutters at the start of week 3 means that 200 frames (gross requirements) must be available at that time. Because none are expected to be on hand, this generates net requirements of 200 frames and necessitates planned receipts of 200 frames by the start of week 3. With a two-week lead time, this means that the firm must order 200 frames at the start of week 1. Similarly, the planned-order release of 150 shutters at week 7 generates gross and net requirements of 300 frames for week 7 as well as planned receipts for that time. The two-week lead time means the firm must order frames at the start of week 5.

The planned-order release of 100 shutters at the start of week 3 also generates gross requirements of 400 wood sections at that time. However, because 70 wood sections are expected to be on hand, net requirements are 400 — 70 = 330. This means a planned receipt

FIGURE 12.9 MRP schedule with lot sizes for components

Master schedule for shutters:

Week number	Beg. Inv.	1	2	3	4	5	6	7	8
Quantity					100				150

Shutters:
LT = 1 week
Lot size = lot-for-lot

	Beg. Inv.	1	2	3	4	5	6	7	8
Gross requirements					100				150
Scheduled receipts									
Projected on hand									
Net requirements					100				150
Planned-order receipts					(100)				(150)
Planned-order releases				(100)				(150)	

times 2

Frames:
LT = 2 weeks
Lot size = multiples of 320

	Beg. Inv.	1	2	3	4	5	6	7	8
Gross requirements				200				300	
Scheduled receipts									
Projected on hand					120	120	120	120	140
Net requirements				200				180	
Planned-order receipts				(320)				(320)	
Planned-order releases		(320)				(320)			

times 4

Wood sections:
LT = 1 week
Lot size = multiples of 70

	Beg. Inv.	1	2	3	4	5	6	7	8
Gross requirements				400				600	
Scheduled receipts		70							
Projected on hand		70	70	70	20	20	20	20	50
Net requirements				330				580	
Planned-order receipts				(350)				(630)	
Planned-order releases			(350)				(630)		

of 330 by the start of week 3. Since fabrication time is one week, the fabrication must start (planned-order release) at the beginning of week 2.

Similarly, the planned-order release of 150 shutters in week 7 generates gross requirements of 600 wood sections at that point. Because no on-hand inventory of wood sections is projected, net requirements are also 600, and planned-order receipt is 600 units. Again, the one-week lead time means 600 sections are scheduled for fabrication at the start of week 6.

d.   Under lot-size ordering, the only difference is the possibility that planned receipts will exceed net requirements. The excess is recorded as projected inventory in the following period. For example, in Figure 12.9, the order size for frames is 320 units. Net requirements for week 3 are 200; thus, there is an excess of 320 — 200 = 120 units, which become projected inventory in the next week. Similarly, net frame requirements of 180 units are 140 less than the 320 order size; again, the excess becomes projected inventory in week 8. The same thing happens with wood sections; an excess of planned receipts in weeks 3 and 7 is added to projected inventory in weeks 4 and 8. Note that the order size must be in *multiples* of the lot size; for week 3 it is 5 times 70, and for week 7 it is 9 times 70.

MRP provides plans for the end item and each of its subassemblies and components. Conceptually, this amounts to what is depicted in Figure 12.10. Practically speaking, however, the number of components in even a relatively simple product would make the width of the resulting spreadsheet far too wide to handle. Consequently, the plans for the individual components are *stacked,* as illustrated in the preceding example. Because of this, it is important to refer to the product tree in order to track relationships between components.

Example 2 is useful for describing some of the main features of MRP processing, but it understates the enormity of the task of keeping track of material requirements, especially in situations where the same subassemblies, parts, or raw materials are used in a number of

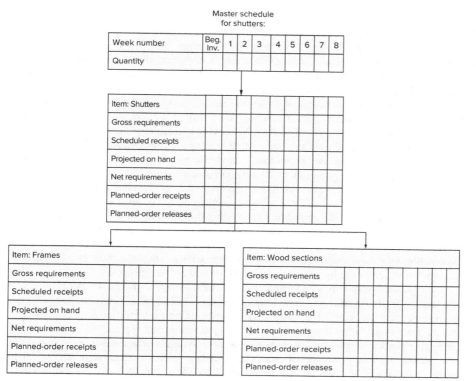

FIGURE 12.10
Net requirements at each level determine gross requirements at the next

FIGURE 12.11
Two different products
have D as a component

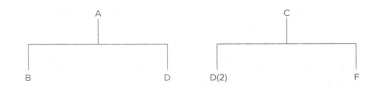

different products. Differences in timing of demands and quantities needed, revisions caused by late deliveries, high scrap rates, and canceled orders all have an impact on processing.

Consider the two product structure trees shown in Figure 12.11. Note that both products have D as a component. Suppose we want to develop a material requirements plan for D given this additional information: There is a beginning inventory of 110 units of D on hand, and all items have lead times of one week. The master schedule calls for 80 units of A in week 4 and 50 units of C in week 5. The plan is shown in Figure 12.12. Note that requirements for B and F are not shown because they are not related to (i.e., neither a "parent" nor a "child" of) D.

The term **pegging** denotes working this process in reverse, that is, identifying the parent items that have generated a given set of material requirements for some item such as D. Although the process may appear simple enough given the product trees and schedules shown in this chapter, when multiple products are involved, the process is more complex. Pegging enables managers to determine which product(s) will be affected if orders are late due to late deliveries, quality problems, or other problems.

The importance of the computer becomes evident when you consider that a typical firm would have not one but many end items for which it needs to develop material requirements plans, each with its own set of components. Inventories on hand and on order, schedules, order releases, and so on must all be updated as changes and rescheduling occur. Without the aid of a computer, the task would be almost hopeless; with the computer, planners can accomplish all of these things with much less difficulty.

pegging The process of identifying the parent items that have generated a given set of material requirements for an item.

Updating the System

A material requirements plan is not a static document. As time passes, some orders will have been completed, other orders will be nearing completion, and new orders will have been entered. In addition, there may have been changes to orders, such as changes in quantity, delays, missed deliveries of parts or raw materials, and so on. Hence, a material requirements plan is a "living" document, one that changes over time. And what we refer to as "Period 1" (i.e., the current period) is continually moving ahead; so what is now Period 2 will soon be Period 1. In a sense, schedules such as these have a *rolling horizon,* which means that plans are updated and revised so that they reflect the moving horizon over time.

The two basic systems used to update MRP records are *regenerative* and *net change.* A **regenerative system** is updated periodically; a **net-change system** is continuously updated.

A regenerative system is essentially a batch-type system, which compiles all changes (e.g., new orders, receipts) that occur within the time interval (e.g., day) and periodically updates the system. Using that information, a revised production plan is developed in the same way that the original plan was developed (e.g., exploding the bill of materials, level by level).

In a net-change system, the production plan is modified to reflect changes as they occur. If some defective purchased parts had to be returned to a vendor, the manager can enter this information into the system as soon as it becomes known. Only the *changes* are exploded through the system, level by level; the entire plan would not be regenerated.

The regenerative system is best suited to fairly stable systems, whereas the net-change system is best suited to systems that have frequent changes. The obvious disadvantage of a regenerative system is the potential amount of lag between the time information becomes available and the time it can be incorporated into the material requirements plan. On the other hand, processing costs are typically less using regenerative systems; changes that occur in a given time period could ultimately cancel each other, thereby avoiding the need to modify and then remodify the plan. The disadvantages of the net-change system relate to the costs involved in

regenerative system Approach that updates MRP records periodically.

net-change system Approach that updates MRP records continuously.

Master schedule

Week number			1	2	3	4	5	6
Quantity of A						80		
Quantity of C							50	

FIGURE 12.12
Material requirements plan for component D

A LT = 1	Beg. Inv.	1	2	3	4	5	6
Gross requirements					80		
Scheduled receipts							
Projected on hand							
Net requirements					80		
Planned-order receipts					80		
Planned-order releases				(80)			

C LT = 1	Beg. Inv.	1	2	3	4	5	6
Gross requirements					50		
Scheduled receipts							
Projected on hand							
Net requirements					50		
Planned-order receipts					50		
Planned-order releases				(50)			

times 2

D LT = 1	Beg. Inv.	1	2	3	4	5	6
Gross requirements				80	100		
Scheduled receipts							
Projected on hand	110	110	110	110	30		
Net requirements					70		
Planned-order receipts					70		
Planned-order releases				70			

continuously updating the system and the constant state of flux in a system caused by many small changes. One way around this is to enter minor changes periodically and major changes immediately. The primary advantage of the net-change system is that management can have up-to-date information for planning and control purposes.

12.5 MRP OUTPUTS

MRP systems have the ability to provide management with a fairly broad range of outputs. These are often classified as *primary reports,* which are the main reports, and *secondary reports,* which are optional outputs.

Primary Reports. Production and inventory planning and control are part of primary reports. These reports normally include the following:

1. **Planned orders**, a schedule indicating the amount and timing of future orders.
2. **Order releases**, authorizing the execution of planned orders.
3. **Changes** to planned orders, including revisions of due dates or order quantities and cancellations of orders.

Secondary Reports. Performance control, planning, and exceptions belong to secondary reports.

1. **Performance-control reports** evaluate system operation. They aid managers by measuring deviations from plans, including missed deliveries and stockouts, and by providing information that can be used to assess cost performance.
2. **Planning reports** are useful in forecasting future inventory requirements. They include purchase commitments and other data that can be used to assess future material requirements.
3. **Exception reports** call attention to major discrepancies such as late and overdue orders, excessive scrap rates, reporting errors, and requirements for nonexistent parts.

The wide range of outputs generally permits users to tailor MRP to their particular needs.

planned orders Schedule indicating the amount and timing of future orders.

order releases Authorization for the execution of planned orders.

changes Revisions of due dates or order quantities, or cancellations of orders.

performance-control reports Evaluation of system operation, including deviations from plans and cost information.

planning reports Data useful for assessing future material requirements.

exception reports Data on any major discrepancies encountered.

12.6 OTHER CONSIDERATIONS

Aside from the main details of inputs, outputs, and processing, managers must be knowledgeable about a number of other aspects of MRP. These include the holding of safety stock, lot-sizing choices, and the possible use of MRP for unfinished products.

Safety Stock

Theoretically, inventory systems with dependent demand should not require safety stock below the end item level. This is one of the main advantages of an MRP approach. Supposedly, safety stock is not needed because the manager can project precise usage quantities once the master schedule has been established because demand is not variable. Practically, however, there may be exceptions. For example, a bottleneck process or one with varying scrap rates can cause shortages in downstream operations. Furthermore, shortages may occur if orders are late or fabrication or assembly times are longer than expected. On the surface, these conditions lend themselves to the use of safety stock to maintain smooth operations; but the problem becomes more complicated when dealing with multiechelon items (i.e., multiple-level arenas such as assembled products) because a shortage of *any* component will prevent manufacture of the final assembly. However, a major advantage of MRP is lost by holding safety stock for all lower-level items.

MRP systems deal with these problems in several ways. The manager's first step is to identify activities or operations that are subject to variability and to determine the extent of that variability. When lead times are variable, the concept of safety *time* instead of safety *stock* is often used. This results in scheduling orders for arrival or completion sufficiently ahead of the time they are needed in order to eliminate or substantially reduce the element of chance in waiting for those items. When quantities tend to vary, some safety stock may be called for, but the manager must carefully weigh the need and cost of carrying extra stock. Frequently, managers elect to carry safety stock for end items, which are subject to random demand, and for selected lower-level operations when safety time is not feasible.

It is important in general to make sure that lead times are accurate, particularly when the objective is to have incoming shipments of parts and materials arrive shortly before they are needed. Early arrivals increase on-hand inventory and carrying costs, but late arrivals can raise havoc, possibly delaying all following operations. Knowing this, managers may inflate lead times (i.e., use safety time) and cause early arrivals, defeating the objective of matching the arrival of orders with production schedules.

If safety stock is needed, planned-order release amounts can be increased by the safety stock quantities for the designated components.

Lot Sizing

Determining a lot size to order or to produce is an important issue in inventory management for both independent- and dependent-demand items. This is called lot sizing. For independent-demand items, managers often use economic order sizes and economic production quantities. For dependent-demand systems, however, a much wider variety of plans is used to determine lot sizes, mainly because no single plan has a clear advantage over the others. Some of the most popular plans for lot sizing are described in this section.

A primary goal of inventory management for both independent- and dependent-demand systems is to minimize the sum of ordering cost (or setup cost) and holding cost. With independent demand, that demand is frequently distributed uniformly throughout the planning horizon (e.g., six months, year). In some cases, demand tends to be lumpy and the planning horizon shorter (e.g., three months), so that economic lot sizes are usually much more difficult to identify. Consider the situation depicted in Figure 12.13. Period demands vary from 1 to 80 units, and no demand size repeats over the horizon shown.

Managers can realize economies by grouping orders. This would be the case if the additional cost incurred by holding the extra units until they were used led to a savings in setup or ordering cost. This determination can be very complex at times, for several reasons. First, combining period demands into a single order, particularly for middle-level or end items, has a cascading effect down through the product tree: To achieve this grouping, it becomes necessary to also group items at lower levels in the tree and incorporate their setup and holding costs into the decision. Second, the uneven period demand and the relatively short planning horizon require a continual recalculation and updating of lot sizes. Not surprisingly, the methods used to handle lot sizing range from the complex, which attempt to include all relevant costs, to the very simple, which are easy to use and understand. In certain cases, the simple models seem to approach cost minimization although generalizations are difficult. Let's consider some of these models.

Lot-for-Lot Ordering. Perhaps the simplest of all the methods is lot-for-lot ordering. The order or run size for each period is set equal to demand for that period. Example 2 demonstrated this method. Not only is the order size obvious, it also virtually eliminates holding costs for parts carried over to other periods. Hence, lot-for-lot ordering minimizes investment in inventory. Its two chief drawbacks are that it usually involves many different order sizes and thus cannot take advantage of the economies of fixed order size (e.g., standard containers and other standardized procedures), and it requires a new setup for each production run. If setup costs can be significantly reduced, this method may approximate a minimum-cost lot size.

Economic Order Quantity Model. Sometimes economic order quantity (EOQ) models are used. They can lead to minimum costs if usage is fairly uniform. This is sometimes the case for lower-level items that are common to different parents and for raw materials. However, the more lumpy demand is, the less appropriate such an approach is, because the mismatch in supply and demand results in leftover inventories.

Fixed-Period Ordering. This type of ordering provides coverage for some predetermined number of periods (e.g., two or three). In some instances, the span is simply arbitrary; in other

	Period				
	1	2	3	4	5
Demand	70	50	1	80	4
Cumulative demand	70	120	121	201	205

FIGURE 12.13
Demand for part K

cases, a review of historical demand patterns may lead to a more rational designation of a fixed period length. A simple rule is: Order to cover a two-period interval. The rule can be modified when common sense suggests a better way. For example, take a look at the demands shown in Figure 12.13. Using a two-period rule, an order size of 120 units would cover the first two periods. The next two periods would be covered by an order size of 81 units. However, the demands in periods 3 and 5 are so small, it would make sense to combine them both with the 80 units and order 85 units.

Other Models. There are other models, such as the part-period model and the Wagner-Whitin model, that are used for lot sizing which are beyond the scope of this book.

12.7 MRP IN SERVICES

MRP has applications in services as well as in manufacturing. These applications may involve material goods that form a part of the product–service package, or they may involve mainly service components.

An example of a product–service package is a food catering service, particularly in instances that require preparing and serving meals for large numbers of people. To estimate quantities and costs of an order, the food manager would have to determine the quantities of the ingredients for each recipe on the menu (i.e., a bill of materials), which would then be combined with the number of each meal to be prepared to obtain a material requirements plan for the event.

Similar examples occur for large-scale renovations, such as a sports stadium or a major hotel, where there are multiple repetitions of activities and related materials that must be "exploded" into their components for purposes of cost estimation and scheduling.

12.8 BENEFITS AND REQUIREMENTS OF MRP

LO12.4 Discuss the benefits and requirements of MRP.

Benefits

MRP enables managers to easily determine the quantities of every component for a given order size, to know when to release orders for each component, and to be alerted when items need attention. Still other benefits include the following:

1. Low levels of in-process inventories, due to an exact matching of supply to demand.
2. The ability to keep track of material requirements.
3. The ability to evaluate capacity requirements generated by a given master schedule.
4. A means of allocating production time.
5. The ability to easily determine inventory usage by *backflushing*.

backflushing Exploding an end item's BOM to determine the quantities of the components that were used to make the item.

Backflushing is a procedure in which an end item's bill of materials (BOM) is periodically exploded to determine the quantities of the various components that were used to make the item, eliminating the need to collect detailed usage information on the production floor.

A range of people in a typical manufacturing company are important users of the information provided by an MRP system. Production planners are obvious users of MRP. Production managers, who must balance workloads across departments and make decisions about scheduling work, and plant foremen, who are responsible for issuing work orders and maintaining production schedules, also rely heavily on MRP output. Other users include customer service representatives, who must be able to supply customers with projected delivery dates; purchasing managers; and inventory managers. The benefits of MRP depend in large measure on the use of a computer to maintain up-to-date information on material requirements.

Requirements

In order to implement and operate an effective MRP system, it is necessary to have:

1. A computer and the necessary software programs to handle computations and maintain records

2. Accurate and up-to-date:
    a. Master schedules
    b. Bills of materials
    c. Inventory records

3. Integrity of file data

Accuracy is absolutely essential for a successful MRP system. Inaccuracies in inventory record files or bill-of-material files can lead to unpleasant surprises, ranging from missing parts to ordering too many of some items and too few of others, and failure to stay on schedule, all of which contribute to inefficient use of resources, missed delivery dates, and poor customer service. Companies also need to exert scheduling discipline and have in place standard procedures for maintaining and updating bills of material.

Other common problems associated with using MRP include those due to the assumption of constant lead times, products being produced differently from the bill of materials, and failure to alter a bill of materials when customizing a product.

Similarly, inaccurate forecasts can have serious consequences for producers of assembled items. If forecasts are overly optimistic, companies will experience relatively high holding costs, considering the excess inventory represented by the components and raw materials. Conversely, forecasts that are too low will result in shortages of component parts and will require long lead times to acquire the needed components and assemble the products to alleviate the shortages.

> **LO12.5** Describe some of the difficulties users have encountered with MRP.

12.9 MRP II

> **LO12.6** Describe MRP II and its benefits.

MRP was developed as a way for manufacturing companies to calculate more precisely what materials were needed to produce a product, and when and how much of those materials were needed. **Manufacturing resources planning (MRP II)** evolved from MRP because manufacturers recognized additional needs. MRP II expanded the scope of materials planning to include capacity requirements planning, and to involve other functional areas of the organization such as marketing and finance in the planning process.

Material requirements planning is at the heart of the process (see Figure 12.14). The process begins with an aggregation of demand from all sources (e.g., firm orders, forecasts, safety stock requirements). Production, marketing, and finance personnel work toward developing a master production schedule. Although manufacturing people will have a major input in determining that schedule and a major responsibility for making it work, marketing and finance will also have important inputs and responsibilities. The rationale for having these functional areas work together is the increased likelihood of developing a plan that works and with which everyone can live. Moreover, because each of these functional areas has been involved in formulating the plan, they will have reasonably good knowledge of the plan and more reason to work toward achieving it.

In addition to the obvious manufacturing resources needed to support the plan, financing resources will be needed and must be planned for, both in amount and timing. Similarly, marketing resources also will be needed in varying degrees throughout the process. In order for the plan to work, the firm must have all of the necessary resources available as needed. Often, an initial plan must be revised based on an assessment of the availability of various resources. Once these have been decided, the master production schedule can be firmed up.

At this point, material requirements planning comes into play, generating material and schedule requirements. Next, management must make more detailed capacity requirements

manufacturing resources planning (MRP II) Expanded approach to production resource planning, involving other areas of a firm in the planning process and enabling capacity requirements planning.

FIGURE 12.14
An overview of MRP II

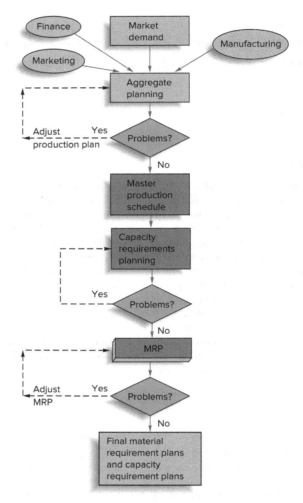

planning to determine whether these more specific capacity requirements can be met. Again, some adjustments in the master production schedule may be required.

As the schedule unfolds and actual work begins, a variety of reports help managers to monitor the process and to make any necessary adjustments to keep operations on track.

In effect, this is a continuing process, where the master production schedule is updated and revised as necessary to achieve corporate goals. The business plan that governs the entire process usually undergoes changes too, although these tend to be less frequent than the changes made at lower levels (i.e., the master production schedule).

Most MRP II systems have the capability of performing simulation, enabling managers to answer a variety of what-if questions so they can gain a better appreciation of available options and their consequences.

Closed-Loop MRP

When MRP was introduced, it did not have the capability to assess the feasibility of a proposed plan (i.e., if sufficient capacity existed at every level to achieve the plan). Thus, there was no way of knowing before executing a proposed plan if it could be achieved, or after executing the plan if it had been achieved. Consequently, a new plan had to be developed each week. When MRP II systems began to include feedback loops, they were referred to as closed-loop MRP. Closed-loop MRP systems evaluate a proposed material plan relative to available capacity. If a proposed plan is not feasible, it must be revised. The evaluation is referred to as capacity requirements planning.

12.10 CAPACITY REQUIREMENTS PLANNING

LO12.7 Explain how an MRP system is useful in capacity requirements planning.

One of the most important features of MRP II is its ability to aid managers in capacity planning.

Capacity requirements planning is the process of determining short-range capacity requirements. The necessary inputs include planned-order releases for MRP, the current shop load, routing information, and job times. Key outputs include load reports for each work center. When variances (underloads or overloads) are projected, managers might consider remedies such as alternative routings, changing or eliminating of lot sizing or safety stock requirements, and lot splitting. Moving production forward or backward can be extremely challenging because of precedence requirements and the availability of components.

A firm usually generates a master schedule initially in terms of what is needed but not what is possible. The initial schedule may or may not be feasible given the limits of the production system and availability of materials when end items are translated into requirements for procurement, fabrication, and assembly. Consequently, it is often necessary to run a proposed master schedule through MRP processing in order to obtain a clearer picture of actual requirements, which can then be compared to available capacity and materials. If it turns out that the current master schedule is not feasible, management may make a decision to increase capacity (e.g., through overtime or subcontracting) or to revise the master schedule. In the latter case, this may entail several revisions, each of which is run through the system until a feasible plan is obtained. At that point, the master schedule is *frozen,* at least for the near term, thus establishing a firm schedule from which to plan requirements.

Stability in short-term production plans is very important; without it, changes in order quantity and/or timing can render material requirements plans almost useless. The term *system nervousness* describes the way a system might react to changes. The reaction can sometimes be greater than the original change. For example, a small change near the top of a product tree can reverberate throughout much of the lower parts of the tree, causing major changes to order quantities and production schedules of many components. That, in turn, might cause queues to form at various portions of the system, leading to late orders, increased work in process, and added carrying costs.

To minimize such problems, many firms establish a series of time intervals, called **time fences**, during which changes can be made to orders. For example, a firm might specify time fences of 4, 8, and 12 weeks, with the nearest fence being the most restrictive and the farthest fence being the least restrictive. Beyond 12 weeks, changes are expected; from 8 to 12 weeks, substitutions of one end item for another may be permitted as long as the components are available and the production plan is not compromised; from 4 to 8 weeks, the plan is fixed, but small changes may be allowed; and the plan is frozen out to the 4-week fence.

Some companies use two fences: One is a near-term *demand* fence, and the other is a long-term *planning* fence. For example, the demand fence might be 4 weeks from the present time while the planning fence might be 10 weeks away. In the near term, customer orders receive precedence over the forecast. The time beyond the planning fence is available for inserting new orders into the master schedule. Between the demand fence and the planning fence, management must make trade-offs when changes are introduced unless excess capacity is expected to be available.

In establishing time fences, a manager must weigh the benefits of stability in the production plan against the possible negative impact on the competitive advantage of being able to quickly respond to new orders.

The capacity planning process begins with a proposed or tentative master production schedule that must be tested for feasibility and possibly adjusted before it becomes permanent. The proposed schedule is processed using MRP to ascertain the material requirements the schedule would generate. These are then translated into resource (i.e., capacity) requirements, often in the form of a series of **load reports** for each department or work center, which compares known and expected future capacity requirements with projected capacity availability. Figure 12.15 illustrates the nature of a load report. It shows expected resource requirements (i.e., usage) for jobs currently being worked on, planned orders, and expected orders for the planning horizon. Given this sort of information, the manager can more easily determine whether capacity is sufficient

capacity requirements planning The process of determining short-range capacity requirements.

time fences Series of time intervals during which order changes are allowed or restricted; the nearest fence is most restrictive to change, the farthest is least restrictive.

load reports Department or work center reports that compare known and expected future capacity requirements with projected capacity availability.

FIGURE 12.15
A hypothetical department
load profile

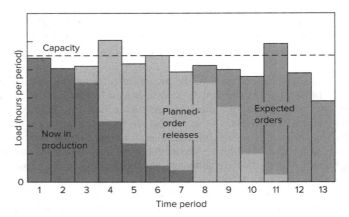

to satisfy these requirements. If there is enough capacity, he or she can freeze the portion of the master production schedule that generates these requirements. In the load profile illustrated in Figure 12.15, planned-order releases in time period 4 will cause an overload. However, it appears possible to accommodate demand by slightly shifting some orders to adjacent periods. Similarly, an overload appears likely in period 11, but that too can be handled by shifting some jobs to adjacent time periods. In cases where capacity is insufficient, a manager may be able to increase capacity (by scheduling overtime, transferring personnel from other areas, or subcontracting some of the work) if this is possible and economical, or else revise the master production schedule and repeat the process until an acceptable production schedule is obtained.

If the master production schedule must be revised, this generally means that the manager must assign priorities to orders, if some orders will be finished later than originally planned.

One note of caution is in order concerning capacity load reports. Often, the load reports are only approximations, and they may not give a true picture because the loading does not take into account scheduling and queuing delays. Consequently, it is possible to experience system backups even though a load report implies sufficient capacity to handle projected loads.

An important aspect of capacity requirements planning is the conversion of quantity requirements into labor and machine requirements. One accomplishes this by multiplying each period's quantity requirements by standard labor and/or machine requirements per unit. For instance, if 100 units of product A are scheduled in the fabrication department, and each unit has a labor standard time of 2 hours and a machine standard time of 1.5 hours, then 100 units of A convert into these capacity requirements:

$$\text{Labor:} \quad 100 \text{ units} \times 2 \text{ hours/unit} \quad = 200 \text{ machine hours}$$
$$\text{Machine:} \quad 100 \text{ units} \times 1.5 \text{ hours/unit} = 150 \text{ machine hours}$$

One can then compare these capacity requirements with available department capacity to determine the extent to which this product utilizes capacity. For example, if the department has 200 labor hours and 200 machine hours available, labor utilization will be 100 percent because all of the labor capacity will be required by this product. However, machine capacity will be underutilized.

$$\frac{\text{Required}}{\text{Available}} \times 100 = \frac{150 \text{ hours}}{200 \text{ hours}} \times 100 = 75 \text{ percent}$$

Underutilization may mean that unused capacity can be used for other jobs; overutilization indicates that available capacity is insufficient to handle requirements. To compensate, production may have to be rescheduled or overtime may be needed.

Distribution Resource Planning for the Supply Chain

distribution resource plan-ning (DRP) A method used for planning orders in a supply chain.

Distribution resource planning (DRP), also referred to as *distribution requirements planning,* is a method used for planning orders in a supply chain. It extends MRP concepts, enabling a planner to compute time-phased inventory requirements for a supply chain. The goal is to achieve a balance of supply and demand throughout the supply chain.

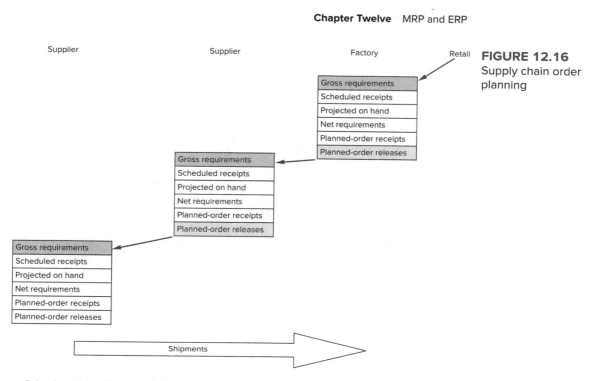

FIGURE 12.16
Supply chain order planning

It begins with a forecast of demand plus actual orders for future periods at the distribution end (e.g., retail) of a supply chain. Other information needed includes the quantity and timing of scheduled receipts at various points in the supply chain as well as on-hand inventories, and any safety stock requirements. Some versions of DRP also include projections for labor, material handling facilities, and storage space that will be needed.

In a procedure similar to MRP, the planned-order release quantities at each level in the supply chain become the gross requirements one level back, as illustrated in Figure 12.16. In effect, the process pulls inventory shipment through the supply chain based on demand.

12.11 ERP

Business organizations are complex systems in which various functions such as purchasing, production, distribution, sales, human resources, finance, and accounting must work together to achieve the goals of the organization. However, in the functional structure used by many business organizations, information flows freely within each function, but not so between functions. That makes information sharing among functional areas burdensome.

Enterprise resource planning (ERP) is a computerized system designed to connect all parts of a business organization as well as key portions of its supply chain to a single database for the purpose of information sharing. Some of the key connections are depicted in Figure 12.17. SAP and PeopleSoft are major vendors, although there are many others.

ERP software provides a system to capture and make data available in real time to decision makers and other users throughout an organization. It also provides a set of tools for planning and monitoring various business processes to achieve the goals of the organization. ERP systems are composed of a collection of integrated modules. There are many modules to choose from, and different software vendors offer different but similar lists of modules. Some are industry specific, and others are general purpose. The modules relate to the functional areas of business organizations. For example, there are modules for accounting and finance, HR, product planning, purchasing, inventory management, distribution, order tracking, finance, accounting, and marketing. Organizations can select the modules that best serve their needs and budgets. Table 12.1 provides an overview of some widely used modules.

LO12.8 Describe ERP, what it provides, and its hidden costs.

enterprise resource planning (ERP) Integration of financial, manufacturing, and human resources in a single database.

522   **Chapter Twelve**   MRP and ERP

FIGURE 12.17
Key connections to the
ERP system

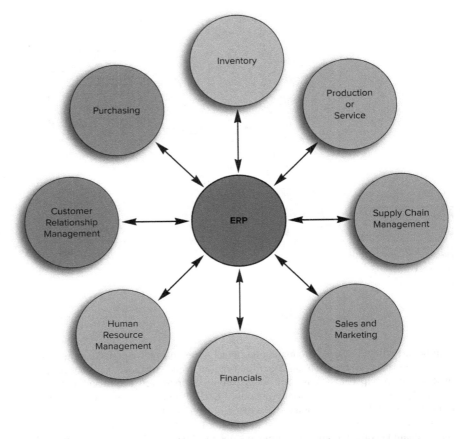

TABLE 12.1
An overview of some ERP
software modules

Module	Brief Description
Accounting/Finance	A central component of most ERP systems. It provides a range of financial reports, including general ledger, accounts payable, accounts receivable, payroll, income statements, and balance sheets.
Marketing	Supports lead generation, target marketing, direct mail, and sales.
Human Resources	Maintains a complete database of employee information such as date of hire, salary, contact information, performance evaluations, and other pertinent information.
Purchasing	Facilitates vendor selection, price negotiation, making purchasing decisions, and bill payment.
Production Planning	Integrates information on forecasts, orders, production capacity, on-hand inventory quantities, bills of material, work in process, schedules, and production lead times.
Inventory Management	Identifies inventory requirements, inventory availability, replenishment rules, and inventory tracking.
Distribution	Contains information on third-party shippers, shipping and delivery schedules, delivery tracking.
Sales	Information on orders, invoices, order tracking, and shipping.
Supply Chain Management	Facilitates supplier and customer management, supply chain visibility, and event management.
Customer Relationship Management	Contact information, buying behavior, shipping preferences, contracts, payment terms, and credit history.

Chapter Twelve   MRP and ERP   **523**

An important feature of the modules is that data entered in one module is automatically routed to other modules, so all data is immediately updated and available to all functional areas.

It should be noted that implementations are costly and time consuming, often lasting many years, and require extensive employee training throughout the organization.

The following reading provides additional insight into ERP.

READING   **THE ABCS OF ERP**

Compiled from Reports by Christopher Koch, Derek Slater, and E. Baatz

What is ERP?
How can ERP improve a company's business performance?
How long will an ERP project take?
What will ERP fix in my business?
Will ERP fit the way I do business?
What does ERP *really* cost?
When will I get payback from ERP—and how much will it be?
The hidden costs of ERP?
How do you configure ERP software?
How do companies organize their ERP projects?
How does ERP fit with electronic commerce?

What Is ERP?

Enterprise resource planning software, or ERP, doesn't live up to its acronym. Forget about planning—it doesn't do that—and forget about resource, a throwaway term. But remember the enterprise part. This is ERP's true ambition. It attempts to integrate all departments and functions across a company onto a single computer system that can serve all those different departments' particular needs.

That is a tall order, building a single software program that serves the needs of people in finance as well as it does the people in human resources and in the warehouse. Each of those departments typically has its own computer system, each optimized for the particular ways that the department does its work. But ERP combines them all together into a single, integrated software program that runs off a single database so that the various departments can more easily share information and communicate with each other.

That integrated approach can have a tremendous payback if companies install the software correctly. Take a customer order, for example. Typically, when a customer places an order, that order begins a mostly paper-based journey from in-basket to in-basket around the company, often being keyed and rekeyed into different departments' computer systems along the way. All that lounging around in in-baskets causes delays and lost orders, and all the keying into different computer systems invites errors. Meanwhile,

no one in the company truly knows what the status of the order is at any given point because there is no way for the finance department, for example, to get into the warehouse's computer system to see whether the item has been shipped. "You'll have to call the warehouse," is the familiar refrain heard by frustrated customers.

How Can ERP Improve a Company's Business Performance?

ERP automates the tasks involved in performing a business process—such as order fulfillment, which involves taking an order from a customer, shipping it, and billing for it. With ERP, when a customer service representative takes an order from a customer, he or she has all the information necessary to complete the order (the customer's credit rating and order history, the company's inventory levels and the shipping dock's trucking schedule). Everyone else in the company sees the same computer screen and has access to the single database that holds the customer's new order. When one department finishes with the order it is automatically routed via the ERP system to the next department. To find out where the order is at any point, one need only log into the ERP system and track it down. With luck, the order process moves like a bolt of lightning through the organization, and customers get their orders faster and with fewer mistakes than before. ERP can apply that same magic to the other major business processes, such as employee benefits or financial reporting.

That, at least, is the dream of ERP. The reality is much harsher.

Let's go back to those inboxes for a minute. That process may not have been efficient, but it was simple. Finance did its job, the warehouse did its job, and if anything went wrong outside of the department's walls, it was somebody else's problem. Not anymore. With ERP, the customer service representatives are no longer just typists entering someone's name into a computer and hitting the return key. The ERP screen makes them business people. It flickers with the customer's credit rating from the finance department and the product inventory levels from the warehouse. Will the customer pay on time? Will we be able to ship the order on time? These are decisions that customer service representatives have never had to make before and which affect the customer and every other department in the company. But it's not just the

(continued)

(*concluded*)

customer service representatives who have to wake up. People in the warehouse who used to keep inventory in their heads or on scraps of paper now need to put that information online. If they don't, customer service will see low inventory levels on their screens and tell customers that their requested item is not in stock. Accountability, responsibility and communication have never been tested like this before.

How Long Will an ERP Project Take?

Companies that install ERP do not have an easy time of it. Don't be fooled when ERP vendors tell you about a three or six month average implementation time. Those short (that's right, six months is short) implementations all have a catch of one kind or another: the company was small, or the implementation was limited to a small area of the company, or the company only used the financial pieces of the ERP system (in which case the ERP system is nothing more than a very expensive accounting system). To do ERP right, the ways you do business will need to change and the ways people do their jobs will need to change too. And that kind of change doesn't come without pain. Unless, of course, your ways of doing business are working extremely well (orders all shipped on time, productivity higher than all your competitors, customers completely satisfied), in which case there is no reason to even consider ERP.

The important thing is not to focus on how long it will take—real transformational ERP efforts usually run between one to three years, on average—but rather to understand why you need it and how you will use it to improve your business.

What Will ERP Fix in My Business?

There are three major reasons why companies undertake ERP:

To integrate financial data—As the CEO tries to understand the company's overall performance, he or she may find many different versions of the truth. Finance has its own set of revenue numbers, sales has another version, and the different business units may each have their own versions of how much they contributed to revenues. ERP creates a single version of the truth that cannot be questioned because everyone is using the same system.

To standardize manufacturing processes—Manufacturing companies—especially those with an appetite for mergers and acquisitions—often find that multiple business units across the company make the same widget using different methods and computer systems. Standardizing those processes and using a single, integrated computer system can save time, increase productivity, and reduce headcount.

To standardize HR information—Especially in companies with multiple business units, HR may not have a unified, simple method for tracking employee time and communicating with them about benefits and services. ERP can fix that.

In the race to fix these problems, companies often lose sight of the fact that ERP packages are nothing more than generic representations of the ways a typical company does business. While most packages are exhaustively comprehensive, each industry has its quirks that make it unique. Most ERP systems were designed to be used by discreet manufacturing companies (who make physical things that can be counted), which immediately left all the process manufacturers (oil, chemical, and utility companies that measure their products by flow rather than individual units) out in the cold. Each of these industries has struggled with the different ERP vendors to modify core ERP programs to their needs.

Will ERP Fit the Ways I Do Business?

It's critical for companies to figure out if their ways of doing business will fit within a standard ERP package before the checks are signed and the implementation begins. The most common reason that companies walk away from multimillion-dollar ERP projects is that they discover that the software does not support one of their important business processes. At that point there are two things they can do: They can change the business process to accommodate the software, which will mean deep changes in long-established ways of doing business (that often provide competitive advantage) and shake up important peoples' roles and responsibilities (something that few companies have the stomach for). Or they can modify the software to fit the process, which will slow down the project, introduce dangerous bugs into the system and make upgrading the software to the ERP vendor's next release excruciatingly difficult, because the customizations will need to be torn apart and rewritten to fit with the new version.

Needless to say, the move to ERP is a project of breathtaking scope, and the price tags on the front end are enough to make the most placid CFO a little twitchy. In addition to budgeting for software costs, financial executives should plan to write checks to cover consulting, process rework, integration testing and a long laundry list of other expenses before the benefits of ERP start to manifest themselves. Underestimating the price of teaching users their new job processes can lead to a rude shock down the line. So can failure to consider data warehouse integration requirements and the cost of extra software to duplicate the old report formats. A few oversights in the budgeting and planning stage can send ERP costs spiraling out of control faster than oversights in planning almost any other information system undertaking.

What Does ERP *Really* Cost?

Meta Group recently did a study looking at the Total Cost of Ownership (TCO) of ERP, including hardware, software, professional services, and internal staff costs. The TCO numbers include getting the software installed and the two years afterward, which is when the real costs of maintaining, upgrading, and optimizing the system for your business are felt. Among the 63 companies surveyed—including small, medium, and large companies in a range of industries—the average TCO was $15 million (the highest was $300 million and lowest was $400,000). While it's hard to draw a solid number from that kind of a range of companies and ERP efforts, Meta came up with one statistic that proves that ERP is expensive no matter what kind of company is using it. The TCO for a "heads-down" user over that period was a staggering $53,320.

When Will I Get Payback from ERP—and How Much Will It Be?

Don't expect to revolutionize your business with ERP. It is a navel gazing exercise that focuses on optimizing the way things are done internally rather than with customers, suppliers, or partners. Yet the navel gazing has a pretty good payback if you're willing to wait for it—a Meta Group study of 63 companies found that it took eight months after the new system was in (31 months total) to see any benefits. But the median annual savings from the new ERP system was $1.6 million per year.

The Hidden Costs of ERP

Although different companies will find different land mines in the budgeting process, those who have implemented ERP packages agree that certain costs are more commonly overlooked or underestimated than others. Armed with insights from across the business, ERP pros vote the following areas as most likely to result in budget overrun.

1. **Training.** Training is the near-unanimous choice of experienced ERP implementers as the most elusive budget item. It's not so much that this cost is completely overlooked as it is consistently underestimated. Training expenses are high because workers almost invariably have to learn a new set of processes, not just a new software interface.

2. **Integration and testing.** Testing the links between ERP packages and other corporate software links that have to be built on a case-by-case basis is another often underestimated cost. A typical manufacturing company may have add-on applications for logistics, tax, production planning, and bar coding. If this laundry list also includes customization of the core ERP package, expect the cost of integrating, testing, and maintaining the system to skyrocket.

    As with training, testing ERP integration has to be done from a process-oriented perspective. Instead of plugging in dummy data and moving it from one application to the next, veterans recommend running a real purchase order through the system, from order entry through shipping and receipt of payment—the whole order-to-cash banana—preferably with the participation of the employees who will eventually do those jobs.

3. **Data conversion.** It costs money to move corporate information, such as customer and supplier records, product design data and the like, from old systems to new ERP homes. Although few CIOs will admit it, most data in most legacy systems is of little use. Companies often deny their data is dirty until they actually have to move it to the new client/server setups that popular ERP packages require. Consequently, those companies are more likely to underestimate the cost of the move. But even clean data may demand some overhaul to match process modifications necessitated—or inspired—by the ERP implementation.

4. **Data analysis.** Often, the data from the ERP system must be combined with data from external systems for analysis purposes. Users with heavy analysis needs should include the cost of a data warehouse in the ERP budget—and they should expect to do quite a bit of work to make it run smoothly. Users are in a pickle here: Refreshing all the ERP data in a big corporate data warehouse daily is difficult, and ERP systems do a poor job of indicating which information has changed from day to day, making selective warehouse updates tough. One expensive solution is custom programming. The upshot is that the wise will check all their data analysis needs before signing off on the budget.

5. **Consultants ad infinitum.** When users fail to plan for disengagement, consulting fees run wild. To avoid this, companies should identify objectives for which [their] consulting partners must aim when training internal staff. Include metrics in the consultants' contract; for example, a specific number of the user company's staff should be able to pass a project-management leadership test—similar to what Big Five consultants have to pass to lead an ERP engagement.

6. **Replacing your best and brightest.** ERP success depends on staffing the project with the best and brightest from the business and IS. The software is too complex and the business changes too dramatic to trust the project to just anyone. The bad news is, a company must be prepared to replace many of those people when the project is over. Though the ERP market is not as hot as it once was, consulting firms and other companies that have lost their best people will be hounding yours with higher salaries and bonus offers than you can afford—or that your HR policies permit. Huddle with HR early on to develop a retention bonus program and to create new salary strata for ERP veterans. If you let them go, you'll wind up hiring them—or someone like them—back as consultants for twice what you paid them in salaries.

7. **Implementation teams can never stop.** Most companies intend to treat their ERP implementations as they would any other software project. Once the software is installed, they figure, the team will be scuttled and everyone will go back to his or her day job. But after ERP, you can't go home again. You're too valuable. Because they have worked intimately with ERP, they know more about the sales process than the salespeople do and more about the manufacturing process than the manufacturing people do. Companies can't afford to send their project people back into the business because there's so much to do after the ERP software is installed. Just writing reports to pull information out of the new ERP system will keep the project team busy for a year at least. And it is in analysis—and, one hopes, insight—that companies make their money back on an ERP implementation. Unfortunately, few IS departments plan for the frenzy of post-ERP installation activity, and fewer still build it into their budgets when they start their ERP projects. Many are forced to beg for more money and staff immediately after the go-live date, long before the ERP project has demonstrated any benefit.

8. **Waiting for ROI.** One of the most misleading legacies of traditional software project management is that the company expects to gain value from the application as soon as it is

(*continued*)

(*concluded*)

installed; the project team expects a break, and maybe a pat on the back. Neither expectation applies to ERP. Most don't reveal their value until after companies have had them running for some time and can concentrate on making improvements in the business processes that are affected by the system. And the project team is not going to be rewarded until their efforts pay off.

9. **Post-ERP depression.** ERP systems often wreak havoc in the companies that install them. In a recent Deloitte Consulting survey of 64 Fortune 500 companies, one in four admitted that they suffered a drop in performance when their ERP systems went live. The true percentage is undoubtedly much higher. The most common reason for the performance problems is that everything looks and works differently from the way it did before. When people can't do their jobs in the familiar way and haven't yet mastered the new way, they panic, and the business goes into spasms.

How Do You Configure ERP Software?

Even if a company installs ERP software for the so-called right reasons and everyone can agree on the optimal definition of a customer, the inherent difficulties of implementing something as complex as ERP is like, well, teaching an elephant to do the hootchy-kootchy. The packages are built from database tables, thousands of them, that IS programmers and end users must set to match their business processes; each table has a decision "switch" that leads the software down one decision path or another. By presenting only one way for the company to do each task—say, run the payroll or close the books—a company's individual operating units and far-flung divisions are integrated under one system. But figuring out precisely how to set all the switches in the tables requires a deep understanding of the existing processes being used to operate the business. As the table settings are decided, these business processes are reengineered, ERP's way. Most ERP systems are not shipped as a shell system in which customers must determine at the minutia level how all the functional procedures should be set, making thousands of decisions that affect how their system behaves in line with their own business activities. Most ERP systems are preconfigured, allowing just hundreds— rather than thousands—of procedural settings to be made by the customer.

How Do Companies Organize Their ERP Projects?

Based on our observations, there are three commonly used ways of installing ERP.

The big bang—In this, the most ambitious and difficult of approaches to ERP implementation, companies cast off all their legacy systems at once and implement a single ERP system across the entire company.

Though this method dominated early ERP implementations, few companies dare to attempt it anymore because it calls for the entire company to mobilize and change at once. Most of the ERP implementation horror stories from the late 90s warn us about companies that used this strategy. Getting everyone to cooperate and accept a new software system at the same time is a tremendous effort, largely because the new system will not have any advocates. No one within the company has any experience using it, so no one is sure whether it will work. Also, ERP inevitably involves compromises. Many departments have computer systems that have been honed to match the ways they work. In most cases, ERP offers neither the range of functionality, nor the comfort of familiarity that a custom legacy system can offer. In many cases, the speed of the new system may suffer because it is serving the entire company rather than a single department. ERP implementation requires a direct mandate from the CEO.

Franchising strategy—This approach suits large or diverse companies that do not share many common processes across business units. Independent ERP systems are installed in each unit, while linking common processes, such as financial bookkeeping, across the enterprise.

This has emerged as the most common way of implementing ERP. In most cases, the business units each have their own "instances" of ERP—that is, a separate system and database. The systems link together only to share the information necessary for the corporation to get a performance big picture across all the business units (business unit revenues, for example), or for processes that don't vary much from business unit to business unit (perhaps HR benefits). Usually, these implementations begin with a demonstration or "pilot" installation in a particularly open-minded and patient business unit where the core business of the corporation will not be disrupted if something goes wrong. Once the project team gets the system up and running and works out all the bugs, the team begins selling other units on ERP, using the first implementation as a kind of in-house customer reference. Plan for this strategy to take a long time.

Slam-dunk—ERP dictates the process design in this method, where the focus is on just a few key processes, such as those contained in an ERP system's financials module. The slam-dunk is generally for smaller companies expecting to grow into ERP.

The goal here is to get ERP up and running quickly and to ditch the fancy reengineering in favor of the ERP system's "canned" processes. Few companies that have approached ERP this way can claim much payback from the new system. Most use it as an infrastructure to support more diligent installation efforts down the road. Yet many discover that a slammed-in ERP system is little better than a legacy system, because it doesn't force employees to change any of their old habits. In fact, doing the hard work of process reengineering after the system is in can be more challenging than if there had been no system at all, because at that point few people in the company will have felt much benefit.

How Does ERP Fit with Electronic Commerce?

After all of that work inventing, perfecting, and selling ERP to the world, the major ERP vendors are having a hard time shifting gears from making the applications that streamline business practices inside a company to those that face outward to the rest of the world.

Chapter Twelve   MRP and ERP   **527**

These days, the hottest areas for outward-looking (that is, Internet) post-ERP work are electronic commerce, planning and managing your supply chain, and tracking and serving customers. Most ERP vendors have been slow to develop offerings for these areas, and they face stiff competition from niche vendors. ERP vendors have the advantage of a huge installed base of customers and a virtual stranglehold on the "back office" functions—such as order fulfillment. Recently ERP vendors have begun to shrink their ambitions and focus on being the back-office engine that powers electronic commerce, rather than trying to own all the software niches that are necessary for a good electronic commerce website. Indeed, as the niche vendors make their software easier to hook into electronic commerce websites, and as middleware vendors make it easier for

IS departments to hook together applications from different vendors, many people wonder how much longer ERP vendors can claim to be the primary platform for the Fortune 500.

Questions

1. What is ERP?
2. What are the three main reasons firms adopt ERP?
3. What are some hidden costs of ERP?
4. How does ERP fit with e-commerce and supply chain management?

Source: Christopher Koch, "ABC: An Introduction to ERP," Cio.com, Copyright © 2008 CXO Media. Used with permission.

ERP in Services

Although ERP was initially developed for manufacturing, it now has a long list of service applications. These include professional services, postal services, retail, banking, health care, higher education, engineering and construction services, logistics services, and real estate management.

In a manufacturing environment, ERP systems generally encompass the major functions such as production planning and scheduling, inventory management, product costing, and distribution. In a service environment, the major functions can differ from one service organization to another. For example, many universities use ERP systems; they typically are used to integrate and access student information, course prerequisites, course schedules, room schedules, human resources, accounting, and financial information. Hospitals' ERP systems include patient records, medication data, treatment plans, and scheduling information (e.g., rooms, equipment, surgery) as well as human resources information.

ERP is now about enterprise applications *integration,* an issue that generally arises with any major technology acquisition. The following reading underscores this point.

READING   # THE TOP 10 ERP MISTAKES

Clive Weightman

Although faulty technology often is blamed for problems, it is frequently other shortcomings that create performance-related problems—such as the people employing the ERP application don't fully understand what it is or how it works.

Execution of a successful ERP project provides the backbone for a company's internal and external operations—from integrating back-office financials with business performance data to building a launch platform for an extended enterprise and collaborative commerce. This foundation can serve as the competitive weapon of the future.

Top 10 Mistakes

10. **Believing the journey is complete at "go live."** Treat the day your ERP project goes live as the start of the next phase

of your journey, not the finish because an ERP implementation represents much more than simply a project. . . . So don't disband the team a month after the project goes live.

9. **Not planning for—and minimizing—the interim performance dip after start up.** Research shows that even the projects that have gone the smoothest in the execution stage suffer a dip in performance after the new system launches. Transactional efficiency, the pace of taking sales orders may slow down, or the speed of pushing products into the warehouse may decline a bit. Recognize that performance is going to suffer some at the outset, but with excellent execution, this effect can be very slim and very short.

8. **Failing to balance the needs and power of integration with seeking quick business hits.** Today, every chief executive officer

(continued)

(*concluded*)

must deliver results now, not in 15 months from now. Given the challenges of a full ERP implementation, it's difficult for them to promise their board of directors that with the ERP project, they are going to see savings in 24 to 36 months of such-and-such amount. They want to see the return on investment now.

7. **Starting too late to address all things data (architecture, standards, management, cleansing, and so on).** These systems are only as good as the fundamental data that enters them. And that's where a common problem erupts. Far too often, research indicates, companies think about the quality and accuracy of their data too late in the project. The consistency and accuracy of data is [*sic*] critical.

6. **Failing to staff the team with "A" players from business and technical sides of the organization, including program management.** This can be a major challenge. You need top-notch players for these projects—not just technical stars but stellar performers from the business side as well. Indeed, if you have to trade off in terms of quality in one area, never skimp on business talent. You can perhaps trade off on technical expertise because the consultant you retain can bring in skilled technicians.

   And the "A" players should encompass program managers to the most junior members of the team.

5. **Starting without an effective and dedicated senior governance council, including a single executive sponsor.** Any major ERP project overhauls a lot of business processes, roles, responsibilities, standards, and data definitions—and these are changes that cannot be pursued from the bottom up. An effective governing council—a steering group—is essential, as is a single executive sponsor, dedicated and effective, to chair it. The project will trigger difficult, sometimes nasty, issues and a senior executive who is accountable can make those decisions and see that the steering group understands and accepts them.

   The project's executive "angel" must be from the corporate suite and, preferably, not the chief information officer.

4. **Selecting a strong systems integrator and then not heeding its advice.** In selecting an SI, a company should:
   - Consider compatibility. Do you want a firm that wants to come in to do it to you rather than do it with you? Some SI firms favor a "let's solve this together" approach, while others prefer the "here are your marching orders, this is how it's going to be, so let's get down to business." Determine which approach you favor for your firm's culture.
   - Clearly look at the SI's track record. Look beyond its marketing, talk to the software vendors you'll be working with and also talk with industry analysts.
   - Spend considerable time examining the members of the actual team that will be working with you every day. Be sure to put language in the contract that at least binds the team leaders and the firm's partner with you for its duration.

3. **Trying to create a solution incompatible with the company's culture.** In the 1990s, research found that many companies

with ERP projects saw them as a silver bullet that would solve all their problems—even if the "style" of solution wasn't compatible with their corporate culture traditions.

An executive might say he or she wants to operate in a globally centralized fashion—to be more like a Wal-Mart, with the strength and discipline of a global head office. However, this doesn't work if your firm's culture is one of decentralized entrepreneurship. You can't use technology to force change in the culture of your company. So if yours is a very decentralized structure, you'd better opt to install a decentralized ERP application or recognize the enormous change-management mountain you face.

2. **Treating this as a technical project vs. a change that balances people, process, and technology; not using the power of the new, integrated information.** The new technology brings integration and, generally, makes information available instantly. For example, when raw material arrives at a company's receiving dock and is scanned into the system, anyone can access that information and use it.

   Real-time integration and accurate data change people's jobs. A traditional sales order taker can change into a full-service customer agent. For example, with full online access to an integrated ERP backbone, the agent enjoys immediate access to the customer's history and other vital identifiers. The agent can examine real-time open inventory at all warehouses (not just local) and future production schedules. The agent can freeze and commit from this schedule to the customer's immediate needs, among other things.

1. **Embarking on the journey without a solid, approved business case, including mechanisms to update the business case continuously and to ensure the savings are baked into operational budgets.** Since an ERP project is going to take a minimum of 12 months and as much as 36 months to employ, and often costs between $5 million and $50 million out-of-pocket costs, stamina is essential. So you must be absolutely certain why you're embarking on this journey; that is, have a solid business case.

   At the same time, if a solid business case hasn't been made for the project, you won't get the commitment from the entire business team to make the journey successful. Many times when a company pursues an ERP implementation, it isn't simply to cut technology costs, because total technical costs may well increase with the application. Most of the time, the project is undertaken for broader business reasons, so if those reasons aren't clearly expressed, fully understood, and approved in both qualitative and quantitative terms, members of the senior executive team won't give their full support.

   While this is far less of an issue than it was five years ago, a number of major companies still complete the business case for an ERP project, submit a capital appropriation request, eventually get it approved, only to park the business case on the shelf to gather dust while the project proceeds.

A business case should be a living, breathing document of how to drive out both the original and updated business benefits from the ERP journey for, say, the next 20 years. It must outline how to track the benefits the application will produce, and it must be used for the CEO to bake into the annual operating budgets the cost-reductions and revenue increases that each vice president has committed to. It must make senior and middle executives accountable for the goals so that the anticipated bottom-line benefits are realized. This type of discipline still is relatively rare, in part because many managers think, "Hey, I'm not going to be here to see the end of this."

But, for an ERP project to succeed, it is critical that this business case is documented and becomes well worn. Just how vital is it? It does head this list of mistakes to avoid!

Source: Condensed from Clive Weightman and Deloitte Consulting, "The Top 10 ERP Mistakes." Copyright © Clive Weightman. Used with permission.

Conversion to an ERP system from a traditional operation is a major undertaking that requires a project approach to manage the process.

12.12 OPERATIONS STRATEGY

Acquisition of technology on the order of ERP has strategic implications. Among the considerations are a high initial cost, a high cost to maintain, the need for future upgrades, and the intensive training required. An ERP team is an excellent example of the value of a cross-functional team. Purchasing, which will ultimately place the order, typically does not have the technical expertise to select the best vendor. Information technology can assess various technical requirements, but won't be the user. Various functional users (marketing, operations, and accounting) will be in the best position to evaluate inputs and outputs, and finance must evaluate the effect on the organization's bottom line. Also, it is important to have a member of the purchasing staff involved from the beginning of negotiations on ERP acquisition because this will have major implications for purchasing.

The real-time aspect of ERP makes it valuable as a strategic planning tool. For example, it can improve supply chain management, with stronger links between their customers and their suppliers, and make the organizations more capable of satisfying changing customer requirements.

Because ERP tracks the flow of information and materials through a company, it offers opportunities for collecting information on waste and environmental costs and, hence, opportunities for process improvement.

SUMMARY

MRP is a planning technique that creates a schedule for all the (dependent-demand) items in an end item's bill of materials based on fixed manufacturing lead times. The end item is exploded using the bill of materials, and material requirements plans are developed that show quantity and timing for ordering or producing components.

The main features of MRP are the time-phasing of requirements, calculating component requirements, and planned-order releases. To be successful, MRP requires accurate master production schedules, bills of materials, and inventory data. Firms without reasonably accurate records or schedules have experienced major difficulties in trying to implement MRP-type systems. A potential weakness of MRP is the assumption of constant lead times.

MRP is utilized by most MRP II and ERP systems. MRP II adds software applications designed to better manage the entire manufacturing process involving finance and marketing, and including capacity planning. ERP is the third generation of manufacturing software that encompasses all business functions, including order entry and an option for financial management *integrated* with the manufacturing functions available in MRP II.

KEY POINTS

1. The usage of components in production of assembled items depends on how many of each component are needed per item, and how many items are to be produced. Hence the term *dependent demand*.

2. MRP is a tool used for dependent-demand components, to assist in making the two basic decisions in inventory management: how much of each component to order, and when to order it.

3. MRP II is an enhancement of MRP that gives management the ability to relate financial and other information to an MRP plan.

4. ERP is a software-based enterprise-wide system that allows access to production, sales, accounting, warehouse, and supply chain information.

KEY TERMS

backflushing 516
bill of materials (BOM) 503
capacity requirements planning
    519
changes 514
cumulative lead time 503
dependent demand 501
distribution resource planning
    (DRP) 520
enterprise resource planning
    (ERP) 521
exception reports 514

gross requirements 507
inventory records 506
load reports 519
low-level coding 506
manufacturing resources
    planning (MRP II) 517
master schedule 502
material requirements planning
    (MRP) 501
net-change system 512
net requirements 507
order releases 514

pegging 511
performance-control reports
    514
planned-order receipts 507
planned-order releases 508
planned orders 514
planning reports 514
product structure tree 503
projected on hand 507
regenerative system 512
scheduled receipts 507
time fences 519

SOLVED PROBLEMS

Problem 1   The following product structure tree indicates the components needed to assemble one unit of product W. Determine the quantities of each component needed to assemble 100 units of W.

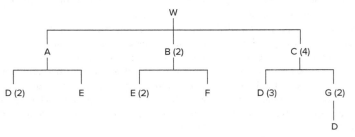

Solution   An easy way to compute and keep track of component requirements is to do it right on the tree, as shown in the following figure. *Note:* For the procedure when there are on-hand inventories, see Example 1.

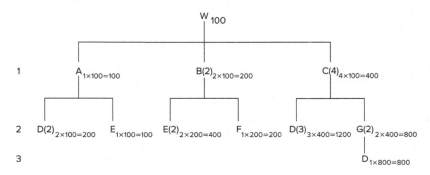

Summary:

Level	Item	Quantity
0	W	100
1	A	100
	B	200
	C	400
2	E	500
	F	200
	G	800
3	D	2,200

Material Requirements Plan Setup Guide

Problem 2

Twelve units of the end item are needed at the beginning of week 6. Prepare a material requirements plan for component D given that there is a scheduled receipt of 10 units of subassembly A in week 3 plus the following information.

Item	End	A	B	C	D
Units on hand	2	6	4	32	15
Lead time (weeks)	1	2	1	2	2

```
                              End
             ┌─────────────────┴───────────────────┐
           A(3)                                      B
      ┌──────┴──────┐                                │
    C(3)          D(2)                              D(4)
```

Steps

1. If a question asks for a materials requirement plan for a component such as D in the tree diagram, circle all occurrences of that component so you will be sure to include them.

2. Label the spreadsheet sections, top to bottom, following the order shown in the tree diagram:

   Top section: End Item
   Next section: A
   Next section: B
   Last section: D

   (You don't need one for C because the problem asks for D, and C isn't needed for D.)

3. Add the LT (lead time) for the end item and each component next to the section labels.

4. Add any beginning inventory (on hand) for the end item and each component to their spreadsheet sections.

5. Place the desired end item quantity in the master schedule in the week it is needed, and in the gross requirements of the end item in that same week.

6. Complete the remainder of the plan.

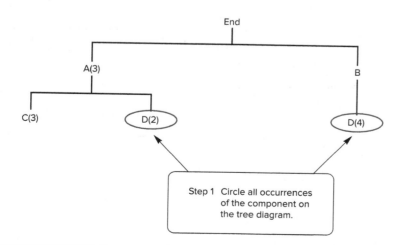

Step 1   Circle all occurrences of the component on the tree diagram.

Master	Week	1	2	3	4	5	6
Schedule	Quantity						

End	Beg. Inv.	1	2	3	4	5	6
Gross requirements							
Scheduled receipts							
Projected on hand							
Net requirements							
Planned-order receipts							
Planned-order releases							

A (3)	Beg. Inv.	1	2	3	4	5	6
Gross requirements							
Scheduled receipts							
Projected on hand							
Net requirements							
Planned-order receipts							
Planned-order releases							

Step 2. Label spreadsheet sections in the order shown in the tree diagram.

B	Beg. Inv.	1	2	3	4	5	6
Gross requirements							
Scheduled receipts							
Projected on hand							
Net requirements							
Planned-order receipts							
Planned-order releases							

D(2) D(4)	Beg. Inv.	1	2	3	4	5	6
Gross requirements							
Scheduled receipts							
Projected on hand							
Net requirements							
Planned-order receipts							
Planned-order releases							

Master	Week	1	2	3	4	5	6
Schedule	Quantity						

End LT = 1	Beg. Inv.	1	2	3	4	5	6
Gross requirements							
Scheduled receipts							
Projected on hand							
Net requirements							
Planned-order receipts							
Planned-order releases							

A (3) LT = 2	Beg. Inv.	1	2	3	4	5	6
Gross requirements							
Scheduled receipts							
Projected on hand							
Net requirements							
Planned-order receipts							
Planned-order releases							

Step 3. Add lead times.

B LT = 1	Beg. Inv.	1	2	3	4	5	6
Gross requirements							
Scheduled receipts							
Projected on hand							
Net requirements							
Planned-order receipts							
Planned-order releases							

D(2) D(4) LT = 2	Beg. Inv.	1	2	3	4	5	6
Gross requirements							
Scheduled receipts							
Projected on hand							
Net requirements							
Planned-order receipts							
Planned-order releases							

Master	Week	1	2	3	4	5	6
Schedule	Quantity						

End	LT = 1	Beg. Inv.	1	2	3	4	5	6
Gross requirements								
Scheduled receipts								
Projected on hand		2						
Net requirements								
Planned-order receipts								
Planned-order releases								

A (3)	LT = 2	Beg. Inv.	1	2	3	4	5	6
Gross requirements								
Scheduled receipts				10				
Projected on hand		6						
Net requirements								
Planned-order receipts								
Planned-order releases								

B	LT = 1	Beg. Inv.	1	2	3	4	5	6
Gross requirements								
Scheduled receipts								
Projected on hand		4						
Net requirements								
Planned-order receipts								
Planned-order releases								

D(2) D(4)	LT = 2	Beg. Inv.	1	2	3	4	5	6
Gross requirements								
Scheduled receipts								
Projected on hand		15						
Net requirements								
Planned-order receipts								
Planned-order releases								

Step 4. Enter specified beginning inventory and scheduled receipts quantities.

Master	Week	1	2	3	4	5	6
Schedule	Quantity						12

Step 5 . Enter the master schedule quantities and end item gross requirements in the specified week(s).

End LT = 1	Beg. Inv.	1	2	3	4	5	6
Gross requirements							12
Scheduled receipts							
Projected on hand	2						
Net requirements							
Planned-order receipts							
Planned-order releases							

A (3) LT = 2	Beg. Inv.	1	2	3	4	5	6
Gross requirements							
Scheduled receipts				10			
Projected on hand	6						
Net requirements							
Planned-order receipts							
Planned-order releases							

B LT = 1	Beg. Inv.	1	2	3	4	5	6
Gross requirements							
Scheduled receipts							
Projected on hand	4						
Net requirements							
Planned-order receipts							
Planned-order releases							

D(2) D(4) LT = 2	Beg. Inv.	1	2	3	4	5	6
Gross requirements							
Scheduled receipts							
Projected on hand	15						
Net requirements							
Planned-order receipts							
Planned-order releases							

Master	Week	1	2	3	4	5	6
Schedule	Quantity						12

End LT = 1	Beg. Inv.	1	2	3	4	5	6
Gross requirements							12
Scheduled receipts							
Projected on hand	2	2	2	2	2	2	2
Net requirements							10
Planned-order receipts							10
Planned-order releases							10	

Step 6. Complete the remainder of the plan, starting with the end item and working down, subtracting projected on hand from gross requirements to get net requirements. Planned order receipts = Net requirements, and all are in the same week. Planned order releases are always the same as planned order receipts, but earlier by lead time (one week in this case).

A (3) LT = 2	Beg. Inv.	1	2	3	4	5	6
Gross requirements						30	
Scheduled receipts				10			
Projected on hand	6	6	6	16	16	16	
Net requirements						14	
Planned-order receipts						14	
Planned-order releases				14			

Subassemblies A and B both come under End in the tree diagram, so their gross requirements are in the same column as the End item's planned-order releases (Week 5), using the multiples given in the tree diagram:
3 times 10 for A = 30
1 times 10 for B = 10

B LT = 1	Beg. Inv.	1	2	3	4	5	6
Gross requirements						10	
Scheduled receipts							
Projected on hand	4	4	4	4	4	4	
Net requirements						6	
Planned-order receipts						6	
Planned-order releases					6		

D(2) comes under A in the tree diagram, so its gross requirements are related to A's planned-order release sand in that same week:
2 times 14 = 28 in week 3

D(4) comes under B in the tree diagram, so its gross requirements are related to B's planned-order releases and in that same week:
4 times 6 = 24 in week 4

D(2) D(4) LT = 2	Beg. Inv.	1	2	3	4	5	6
Gross requirements				28	24		
Scheduled receipts							
Projected on hand	15	15	15	15			
Net requirements				13	24		
Planned-order receipts				13	24		
Planned-order releases			13	24			

The product structure tree for end item E follows. The manager wants to know the material requirements for ordered part R that will be needed to complete 120 units of E by the start of week 5. Lead times for items are one week for level 0 items, one week for level 1 items, and two weeks for level 2 items. There is a scheduled receipt of 60 units of M at the *start* of week 2 and 100 units of R at the *start* of week 1. Lot-for-lot ordering is used.

Problem 3

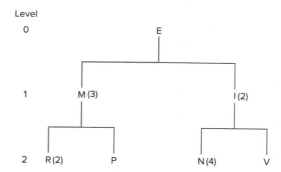

A partial assembly-time chart that includes R and leads to completion of E by the start of week 5 looks like this:

Solution

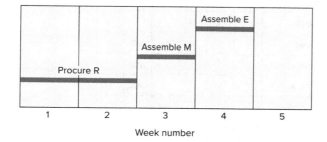

Week number

The table entries are arrived at as follows:

Master schedule: 120 units of E to be available at the start of week 5.

Item E: Gross requirements equal the quantity specified in the master production schedule. Since there is no on-hand inventory, net requirements also equal 120 units. Using lot-for-lot ordering, 120 units must be scheduled to be available at the start of week 5. Because there is a one-week lead time for assembly of Es, an order will need to be released (i.e., work started) at the beginning of week 4.

Item M: The *gross* requirements for M are three times the *net* requirements for E, because each E requires three Ms. These must be available at the start of week 4. The net requirements are 60 units fewer due to the 60 units expected to be on hand at that time. Hence, 300 additional units of M must be available at the start of week 4. With the one-week lead time, there must be an order release at the start of week 3.

Item R: Because each M requires two units of R, 600 Rs will be needed to assemble 300 units of M. However, 100 units will be on hand, so only 500 need to be ordered. Because there is a lead time of two weeks, the 500 Rs must be ordered at the start of week 1.

The master schedule for E and requirements plans for E, M, and R follow.

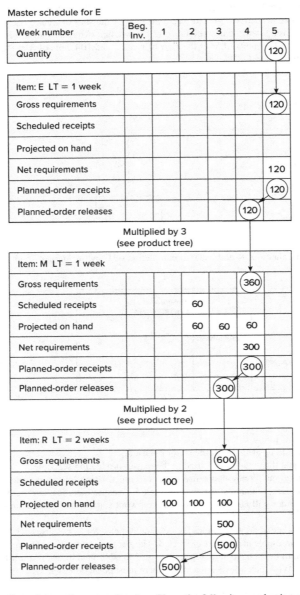

Master schedule for E

Week number	Beg. Inv.	1	2	3	4	5
Quantity						(120)

Item: E LT = 1 week		1	2	3	4	5
Gross requirements						(120)
Scheduled receipts						
Projected on hand						
Net requirements						120
Planned-order receipts						(120)
Planned-order releases					(120)	

Multiplied by 3
(see product tree)

Item: M LT = 1 week		1	2	3	4	5
Gross requirements					(360)	
Scheduled receipts			60			
Projected on hand			60	60	60	
Net requirements					300	
Planned-order receipts					(300)	
Planned-order releases				(300)		

Multiplied by 2
(see product tree)

Item: R LT = 2 weeks		1	2	3	4	5
Gross requirements					(600)	
Scheduled receipts		100				
Projected on hand		100	100	100		
Net requirements					500	
Planned-order receipts					(500)	
Planned-order releases			(500)			

Problem 4   *Capacity requirements planning.* Given the following production schedule in units and the production standards for labor and machine time for this product, determine the labor and machine capacity requirements for each week. Then compute the percent utilization of labor and machines in each week if labor capacity is 200 hours per week and machine capacity is 250 hours per week.

Production Schedule:

Week	1	2	3	4
Quantity	200	300	100	150

Standard Times:

Labor	.5 hour/unit
Machine	1.0 hour/unit

Convert the quantity requirements into labor and machine requirements by multiplying the quantity requirements by the respective standard times (i.e., multiply each quantity by .5 to obtain the labor hours and multiply each quantity by 1.0 to obtain the machine hours):

Solution

Week	1	2	3	4
Quantity	200	300	100	150
Labor hours	100	150	50	75
Machine hours	200	300	100	150

To compute utilization, divide the capacity requirements by the available capacity (200 hours per week for labor and 250 hours per week for machine) and multiply by 100. The results are

Week	1	2	3	4
Labor	50%	75%	25%	37.5%
Machine	80%	120%	40%	60%

Note that machine capacity in week 2 is overutilized (i.e., capacity is insufficient) because the utilization exceeds 100 percent. To compensate, some production could be shifted to weeks 1 and/or 3 where labor and machine time are available.

DISCUSSION AND REVIEW QUESTIONS

1. Contrast independent and dependent demand.
2. When is MRP appropriate?
3. Briefly define or explain each of these terms:
   a. Master schedule
   b. Bill of materials
   c. Inventory records
   d. Gross requirements
   e. Net requirements
   f. Time-phased plan
4. How is safety stock included in a material requirements plan?
5. What factors can create safety stock requirements in an MRP system?
6. What is meant by the term *safety time?*
7. Contrast *net-change* systems and *regenerative* systems for MRP.
8. Briefly discuss the requirements for effective MRP.
9. What are some of the main advantages and limitations of MRP?
10. How can the use of MRP contribute to productivity?
11. Briefly describe MRP II and closed-loop MRP.
12. What is lot sizing, what is its goal, and why is it an issue with lumpy demand?
13. Contrast planned-order receipts and scheduled receipts.
14. If seasonal variations are present, is their incorporation into MRP fairly simple or fairly difficult? Explain briefly.
15. How does the purpose of ERP differ from the purpose of MRP II?
16. What are some unforeseen costs of ERP?

TAKING STOCK

1. What trade-offs are involved in the decision to purchase an ERP software package?
2. Who in the organization needs to be involved in designing and implementing MRP II? Who needs to be involved in the decision to purchase an ERP system? Who needs to be trained to use ERP?
3. To what extent has technology such as ERP software improved the ability to manage a business organization? How important are each of the following considerations?
   a. Ease of use
   b. Complete integration
   c. Reliability

540   **Chapter Twelve**   MRP and ERP

1. Suppose you work for a furniture manufacturer, one of whose products is the chair depicted in Figure 12.5. Finished goods inventory is held in a central warehouse in anticipation of customer orders. Finished goods are controlled using EOQ/ROP methods. The warehouse manager, Juan Villa, has suggested using the same methods for controlling component inventory. Write him a brief memo outlining your opinion on doing that.

2. Give one example of unethical behavior involving MRP and one involving ERP, and state the ethical principle violated for each example.

PROBLEMS

1. a. Given the following diagram for a product, determine the quantity of each component required to assemble one unit of the finished product.

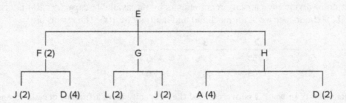

   b. Draw a tree diagram for a stapler given the following bill of materials:

Item	Components
Stapler	Top assembly, base assembly
Top assembly	Cover, spring, slide assembly
Cover	
Spring	
Slide assembly	Slide, spring
Slide	
Spring	
Base assembly	Base, strike plate, rubber pad (2)
Base	
Strike plate	
Rubber pad (2)	

2. The following table lists the components needed to assemble an end item, lead times, and quantities on hand.

Item	End	B	C	D	E	F	G	H
LT (wk)	1	2	3	3	1	2	1	2
Amount on hand	0	10	10	25	12	30	5	0

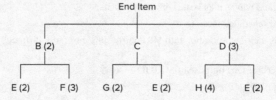

   a. If 20 units of the end item are to be assembled, how many additional units of E are needed? (*Hint:* You don't need to develop an MRP plan to determine this.)

   b. An order for the end item is scheduled to be shipped at the start of week 11. What is the latest week that the order can be started and still be ready to ship on time? (*Hint:* You don't need to develop an MRP plan for this part either.)

3. The following table lists the components needed to assemble an end item, lead times (in weeks), and quantities on hand.

Item	Lead Time	Amount on Hand	Direct Components
End	1	—	L(2), C(1), K(3)
L	2	10	B(2), J(3)
C	3	15	G(2), B(2)
K	3	20	H(4), B(2)
B	2	30	
J	3	30	
G	3	5	
H	2	—	

   a. If 40 units of the end item are to be assembled, how many additional units of B are needed? (*Hint:* You don't need to develop an MRP plan.)

   b. An order for the end item is scheduled to be shipped at the start of week 8. What is the latest week that the order can be started and still be ready to ship on time? (*Hint:* You don't need to develop an MRP plan.)

4. Eighty units of end item E are needed at the beginning of week 6. Three cases (30 units per case) of J have been ordered and one case is scheduled to arrive in week 3, one in week 4, and one in week 5. *Note:* J must be ordered by the case, and B must be produced in multiples of 120 units. There are 60 units of B and 20 units of J now on hand. Lead times are two weeks each for E and B, and one week for J.

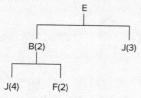

   a. Prepare a material requirements plan for component J.

   b. Suppose that in week 4 the quantity of E needed is changed from 80 to 70. The planned-order releases through week 3 have all been executed. How many more Bs and Js will be on hand in week 6?

5. a. One hundred twenty units of end item Z are needed at the beginning of week 7. Prepare a material requirements plan for component C. Take into account that on hand there are 40 units of Z, 70 units of A, 100 units of B, and 30 units of C. Also, there is a scheduled receipt of 20 units of component C in week 4. Lead times are two weeks for Z and B, and one week for the other components. Lot-for-lot ordering will be used for all items.

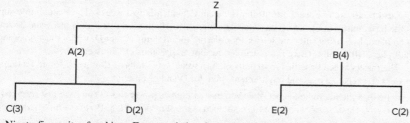

   b. Ninety-five units of end item E are needed at the beginning of week 7. Prepare a material requirements plan *for component D*. Take into account that 5 units of E are currently on hand, as well as 50 units of B, 100 units of C, and 80 units of D. Also, 30 units of C have been outsourced and are expected to arrive in week 4. Lead times are two weeks for E and C, and one week for the other components. Assume lot-for-lot ordering except for D, where multiples of 40 must be used.

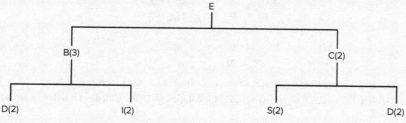

6. A table is assembled using three components, as shown in the accompanying product structure tree. The company that makes the table wants to ship 100 units at the beginning of day 4, 150 units at the beginning of day 5, and 200 units at the beginning of day 7. Receipts of 100 wood sections are scheduled at the beginning of day 2. There are 120 legs on hand. There are 60 braces on hand. Lead times (in days) for all items are shown in the following table. Prepare a material requirements plan using lot-for-lot ordering.

Quantity	Lead Time
1–200	1
201–550	2
551–999	3

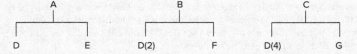

7. Eighty units of end item X are needed at the beginning of week 6, and another 30 units are needed at the beginning of week 8. Prepare a material requirements plan for component D. D can only be ordered in whole cases (50 units per case). One case of D is automatically received every other week, beginning in week 1 (i.e., weeks 1, 3, 5, 7). Lot-for-lot ordering will be used for all items except D. Also, there are 30 units of B and 20 units of D now on hand. Lead times for all items are a function of quantity: one week for up to 100 units, two weeks for 101 to 200 units, three weeks for 201 to 300 units, and four weeks for 301 or more units.

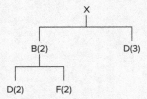

8. Oh No!, Inc., sells three models of radar detector units. It buys the three basic models (E, F, and G) from a Japanese manufacturer and adds one, two, or four lights (component D) to further differentiate the models. D is bought from a domestic producer.

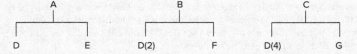

Lead times are one week for all items except C, which is two weeks. There are ample supplies of the basic units (E, F, and G) on hand. There are also 10 units of B, 10 units of C, and 25 units of D on hand. Lot-sizing rules are lot-for-lot ordering for all items except D, which must be ordered in multiples of 100 units. There is a scheduled receipt of 100 units of D in week 1.

The master schedule calls for 40 units of A in week 4, 60 units of B in week 5, and 30 units of C in week 6. Prepare a material requirements plan for D and its parents.

9. Assume that you are the manager of a shop that assembles power tools. You have just received an order for 50 chain saws, which are to be shipped at the start of week 8. Pertinent information on the saws follows:

Item	Lead Time (weeks)	On Hand	Components
Saw	2	15	A(2), B(1), C(4)
A	1	10	E(3), D(1)
B	2	5	D(2), F(3)
C	2	65	E(2), D(2)
D	1	20	
E	1	10	
F	2	30	

a. Develop a product structure tree, an assembly time chart, and a master schedule.

b. Develop the material requirements plan for component E using lot-for-lot ordering for all items.

10. Assume that you are the manager of Assembly, Inc. You have just received an order for 40 units of an industrial robot, which is to be delivered at the start of week 7 of your schedule. Using the following information, determine how many units of subassembly G to order and the timing of those orders, given that subassembly G must be ordered in multiples of 80 units and all other components are ordered lot-for-lot. Assume that the components are used only for this particular robot.

Item	Lead Time (weeks)	On Hand	Components
Robot	2	10	B, G, C(3)
B	1	5	E, F
C	1	20	G(2), H
E	2	4	—
F	3	8	—
G	2	15	—
H	1	10	—

11. Determine material requirements plans for parts N and V and subassembly I as described in Solved Problem 3 for each of the following:

    a. Assume that there are currently 100 Ns on hand and scheduled receipts of 40 Is and 10 Vs at the beginning of week 3. No Es are on hand; 120 Es are needed at the start of week 5.

    b. Assume on-hand and scheduled receipts as in part *a*. Now suppose that 100 Es are needed at the start of week 5 and 55 at the start of week 7. Also, use multiples of these order sizes: N, 800; V, 200. Use lot-for-lot ordering for I.

    c. Using your answer to part *b,* update the MRP for V, using the following additional information for each of these cases: (1) one week has elapsed (making it the start of week 2), and (2) three weeks have elapsed (making it the start of week 4).

       The updated master schedule now has an order for 100 units of E in week 9. Your plan should cover weeks 2 through 9 for case 1, and weeks 4 through 11 for case 2. Assume all orders are released and received as planned.

12. A firm that produces electric golf carts has just received an order for 200 carts, which must be ready for delivery at the start of week 8. Information concerning the product structure, lead times, and quantities on hand is shown in the following table. Use this information to do each of the following:

    a. Construct a product tree.

    b. Construct an assembly time chart.

    c. Develop a material requirements plan that will provide 200 golf carts by week 8 assuming lot-for-lot ordering.

Parts List for Electric Golf Cart	Lead Time	Quantity on Hand
Electric golf cart	1	0
Top	1	40
Supports (4)	1	200
Cover	1	0
Base	1	20
Motor	2	300
Body	3	50
Frame	1	35
Controls	1	0
Wheel assemblies (4)	1	240
Seats (2)	2	120

13. Refer to Problem 12. Assume that unusually mild weather has caused a change in the quantity and timing of orders for golf carts. The revised plan calls for 100 golf carts at the start of week 6, 100 at the start of week 8, and 100 at the start of week 9.

    a. Develop a master schedule for this revised plan.

    b. Determine the timing and quantities for orders for tops and bases.

    c. Assume that equipment problems reduce the firm's capacity for assembling bases to 50 units per week. Revise your material plan for bases to reflect this, but still meet delivery dates.

14. Using the accompanying diagram, do the following:

   a. Draw a tree diagram for the scissors.

   b. Prepare an MRP plan for scissors. Lead times are one day for each component and final scissor assembly, but two days for the plastic grips. Six hundred pairs of scissors are needed on day 6. *Note:* There are 200 straight blades and 350 bent blades on hand, and 40 top blade assemblies on hand. Use lot-for-lot ordering for all items.

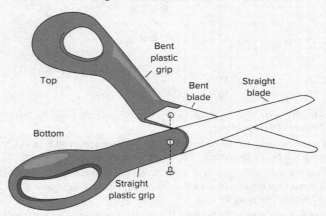

15. A company that manufactures paving material for driveways and parking lots expects the following demand for its product for the next four weeks.

Week number	1	2	3	4
Material (tons)	40	80	60	70

The company's labor and machine standards and available capacities are as follows.

	Labor	Machine
Production standard (hours per ton)	4	3
Weekly production capacity (hours)	300	200

   a. Determine the capacity utilization for labor and machine for each of the four weeks.

   b. In which weeks do you foresee a problem? What options would you suggest to resolve any problems? What costs are relevant in making a decision on choosing an option?

16. A company produces two very similar products that go through a three-step sequence of fabrication, assembly, and packaging. Each step requires one day for a lot to be completely processed and moved to the next department. Processing requirements for the departments (hours per unit) are as follows.

Product	FABRICATION		ASSEMBLY		PACKAGING	
	Labor	Machine	Labor	Machine	Labor	Machine
A	2	1	1.5	1	1	.5
B	1	1	1	1	1.5	.5

Department capacities are all 700 hours of labor and 500 hours of machine time, except Friday, when capacities are 200 hours for both labor and machine time. The following production schedule is for next week.

Product	Mon	Tues	Wed	Thurs	Fri
A	200	400	100	300	100
B	300	200	200	200	200

   a. Determine the labor and machine capacity requirements for each product and the total load for each department for each day. Ignore changeover time.

   b. Evaluate the projected loading for the first three days of the week. Is the schedule feasible? What do you suggest for balancing the load?

17. The MRP Department has a problem. Its computer "died" just as it spit out the following information: Planned order release for item J27 = 640 units in week 2. The firm has been able to reconstruct all the information they lost except the master schedule for end item 565. The firm is fortunate because J27 is used only in 565s. Given the following product structure tree and associated inventory status record information, determine what master schedule entry for 565 was exploded into the material requirements plan that killed the computer.

Part Number	On Hand	Lot Size	Lead Time
565	0	Lot-for-lot	1 week
X43	60	Multiples of 120	1 week
N78	0	Lot-for-lot	2 weeks
Y36	200	Lot-for-lot	1 week
J27	0	Lot-for-lot	2 weeks

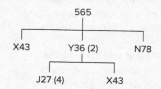

18. Develop a material requirements plan for component H. Lead times for the end item and each component except B are one week. The lead time for B is three weeks. Sixty units of A are needed at the start of week 8. There are currently 15 units of B on hand and 130 of E on hand, and 50 units of H are in production and will be completed by the start of week 2. Lot-for-lot ordering will be used for all items.

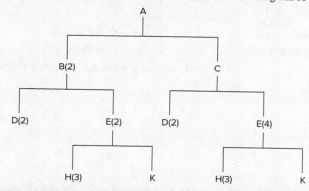

CASE   # PROMOTIONAL NOVELTIES

Promotional Novelties provides a wide range of novelty items for its corporate customers. It has just received an order for 20,000 toy tractor-trailers that will be sold by a regional filling station company as part of a holiday promotion. The order is to be shipped at the beginning of week 8. The tree diagram shows the various components of the trucks.

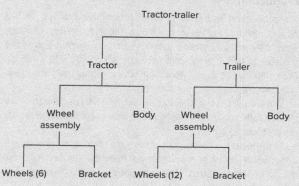

The company can complete final assembly of the tractor-trailers at the rate of 10,000 a week. The tractor and trailer bodies are purchased; lead time is three weeks. The wheels are the manager's main concern.

The company has a sufficient supply of brackets on hand. Assembly time is one week each for tractors, trailers, and wheel assembly. However, the wheel department can only produce wheels at the rate of 100,000 a week. The manager plans to use the wheel department to full capacity, starting in week 2 of the schedule, and order additional wheels from a supplier as needed. Ordered wheels come in sets of 6,400. The lead time for delivery from the supplier is expected to be two to three weeks. Use lot-for-lot ordering for all items except the purchased wheels.

Questions

1. How many wheels sets should the manager order?
2. When should the wheel sets be ordered?

CASE   DMD ENTERPRISES

After the dot-com business he tried to start folded, David "Marty" Dawkins decided to pursue his boyhood dream of owning a bike factory. After several false starts, he finally got the small company up and running. The company currently assembles two models Marty designed: the Arrow and the Dart. The company hasn't turned a profit yet, but Marty feels that once he resolves some of the problems he's having with inventory and scheduling, he can increase productivity and reduce costs.

At first, he ordered enough bike parts and subassemblies for four months' worth of production. Parts were stacked all over the place, seriously reducing work space and hampering movement of workers and materials. And no one knew exactly where anything was. In Marty's words, "It was a solid mess!"

He and his two partners eventually managed to work off most of the inventory. They hope to avoid similar problems in the future by using a more orderly approach. Marty's first priority is to develop a materials requirement plan for upcoming periods. He wants to assemble 15 Arrows and 10 Darts each week, to have them ready at the start of weeks 4 through 8. The product structure trees for the two bikes follow.

One of Marty's partners, Ann, has organized information on lead times, inventory on hand, and lot-sizing rules (established by suppliers):

Item	Lead Time(weeks)	On Hand	Lot-Sizing Rule
Arrow	2	5	Lot-for-lot
Dart	2	2	Lot-for-lot
X	1	5	Multiples of 25
W	2*	2	Multiples of 12
F	1	10	Multiples of 30
K	1	3	Lot-for-lot
Q	1	15	Multiples of 30
M	1	0	Lot-for-lot

*LT = 3 weeks for orders of 36 or more units on this item.

Scheduled receipts are:

Period 1: 20 Arrows and 18 Ws

Period 2: 20 Darts and 15 Fs

As the third partner, it is your job to develop the material requirements plan.

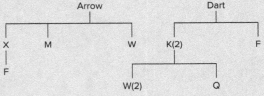

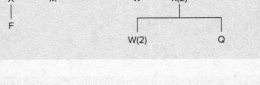

OPERATIONS TOUR   STICKLEY FURNITURE

Introduction

www.stickley.com

L. & J.G. Stickley was founded in 1900 by brothers Leopold and George Stickley. Located just outside of Syracuse, New York, the company is a producer of fine cherry, white oak, and mahogany furniture. In the 1980s, the company reintroduced the company's original line of mission oak furniture, which now accounts for nearly 50 percent of the company's sales.

Over the years, the company experienced both good and bad times, and at one point, it employed over 200 people. But by the early 1970s, the business was in disarray; there were only about 20 full-time employees, and the company was on the brink of bankruptcy. The present owners bought the ailing firm in 1974, and under their leadership, the company has prospered and grown, and now has 1,350 employees. Stickley has five retail showrooms

in New York State, two in Connecticut, one in North Carolina, and its furniture is sold nationally by some 120 dealers.

Production

The production facility is a large, rectangular building with a 30-foot ceiling. Furniture making is labor intensive, although saws, sanders, and other equipment are very much a part of the process. In fact, electric costs average about $60,000 a month. The company has its own tool room where cutting tools are sharpened, and replacement parts are produced as needed.

Worker skills range from low-skilled material handlers to highly skilled craftsmen. For example, seven master cabinet makers handle customized orders.

The process (see figure) begins with various sawing operations where large boards received from the lumber mills are cut into smaller sizes. The company recently purchased a

© Khakimullin Aleksandr/Shutterstock

computer-controlled "optimizer" saw that greatly improves sawing productivity, and eliminates some waste. Workers inspect and mark knot locations and other defects they find on each piece of lumber before feeding it into the saw. The computer then determines the optimal set of cuttings, given the location of knots and other defects, and standard lengths needed for subsequent operations. Approximately 20,000 board feet are cut each day. Subsequent sawing operations provide additional cuts for specific jobs.

Workers then glue some of the pieces together; they will end up as tops of tables, desks, dressers, or a similar item. Large presses hold 20 to 30 glued sections at a time. Other pieces that will become table or chair legs, chair backs or other items go through various shaping operations. Next comes a series of sanding operations, which remove excess glue from the glued sections, and smooth the surface of both glued pieces and other pieces.

Some of the pieces may require drilling or mortising, an operation in which rectangular holes and other shapes are cut into the wood. The company has a CNC (numerically controlled) router that can be programmed to make grooves and other specialty cuts. Some items require carving, which involves highly skilled workers.

Next, workers assemble the various components, either into subassemblies, or sometimes directly to other components to obtain completed pieces. Each item is stamped with the date of production, and components such as dresser drawers, cabinet doors, and expansion leaves of tables also are stamped to identify their location (e.g., top drawer, left door). Careful records are kept so that if a piece of furniture is ever returned for repairs, complete instructions are available (type of wood, finish, etc.) to enable repair people to closely match the original piece.

The furniture items then usually move to the "white inventory" (unfinished) section, and eventually to the finishing department where workers apply linseed oil or another finish before the items

are moved to the finished goods inventory to await shipment to stores or customers.

The company uses a level production plan (maintain steady output and steady labor force). Demand is seasonal; it is highest in the first and third quarters. During the second and fourth quarters, excess output goes into inventory; during the first and third quarters, excess demand is met using inventory. The production scheduler uses a schedule that is set for the next 8 to 10 weeks.

Production Control

Job sequence is determined by the amount of remaining inventory (days' supply on hand), and processing time. Lot sizes are determined by factoring in demand, setup costs, and carrying costs. Typical lot sizes are 25 to 60 pieces. There are many jobs being done concurrently. Each job is accompanied by a set of bar codes that identify the job and the operation. As each operation is completed, the operator removes a bar code sticker and delivers it to the scheduling office where it is scanned into the computer, thereby enabling production control to keep track of progress on a job, and to know its location in the shop.

The company's policy of level output coupled with seasonal demand patterns means that prior to peak demand periods, excess output is used to build up inventories, which is then drawn down when demand exceeds production capacity during periods of peak production.

Inventory

In addition to the "white" inventory and a small finished goods inventory, the company maintains an inventory of furniture pieces (e.g., table and chair legs) and partially assembled items. This inventory serves two important functions. One is to reduce the amount of time needed to respond to customer

(*continued*)

(concluded))

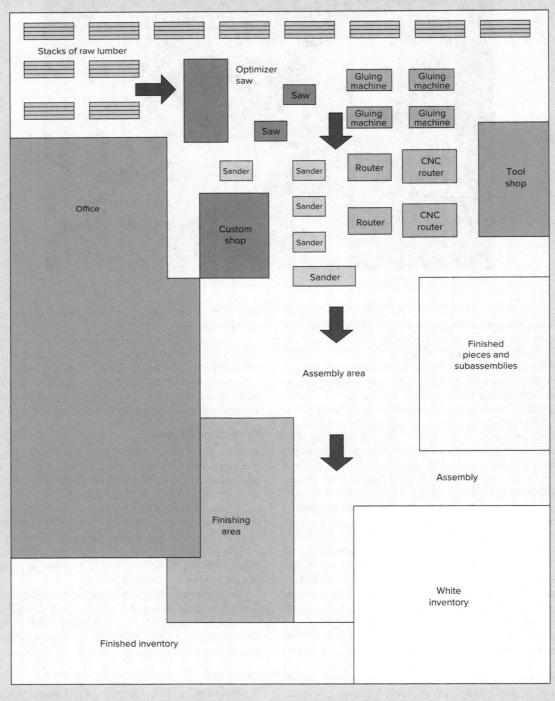

orders rather than having to go through the entire production process to obtain needed items, and the other is that it helps to smooth production and utilize idle machinery/workers. Because of unequal job times on successive operations, some workstations invariably have slack time while others work at capacity. This is used to build an inventory of commonly used pieces and subassemblies. Moreover, because pieces are being made for inventory, there is flexibility in sequencing. This permits jobs that have similar setups to be produced in sequence, thereby reducing setup time and cost.

Quality

Each worker is responsible for checking his or her quality, as well as the quality of materials received from preceding operations, and to report any deficiencies. In addition, on several difficult operations, quality control people handle inspections and work with operators to correct any deficiencies. The company is considering a TQM approach, but has not yet made a decision on whether to go in that direction.

Questions

1. Which type of production processing—job shop, batch, repetitive, or continuous—is the primary mode of operation at Stickley Furniture?

Why? What other type of processing is used to a lesser extent? Explain.

2. How does management keep track of job status and location during production?

3. Suppose the company has just received an order for 40 mission oak dining room sets. Briefly list the kinds of information the company will need to plan, schedule, and process this job.

4. What benefits and what problems would you expect given the company's level production policy?

5. Can you suggest any changes that might be beneficial to the company? What are they?

Hopp, Wallace, and Mark L. Spearman. *Factory Physics,* 3rd ed. New York: Irwin/McGraw-Hill, 2007.

Jacobs, F. Robert, William L. Berry, D. Clay Whybark, and Thomas E. Vollman. *Manufacturing Planning*

and Control for Supply Chain Management, 6th ed. Burr Ridge, IL: McGraw-Hill/Irwin, 2011.

Wagner, Brett, and Ellen Monk. *Enterprise Resource Planning,* 3rd ed. Boston, MA: Cengage Learning, 2008.

SELECTED BIBLIOGRAPHY AND FURTHER READINGS

13 Inventory Management

CHAPTER OUTLINE

13.1 **Introduction** 551

13.2 **The Nature and Importance of Inventories** 552

Functions of Inventory 553

Objective of Inventory Management 554

13.3 **Requirements for Effective Inventory Management** 555

Inventory Counting Systems 555

Demand Forecasts and Lead-Time Information 557

Inventory Costs 557

Classification System 558

13.4 **Inventory Ordering Policies** 561

13.5 **How Much to Order: Economic Order Quantity Models** 561

Basic Economic Order Quantity (EOQ) Model 561

Economic Production Quantity (EPQ) 565

Quantity Discounts 568

13.6 **Reorder Point Ordering** 573

13.7 **How Much to Order: Fixed-Order-Interval Model** 577

Reasons for Using the Fixed-Order-Interval Model 578

Determining the Amount to Order 578

Benefits and Disadvantages 580

13.8 **The Single-Period Model** 580

Continuous Stocking Levels 581

Discrete Stocking Levels 582

13.9 **Operations Strategy** 585

Cases: UPD Manufacturing 600

Harvey Industries 601

Grill Rite 602

Farmers Restaurant 603

Operations Tours: Bruegger's Bagel Bakery, 604; PSC, Inc. 605

© Kris Tripplaar/Sipa USA/Newscom

Inventory management is a core operations management activity. Effective inventory management is important for the successful operation of most businesses and their supply chains. Inventory management impacts operations, marketing, and finance. Poor inventory management hampers operations, diminishes customer satisfaction, and increases operating costs.

Some organizations have excellent inventory management, and many have satisfactory inventory management. Too many, however, have unsatisfactory inventory management. They either have too little or too much inventory, inaccurate inventory tracking, or incorrect priorities. What is lacking is an understanding of what needs to be done and how to do it. This chapter presents the concepts and knowledge base for effective inventory management.

13.1 INTRODUCTION

An **inventory** is a stock or store of goods. Firms typically stock hundreds or even thousands of items in inventory, ranging from small things such as pencils, paper clips, screws, nuts, and bolts to large items such as machines, trucks, construction equipment, and airplanes. Naturally, many of the items a firm carries in inventory relate to the kind of business it engages in. Thus, manufacturing firms carry supplies of raw materials, purchased parts, partially finished items, and finished goods, as well as spare parts for machines, tools, and other supplies. Department stores carry clothing, furniture, carpeting, stationery, cosmetics, gifts, cards, and toys. Some also stock sporting goods, paints, and tools. Hospitals stock drugs, surgical supplies, life-monitoring equipment, sheets and pillow cases, and more. Supermarkets stock fresh and canned foods, packaged and frozen foods, household supplies, magazines, baked goods, dairy products, produce, and other items.

The inventory models described in this chapter relate primarily to what are referred to as *independent-demand* items, that is, items that are ready to be sold or used. Chapter 12 described models that are used for *dependent-demand* items, which are components of

Inventory A stock or store of goods.

LO13.1 Define the term *inventory*.

READING $$$

A local factory was having difficulties with managing its inventory, so they asked Bill, a consultant, for his help. Here is what he found: In a recent round of layoffs, a number of older supervisors who had managed ordering had been let go. A newly hired production manager decided to allow newly hired supervisors more freedom in how ordering was accomplished. The new hires eschewed the inventory models that had been used, referring to them as "old school" because they didn't allow for "intuitive input" from supervisors. As Bill toured the facility, in some areas he found excessive inventories of parts and raw materials ($$$), while in others, he heard complaints about shortages that were severely hampering operations ($$$). When he presented his findings to the production manager that revealed how much the "intuitive approach" was costing the company, the astounded production manager immediately scrapped the "intuitive approach" and replaced it with more appropriate "real world" models. The new supervisors were treated to educational sessions that helped them understand how to use the inventory ordering models. Before long the problems of inventory excesses and shortages were a thing of the past. Costs decrease substantially, and profits, customer satisfaction, and employee morale all increased.

finished products, rather than the finished products themselves. Thus, a computer would be an independent-demand item, while the components that are used to assemble a computer would be dependent-demand items: The demand for those items would depend on how many of each item is needed for a computer, as well as how many computers are going to be made.

13.2 THE NATURE AND IMPORTANCE OF INVENTORIES

Inventories are a vital part of business. Not only are they necessary for operations, but they also contribute to customer satisfaction. To get a sense of the significance of inventories, consider the following: Some very large firms have tremendous amounts of inventory. For example, General Motors was at one point reported to have as much as $40 billion worth of materials, parts, cars, and trucks in its supply chain! Although the amounts and dollar values of inventories carried by different types of firms vary widely, a typical firm probably has about 30 percent of its current assets and perhaps as much as 90 percent of its working capital invested in inventory. One widely used measure of managerial performance relates to *return on investment* (ROI), which is profit after taxes divided by total assets. Because inventories may represent a significant portion of total assets, a reduction of inventories can result in a significant increase in ROI, although that benefit has to be weighed against a possible risk of a decrease in customer service. It is interesting to note that the ratio of inventories to sales in the manufacturing, wholesale, and retail sectors is one measure that is used to gauge the health of the U.S. economy.

Inventory decisions in service organizations can be especially critical. Hospitals, for example, carry an array of drugs and blood supplies that might be needed on short notice. Being out of stock on some of these could imperil the well-being of a patient. However, many of these items have a limited shelf life, so carrying large quantities would mean having to dispose of unused, costly supplies. On-site repair services for computers, printers, copiers, and fax machines also have to carefully consider which parts to bring to the site to avoid having to make an extra trip to obtain parts. The same goes for home repair services such as electricians, appliance repairers, and plumbers.

The major source of revenues for retail and wholesale businesses is the sale of merchandise (i.e., inventory). In fact, in terms of dollars, the inventory of goods held for sale is one of the largest assets of a merchandising business. Retail stores that sell clothing wrestle with decisions about which styles to carry, and how much of each to carry, knowing full well that fast-selling items will mean greater profits than having to heavily discount goods that didn't sell.

© Fuse/Getty Images

By initiating a program that utilizes bar codes and scanners, hospitals can control inventory supply areas, as well as keep track of all equipment in use across the enterprise. Stockroom inventory applications track consumable items such as medication and supplies, while check in/out applications track shared or reusable items such as X-rays, lab results, diagnostic tools, and other medical equipment.

The different kinds of inventories include the following:

Raw materials and purchased parts.

Partially completed goods, called *work-in-process (WIP)*.

Finished-goods inventories (manufacturing firms) or merchandise (retail stores).

Tools and supplies.

Maintenance and repairs (MRO) inventory.

Goods-in-transit to warehouses, distributors, or customers (pipeline inventory).

> **LO13.2** List the different types of inventory.

Both manufacturing and service organizations have to take into consideration the space requirements of inventory. In some cases, space limitations may pose restrictions on inventory storage capability, thereby adding another dimension to inventory decisions.

To understand why firms have inventories at all, you need to be aware of the various functions of inventory.

Functions of Inventory

Inventories serve a number of functions. Among the most important are the following.

1. **To meet anticipated customer demand.** A customer can be a person who walks in off the street to buy a new stereo system, a mechanic who requests a tool at a tool crib, or a manufacturing operation. These inventories are referred to as *anticipation stocks* because they are held to satisfy expected (i.e., *average*) demand.

2. **To smooth production requirements.** Firms that experience seasonal patterns in demand often build up inventories during preseason periods to meet overly high requirements during seasonal periods. These inventories are aptly named *seasonal inventories*. Companies that process fresh fruits and vegetables deal with seasonal inventories. So do stores that sell greeting cards, skis, snowmobiles, or Christmas trees.

3. **To decouple operations.** Historically, manufacturing firms have used inventories as buffers between successive operations to maintain continuity of production that would

> **LO13.3** Describe the main functions of inventories.

otherwise be disrupted by events such as breakdowns of equipment and accidents that cause a portion of the operation to shut down temporarily. The buffers permit other operations to continue temporarily while the problem is resolved. Similarly, firms have used buffers of raw materials to insulate production from disruptions in deliveries from suppliers, and finished goods inventory to buffer sales operations from manufacturing disruptions. More recently, companies have taken a closer look at buffer inventories, recognizing the cost and space they require, and realizing that finding and eliminating sources of disruptions can greatly decrease the need for decoupling operations.

Inventory buffers are also important in *supply chains*. Careful analysis can reveal both points where buffers would be most useful and points where they would merely increase costs without adding value.

4. **To reduce the risk of stockouts.** Delayed deliveries and unexpected increases in demand increase the risk of shortages. Delays can occur because of weather conditions, supplier stockouts, deliveries of wrong materials, quality problems, and so on. The risk of shortages can be reduced by holding *safety stocks,* which are stocks in excess of expected demand to compensate for *variabilities* in demand and lead time.

5. **To take advantage of order cycles.** To minimize purchasing and inventory costs, a firm often buys in quantities that exceed immediate requirements. This necessitates storing some or all of the purchased amount for later use. Similarly, it is usually economical to produce in large rather than small quantities. Again, the excess output must be stored for later use. Thus, inventory storage enables a firm to buy and produce in *economic lot sizes* without having to try to match purchases or production with demand requirements in the short run. This results in *periodic* orders or order *cycles.*

6. **To hedge against price increases.** Occasionally a firm will suspect that a substantial price increase is about to occur and purchase larger-than-normal amounts to beat the increase.

7. **To permit operations.** The fact that production operations take a certain amount of time (i.e., they are not instantaneous) means that there will generally be some work-in-process inventory. In addition, intermediate stocking of goods—including raw materials, semifinished items, and finished goods at production sites, as well as goods stored in warehouses—leads to *pipeline* inventories throughout a production-distribution system. **Little's Law** can be useful in quantifying pipeline inventory. It states that the average amount of inventory in a system is equal to the product of the average rate at which inventory units leave the system (i.e., the average demand rate) and the average time a unit is in the system. Thus, if units are in the system for an average of 10 days, and the demand rate is 5 units per day, the average inventory is 50 units: 5 units/day × 10 days = 50 units.

8. **To take advantage of quantity discounts.** Suppliers may give discounts on large orders.

Little's Law The average amount of inventory in a system is equal to the product of the average demand rate and the average time a unit is in the system.

Objective of Inventory Management

Inadequate control of inventories can result in both under- and overstocking of items. Understocking results in missed deliveries, lost sales, dissatisfied customers, and production bottlenecks; overstocking unnecessarily takes up space and ties up funds that might be more productive elsewhere. Although overstocking may appear to be the lesser of the two evils, the price tag for excessive overstocking can be staggering when inventory holding costs are high—as illustrated by the reading about the bin of gears at the beginning of the chapter—and matters can easily get out of hand.

The overall objective of inventory management is to achieve satisfactory levels of *customer service* while keeping inventory *costs* within reasonable bounds. The two basic issues (decisions) for inventory management are *when to order* and *how much to order*. The greater part of this chapter is devoted to models that can be applied to assist in making those decisions.

Managers have a number of performance measures they can use to judge the effectiveness of inventory management. The most obvious, of course, are costs and customer satisfaction, which they might measure by the number and quantity of backorders and/or customer complaints. A widely used measure is **inventory turnover**, which is the ratio of annual cost of goods sold to average inventory investment. The turnover ratio indicates how many times a year the inventory is sold. Generally, the higher the ratio, the better, because that implies more efficient use of inventories. However, the desirable number of turns depends on the industry and what the profit margins are. The higher the profit margins, the lower the acceptable number of inventory turns, and vice versa. Also, a product that takes a long time to manufacture, or a long time to sell, will have a low turnover rate. This is often the case with high-end retailers (high profit margins). Conversely, supermarkets (low profit margins) have a fairly high turnover rate. Note, though, that there should be a balance between inventory investment and maintaining good customer service. Managers often use inventory turnover to evaluate inventory management performance; monitoring this metric over time can yield insights into changes in performance.

> **Inventory turnover** Ratio of annual cost of goods sold to average inventory investment.

Another useful measure is days of inventory on hand, a number that indicates the expected number of days of sales that can be supplied from existing inventory. Here, a balance is desirable; a high number of days might imply excess inventory, while a low number might imply a risk of running out of stock.

13.3 REQUIREMENTS FOR EFFECTIVE INVENTORY MANAGEMENT

> **LO13.4** Discuss the main requirements for effective management.

Management has two basic functions concerning inventory. One is to establish a system to keep track of items in inventory, and the other is to make decisions about how much and when to order. To be effective, management must have the following:

1. A system to **keep track of the inventory** on hand and on order.
2. A reliable **forecast of demand** that includes an indication of possible *forecast error.*
3. Knowledge of **lead times** and **lead time variability.**
4. Reasonable estimates of inventory **holding costs, ordering costs,** and **shortage costs.**
5. A **classification system** for inventory items.

Let's take a closer look at each of these requirements.

Inventory Counting Systems

Inventory counting systems can be periodic or perpetual. Under a **periodic system**, a physical count of items in inventory is made at periodic, fixed intervals (e.g., weekly, monthly) in order to decide how much to order of each item. Many small retailers use this approach: A manager periodically checks the shelves and stockroom to determine the quantity on hand. Then the manager estimates how much will be demanded prior to the next delivery period and bases the order quantity on that information. An advantage of this type of system is that orders for many items occur at the same time, which can result in economies in processing and shipping orders. There are also several disadvantages of periodic reviews. One is a lack of control between reviews. Another is the need to protect against shortages between review periods by carrying extra stock.

> **Periodic system** Physical count of items in inventory made at periodic intervals (weekly, monthly).

> **LO13.5** Explain periodic and perpetual review systems.

A **perpetual inventory system** (also known as a *continuous review* system) keeps track of removals from inventory on a continuous basis, so the system can provide information on the current level of inventory for each item. When the amount on hand reaches a predetermined minimum, a fixed quantity, Q, is ordered. An obvious advantage of this system is the control provided by the continuous monitoring of inventory withdrawals. Another advantage is the fixed-order quantity; management can determine an optimal order quantity. One disadvantage of this approach is the added cost of record keeping. Moreover, a physical count of inventories must still be performed periodically to verify records because of possible errors, pilferage, spoilage, and other factors that can reduce the effective amount of inventory.

> **Perpetual inventory system** System that keeps track of removals from inventory continuously, thus monitoring current levels of each item.

Bank transactions such as customer deposits and withdrawals are examples of continuous recording of inventory changes.

Perpetual systems range from very simple to very sophisticated. A **two–bin system**, a very elementary system, uses two containers for inventory. Items are withdrawn from the first bin until its contents are exhausted. It is then time to reorder. Sometimes an order card is placed at the bottom of the first bin. The second bin contains enough stock to satisfy expected demand until the order is filled, plus an extra cushion of stock that will reduce the chance of a stockout if the order is late or if usage is greater than expected. The advantage of this system is that there is no need to record each withdrawal from inventory; the disadvantage is that the reorder card may not be turned in for a variety of reasons (e.g., misplaced, the person responsible forgets to turn it in).

Supermarkets, discount stores, and department stores have always been major users of periodic counting systems. Today, most have switched to computerized checkout systems using a laser scanning device that reads a **universal product code (UPC)**, or *bar code*, printed on an item tag or on packaging. A typical grocery product code is illustrated here:

0 14800 23208

The zero on the left of the bar code identifies this as a grocery item, the first five numbers (14800) indicate the manufacturer (Mott's), and the last five numbers (23208) indicate the specific item (natural-style applesauce). Items in small packages, such as candy and gum, use a six-digit number.

Point-of-sale (POS) systems electronically record actual sales. Knowledge of actual sales can greatly enhance forecasting and inventory management: By relaying information about actual demand in real time, these systems enable management to make any necessary changes to restocking decisions. These systems are being increasingly emphasized as an important input to effective supply chain management by making this information available to suppliers.

UPC scanners represent major benefits to supermarkets. In addition to their increase in speed and accuracy, these systems give managers continuous information on inventories, reduce the need for periodic review and order–size determinations, and improve the level of customer service by indicating the price and quantity of each item on the customer's receipt.

Two-bin system Two containers of inventory; reorder when the first is empty.

Universal product code (UPC) Bar code printed on a label that has information about the item to which it is attached.

Point-of-sale (POS) systems Record items at time of sale.

Poor inventory accuracy leads to too much inventory or shortages. Software systems maintain enormous amounts of data and have a great amount of functionality. Systems can analyze inventory levels, allocate stock plan purchases, and allocate deliveries accordingly. They can identify key suppliers of each stocked item and can give lead times and dock-to-stock times for realistic time-phasing.

© DreamPictures/Shannon Faulk/Getty RF

READING   RADIO FREQUENCY IDENTIFICATION (RFID) TAGS

Keeping track of inventories in-house and throughout a supply chain is vitally important for manufacturing, service, and retail operations. Bar codes have long been used for that purpose, but they carry only a limited amount of information and require direct line-of-sight to be scanned. Radio frequency identification (RFID) tags are a technological breakthrough in inventory management, providing real-time information that increases the ability to track and process shipping containers, parts in warehouses, items on supermarket shelves, and a whole lot more. They carry much more information than bar codes, and they don't require line-of-sight to be scanned.

RFID tags transmit product information or other data to network-connected RFID readers via radio waves. Tags attached to pallets, boxes, or individual items can enable a business to identify, track, monitor, or locate any object that is within range of a reader. For example, the tags are used in "speed passes" for toll roads.

In agriculture, fruit growers might use RFID tags to constantly monitor temperatures around fruit during shipping. This ensures that the fruit is kept at the appropriate temperature. The tags can be used for a wide range of agricultural products, containing information such as cultivation history, as well as whether the fruit is organically grown and what fertilizers or chemicals have been used.

Because major retail chains, such as Walmart and Target, and governmental agencies now require their suppliers to use RFID tags, many companies have already made RFID a priority in their business strategies.

Although RFID technology holds the potential for improved safety, convenience, and inventory management, widespread adoption, particularly in retail operations, could take several years. Until a global standard is established and cheap disposable tags are developed, the main areas of growth continue to be in nonretail operations.

Bar coding is important for other sectors of business besides retailing. Manufacturing and service industries benefit from the simplified production and inventory control it provides. In manufacturing, bar codes attached to parts, subassemblies, and finished goods greatly facilitate counting and monitoring activities. Automatic routing, scheduling, sorting, and packaging can also be done using bar codes. In health care, the use of bar codes can help to reduce drug dispensing errors.

Radio frequency identification (RFID) tags are also used to keep track of inventory in certain applications.

Demand Forecasts and Lead–Time Information

Inventories are used to satisfy demand requirements, so it is essential to have reliable estimates of the amount and timing of demand. Similarly, it is essential to know how long it will take for orders to be delivered. In addition, managers need to know the extent to which demand and **lead time** (the time between submitting an order and receiving it) might vary; the greater the potential variability, the greater the need for additional stock to reduce the risk of a shortage between deliveries. Thus, there is a crucial link between forecasting and inventory management.

Lead time Time interval between ordering and receiving the order.

Inventory Costs

Four basic costs are associated with inventories: purchase, holding, ordering, and shortage costs.

Purchase cost is the amount paid to a vendor or supplier to buy the inventory. It is typically the largest of all inventory costs.

Holding, or carrying, costs relate to physically having items in storage. Costs include interest, insurance, taxes (in some states), depreciation, obsolescence, deterioration, spoilage, pilferage, breakage, tracking, picking, and warehousing costs (heat, light, rent, workers, equipment, security). They also include opportunity costs associated with having funds that could be used elsewhere tied up in inventory. Note that it is the *variable* portion of these costs that is pertinent.

The significance of the various components of holding cost depends on the type of item involved, although taxes, interest, and insurance are generally based on the dollar value of an inventory. Items that are easily concealed (e.g., pocket cameras, transistor radios, calculators) or fairly expensive (cars, TVs) are prone to theft. Fresh seafood, meats and poultry, produce, and baked goods are subject to rapid deterioration and spoilage. Dairy products, salad dressings, medicines, and batteries also have limited shelf lives.

Holding costs are stated in either of two ways: as a percentage of unit price or as a dollar amount per unit. Typical annual holding costs range from 20 percent to 40 percent or more of the value of an item. In other words, to hold a $100 item in inventory for one year could cost from $20 to $40.

Purchase cost The amount paid to buy the inventory.

Holding (carrying) cost Cost to carry an item in inventory for a length of time, usually a year.

LO13.6 Describe the costs that are relevant for inventory management.

Chapter Thirteen   Inventory Management

Ordering costs Costs of ordering and receiving inventory.

Ordering costs are the costs of ordering and receiving inventory. They are the costs that occur with the actual placement of an order. They include determining how much is needed, preparing invoices, inspecting goods upon arrival for quality and quantity, and moving the goods to temporary storage. Ordering costs are generally expressed as a fixed dollar amount per order, regardless of order size.

When a firm produces its own inventory instead of ordering it from a supplier, machine **setup costs** (e.g., preparing equipment for the job by adjusting the machine, changing cutting tools) are analogous to ordering costs; that is, they are expressed as a fixed charge per production run, regardless of the size of the run.

Setup costs The costs involved in preparing equipment for a job.

Shortage costs Costs resulting when demand exceeds the supply of inventory; often unrealized profit per unit.

Shortage costs result when demand exceeds the supply of inventory on hand. These costs can include the opportunity cost of not making a sale, loss of customer goodwill, late charges, backorder costs, and similar costs. Furthermore, if the shortage occurs in an item carried for internal use (e.g., to supply an assembly line), the cost of lost production or downtime is considered a shortage cost. Such costs can easily run into hundreds of dollars a minute or more. Shortage costs are sometimes difficult to measure, and they may be subjectively estimated.

Classification System

LO13.7 Describe the A-B-C approach and explain how it is useful.

An important aspect of inventory management is that items held in inventory are not of equal importance in terms of dollars invested, profit potential, sales or usage volume, or stockout penalties. Therefore, it would be unrealistic to devote equal attention to each of these items. Instead, a more reasonable approach would be to allocate control efforts according to the *relative importance* of various items in inventory.

A-B-C approach Classifying inventory according to some measure of importance, and allocating control efforts accordingly.

The **A-B-C approach** classifies inventory items according to some measure of importance, usually annual dollar value (i.e., dollar value per unit multiplied by annual usage rate), and then allocates control efforts accordingly. Typically, three classes of items are used: A (very important), B (moderately important), and C (least important). However, the actual number of categories may vary from organization to organization, depending on the extent to which a firm wants to differentiate control efforts. With three classes of items, A items generally only account for about 10 to 20 percent of the *number* of items in inventory but about 60

One way to lower inventory holding costs is to improve space utilization through narrow aisle handling equipment, mezzanines, layout, or other appropriate storage modes. Another is an inventory management system that allows companies to maintain tight control over inventory levels. This allows process planners to optimize material and maintain accurate quantities.

© Getty

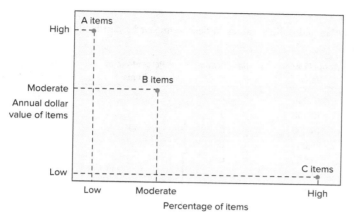

FIGURE 13.1
A typical A-B-C breakdown in relative annual dollar value of items and number of items by category

to 70 percent of the *annual dollar value.* At the other end of the scale, C items might account for about 50 to 60 percent of the number of items but only about 10 to 15 percent of the dollar value of an inventory. These percentages vary from firm to firm, but in most instances a relatively small number of items will account for a large share of the value or cost associated with an inventory, and these items should receive a relatively greater share of control efforts. For instance, A items should receive close attention through frequent reviews of amounts on hand and control over withdrawals, where possible, to make sure that customer service levels are attained. The C items should receive only loose control (two-bin system, bulk orders), and the B items should have controls that lie between the two extremes.

Note that C items are not necessarily *un*important; incurring a stockout of C items such as the nuts and bolts used to assemble manufactured goods can result in a costly shutdown of an assembly line. However, due to the low annual dollar value of C items, there may not be much additional cost incurred by ordering larger quantities of some items, or ordering them a bit earlier.

Figure 13.1 illustrates the A-B-C concept.

To conduct an A-B-C analysis, follow these steps:

1. For each item, multiply annual volume by unit price to get the annual dollar value.

2. Arrange annual dollar values in descending order.

3. The few (10 to 15 percent) with the highest annual dollar value are A items. The most (about 50 percent) with the lowest annual dollar value are C items. Those in between (about 35 percent) are B items.

Determining A, B, and C Designations

EXAMPLE 1

mhhe.com/stevenson13e

A manager has obtained a list of unit costs and estimated annual demands for 10 inventory items and now wants to categorize the items on an A-B-C basis. Multiplying each item's annual demand by its unit cost yields its annual dollar value:

Item Number	Annual Demand (00)	×	Unit Cost	=	Annual Dollar Value (00)
1	25		$ 360		$ 9,000
2	10		70		700
3	24		500		12,000
4	15		100		1,500
5	7		70		490
6	10		1,000		10,000
7	2		210		420
8	10		4,000		40,000
9	80		10		800
10	5		200		1,000
					75,910

SOLUTION

Arranging the annual dollars values in descending order can facilitate assigning items to categories:

Item Number	Annual Dollar Value	Classification	Percentage of Items	Percentage of Annual Dollar Value
8	$40,000	A	10	52.7
3	12,000	B		
6	10,000	B	30	40.8
1	9,000	B		
4	1,500	C		
10	1,000	C		
9	800	C	60	6.5
2	700	C		
5	490	C		
7	420	C		
	75,910		100	100

Note that category A has the fewest number of items but the highest percentage of annual dollar value, while category C has the most items but only a small percentage of the annual dollar value.

Although annual dollar value may be the primary factor in classifying inventory items, a manager may take other factors into account in making exceptions for certain items (e.g., changing the classification of a B item to an A item). Factors may include the risk of obsolescence, the risk of a stockout, the distance of a supplier, and so on.

Managers use the A-B-C concept in many different settings to improve operations. One key use occurs in customer service, where a manager can focus attention on the most important aspects of customer service by categorizing different aspects as very important, important, or of only minor importance. The point is to not overemphasize minor aspects of customer service at the expense of major aspects.

Cycle counting A physical count of items in inventory.

Another application of the A-B-C concept is as a guide to **cycle counting**, which is a physical count of items in inventory. The purpose of cycle counting is to reduce discrepancies between the amounts indicated by inventory records and the actual quantities of inventory on hand. Accuracy is important because inaccurate records can lead to disruptions in operations, poor customer service, and unnecessarily high inventory carrying costs. The counts are conducted more frequently than once a year, which reduces the costs of inaccuracies compared to only doing an annual count, by allowing for investigation and correction of the causes of inaccuracies.

The key questions concerning cycle counting for management are

1. How much accuracy is needed?
2. When should cycle counting be performed?
3. Who should do it?

APICS recommends the following guidelines for inventory record accuracy: $\pm$ .2 percent for A items, $\pm$ 1 percent for B items, and $\pm$ 5 percent for C items. A items are counted frequently, B items are counted less frequently, and C items are counted the least frequently.

Some companies use certain events to trigger cycle counting, whereas others do it on a periodic (scheduled) basis. Events that can trigger a physical count of inventory include an out-of-stock report written on an item indicated by inventory records to be in stock, an inventory report that indicates a low or zero balance of an item, and a specified level of activity (e.g., every 2,000 units sold).

Some companies use regular stockroom personnel to do cycle counting during periods of slow activity, while others contract with outside firms to do it on a periodic basis. Use of an outside firm provides an independent check on inventory and may reduce the risk of problems created by dishonest employees. Still other firms maintain full-time personnel to do cycle counting.

13.4 INVENTORY ORDERING POLICIES

Inventory ordering policies address the two basic issues of inventory management, which are how much to order and when to order. In the following sections, a number of models are described that are used for these issues.

Inventory that is intended to meet expected demand is known as **cycle stock**, while inventory that is held to reduce the probability of experiencing a stockout (i.e., running out of stock) due to demand and/or lead time variability is known as **safety stock**.

The discussion begins with the issue of how much to order.

Cycle stock The amount of inventory needed to meet expected demand.

Safety stock Extra inventory carried to reduce the probability of a stockout due to demand and/or lead time variability.

13.5 HOW MUCH TO ORDER: ECONOMIC ORDER QUANTITY MODELS

The question of how much to order can be determined by using an **economic order quantity** **(EOQ)** model. EOQ models identify the optimal order quantity by minimizing the sum of certain annual costs that vary with order size and order frequency. Three order size models are described here:

1. The basic economic order quantity model
2. The economic production quantity model
3. The quantity discount model

Economic order quantity (EOQ) The order size that minimizes total annual cost.

SCREENCAM TUTORIAL

Basic Economic Order Quantity (EOQ) Model

The basic EOQ model is the simplest of the three models. It is used to identify a *fixed* order size that will minimize the sum of the annual costs of holding inventory and ordering inventory. The unit purchase price of items in inventory is not generally included in the total cost because the unit cost is unaffected by the order size unless quantity discounts are a factor. If holding costs are specified as a percentage of unit cost, then unit cost is indirectly included in the total cost as a part of holding costs.

The basic model involves a number of assumptions. They are listed in Table 13.1.

Inventory ordering and usage occur in cycles. Figure 13.2 illustrates several inventory cycles. A cycle begins with receipt of an order of Q units, which are withdrawn at a constant rate over time. When the quantity on hand is just sufficient to satisfy demand during lead time, an order for Q units is submitted to the supplier. Because it is assumed that both the usage rate and the lead time do not vary, the order will be received at the precise instant that the inventory on hand falls to zero. Thus, orders are timed to avoid both excess stock and stockouts.

The optimal order quantity reflects a balance between carrying costs and ordering costs: As order size varies, one type of cost will increase while the other decreases. For example, if the order size is relatively small, the average inventory will be low, resulting in low carrying costs. However, a small order size will necessitate frequent orders, which will drive up annual ordering costs. Conversely, ordering large quantities at infrequent intervals can hold down annual ordering costs, but that would result in higher average inventory levels and therefore increased carrying costs. Figure 13.3 illustrates these two extremes.

LO13.8 Describe the basic EOQ model and its assumptions and solve typical problems.

1. Only one product is involved.
2. Annual demand requirements are known.
3. Demand is spread evenly throughout the year so that the demand rate is reasonably constant.
4. Lead time is known and constant.
5. Each order is received in a single delivery.
6. There are no quantity discounts.

TABLE 13.1

Assumptions of the basic EOQ model

562   **Chapter Thirteen**   Inventory Management

FIGURE 13.2
The inventory cycle: profile
of inventory level over time

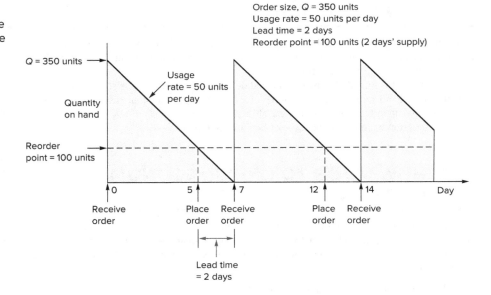

Order size, Q = 350 units
Usage rate = 50 units per day
Lead time = 2 days
Reorder point = 100 units (2 days' supply)

FIGURE 13.3
Average inventory level
and number of orders per
year are inversely related:
As one increases, the other
decreases

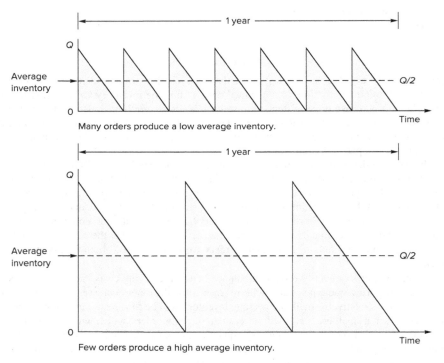

Thus, the ideal solution is an order size that causes neither a few very large orders nor many small orders, but one that lies somewhere between. The exact amount to order will depend on the relative magnitudes of carrying and ordering costs.

Annual carrying cost is computed by multiplying the average amount of inventory on hand by the cost to carry one unit for one year, even though any given unit would not necessarily be held for a year. The average inventory is simply half of the order quantity: The amount

FIGURE 13.4   Carrying cost, ordering cost, and total cost curve

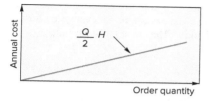

A. Carrying costs are linearly related to order size.

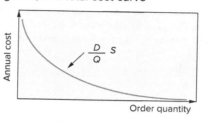

B. Ordering costs are inversely and nonlinearly related to order size.

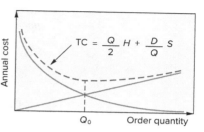

C. The total-cost curve is U-shaped.

on hand decreases steadily from Q units to 0, for an average of $(Q + 0)/2$, or $Q/2$. Using the symbol H to represent the average annual carrying cost per unit, the *total annual carrying cost* is

$$\text{Annual carrying cost} = \frac{Q}{2}H$$

where

Q = Order quantity in units

H = Holding (carrying) cost per unit per year

Carrying cost is thus a linear function of Q: Carrying costs increase or decrease in direct proportion to changes in the order quantity Q, as Figure 13.4A illustrates.

On the other hand, annual ordering cost will decrease as order size increases because, for a given annual demand, the larger the order size, the fewer the number of orders needed. For instance, if annual demand is 12,000 units and the order size is 1,000 units per order, there must be 12 orders over the year. But if Q = 2,000 units, only six orders will be needed; if Q = 3,000 units, only four orders will be needed. In general, the number of orders per year will be D/Q, where D = Annual demand and Q = Order size. Unlike carrying costs, ordering costs are relatively insensitive to order size; regardless of the amount of an order, certain activities must be done, such as determining how much is needed, periodically evaluating sources of supply, and preparing the invoice. Even inspection of the shipment to verify quality and quantity characteristics is not strongly influenced by order size since large shipments are sampled rather than completely inspected. Hence, ordering cost is treated as a constant. *Annual ordering cost* is a function of the number of orders per year and the ordering cost per order:

$$\text{Annual ordering cost} = S\frac{D}{Q}$$

where

D = Demand, usually in units per year

S = Ordering cost per order

Because the number of orders per year, D/Q, decreases as Q increases, annual ordering cost is inversely related to order size, as Figure 13.4B illustrates.

The total annual cost (TC) associated with carrying and ordering inventory when Q units are ordered each time is

$$\text{TC} = \begin{matrix}\text{Annual} \\ \text{carrying} \\ \text{cost}\end{matrix} + \begin{matrix}\text{Annual} \\ \text{ordering} \\ \text{cost}\end{matrix} = \frac{Q}{2}H + \frac{D}{Q}S \qquad (13\text{--}1)$$

(Note that D and H must be in the same units, e.g., months, years.) Figure 13.4C reveals that the total-cost curve is U-shaped (i.e., convex, with one minimum) and that *it reaches its minimum at the quantity where carrying and ordering costs are equal*. An expression for the optimal order quantity, Q_0, can be obtained using calculus.[1] The result is the formula

$$Q_0 = \sqrt{\frac{2DS}{H}} \qquad (13\text{--}2)$$

Thus, given annual demand, the ordering cost per order, and the annual carrying cost per unit, one can compute the optimal (economic) order quantity. The minimum total cost is then found by substituting Q_0 for Q in Formula 13–1.

The length of an order cycle (i.e., the time between orders) is

$$\text{Length of order cycle} = \frac{Q}{D} \qquad (13\text{--}3)$$

EXAMPLE 2   **Computing and Using the EOQ**

mhhe.com/stevenson13e

A local distributor for a national tire company expects to sell approximately 9,600 steel-belted radial tires of a certain size and tread design next year. Annual carrying cost is $16 per tire, and ordering cost is $75. The distributor operates 288 days a year.a.

a.   What is the EOQ?

b.   How many times per year does the store reorder?

c.   What is the length of an order cycle?

d.   What will the total annual cost be if the EOQ quantity is ordered?

SOLUTION $D = 9,600$ tires per year

$H = \$16$ per unit per year

$S = \$75$

a. $Q_0 = \sqrt{\dfrac{2DS}{H}} = \sqrt{\dfrac{2(9,600)75}{16}} = 300$ tires.

b.   Number of orders per year: $D/Q = \dfrac{9,600 \text{ tires/year}}{300 \text{ tires/order}} = 32$ orders.

c.   Length of order cycle: $Q/D = \dfrac{300 \text{ tires}}{9,600 \text{ tires/year}} = 1/32$ of a year, which is $1/32 \times 288$, or 9 workdays.

d.   TC = Carrying cost + Ordering to

$= (Q/2)H + (D/Q)S$

$= (300/2)16 + (9,600/300)75$

$= \$2,400 + \$2,400$

$= \$4,800$

Note that the ordering and carrying costs are equal at the EOQ, as illustrated in Figure 13.4C.

---

[1] We can find the minimum point of the total-cost curve by differentiating TC with respect to Q, setting the result equal to zero, and solving for Q. Thus,

1. $\dfrac{d\text{TC}}{dQ} = H/2 - DS/Q^2$

2. $0 = H/2 - DS/Q^2$, so $Q^2 = \dfrac{2DS}{H}$ and $Q = \sqrt{\dfrac{2DS}{H}}$

Note that the second derivative is positive, which indicates a minimum has been obtained.

Carrying cost is sometimes stated as a percentage of the price of an item rather than as a dollar amount per unit. However, as long as the percentage is converted into a dollar amount, the EOQ formula is still appropriate.

Computing the EOQ

Piddling Manufacturing assembles security systems. It purchases 3,600 high-definition security cameras a year at $180 each. Ordering costs are $50, and annual carrying costs are 20 percent of the purchase price. Compute the optimal quantity and the total annual cost of ordering and carrying the inventory.

$$D = 3{,}600 \text{ security cameras per year}$$
$$S = \$50$$
$$H = .20(\$180) = \$36$$
$$Q_0 = \sqrt{\frac{2DS}{H}} = \sqrt{\frac{2(3{,}600)(50)}{36}} = 100 \text{ security cameras}$$
$$TC = \text{Carrying costs} + \text{Ordering costs}$$
$$= (Q_0/2)H + (D/Q_0)S$$
$$= (100/2)36 + (3{,}600/100)50$$
$$= \$1{,}800 + \$1{,}800 = \$3{,}600$$

Comment Holding and ordering costs, and annual demand, are typically estimated values rather than values that can be precisely determined, say, from accounting records. Holding costs are sometimes *designated* by management rather than computed. Consequently, the EOQ should be regarded as an *approximate* quantity rather than an exact quantity. Thus, rounding the calculated value (to a whole number) is perfectly acceptable; stating a value to several decimal places would tend to give an unrealistic impression of the precision involved. An obvious question is: How good is this "approximate" EOQ in terms of minimizing cost? The answer is that the EOQ is fairly robust; the total cost curve is relatively flat near the EOQ. In other words, even if the order quantity differs from the actual EOQ, total costs will not increase much at all. This is particularly true for quantities larger than the real EOQ, because the total cost curve rises very slowly to the right of the EOQ. (See Figure 13.5.)

Because the total cost curve is relatively flat around the EOQ, there can be some flexibility to modify the order quantity a bit from the EOQ (say, to achieve a round lot or full truckload) without incurring much of an increase in total cost.

Economic Production Quantity (EPQ)

The batch mode is widely used in production. Even in assembly operations, portions of the work are done in batches. The reason for this is that in certain instances, the capacity to

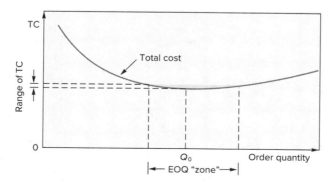

FIGURE 13.5
The total cost curve is relatively flat near the EOQ

produce a part exceeds the part's usage or demand rate. As long as production continues, inventory will continue to grow. In such instances, it makes sense to periodically produce such items in batches, or *lots,* instead of producing continually.

The assumptions of the EPQ model are similar to those of the EOQ model, except that instead of orders received in a single delivery, units are received incrementally during production. The assumptions are:

1. Only one product is involved
2. Annual demand is known
3. The usage rate is constant
4. Usage occurs continually, but production occurs periodically
5. The production rate is constant when production is occurring
6. Lead time is known and constant
7. There are no quantity discounts

Figure 13.6 illustrates how inventory is affected by periodically producing a batch of a particular item.

During the production phase of the cycle, inventory builds up at a rate equal to the difference between production and usage rates. For example, if the daily production rate is 20 units and the daily usage rate is 5 units, inventory will build up at the rate of $20 - 5 = 15$ units per day. As long as production occurs, the inventory level will continue to build; when production ceases, the inventory level will begin to decrease. Hence, the inventory level will be maximum at the point where production ceases. Inventory will then decrease at the constant usage rate. When the amount of inventory on hand is exhausted, production is resumed, and the cycle repeats itself.

Because the company makes the product itself, there are no ordering costs as such. Nonetheless, with every production run (batch) there are setup costs—the costs required to prepare the equipment for the job, such as cleaning, adjusting, and changing tools and fixtures. Setup costs are analogous to ordering costs because they are independent of the lot (run) size. They are treated in the formula in exactly the same way. The larger the run size, the fewer the number of runs needed and, therefore, the lower the annual setup cost. The number of runs or batches per year is D/Q, and the annual setup cost is equal to the number of runs per year times the setup cost, S, per run: $(D/Q)S$.

The total cost is

$$TC_{min} = \text{Carrying cost} + \text{Setup cost} = \left(\frac{I_{max}}{2}\right)H + (D/Q)S \qquad (13\text{–}4)$$

where

$I_{max} = \text{Maximum inventory}$

Unlike the EOQ case, where the entire quantity, Q, goes into inventory, in this case usage continually draws off some of the output, and what's left goes into inventory. So the inventory level will never be at the run size, Q_0. You can see that in Figure 13.6.

LO13.9 Describe the economic production quantity model and solve typical problems.

FIGURE 13.6
EPQ with incremental inventory buildup

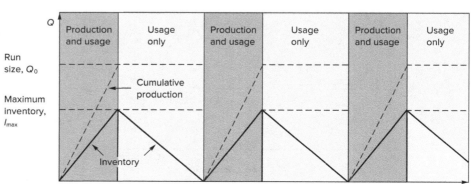

The economic run quantity is

$$Q_p = \sqrt{\frac{2DS}{H}} \sqrt{\frac{p}{p - u}}$$ (13–5)

SCREENCAM TUTORIAL

where

p = Production or delivery rate
u = Usage rate

Note: p and u must be in the same units (e.g., both in units per day, or units per week).

The cycle time (the time between setups of consecutive runs) for the economic run size model is a function of the run size and usage (demand) rate:

$$\text{Cycle time} = \frac{Q_p}{u}$$ (13–6)

Similarly, the run time (the production phase of the cycle) is a function of the run (lot) size and the production rate:

$$\text{Run time} = \frac{Q_p}{p}$$ (13–7)

The maximum and average inventory levels are

$$I_{max} = \frac{Q_p}{p}(p - u) \quad \text{or} \quad Q_p - \left(\frac{Q_p}{P}\right)u \quad \text{and} \quad I_{average} = \frac{I_{max}}{2}$$ (13–8)

Computing and Using the Production Lot Quantity

EXAMPLE 4

mhhe.com/stevenson13e

A toy manufacturer uses 48,000 rubber wheels per year for its popular dump truck series. The firm makes its own wheels, which it can produce at a rate of 800 per day. The toy trucks are assembled uniformly over the entire year. Carrying cost is $1 per wheel a year. Setup cost for a production run of wheels is $45. The firm operates 240 days per year. Determine the following:

a.   Optimal run size

b.   Minimum total annual cost for carrying and setup

c.   Cycle time for the optimal run size

d.   Run time

SOLUTION

D = 48,000 wheels per year
S = $45
H = $1 per wheel per year
p = 800 wheels per day
u = 48,000 wheels per 240 days, or 200 wheels per day

a. $Q_p = \sqrt{\dfrac{2DS}{H}} \sqrt{\dfrac{p}{p - u}} = \sqrt{\dfrac{2(48,000)45}{1}} \sqrt{\dfrac{800}{800 - 200}} = 2{,}400$ wheels

b. TC_{min} = Carrying cost + Setup cost = $\left(\dfrac{I_{max}}{2}\right)H + (D/Q_p)S$

Thus, first compute I_{max} :

$$I_{max} = \frac{Q_p}{p}(p - u) = \frac{2,400}{800}(800 - 200) = 1{,}800 \text{ wheels}$$

$$TC = \frac{1,800}{2} \times \$1 + \frac{48,000}{2,400} \times \$45 = \$900 + \$900 = \$1{,}800$$

Note again the equality of cost (in this example, setup and carrying costs) at the EOQ.

c. Cycle time $= \dfrac{Q_p}{u} = \dfrac{2,400 \text{ wheels}}{200 \text{ wheels per day}} = 12$ days

Thus, a run of wheels will be made every 12 days.

d. Run time $= \dfrac{Q_p}{p} = \dfrac{2,400 \text{ wheels}}{800 \text{ wheels per day}} = 3$ days

Thus, each run will require three days to complete.

Quantity Discounts

Quantity discounts Price reductions for larger orders.

Quantity discounts are price reductions for larger orders offered to customers to induce them to buy in large quantities. For example, a Chicago surgical supply company publishes the price list shown in Table 13.2 for boxes of gauze strips. Notice how the price per box decreases as order quantity increases.

When quantity discounts are available, there are a number of questions that must be addressed to decide whether to take advantage of a discount. These include:

1. Will storage space be available for the additional items?
2. Will obsolescence or deterioration be an issue?
3. Can we afford to tie up extra funds in inventory?

LO13.10 Describe the quantity discount model and solve typical problems.

If the decision is made to take advantage of a quantity discount, the goal is to select the order quantity that will minimize total cost, where total cost is the sum of carrying cost, ordering cost, *and* purchasing (i.e., product) cost:

TC = Carrying cost + Ordering cost + Purchasing cost

$$= \left(\frac{Q}{2}\right)H + \left(\frac{D}{Q}\right)S + PD \tag{13–9}$$

Where

Q = Order quantity
H = Holding cost per unit (usually annual)
D = Demand (usually annual)
S = Ordering cost
P = Unit price or cost

Recall that in the basic EOQ model, determination of order size does not involve the purchasing cost. The rationale for not including unit price is that under the assumption of no quantity discounts, price per unit is the same for all order sizes. Inclusion of unit price in the total-cost computation in that case would merely increase the total cost by the amount P times D. A graph of total annual purchase cost versus quantity would be a horizontal line. Hence, including purchasing costs would merely raise the total-cost curve by the same amount *(PD)* at every point. That would not change the EOQ. (See Figure 13.7.)

When quantity discounts are offered, there is a separate U-shaped total-cost curve for each unit price. Again, including unit prices merely raises each curve by a constant amount. However,

TABLE 13.2
Price list for extra-wide gauze strips

Order Quantity	Price per Box
1 to 44	$2.00
45 to 69	1.70
70 or more	1.40

FIGURE 13.7

Adding PD doesn't change the EOQ

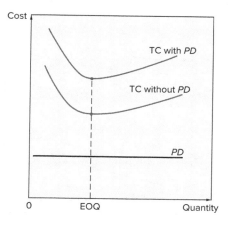

FIGURE 13.8

The total-cost curve with quantity discounts is composed of a portion of the total-cost curve for each price

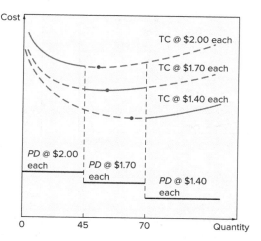

because the unit prices are all different, each curve is raised by a different amount: Smaller unit prices will raise a total-cost curve less than larger unit prices. Note that no one curve applies to the entire range of quantities; each curve applies to only a *portion* of the range. (See Figure 13.8.) Hence, the applicable or *feasible* total cost is initially on the curve with the highest unit price and then drops down, curve by curve, at the *price breaks,* which are the minimum quantities needed to obtain the discounts. Thus, in Table 13.2, the price breaks for gauze strips are at 45 and 70 boxes. The result is a total-cost curve with *steps* at the price breaks.

Even though each curve has a minimum, those points are not necessarily feasible. For example, the minimum point for the $1.40 curve in Figure 13.8 appears to be about 65 units. However, the price list shown in Table 13.2 indicates that an order size of 65 boxes will involve a unit price of $1.70. The actual total-cost curve is denoted by the solid lines; only those price–quantity combinations are feasible. The objective of the quantity discount model is to identify the order quantity that will represent the lowest total cost for the entire set of curves.

Analysis of quantity discount problems differs slightly, depending on whether holding costs are independent of unit price (i.e., constant), or whether they are a percentage of unit price. The following table illustrates the two ways, using 20 percent to illustrate holding costs that are a percentage of unit price.

Order Quality	Unit Price	H constant @ $4	H 20% of Unit Price
1 to 99	$10	4	.20(10) = 2.00
100 to 299	9	4	.20(9) = 1.80
300 or more	8	4	.20(8) = 1.60

When carrying costs are constant, there will be a single minimum point. All curves will have their minimum point at the same quantity. Consequently, the total-cost curves line up vertically, differing only in that the lower unit prices are reflected by lower total-cost curves as shown in Figure 13.9A. (For purposes of illustration, the horizontal purchasing cost lines have been omitted.)

When carrying costs are specified as a percentage of unit price, each curve will have a different minimum point. Because carrying costs are a percentage of price, lower prices will mean lower carrying costs and larger minimum points. Thus, as price decreases, each curve's minimum point will be to the right of the next higher curve's minimum point. (See Figure 13.9B.)

FIGURE 13.9
Comparison of TC curves for constant carrying costs and carrying costs that are a percentage of unit costs

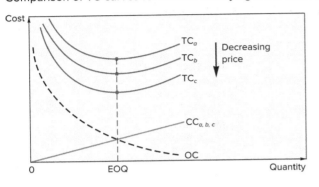
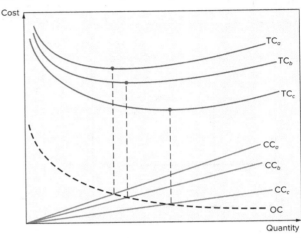

A. When carrying costs are constant, all curves have their minimum points at the same quantity.

B. When carrying costs are stated as a percentage of unit price, the minimum points do not line up.

The procedure for determining the overall EOQ differs slightly, depending on which of these two cases is relevant. For carrying costs that are constant, the procedure is as follows:

1. Compute the common minimum point. and then identify the price range in which the minimum point is feasible.

   a. If the minimum point is feasible in the lowest cost price range, that is the optimal order quantity.

   b. If the minimum point is in a higher cost range, compute the total cost for the feasible minimum point and for the price break quantity (i.e., small quantity to buy for that unit price) for all *lower* unit costs. Compare the total costs; the quantity (minimum point or price break quantity) that yields the lowest total cost is the optimal order quantity.

EXAMPLE 5

mhhe.com/stevenson13e

Determining the Optimal Order Quantity When There Are Quantity Discounts and Carrying Costs are Constant

The maintenance department of a large hospital uses about 816 cases of liquid cleanser annually. Ordering costs are $12, carrying costs are $4 per case a year, and the new price schedule indicates that orders of less than 50 cases will cost $20 per case, 50 to 79 cases will cost $18 per case, 80 to 99 cases will cost $17 per case, and larger orders will cost $16 per case. Determine the optimal order quantity and the total cost.

SOLUTION   See Figure 13.10:

$D = 816$ cases per year $S = \$12$ $H = \$4$ per case per year

Range	Price
1 to 49	$20
50 to 79	18
80 to 99	17
100 or more	16

1. Compute the common minimum quantity $Q: = \sqrt{\dfrac{2DS}{H}} = \sqrt{\dfrac{2(816)12}{4}} = 69.97 \approx 70$ cases.

Note: The curves are shown for illustration. You do not need to draw the curves.

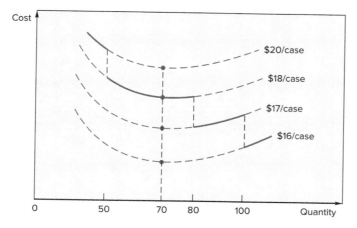

FIGURE 13.10
Total-cost curves for
Example 5

2.   The 70 cases can be bought at $18 per case because 70 falls in the range of 50 to 79 cases.
    The total cost to purchase 816 cases a year, at the rate of 70 cases per order, will be

$$TC_{70} = \text{Carrying cost} + \text{Order cost} + \text{Purchase cost}$$
$$= (Q/2)H + (D/Q)S + PD$$
$$= (70/2)4 + (816/70)12 + 18(816) = \$14{,}968$$

Because lower cost ranges exist, each must be checked against the minimum cost generated
by 70 cases at $18 each. In order to buy at $17 per case, at least 80 cases must be purchased.
(Because the TC curve is rising, 80 cases will have the lowest TC for that curve's feasible
region.) The total cost at 80 cases will be

$$TC_{80} = (80/2)4 + (816/80)12 + 17(816) = \$14{,}154$$

To obtain a cost of $16 per case, at least 100 cases per order are required, and the total cost
at that price break will be

$$TC_{100} = (100/2)4 + (816/100)12 + 16(816) = \$13{,}354$$

Therefore, because 100 cases per order yields the lowest total cost, 100 cases is the overall
optimal order quantity.

When carrying costs are expressed as a percentage of price, determine the best purchase
quantity with the following procedure:

1.   Beginning with the lowest unit price, compute the minimum points for each price range
    until you find a feasible minimum point (i.e., until a minimum point falls in the quantity
    range for its price).

2.   If the minimum point for the lowest unit price is feasible, it is the optimal order quantity.
    If the minimum point is not feasible in the lowest price range, compare the total cost at
    the price break for all *lower* price ranges with the total cost of the feasible minimum
    point. The quantity that yields the lowest total cost is the optimum.

Determining the Optimal Order Quantity When There Are Quantity Discounts and Carrying Costs are a Percentage of Unit Prices

EXAMPLE 6

mhhe.com/stevenson13e

Surge Electric uses 4,000 toggle switches a year. Switches are priced as follows: 1 to 499, 90
cents each; 500 to 999, 85 cents each; and 1,000 or more, 80 cents each. It costs approximately
$30 to prepare an order and receive it, and carrying costs are 40 percent of purchase price per
unit on an annual basis. Determine the optimal order quantity and the total annual cost.

FIGURE 13.11
Total-cost curves for
Example 6

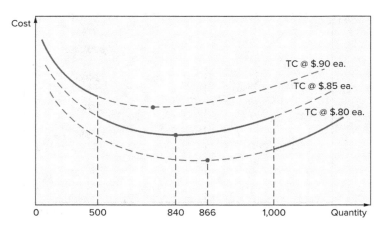

SOLUTION

See Figure 13.11:

$$D = 4{,}000 \text{ switches per year} \qquad S = \$30 \qquad H = .40P$$

Range	Unit Price	H
1 to 499	$.90	.40(.90) = .36
500 to 999	$.85	.40(.85) = .34
1,000 or more	$.80	.40(.80) = .32

Find the minimum point for each price, starting with the lowest price, until you locate a feasible minimum point.

$$\text{Minimum point.}_{80} = \sqrt{\frac{2DS}{H}} = \sqrt{\frac{2(4{,}000)30}{.32}} = 866 \text{ switches}$$

Because an order size of 866 switches will cost $.85 each rather than $.80 each, 866 is not a feasible minimum point for $.80 per switch. Next, try $.85 per unit.

$$\text{Minimum point.}_{85} = \sqrt{\frac{2(4{,}000)30}{.34}} = 840 \text{ switches}$$

This is feasible; it falls in the $.85 per switch range of 500 to 999.

Now compute the total cost for 840, and compare it to the total cost of the minimum quantity necessary to obtain a price of $.80 per switch.

$$\text{TC} = \text{Carrying costs} + \text{Ordering costs} + \text{Purchasing costs}$$

$$= \left(\frac{Q}{2}\right)H + \left(\frac{D}{Q}\right)S + PD$$

$$\text{TC}_{840} = \frac{840}{2}(.34) + \frac{4{,}000}{840}(30) + .85(4{,}000) = \$3{,}686$$

$$\text{TC}_{1000} = \frac{1{,}000}{2}(.32) + \frac{4{,}000}{1{,}000}(30) + .80(4{,}000) = \$3{,}480$$

Thus, the minimum-cost order size is 1,000 switches.

13.6 REORDER POINT ORDERING

EOQ models answer the question of how much to order, but not the question of when to order. The latter is the function of models that identify the **reorder point (ROP)** in terms of a *quantity:* The reorder point occurs when the quantity on hand drops to a predetermined amount. That amount generally includes expected demand during lead time and perhaps an extra cushion of stock, which serves to reduce the probability of experiencing a stockout during lead time. Note that in order to know when the reorder point has been reached, *perpetual* inventory monitoring is required.

The goal in ordering is to place an order when the amount of inventory on hand is sufficient to satisfy demand during the time it takes to receive that order (i.e., lead time). There are four determinants of the reorder point quantity:

1. The rate of demand (usually based on a forecast)
2. The lead time
3. The extent of demand and/or lead time variability
4. The degree of stockout risk acceptable to management

If demand and lead time are both constant, the reorder point is simply

$$ROP = d \times LT \qquad (13\text{–}10)$$

where

$$d = \text{Demand rate (units per day or week)}$$
$$LT = \text{Lead time in days or weeks}$$

Note: Demand and lead time must be expressed in the same time units.

> **Reorder point (ROP)** When the quantity on hand of an item drops to this amount, the item is reordered.

> **LO13.11** Describe reorder point models and solve typical problems.

SCREENCAM TUTORIAL

Computing the ROP When Usage and Lead Time are Constant

Tingly takes Two-a-Day vitamins, which are delivered to his home by a routeman seven days after an order is called in. At what point should Tingly reorder?

EXAMPLE 7

mhhe.com/stevenson13e

SOLUTION

Usage   = 2 vitamins a day
Lead time = 7 days
ROP   = Usage × Lead time
           = 2 vitamins per day × 7 days = 14 vitamins

Thus, Tingly should reorder when 14 vitamin tablets are left, which is equal to a seven-day supply of two vitamins a day.

When variability is present in demand or lead time, it creates the possibility that actual demand will exceed expected (average) demand. Consequently, it becomes necessary to carry additional inventory, called **safety stock**, to reduce the risk of running out of inventory (a stockout) during lead time. The reorder point then increases by the amount of the safety stock:

$$ROP = \frac{\text{Expected demand}}{\text{during lead time}} + \text{Safety stock} \qquad (13\text{–}11)$$

For example, if expected demand during lead time is 100 units, and the desired amount of safety stock is 10 units, the ROP would be 110 units.

Figure 13.12 illustrates how safety stock can reduce the risk of a stockout during lead time (LT). Note that stockout protection is needed only during lead time. If there is a sudden surge at any point during the cycle, that will trigger another order. Once that order is received, the danger of an imminent stockout is negligible.

> **Safety stock** Stock that is held in excess of expected demand due to variable demand and/or lead time.

FIGURE 13.12
Safety stock reduces risk
of stockout during lead
time

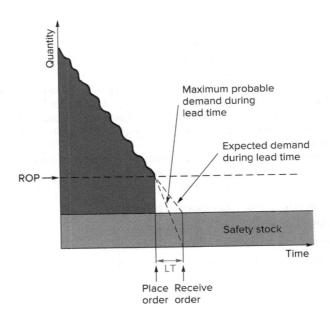

Service level Probability
that demand will not exceed
supply during lead time.

Because it costs money to hold safety stock, a manager must carefully weigh the cost of carrying safety stock against the reduction in stockout risk it provides. The customer *service level* increases as the risk of stockout decreases. Order cycle **service level** can be defined as the probability that demand will not exceed supply during lead time (i.e., that the amount of stock on hand will be sufficient to meet demand). Hence, a service level of 95 percent implies a probability of 95 percent that demand will not exceed supply during lead time. An equivalent statement that demand will be satisfied in 95 percent of such instances does *not* mean that 95 percent of demand will be satisfied. The risk of a stockout is the complement of service level; a customer service level of 95 percent implies a stockout risk of 5 percent. That is,

Service level = 100 percent – Stockout risk

Later you will see how the order cycle service level relates to the *annual* service level.

Consider for a moment the importance of stockouts. When a stockout occurs, demand cannot be satisfied at that time. In manufacturing operations, stockouts mean that jobs will be delayed and additional costs will be incurred. If the stockout involves parts for an assembly line, or spare parts for a machine or conveyor belt on the line, the line will have to shut down, typically at a very high cost per hour, until parts can be obtained. For service operations, stockouts mean that services cannot be completed on time. Aside from the added cost that results from the time delay, there is not only the matter of customer dissatisfaction but also the fact that schedules will be disrupted, sometimes creating a "domino effect" on following jobs. In the retail sector, stockouts create a competitive *disadvantage* that can result in customer dissatisfaction and, ultimately, the loss of customers.

The amount of safety stock that is appropriate for a given situation depends on the following factors:

1.   The average demand rate and average lead time
2.   Demand and lead time variability
3.   The desired service level

For a given order cycle service level, the greater the variability in either demand rate or lead time, the greater the amount of safety stock that will be needed to achieve that service level. Similarly, for a given amount of variation in demand rate or lead time, achieving an increase in the service level will require increasing the amount of safety stock. Selection of a service level

FIGURE 13.13
The ROP based on a normal distribution of lead time demand

may reflect stockout costs (e.g., lost sales, customer dissatisfaction) or it might simply be a policy variable (e.g., the manager wants to achieve a specified service level for a certain item).

Let us look at several models that can be used in cases when variability is present. The first model can be used if an estimate of expected demand during lead time and its standard deviation are available. The formula is

$$\text{ROP} = \frac{\text{Expected demand}}{\text{during lead time}} + z\sigma_{d\text{LT}} \qquad (13\text{--}12)$$

where

z = Number of standard deviations
$S_{d\text{LT}}$ = The standard deviation of lead time demand

The models generally assume that any variability in demand rate or lead time can be adequately described by a normal distribution. However, this is not a strict requirement; the models provide approximate reorder points even where actual distributions depart from normal.

The value of z (see Figure 13.13) used in a particular instance depends on the stockout risk that the manager is willing to accept. Generally, the smaller the risk the manager is willing to accept, the greater the value of z. Use Appendix B, Table B, to obtain the value of z, given a desired service level for lead time.

Computing the ROP and Safety Stock When the Mean and Standard Deviation of Lead Time Demand Are Given

EXAMPLE 8

eXcel
mhhe.com/stevenson13e

Suppose that the manager of a construction supply house determined from historical records that demand for sand during lead time averages 50 tons. In addition, suppose the manager determined that demand during lead time could be described by a normal distribution that has a mean of 50 tons and a standard deviation of 5 tons. Answer these questions, assuming that the manager is willing to accept a stockout risk of no more than 3 percent:

a. What value of z is appropriate?
b. How much safety stock should be held?
c. What reorder point should be used?

SOLUTION

Expected lead time demand = 50 tons
   $\sigma_{d\text{LT}}$ = 5 tons
   Risk = 3 percent

a. From Appendix B, Table B, using a service level of $1 - .03 = .9700$, you obtain a value of $z = +1.88$.
b. Safety stock = $z\sigma_{d\text{LT}}$ = 1.88(5) = 9.40 tons.
c. ROP = Expected lead time demand + Safety stock = 50 + 9.40 = 59.40 tons.

When data on lead time demand are not readily available, Formula 13-12 cannot be used. Nevertheless, data are generally available on daily or weekly demand, and on the length of lead time. Using those data, a manager can determine whether demand and/or lead time is variable, if variability exists in one or both, and the related standard deviation(s). For those situations, one of the following formulas can be used:

If only demand is variable, then $\sigma_{dLT} = \sigma_d\sqrt{LT}$, and the reorder point is

$$ROP = \bar{d} \times LT + z\sigma_d\sqrt{LT} \qquad (13\text{--}13)$$

where

$\bar{d}$ = *Average* daily or weekly demand

σ_d = Standard deviation of demand in days or weeks

LT = Lead time in days or weeks

If only lead time is variable, then $\sigma_{dLT} = d\sigma_{LT}$, and the reorder point is

$$ROP = d \times \overline{LT} + zd\sigma_{LT} \qquad (13\text{--}14)$$

where

d = Daily or weekly demand

$\overline{LT}$ = *Average* lead time in days or weeks

σ_{LT} = Standard deviation of lead time in days or weeks

If both demand and lead time are variable, then

$$\sigma_{dLT} = \sqrt{\overline{LT}\,\sigma_d^2 + \bar{d}^2\sigma_{LT}^2}$$

and the reorder point is

$$ROP = \bar{d} \times \overline{LT} + z\sqrt{\overline{LT}\,\sigma_d^2 + \bar{d}^2\sigma_{LT}^2} \qquad (13\text{--}15)$$

Note: Each of these models assumes that demand and lead time are *independent*.

EXAMPLE 9	**Computing the ROP When Demand is Variable**
e**X**cel mhhe.com/stevenson13e	A restaurant uses an average of 50 jars of a special sauce each week. Weekly usage of sauce has a standard deviation of 3 jars. The manager is willing to accept no more than a 10 percent risk of stockout during lead time, which is two weeks. Assume the distribution of usage is normal.

    a.   Which of the given formulas is appropriate for this situation? Why?

    b.   Determine the value of z.

    c.   Determine the ROP.

SOLUTION

$\bar{d}$ = 50 jars per week   LT = 2 weeks

σ_d = 3 jars per week   Acceptable risk = 10 percent, so service level is .90

    a.   Because only demand is variable (i.e., has a standard deviation), Formula 13–13 is appropriate.

    b.   From Appendix B, Table B, using a service level of .9000, you obtain $z = +1.28$.

    c. $ROP = \bar{d} \times LT + z\sigma_d\sqrt{LT} = 50 \times 2 + 1.28(3)\sqrt{2} = 100 + 5.43 = 105.43$.

    d.   Because the inventory is discrete units (jars), we round this amount to 106. (Generally, round up.)

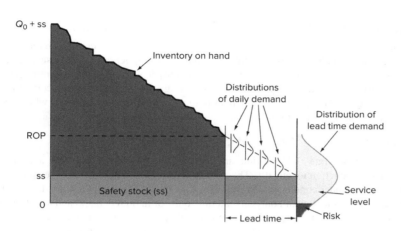

FIGURE 13.14
Lead time demand

Note that a two-bin ordering system (see p. 552) involves ROP reordering: The quantity in the second bin is equal to the ROP.

The logic of the three formulas for the reorder point may not be immediately obvious. The first part of each formula is the expected demand, which is the product of daily (or weekly) demand and the number of days (or weeks) of lead time. The second part of the formula is z times the standard deviation of lead time demand. For the formula in which only demand is variable, daily (or weekly) demand is assumed to be normally distributed and has the same mean and standard deviation (see Figure 13.14). The standard deviation of demand for the entire lead time is found by summing the *variances* of daily (or weekly) demands, and then finding the square root of that number because, unlike variances, standard deviations are not additive. Hence, if the daily standard deviation is σ_d, the *variance* is σ_d^2, and if lead time is four days, the variance of lead time demand will equal the sum of the four variances, which is $4\sigma_d^2$. The standard deviation of lead time demand will be the square root of this, which is equal to $2\sigma_d$. In general, this becomes $\sqrt{LT}\sigma_d$ and, hence, the last part of Formula 13–13.

When only lead time is variable, the explanation is much simpler. The standard deviation of lead time demand is equal to the constant daily demand multiplied by the standard deviation of lead time.

When both demand and lead time are variable, the formula appears truly impressive. However, it is merely the result of squaring the standard deviations of the two previous formulas to obtain their variances, summing them, and then taking the square root.

It is sometimes convenient to think of service level in annual terms. One definition of annual service level is the percentage of demand filled directly from inventory. This is also known as the **fill rate**. Thus, if $D = 1,000$, and 990 units were filled directly from inventory (shortages totaling 10 units over the year were recorded), the annual service level (fill rate) would be 990/1,000 = 99 percent.

Fill rate The percentage of demand filled by the stock on hand.

13.7 HOW MUCH TO ORDER: FIXED-ORDER-INTERVAL MODEL

The **fixed-order-interval (FOI) model** is used when orders must be placed at fixed time intervals (weekly, twice a month, etc.): The timing of orders is set. The question, then, at each order point, is how much to order. Fixed-interval ordering systems are widely used by retail businesses. If demand is variable, the order size will tend to vary from cycle to cycle. This is quite different from an EOQ/ROP approach in which the order size generally remains fixed from cycle to cycle, while the length of the cycle varies (shorter if demand is above average, and longer if demand is below average).

Fixed-order-interval (FOI) model Orders are placed at fixed time intervals.

LO13.12 Describe situations in which the fixed-order-interval model is appropriate, and solve typical problems.

Reasons for Using the Fixed-Order-Interval Model

In some cases, a supplier's policy might encourage orders at fixed intervals. Even when that is not the case, grouping orders for items from the same supplier can produce savings in shipping costs. Furthermore, some situations do not readily lend themselves to continuous monitoring of inventory levels. Many retail operations (e.g., drugstores, small grocery stores) fall into this category. The alternative for them is to use fixed-interval ordering, which requires only periodic checks of inventory levels.

Determining the Amount to Order

If both the demand rate and lead time are constant, the fixed-interval model and the fixed-quantity model function identically. The differences in the two models become apparent only when examined under conditions of variability. Like the ROP model, the fixed-interval model can have variations in demand only, in lead time only, or in both demand and lead time. However, for the sake of simplicity and because it is perhaps the most frequently encountered situation, the discussion here will focus only on *variable demand* and *constant lead time*.

Figure 13.15 provides a comparison of the fixed-quantity and fixed-interval systems. In the fixed-quantity arrangement, orders are triggered by a *quantity* (ROP), while in the

FIGURE 13.15
Comparison of fixed-quantity and fixed-interval ordering

A. Fixed quantity

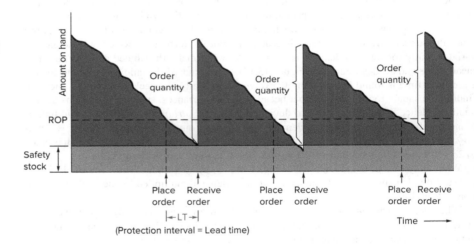

B. Fixed interval

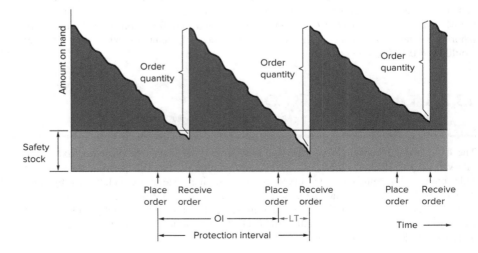

fixed-interval arrangement orders are triggered by a *time*. Therefore, the fixed-interval system must have stockout protection for lead time plus the next order cycle, but the fixed-quantity system needs protection only during lead time because additional orders can be placed at any time and will be received shortly (lead time) thereafter. Consequently, there is a greater need for safety stock in the fixed-interval model than in the fixed-quantity model. Note, for example, the large dip into safety stock during the second order cycle with the fixed-interval model.

Both models are sensitive to demand experience just prior to reordering, but in somewhat different ways. In the fixed-quantity model, a higher-than-normal demand causes a *shorter time* between orders, whereas in the fixed-interval model, the result is *a larger order size*. Another difference is that the fixed-quantity model requires close monitoring of inventory levels in order to know *when* the amount on hand has reached the reorder point. The fixed-interval model requires only a periodic review (i.e., physical count) of inventory levels just prior to placing an order to determine how much is needed.

Order size in the fixed-interval model is determined by the following computation:

$$
\begin{array}{ccccccc}
\text{Amount} \\ \text{to order} & = & \begin{array}{c}\text{Expected demand} \\ \text{during protection} \\ \text{interval}\end{array} & + & \begin{array}{c}\text{Safety} \\ \text{stock}\end{array} & - & \begin{array}{c}\text{Amount on hand} \\ \text{at reorder time}\end{array}
\end{array} \quad \text{(13-16)}
$$

$$
Q = \bar{d}(OI + LT) + z\sigma_d\sqrt{OI + LT} - A
$$

where

   OI = Order interval (length of time between orders)

   A = Amount on hand at reorder time

As in previous models, we assume that demand during the protection interval is normally distributed.

Computing the Order Quantity for the Fixed-Interval Model

EXAMPLE 10

mhhe.com/stevenson13e

Given the following information, determine the amount to order.

$\bar{d}$ = 30 units per day   Desired service level = 99 percent

σ_d = 3 units per day   Amount on hand at reorder time = 71 units

LT = 2 days   OI = 7 days

SOLUTION

$z = 2.33$ for 99 percent service level

$$
\begin{array}{c}\text{Amount} \\ \text{to order}\end{array} = \bar{d}(OI+LT) + z\sigma_d\sqrt{OI + LT} - A
$$

$$
Q = 30(7 + 2) + 2.33(3)\sqrt{7 + 2} - 71 = 220 \text{ units}
$$

An issue related to fixed-interval ordering is the risk of a stockout. From the perspective (i.e., the point in time) of placing an order, there are two points in the order cycle at which a stockout could occur. One is shortly after the order is placed, while waiting to receive the current order (refer to Figure 13.15). The second point is near the end of the cycle, while waiting to receive the next order.

To find the initial risk of a stockout, use the ROP formula (13–13), setting ROP equal to the quantity on hand when the order is placed, and solve for *z*, then obtain the service level for that value of *z* from Appendix B, Table B, and subtract it from 1.0000 to get the risk of a stockout.

To find the risk of a stockout at the end of the order cycle, use the fixed-interval formula (13–16) and solve for *z*. Then obtain the service level for that value of *z* from Appendix B, Table B, and subtract it from 1.0000 to get the risk of a stockout.

Let's look at an example.

EXAMPLE 11

eXcel
mhhe.com/stevenson13e

Computing Stockout Risk for the Fixed-Interval Model

Given the following information:

$LT = 4$ days $A = 43$ units
$OI = 12$ days $Q = 171$ units
$\bar{d} = 10$ units/day
$\sigma_d = 2$ units/day

Determine the risk of a stockout at

a.   The end of the initial lead time.
b.   The end of the second lead time.

SOLUTION

a.   For the risk of stockout for the first lead time, we use Formula 13–13. Substituting the given values, we get $43 = 10 \times 4 + z(2)(2)$. Solving, $z = +.75$. From Appendix B, Table B, the service level is .7734. The risk is $1 - .7734 = .2266$, which is fairly high.

b.   For the risk of a stockout at the end of the second lead time, we use Formula 13–16. Substituting the given values we get $171 = 10 \times (4 + 12) + z(2)(4) - 43$. Solving, $z = 16.75$. This value is way out in the right tail of the normal distribution, making the service level virtually 100 percent, and, thus, the risk of a stockout at this point is essentially equal to zero.

Benefits and Disadvantages

The fixed-interval system results in tight control. In addition, when multiple items come from the same supplier, grouping orders can yield savings in ordering, packing, and shipping costs. Moreover, it may be the only practical approach if inventory withdrawals cannot be closely monitored.

On the negative side, the fixed-interval system necessitates a larger amount of safety stock for a given risk of stockout because of the need to protect against shortages during an entire order interval plus lead time (instead of lead time only), and this increases the carrying cost. Also, there are the costs of the periodic reviews.

13.8 THE SINGLE-PERIOD MODEL

Single-period model Model for ordering of perishables and other items with limited useful lives.

LO13.13 Describe situations in which the single-period model is appropriate and solve typical problems.

Shortage cost Generally, the unrealized profit per unit (i.e. profit/unit - cost per unit).

The **single-period model** (sometimes referred to as the *newsboy problem*) is used to handle ordering of perishables (fresh fruits, vegetables, seafood, cut flowers) and items that have a limited useful life (newspapers, magazines, spare parts for specialized equipment). The *period* for spare parts is the life of the equipment, assuming that the parts cannot be used for other equipment. What sets unsold or unused goods apart is that they are not typically carried over from one period to the next, at least not without penalty. Day-old baked goods, for instance, are often sold at reduced prices; leftover seafood may be discarded; and out-of-date magazines may be offered to used book stores at bargain rates. There may even be some cost associated with disposal of leftover goods.

Analysis of single-period situations generally focuses on two costs: shortage and excess. Shortage cost may include a charge for loss of customer goodwill as well as the opportunity cost of lost sales. Generally, **shortage cost** is simply unrealized profit per unit. That is,

$$C_{\text{shortage}} = C_s = \text{Revenue per unit} - \text{Cost per unit}$$

If a shortage or stockout relates to an item used in production or to a spare part for a machine, then shortage cost refers to the actual cost of lost production.

FIGURE 13.16
The optimal stocking level balances unit shortage and excess costs

Excess cost pertains to items left over at the end of the period. In effect, excess cost is the difference between purchase cost and salvage value. That is,

$$C_{excess} = C_e = \text{Original cost per unit} - \text{Salvage value per unit}$$

If there is cost associated with disposing of excess items, the salvage will be negative and will therefore *increase* the excess cost per unit.

The goal of the single-period model is to identify the order quantity, or stocking level, that will minimize the long-run excess and shortage costs.

There are two general categories of problems that we will consider: those for which demand can be approximated using a continuous distribution (perhaps a theoretical one such as a uniform or normal distribution) and those for which demand can be approximated using a discrete distribution (say, historical frequencies or a theoretical distribution such as the Poisson). The kind of inventory can indicate which type of model might be appropriate. For example, demand for petroleum, liquids, and gases tends to vary over some *continuous scale,* thus lending itself to description by a continuous distribution. Demand for tractors, cars, and computers is expressed in terms of the *number of units* demanded and lends itself to description by a discrete distribution.

Excess cost Difference between purchase cost and salvage value of items left over at the end of a period.

Continuous Stocking Levels

The concept of identifying an optimal stocking level is perhaps easiest to visualize when demand is *uniform.* Choosing the stocking level is similar to balancing a seesaw, but instead of a person on each end of the seesaw, we have excess cost per unit (C_e) on one end of the distribution and shortage cost per unit (C_s) on the other. The optimal stocking level is analogous to the fulcrum of the seesaw; the stocking level equalizes the cost weights, as illustrated in Figure 13.16.

The *service level* is the *probability* that demand will not exceed the stocking level, and computation of the service level is the key to determining the optimal stocking level, S_o.

$$\text{Service level} = \frac{C_s}{C_s + C_e} \qquad\qquad (13\text{--}17)$$

where

C_s = Shortage cost per unit

C_e = Excess cost per unit

If actual demand exceeds S_o, there is a shortage; hence, C_s is on the right end of the distribution. Similarly, if demand is less than S_o, there is an excess, so C_e is on the left end of the distribution. When $C_e = C_s$, the optimal stocking level is halfway between the endpoints of the distribution. If one cost is greater than the other, S_o will be closer to the larger cost.

Finding the Optimal Stocking Level and Stockout Risk for the Single-Period Model when Demand is Uniformly Distributed

Sweet cider is delivered weekly to Cindy's Cider Bar. Demand varies uniformly between 300 liters and 500 liters per week. Cindy pays 20 cents per liter for the cider and charges 80 cents per liter for it. Unsold cider has no salvage value and cannot be carried over into the next week due to spoilage. Find the optimal stocking level and its stockout risk for that quantity.

EXAMPLE 12

eXcel
mhhe.com/stevenson13e

SOLUTION

C_e = Cost per unit − Salvage value per unit

    = \$.20   − \$0

    = \$.20 per unit

C_s = Revenue per unit − Cost per unit

    = \$.80   − \$.20

    = \$.60 per unit

$$SL = \frac{C_s}{C_s + C_e} = \frac{\$.60}{\$.60 + \$.20} = .75$$

Thus, the optimal stocking level must satisfy demand 75 percent of the time. For the uniform distribution, this will be at a point equal to the minimum demand plus 75 percent of the difference between maximum and minimum demands:

$$S_o = 300 + .75(500 - 300) = 450 \text{ liters}$$

The stockout risk is $1.00 - .75 = .25$.

A similar approach applies when demand is normally distributed.

EXAMPLE 13

mhhe.com/stevenson13e

Finding the Optimal Stocking Level When Demand is Normally Distributed

Cindy's Cider Bar also sells a blend of cherry juice and apple cider. Demand for the blend is approximately normal, with a mean of 200 liters per week and a standard deviation of 10 liters per week. C_s = 60 cents per liter, and C_e = 20 cents per liter. Find the optimal stocking level for the apple-cherry blend.

SOLUTION

$$SL = \frac{C_s}{C_s + C_e} = \frac{\$.60}{\$.60 + \$.20} = .75$$

This indicates that 75 percent of the area under the normal curve must be to the left of the stocking level. Appendix B, Table B, shows that a value of z between + .67 and + .68. Use the value of z that has a probability nearest to .75. In this case, it is .67. The optimal stocking level is S_o = mean + $z\sigma$. Thus,

$$S_o = 200 \text{ liters} + .67(10 \text{ liters}) = 206.7 \text{ liters}$$

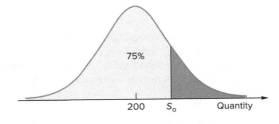

Discrete Stocking Levels

When stocking levels are discrete rather than continuous, the service level computed using the ratio $C_s/(C_s + C_e)$ usually does not coincide with a feasible stocking level (e.g., the optimal amount may be *between* five and six units). The solution is to stock at the *next higher level*

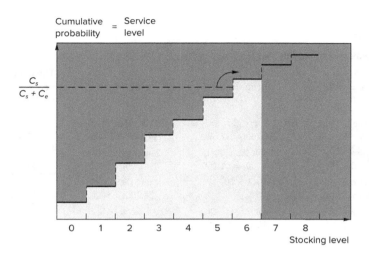

Cumulative probability = Service level

$\dfrac{C_s}{C_s + C_e}$

Stocking level

FIGURE 13.17
The service level achievement must equal or exceed the ratio $C_s/(C_s + C_e)$

(e.g., six units). In other words, choose the stocking level so that the desired service level is equaled or *exceeded*. Figure 13.17 illustrates this concept.

Example 14 illustrates the use of an empirical distribution.

EXAMPLE 14

e**X**cel
mhhe.com/stevenson13e

Finding the Optimal Stocking Level Given an Empirical Frequency Distribution

Historical records on the use of spare parts for several large hydraulic presses are to serve as an estimate of usage for spares of a newly installed press. Stockout costs involve downtime expenses and special ordering costs. These average $4,200 per unit short. Spares cost $800 each, and unused parts have zero salvage. Determine the optimal stocking level.

Spares Used	Relative Frequency	Cumulative Frequency
0	.20	.20
1	.40	.60
2	.30	.90
3	.10	1.00
4 or more	.00	
	1.00	

SOLUTION

$C_s = \$4,200$ $C_e = \$800$ $\text{SL} = \dfrac{C_s}{C_s + C_e} = \dfrac{\$4,200}{\$4,200 + \$800} = .84$

The cumulative-frequency column indicates the percentage of time that demand did not exceed (was equal to or less than) some amount. For example, demand does not exceed one spare 60 percent of the time, or two spares 90 percent of the time. Thus, in order to achieve a service level of *at least* 84 percent, it will be necessary to stock two spares (i.e., to go to the next higher stocking level).

The logic behind Formula 13–17 can be seen by solving the problem using a *decision table* approach. Table 13.3 illustrates this approach. The table enumerates the expected cost of each combination of stocking level and demand. For instance, if the stocking level is three, and demand turns out to be zero (see the blue-shaded cell), that would result in an excess of three units, at a cost of $800 each. The probability of a demand of zero units is .20, so the expected cost of that cell is .20(3)($800) = $480. Similarly, if no units are stocked and

TABLE 13.3
Expected cost for each possible outcome

If the stocking level is	**And the demand probabilities are**				The expected cost will be
	0 prob. = .20	1 prob. = .40	2 prob. = .30	3 prob. = .10	
0	**S = D** $0	1 unit short .40(1) ($4,200) = $1,680	2 units short .30(2) ($4,200) = $2,520	3 units short .10(3) ($4,200) = $1,260	$5,460
1	1-unit excess .20(1) ($800) = $160	**S = D** $0	1 unit short .30(1) ($4,200) = $1,260	2 units short .10(2) ($4,200) = $840	$2,260
2	2-unit excess .20(2) ($800) = $320	1-unit excess .40(1) ($800) = $320	**S = D** $0	1 unit short .10(1) ($4,200) = $420	$1,060
3	3-unit excess .20(3) ($800) = $480	2-unit excess .40(2) ($800) = $640	1-unit excess .30(1) ($800) = $240	**S = D** $0	$1,360

demand is two (see the yellow-shaded cell), the expected cost is the probability of demand being two (i.e., .30) multiplied by two units multiplied by the shortage cost per unit. Thus, the expected cost is .30(2)($4,200) = $2,520. For the cases in which the demand and stocking level are the same (the green-shaded cells), supply = demand, so there is neither a shortage nor an excess, and thus the cost is $0.

The lowest expected cost is $1,060, which occurs for a stocking level of two units, so two is the optimal stocking level, which agrees with the ratio approach.

Example 15 illustrates how to solve a problem when demand is described by a Poisson distribution.

EXAMPLE 15

mhhe.com/stevenson13e

Finding the Optimal Stocking Level when Demand has a Poisson Distribution

Demand for long-stemmed red roses at a small flower shop can be approximated using a Poisson distribution that has a mean of four dozen per day. Profit on the roses is $3 per dozen. Leftover flowers are marked down and sold the next day at a loss of $2 per dozen. Assume that all marked-down flowers are sold. What is the optimal stocking level?

SOLUTION

$$C_s = \$3 \qquad C_e = \$2 \qquad SL = \frac{C_s}{C_s + C_e} = \frac{\$3}{\$3 + \$2} = .60$$

Obtain the cumulative frequencies from the Poisson table (Appendix B, Table C) for a mean of 4.0:

Demand (dozen per day)	Cumulative Frequency
0	.018
1	.092
2	.238
3	.433
4	.629
5	.785
⋮	⋮

Compare the service level to the cumulative frequencies. In order to attain a service level of at least .60, it is necessary to stock four dozen.

One final point about discrete stocking levels: If the computed service level is *exactly* equal to the cumulative probability associated with one of the stocking levels, there are *two* equivalent stocking levels in terms of minimizing long-run cost—the one with equal probability and the next higher one. In the preceding example, if the ratio had been equal to .629, we would be indifferent between stocking four dozen and stocking five dozen roses each day.

13.9 OPERATIONS STRATEGY

Inventories often represent a substantial investment. More important, improving inventory processes can offer significant benefits in terms of cost reduction and customer satisfaction. Among the areas that have potential are the following:

Record keeping. It is important to have inventory records that are accurate and up-to-date, so that inventory decisions are based on correct information. Estimates of holding, ordering, and setup costs, as well as demand and lead times, should be reviewed periodically and updated when necessary.

Variation reduction. Lead time variations and forecast errors are two key factors that impact inventory management, and variation reduction in these areas can yield significant improvement in inventory management.

Lean operation. Lean systems are demand driven, which means that goods are pulled through the system to match demand instead of being pushed through without a direct link to demand. Moreover, lean systems feature smaller lot sizes than more traditional systems, based in part on the belief that holding costs are higher than those assigned by traditional systems, and partly as a deliberate effort to reduce ordering and setup costs by simplifying and standardizing necessary activities. An obvious benefit is a decrease in average inventory on hand and, hence, lower carrying costs. Other benefits include fewer disruptions of work flow, reduction in space needs, enhanced ability to spot problems, and increased feasibility to place machines and workers closer together, which allows more opportunities for socialization, communication, and cooperation.

Supply chain management. Working more closely with suppliers to coordinate shipments, reduce lead times, and reduce supply chain inventories can reduce the size and frequency of stockouts while lowering inventory carrying costs. Blanket orders and vendor-managed inventories can reduce transaction costs. Also, consignment agreements, where buyers are not charged for inventory items until the items are sold, may be an option. Storage costs can sometimes be reduced by using cross-docking, whereby inbound trucks with goods arriving at distributor warehouses from suppliers are directly loaded onto outbound trucks for store or dealer delivery, avoiding warehouse handling and storage costs.

SUMMARY

Inventory management is a core operations management activity. Effective inventory management is often the mark of a well-run organization. Inventory levels must be planned carefully in order to balance the cost of holding inventory and the cost of providing reasonable levels of customer service. Successful inventory management requires a system to keep track of inventory transactions, accurate information about demand and lead times, realistic estimates of certain inventory-related costs, and a priority system for classifying the items in inventory and allocating control efforts.

Four classes of models are described: EOQ, ROP, fixed-order-interval, and single-period models. The first three are appropriate if unused items can be carried over into subsequent periods. The single-period model is appropriate when items cannot be carried over. EOQ models address the question of how much to order. The ROP models address the question of when to order and are particularly helpful in dealing with situations that include variations in either demand rate or lead time. ROP models involve service level and safety stock considerations. When the time between orders is fixed, the FOI model is useful for determining the order quantity. The single-period model is used for items that have a "shelf life" of one period. The models presented in this chapter are summarized in Table 13.4.

TABLE 13.4
Summary of inventory formulas

Model	Formula	Symbols
1. Basic EOQ	$Q_0 = \sqrt{\dfrac{2DS}{H}}$ (13–2) $TC = \dfrac{Q}{2}H + \dfrac{D}{Q}S$ (13–1) Length of order cycle $= \dfrac{Q}{D}$ (13–3) Average inventory $= \dfrac{Q}{2}$	Q_0 = Economic order quantity D = Annual demand S = Order cost per order H = Annual carrying cost per unit Q = Order quantity
2. Economic production quantity	$Q_p = \sqrt{\dfrac{2DS}{H}}\sqrt{\dfrac{p}{p-u}}$ (13–5) $TC = \dfrac{I_{max}}{2}H + \dfrac{D}{Q}S$ (13–4) Cycle time $= \dfrac{Q}{u}$ (13–6) Run time $= \dfrac{Q}{p}$ (13–7) $I_{max} = \dfrac{Q_p}{p}(p-u)$ (13–8) Average inventory $= \dfrac{I_{max}}{2}$	Q_p = Optimal run or order size p = Production or delivery rate u = Usage rate I_{max} = Maximum inventory level
3. Quantity discounts	$TC = \dfrac{Q}{2}H + \dfrac{D}{Q}S + PD$ (13–9)	P = Unit price
4. Reorder point under: a. Constant demand and lead time b. Variable demand rate c. Variable lead time d. Variable lead time and demand	$ROP = d(LT)$ (13–10) $ROP = \bar{d}LT + z(\sigma_d)\sqrt{LT}$ (13–13) $ROP = d\overline{LT} + z(\sigma_{LT})d$ (13–14) $ROP = \overline{d}\overline{LT} + z\sqrt{\overline{LT}\sigma_d^2 + \overline{d}^2\sigma_{LT}^2}$ (13–15)	ROP = Quantity on hand at reorder point d = Demand rate LT = Lead time $\bar{d}$ = Average demand rate σ_d = Standard deviation of demand rate z = Standard normal deviation $\overline{LT}$ = Average lead time σ_{LT} = Standard deviation of lead time
5. Fixed interval	$Q = \bar{d}(OI + LT)$ $\quad + z\sigma_d\sqrt{OI + LT} - A$ (13–16)	OI = Time between orders A = Amount on hand at order time
6. Single period	$SL = \dfrac{C_s}{C_s + C_e}$ (13–17)	SL = Service level C_s = Shortage cost per unit C_e = Excess cost per unit

KEY POINTS

1. All businesses carry inventories, which are goods held for future use or potential future use. Inventory represents money that is tied up in goods or materials.

2. The two basic decisions (issues) in inventory management are how much to order, and when to re-order.

3. Effective inventory decisions depend on having good inventory records, good cost information, and good estimates of demand.

4. The decision of how much inventory to have on hand reflects a trade-off, for example, how much money to tie up in inventory versus having it available for other uses. Factors related to the

decision include purchase costs, holding costs, ordering costs, shortage and backlog costs, available space to store the inventory, and the return that can be had from other uses of the money.

5. As with other areas of operations, variations are present and must be taken into account. Uncertainties can be offset to some degree by holding safety stock, although that adds to the cost of holding inventory.

A-B-C approach 558
cycle counting 560
cycle stock 561
economic order quantity
  (EOQ) 561
excess cost 581
fill rate 577
fixed-order-interval (FOI)
  model 577
holding (carrying) cost 557

inventory 551
inventory turnover 555
lead time 557
Little's Law 554
ordering costs 558
periodic system 555
perpetual inventory system 555
point-of-sale (POS)
  system 555
purchase cost 557

quantity discounts 568
reorder point (ROP) 573
safety stock 561, 573
service level 574
setup costs 558
shortage cost 558, 580
single-period model 580
two-bin system 556
universal product code
  (UPC) 556

KEY TERMS

SOLVED PROBLEM

Basic EOQ. This type of problem can be recognized when annual demand (*D*), ordering cost (*S*), and holding or carrying cost per unit *(H)* are given. Use Formula 13–2 for order quantity, Formula 13–1 for total cost, and *D/Q* for number of orders a year.

  A toy manufacturer uses approximately 32,000 silicon chips annually. The chips are used at a steady rate during the 240 days a year that the plant operates. Annual holding cost is $3 per chip, and ordering cost is $120. Determine the following:

a. The optimal order quantity

b. The number of workdays in an order cycle

Problem 1

$D = 32{,}000$ chips per year $S = \$120$
$H = \$3$ per unit per year

a. $Q_0 = \sqrt{\dfrac{2DS}{H}} = \sqrt{\dfrac{2(32{,}000)120}{3}} = 1{,}600$ chips.

b. $\dfrac{Q}{D} = \dfrac{1{,}600 \text{ chips}}{32{,}000 \text{ chips/yr.}} = \dfrac{1}{20}$ year (i.e., $^1\!/_{20} \times 240$ days), or 12 days

Solution

Economic production quantity. This type of problem can be recognized when a production rate (*p*) is given in addition to the basic EOQ information. Use Formula 13–5 to compute the optimal run quantity. Production (run) time is Q/p. I_{max} is $(Q/p)(p-u)$. The time between the end of one run and the start of the next is $(I_{max})/u$ – setup time.

  The Dine Corporation is both a producer and a user of brass couplings. The firm operates 220 days a year and uses the couplings at a steady rate of 50 per day. Couplings can be produced at a rate of 200 per day. Annual storage cost is $2 per coupling, and machine setup cost is $70 per run.

a. Determine the economic run quantity.

b. Approximately how many runs per year will there be?

c. Compute the maximum inventory level.

d. What is the average inventory on hand?

e. Determine the length of the *pure consumption* portion of the cycle.

Problem 2

$D = 50$ units per day $\times$ 220 days per year $= 11{,}000$ units per year
$S = \$70$ per order
$H = \$2$ per unit per year
$p = 200$ units per day
$u = 50$ units per day

a. $Q_p = \sqrt{\dfrac{2DS}{H}} \sqrt{\dfrac{p}{p-u}} = \sqrt{\dfrac{2(11{,}000)70}{2}} \sqrt{\dfrac{200}{200-50}} \approx 1{,}013$ units.

b. Number of runs per year: $D/Q_0 = 11{,}000/1{,}013 = 10.86$, or approximately 11.

Solution

c. $I_{max} = \dfrac{Q_p}{p}(p - u) = \dfrac{1,013}{200}(200 - 50) = 759.75$ or 760 units.

d. Average inventory $= I_{max}/2 = 760/2 = 380$ units.

e. $I_{max}/u = 760/50 = 15.2$ days.

Problem 3

Quantity discounts. This type of problem can be recognized when a list showing prices for each quantity range is given along with the basic EOQ information.

a. If unit holding cost is constant, use these steps to solve the problem:

 1. Use Formula 13–2 to find Q.

 2. Locate Q in the price schedule.

 3. Compute TC using Formula 13–1 for Q and for all lower-cost price breaks.

b. If unit holding cost is a percentage of unit price, use these steps to solve the problem:

 1. Beginning with the lowest cost, and using the corresponding H for that cost, compute Q using Formula 13–2. Continue moving up in unit cost until a feasible Q is found.

 2. Locate the feasible Q in the price schedule.

 3. Compute TC using Formula 13–9 for Q and for all lower-cost price breaks. Remember to use the corresponding H for each price.

A small manufacturing firm uses roughly 3,400 pounds of chemical dye a year. Currently the firm purchases 300 pounds per order and pays $3 per pound. The supplier has just announced that orders of 1,000 pounds or more will be filled at a price of $2 per pound. The manufacturing firm incurs a cost of $100 each time it submits an order and assigns an annual holding cost of 17 percent of the purchase price per pound.

a. Determine the order size that will minimize the total cost.

b. If the supplier offered the discount at 1,500 pounds instead of 1,000 pounds, what order size would minimize total cost?

$$D = 3,400 \text{ pounds per year} \qquad S = \$100 \text{ per order} \qquad H = .17P$$

Solution

a. Compute the EOQ for $2 per pound: The quantity ranges are as follows.

Range	Unit Price
1 to 999	$3
1,000 +	$2

$$Q_{\$2/pound} = \sqrt{\dfrac{2DS}{H}} = \sqrt{\dfrac{2(3,400)(100)}{.17(2)}} = 1,414 \text{ pounds}$$

Because this quantity is feasible at $2 per pound, it is the optimum.

b. When the discount is offered at 1,500 pounds, the EOQ for the $2 per pound range is no longer feasible. Consequently, it becomes necessary to compute the EOQ for $3 per pound and compare the total cost for that order size with the total cost using the price break quantity (i.e., 1,500).

$$Q_{\$3/pound} = \sqrt{\dfrac{2DS}{H}} = \sqrt{\dfrac{2(3,400)100}{.17(3)}} \approx 1,155 \text{ pounds}$$

$$\text{TC} = \left(\dfrac{Q}{2}\right)H + \left(\dfrac{D}{Q}\right)S + PD$$

$$\text{TC}_{1,155} = \left(\dfrac{1,155}{2}\right).17(3) + \left(\dfrac{3,400}{1,155}\right)100 + 3(3,400)$$

$$= \$294.53 + \$294.37 + \$10,200 = \$10,789$$

$$\text{TC}_{1,500} = \left(\dfrac{1,500}{2}\right).17(2) + \left(\dfrac{3,400}{1,500}\right)100 + 2(3,400)$$

$$= \$255 + \$226.67 + \$6,800 = \$7,282$$

Hence, because it would result in a lower total cost, 1,500 is the optimal order size.

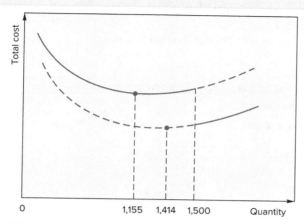

Reorder point. This type of problem can be recognized when the demand rate *(d)*, lead time (LT), and desired service level or stockout risk are given. Use these steps to solve this type of problem: **Problem 4**

1. Match the choice of formula to the standard deviation(s) that are given in the problem (e.g., if both demand and lead time standard deviations are given, use Formula 13–15 for the ROP).

2. If the problem asks for the amount of safety stock, use the second part of the appropriate ROP formula.

3. If the "expected demand during lead time" and the "standard deviation of lead time demand" are given, use Formula 13–12.

ROP for variable demand and constant lead time. The **Problem 4** housekeeping department of a motel uses approximately 400 washcloths per day. The actual number tends to vary with the number of guests on any given night. Usage can be approximated by a normal distribution that has a mean of 400 and a standard deviation of nine washcloths per day. A linen supply company delivers towels and washcloths with a lead time of three days. If the motel policy is to maintain a stockout risk of 2 percent, what is the minimum number of washcloths that must be on hand at reorder time, and how much of that amount can be considered safety stock?

$\bar{d}$ = 400 washcloths per day   LT = 3 days   **Solution**
σ_d = 9 washcloths per day   Risk = 2 percent, so service level = 98 percent

From Appendix B, Table B, the nearest z value that corresponds to an area under the normal curve to the left of z for 98 percent is +2.05.

$$ROP = \bar{d}LT \quad + z\sigma_d\sqrt{LT} = 400(3) + 2.05(9)\sqrt{3}$$
$$= 1,200 + 31.96, \text{ or approximately } 1,232 \text{ washcloths}$$

Safety stock is approximately 32 washcloths.

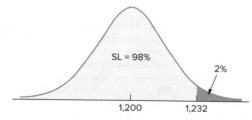

ROP for constant demand and variable lead time. The motel in the preceding example uses approximately 600 bars of soap each day, and this tends to be fairly constant. Lead time for soap delivery is normally distributed with a mean of six days and a standard deviation of two days. A service level of 90 percent is desired.   **Problem 5**

a. Find the ROP.

b. How many days of supply are on hand at the ROP?

Solution

d = 600 bars per day

SL = 90 percent, so $z = +1.28$ (from Appendix B, Table B2)

$\overline{LT}$ = 6 days

σ_{LT} = 2 days

a. ROP = $d\overline{LT} + z(\sigma_{LT})d = 600(6) + 1.28(2)(600)$

    = 5,136 bars of soap

b. $\dfrac{ROP}{d} = \dfrac{5,136}{600} = 8.56$ days

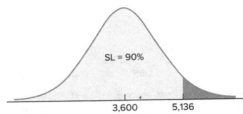

SL = 90%

3,600   5,136

Problem 6

ROP for variable demand rate and variable lead time. The motel replaces broken glasses at a rate of 25 per day. In the past, this quantity has tended to vary normally and have a standard deviation of three glasses per day. Glasses are ordered from a Cleveland supplier. Lead time is normally distributed with an average of 10 days and a standard deviation of 2 days. What ROP should be used to achieve a service level of 95 percent?

Solution

$\overline{d}$ = 25 glasses per day $\overline{LT}$ = 10 days

σ_d = 3 glasses per day σ_{LT} = 2 days

SL = 95 percent, so $z = +1.65$ (Appendix B, Table B2)

$ROP = \overline{d}\overline{LT} + z\sqrt{\overline{LT}\sigma_d^2 + \overline{d}^2\sigma_{LT}^2}$

$= 25(10) + 1.65\sqrt{10(3)^2 + (25)^2(2)^2} = 334$ glasses

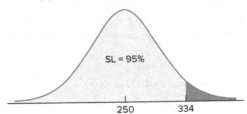

SL = 95%

250   334

Problem 7

Fixed-order-interval. This type of problem can be recognized when an order interval is given (e.g., inventory is ordered every 10 days) along with the demand rate, lead time, and quantity on hand at order time. Use Formula 13–16 to find the optimal order size.

A lab orders a number of chemicals from the same supplier every 30 days. Lead time is five days. The assistant manager of the lab must determine how much of one of these chemicals to order. A check of stock revealed that eleven 25-milliliter (ml) jars are on hand. Daily usage of the chemical is approximately normal with a mean of 15.2 ml per day and a standard deviation of 1.6 ml per day. The desired service level for this chemical is 95 percent.

a. How many jars of the chemical should be ordered?

b. What is the average amount of safety stock of the chemical?

Solution

$\overline{d}$ = 15.2 ml per day   OI = 30 days   SL = 95 percent requires $z = 1.65$

σ_d = 1.6 ml per day   LT = 5 days   A = 11 jars × 25 ml per jar = 275 ml

a. Amount to order $= \bar{d}(OI + LT) + z\sigma_d\sqrt{OI + LT} - A$

$\qquad\qquad\qquad = 15.2(30 + 5) + 1.65(1.6)\sqrt{30 + 5} - 275 = 272.62$ ml

Convert this to number of jars:

$$\frac{272.62 \text{ ml}}{25 \text{ ml per jar}} = 10.90 \text{ or } 11 \text{ jars}$$

b. Safety stock $= z\sigma_d\sqrt{OI + LT} = 1.65(1.6)\sqrt{30 + 5} = 15.62$ ml.

Single-period. This type of problem can be recognized when a probability distribution or empirical distribution for demand for a "perishable" item is given along with unit shortage and excess costs, or information that can be used to calculate them. Use these steps to solve the problem:

Problem 8

1. Compute the optimal service level using Formula 13–17.

2. If the given distribution is uniform or normal, use that to obtain the exact stocking level.

3. If the distribution is Poisson or empirical, SL will fall between two cumulative frequencies. Round up to the higher frequency to find the optimal stocking level. *Note:* If the distribution is empirical, first obtain the cumulative frequencies or probabilities.

A firm that installs cable TV systems uses a certain piece of equipment for which it carries two spare parts as optimal. The parts cost $500 each and have no salvage value or useful life after one period. Part failures can be modeled by a Poisson distribution with a mean of two failures during the useful life of the equipment. Holding and disposal costs are negligible. Estimate the apparent range of shortage cost.

C_s is unknown $\qquad\qquad C_e = \$500$

Solution

The Poisson table (Appendix B, Table C) provides these values for a mean of 2.0:

Number of Failures	Cumulative Probability
0	.135
1	.406
2	.677
3	.857
4	.947
5	.983
⋮	⋮

For the optimal stocking level, the service level must usually be rounded up to a feasible stocking level. Hence, you know that the service level must have been between .406 and .677 in order to make two units the optimal level. By setting the service level equal first to .406 and then to .677, you can establish bounds on the possible range of shortage costs.

$$\frac{C_s}{C_s + \$500} = .406, \text{ so } C_s = .406(\$500 + C_s)$$

Solving, you find $C_s = \$341.75$. Similarly,

$$\frac{C_s}{C_s + \$500} = .677, \text{ so } C_s = .677(\$500 + C_s)$$

Solving, you find $C_s = \$1,047.99$. Hence, the apparent range of shortage cost is $341.75 to $1,047.99.$_s = \$1,047.99$. Hence, the apparent range of shortage cost is $341.75 to $1,047.99.

592   **Chapter Thirteen**   Inventory Management

1. What are the primary reasons for holding inventory?
2. What are the requirements for effective inventory management?
3. Briefly describe each of the costs associated with inventory.
4. What potential benefits and risks do RFID tags have for inventory management?
5. Why might it be inappropriate to use inventory turnover ratios to compare inventory performance of companies that are in different industries?
6. How can managers use the results of A-B-C classification?
7. a. List the major assumptions of the EOQ model.
    b. How would you respond to the criticism that EOQ models tend to provide misleading results because values of D, S, and H are, at best, educated guesses?
8. Explain briefly how a higher carrying cost can result in a decrease in inventory.
9. What is safety stock, and what is its purpose?
10. Under what circumstances would the amount of safety stock held be large? Small? Zero?
11. What is meant by the term *service level?* Generally speaking, how is service level related to the amount of safety stock held?
12. Describe briefly the A-B-C approach to inventory control.
13. The purchasing agent for a company that assembles and sells air-conditioning equipment in a Latin American country noted that the cost of compressors has increased significantly each time they have been reordered. The company uses an EOQ model to determine order size. What are the implications of this price escalation with respect to order size? What factors other than price must be taken into consideration?
14. Explain how a decrease in setup time can lead to a decrease in the average amount of inventory a firm holds, and why that would be beneficial.
15. What is the single-period model, and under what circumstances is it appropriate?
16. Can the optimal stocking level in the single-period model ever be less than expected demand? Explain briefly.
17. What are some ways in which a company can reduce the need for inventories?

1. What trade-offs are involved in each of these aspects of inventory management?
    a. Buying additional amounts to take advantage of quantity discounts.
    b. Treating holding cost as a percentage of unit price instead of as a constant amount.
    c. Conducting cycle counts once a quarter instead of once a year.
2. Who needs to be involved in inventory decisions involving holding costs? Setting inventory levels? Quantity discount purchases?
3. How has technology aided inventory management? How have technological improvements in products such as automobiles and computers impacted inventory decisions?

1. To be competitive, many fast-food chains began to expand their menus to include a wider range of foods. Although contributing to competitiveness, this has added to the complexity of operations, including inventory management. Specifically, in what ways does the expansion of menu offerings create problems for inventory management?
2. As a supermarket manager, how would you go about evaluating the criticalness of an inventory shortage?
3. Sam is at the post office to mail a package. After he pays for mailing the package, the clerk asks if he would like to buy some stamps. Sam pauses to think before he answers. He doesn't have a credit card with him. After paying for the package, he has about $30 in his pocket. Analyze this from an inventory standpoint. Identify the relevant considerations.
4. Give two examples of unethical conduct involving inventory management and the ethical principle each one violates.

Chapter Thirteen   Inventory Management   593

1. a. Determine an A-B-C classification for these items:

Item	Unit Cost	Annual Volume (00)
1	$100	25
2	80	30
3	15	60
4	50	10
5	11	70
6	60	85
7	10	60

b. Find the EOQ given this information: $D = 4{,}500$ units/year, $S = \$36$, and $H = \$10$ per unit per year.

c. Find the economic production quantity given this information.

$D = 18{,}000$ units/year, $S = \$100$, $H = \$40$ per unit per year, $p = 120$ units per day, and $u = 90$ units/day

2. a. The following table contains figures on the monthly volume and unit costs for a random sample of 16 items from a list of 2,000 inventory items at a health care facility. Develop an A-B-C classification for these items.

Item	Unit Cost	Usage	Item	Unit Cost	Usage
K34	$10	200	F99	20	60
K35	25	600	D45	10	550
K36	36	150	D48	12	90
M10	16	25	D52	15	110
M20	20	80	D57	40	120
Z45	80	200	N08	30	40
F14	20	300	P05	16	500
F95	30	800	P09	10	30

b. Given the monthly usages in the following table, classify the items in A, B, and C categories according to dollar usage.

Item	Usage	Unit Cost
4021	90	$1,400
9402	300	12
4066	30	700
6500	150	20
9280	10	1,020
4050	80	140
6850	2,000	10
3010	400	20
4400	5,000	5

c. Determine the percentage of items in each category and the annual dollar value for each category for part *b*.

3. A bakery buys flour in 25-pound bags. The bakery uses 1,215 bags a year. Ordering cost is $10 per order. Annual carrying cost is $75 per bag.

a. Determine the economic order quantity.

b. What is the average number of bags on hand?

c. How many orders per year will there be?

d. Compute the total cost of ordering and carrying flour.

e. If holding costs were to increase by $9 per year, how much would that affect the minimum total annual cost?

4. A large law firm uses an average of 40 boxes of copier paper a day. The firm operates 260 days a year. Storage and handling costs for the paper are $30 a year per box, and it costs approximately $60 to order and receive a shipment of paper.

   a. What order size would minimize the sum of annual ordering and carrying costs?

   b. Compute the total annual cost using your order size from part *a*.

   c. Except for rounding, are annual ordering and carrying costs always equal at the EOQ?

   d. The office manager is currently using an order size of 200 boxes. The partners of the firm expect the office to be managed "in a cost-efficient manner." Would you recommend that the office manager use the optimal order size instead of 200 boxes? Justify your answer.

5. Garden Variety Flower Shop uses 750 clay pots a month. The pots are purchased at $2 each. Annual carrying costs per pot are estimated to be 30 percent of cost, and ordering costs are $20 per order. The manager has been using an order size of 1,500 flower pots.

   a. What additional annual cost is the shop incurring by staying with this order size?

   b. Other than cost savings, what benefit would using the optimal order quantity yield?

6. A produce distributor uses 800 packing crates a month, which it purchases at a cost of $10 each. The manager has assigned an annual carrying cost of 35 percent of the purchase price per crate. Ordering costs are $28. Currently the manager orders once a month. How much could the firm save annually in ordering and carrying costs by using the EOQ?

7. A manager receives a forecast for next year. Demand is projected to be 600 units for the first half of the year and 900 units for the second half. The monthly holding cost is $2 per unit, and it costs an estimated $55 to process an order.

   a. Assuming that monthly demand will be level during each of the six-month periods covered by the forecast (e.g., 100 per month for each of the first six months), determine an order size that will minimize the sum of ordering and carrying costs for each of the six-month periods.

   b. Why is it important to be able to assume that demand will be level during each six-month period?

   c. If the vendor is willing to offer a discount of *$10 per order* for ordering in multiples of 50 units (e.g., 50, 100, 150), would you advise the manager to take advantage of the offer in either period? If so, what order size would you recommend?

8. A food processor uses approximately 27,000 glass jars a month for its fruit juice product. Because of storage limitations, a lot size of 4,000 jars has been used. Monthly holding cost is 18 cents per jar, and reordering cost is $60 per order. The company operates an average of 20 days a month.

   a. What penalty is the company incurring by its present order size?

   b. The manager would prefer ordering 10 times each month but would have to justify any change in order size. One possibility is to simplify order processing to reduce the ordering cost. What ordering cost would enable the manager to justify ordering every other day (i.e., 10 times a month)?

9. The Friendly Sausage Factory (FSF) can produce hot dogs at a rate of 5,000 per day. FSF supplies hot dogs to local restaurants at a steady rate of 250 per day. The cost to prepare the equipment for producing hot dogs is $66. Annual holding costs are 45 cents per hot dog. The factory operates 300 days a year. Find the following:

   a. The optimal run size

   b. The number of runs per year

   c. How many days it takes to produce the optimal run quantity

10. A chemical firm produces sodium bisulfate in 100-pound bags. Demand for this product is 20 tons per day. The capacity for producing the product is 50 tons per day. Setup costs $100, and storage and handling costs are $5 per ton a year. The firm operates 200 days a year. (*Note:* 1 ton = 2,000 pounds.)

   a. How many bags per run are optimal?

   b. What would the average inventory be for this lot size?

   c. Determine the approximate length of a production run, in days.

   d. About how many runs per year would there be?

   e. How much could the company save annually if the setup cost could be reduced to $25 per run?

11. A company is about to begin production of a new product. The manager of the department that will produce one of the components for the product wants to know how often the machine used to produce the item will be available for other work. The machine will produce the item at a rate of 200 units a day. Eighty units will be used daily in assembling the final product. Assembly will take place five days a week, 50 weeks a year. The manager estimates that it will take almost a full day to get the machine ready for a production run, at a cost of $300. Inventory holding costs will be $10 a year.

    a. What run quantity should be used to minimize total annual costs?

    b. How many days does it take to produce the optimal run quantity?

    c. What is the average amount of inventory?

    d. If the manager wants to run another job between runs of this item, and needs a minimum of 10 days per cycle for the other work, will there be enough time?

    e. Given your answer to part *d*, the manager wants to explore options that will allow this other job to be performed using this equipment. Name three options the manager can consider.

    f. Suppose the manager decides to increase the run size of the new product. How many additional units would be needed to just accommodate the other job? How much will that increase the total annual cost?

12. A company manufactures hair dryers. It buys some of the components, but it makes the heating element, which it can produce at the rate of 800 per day. Hair dryers are assembled daily, 250 days a year, at a rate of 300 per day. Because of the disparity between the production and usage rates, the heating elements are periodically produced in batches of 2,000 units.

    a. Approximately how many *batches* of heating elements are produced annually?

    b. If production on a batch begins when there is no inventory of heating elements on hand, how much inventory will be on hand *two days later?*

    c. What is the average inventory of elements, assuming each production cycle begins when there are none on hand?

    d. The same equipment that is used to make the heating elements could also be used to make a component for another of the firm's products. That job would require four days, including setup. Setup time for making a batch of the heating elements is a half day. Is there enough time to do this job between production of batches of heating elements? Explain.

13. A mail-order house uses 18,000 boxes a year. Carrying costs are 60 cents per box a year, and ordering costs are $96. The following price schedule applies. Determine the following:

    a. The optimal order quantity

    b. The number of orders per year

Number of Boxes	Price per Box
1,000 to 1,999	$1.25
2,000 to 4,999	1.20
5,000 to 9,999	1.15
10,000 or more	1.10

14. A jewelry firm buys semiprecious stones to make bracelets and rings. The supplier quotes a price of $8 per stone for quantities of 600 stones or more, $9 per stone for orders of 400 to 599 stones, and $10 per stone for lesser quantities. The jewelry firm operates 200 days per year. Usage rate is 25 stones per day, and ordering costs are $48.

    a. If carrying costs are $2 per year for each stone, find the order quantity that will minimize total annual cost.

    b. If annual carrying costs are 30 percent of unit cost, what is the optimal order size?

    c. If lead time is six working days, at what point should the company reorder?

15. A manufacturer of exercise equipment purchases the pulley section of the equipment from a supplier who lists these prices: less than 1,000, $5 each; 1,000 to 3,999, $4.95 each; 4,000 to 5,999, $4.90 each; and 6,000 or more, $4.85 each. Ordering costs are $50, annual carrying costs per unit are 40 percent of purchase cost, and annual usage is 4,900 pulleys. Determine an order quantity that will minimize total cost.

16. A company will begin stocking remote control devices. Expected monthly demand is 800 units. The controllers can be purchased from either supplier A or supplier B. Their price lists are as follows:

SUPPLIER A		SUPPLIER B	
Quantity	Unit Price	Quantity	Unit Price
1–199	$14.00	1–149	$14.10
200–499	13.80	150–349	13.90
500 +	13.60	350 +	13.70

Ordering cost is $40 and annual holding cost is 25 percent of unit price per unit. Which supplier should be used and what order quantity is optimal if the intent is to minimize total annual costs?

17. A manager just received a new price list from a supplier. It will now cost $1.00 a box for order quantities of 801 or more boxes, $1.10 a box for 200 to 800 boxes, and $1.20 a box for smaller quantities. Ordering cost is $80 per order and carrying costs are $10 per box a year. The firm uses 3,600 boxes a year. The manager has suggested a "round number" order size of 800 boxes. The manager's rationale is that with a U-shaped cost curve that is fairly flat at its minimum, the difference in total annual cost between 800 and 801 units would be small anyway. How would you reply to the manager's suggestion? What order size would you recommend?

18. A newspaper publisher uses roughly 800 feet of baling wire each day to secure bundles of newspapers while they are being distributed to carriers. The paper is published Monday through Saturday. Lead time is six workdays. What is the appropriate reorder point quantity, given that the company desires a service level of 95 percent, if that stockout risk for various levels of safety stock is as follows: 1,500 feet, .10; 1,800 feet, .05; 2,100 feet, .02; and 2,400 feet, .01?

19. Given this information:

Expected demand during lead time = 300 units

Standard deviation of lead time demand = 30 units

Determine each of the following, assuming that lead time demand is distributed normally:

a. The ROP that will provide a risk of stockout of 1 percent during lead time.

b. The safety stock needed to attain a 1 percent risk of stockout during lead time.

c. Would a stockout risk of 2 percent require more or less safety stock than a 1 percent risk? Explain. Would the ROP be larger, smaller, or unaffected if the acceptable risk were 2 percent instead of 1 percent? Explain.

20. Given this information:

Lead-time demand = 600 pounds

Standard deviation of lead time demand = 52 pounds (Assume normality.)

Acceptable stockout risk during lead time = 4 percent

a. What amount of safety stock is appropriate?

b. When should this item be reordered?

c. What risk of stockout would result from a decision not to have any safety stock?

21. Demand for walnut fudge ice cream at the Sweet Cream Dairy can be approximated by a normal distribution with a mean of 21 gallons per week and a standard deviation of 3.5 gallons per week. The new manager desires a service level of 90 percent. Lead time is two days, and the dairy is open seven days a week. (*Hint:* Work in terms of weeks.)

a. If an ROP model is used, what ROP would be consistent with the desired service level? How many days of supply are on hand at the ROP, assuming average demand?

b. If a fixed-interval model is used instead of an ROP model, what order size would be needed for the 90 percent service level with an order interval of 10 days and a supply of 8 gallons on hand at the order time? What is the probability of experiencing a stockout before this order arrives?

c. Suppose the manager is using the ROP model described in part *a*. One day after placing an order with the supplier, the manager receives a call from the supplier that the order will be delayed because of problems at the supplier's plant. The supplier promises to have the order there in two days. After hanging up, the manager checks the supply of walnut fudge ice cream and finds that 2 gallons have been sold since the order was placed. Assuming the supplier's promise is valid, what is the probability that the dairy will run out of this flavor before the shipment arrives?

22. The injection molding department of a company uses an average of 30 gallons of special lubricant a day. The supply of the lubricant is replenished when the amount on hand is 170 gallons. It takes four days for an order to be delivered. Safety stock is 50 gallons, which provides a stockout risk of 9 percent. What amount of safety stock would provide a stockout risk of 3 percent? Assume normality.

23. A company uses 85 circuit boards a day in a manufacturing process. The person who orders the boards follows this rule: Order when the amount on hand drops to 625 boards. Orders are

delivered approximately six days after being placed. The delivery time is normal with a mean of six days and a standard deviation of 1.10 days. What is the probability that the supply of circuit boards will be exhausted before the order is received if boards are reordered when the amount on hand drops to 625 boards?

24. One item a computer store sells is supplied by a vendor who handles only that item. Demand for that item recently changed, and the store manager must determine when to replenish it. The manager wants a probability of at least 96 percent of not having a stockout during lead time. The manager expects demand to average a dozen units a day and have a standard deviation of two units a day. Lead time is variable, averaging four days with a standard deviation of one day. Assume normality and that seasonality is not a factor.

    a. When should the manager reorder to achieve the desired probability?

    b. Why might the model not be appropriate if seasonality were present?

25. The manager of a car wash received a revised price list from the vendor who supplies soap, and a promise of a shorter lead time for deliveries. Formerly the lead time was four days, but now the vendor promises a reduction of 25 percent in that time. Annual usage of soap is 4,500 gallons. The car wash is open 360 days a year. Assume that daily usage is normal, and that it has a standard deviation of 2 gallons per day. The ordering cost is $30 and annual carrying cost is $3 a gallon. The revised price list (cost per gallon) is shown in the following table.

Quantity	Unit Price
1–399	$2.00
400–799	1.70
800 +	1.62

    a. What order quantity is optimal?

    b. What ROP is appropriate if the acceptable risk of a stockout is 1.5 percent?

26. A small copy center uses five 500-sheet boxes of copy paper a week. Experience suggests that usage can be well approximated by a normal distribution with a mean of five boxes per week and a standard deviation of one-half box per week. Two weeks are required to fill an order for letterhead stationery. Ordering cost is $2, and annual holding cost is 20 cents per box.

    a. Determine the economic order quantity, assuming a 52-week year.

    b. If the copy center reorders when the supply on hand is 12 boxes, compute the risk of a stockout.

    c. If a fixed interval of seven weeks instead of an ROP is used for reordering, what risk does the copy center incur that it will run out of stationery before this order arrives if it orders 36 boxes when the amount on hand is 12 boxes?

27. Ned's Natural Foods sells unshelled peanuts by the pound. Historically, Ned has observed that daily demand is normally distributed with a mean of 80 pounds and a standard deviation of 10 pounds. Lead time also appears normally distributed with a mean of eight days and a standard deviation of one day. What ROP would provide a stockout risk of 10 percent during lead time?

28. Regional Supermarket is open 360 days per year. Daily use of cash register tape averages 10 rolls. Usage appears normally distributed with a standard deviation of 2 rolls per day. The cost of ordering tape is $1, and carrying costs are 40 cents per roll a year. Lead time is three days.

    a. What is the EOQ?

    b. What ROP will provide a lead time service level of 96 percent?

29. A service station uses 1,200 cases of oil a year. Ordering cost is $40, and annual carrying cost is $3 per case. The station owner has specified a service level of 99 percent.

    a. What is the optimal order quantity?

    b. What level of safety stock is appropriate if lead time demand is normally distributed with a mean of 80 cases and a standard deviation of 6 cases?

30. Caring Hospital's dispensary reorders doses of a drug when the supply on hand falls to 18 units. Lead time for resupply is three days. Given the typical usage over the last 10 days, what service level is achieved with the hospital's reorder policy? (*Hint:* Use Formula 13–13.)

Day	1	2	3	4	5	6	7	8	9	10
Units	3	4	7	5	5	6	4	3	4	5

31. A drugstore uses fixed-order cycles for many of the items it stocks. The manager wants a service level of .98. The order interval is 14 days, and lead time is 2 days. Average demand for one item is 40 units per day, and the standard deviation of demand is 3 units per day. Given the on-hand inventory at the reorder time for each order cycle shown in the following table, determine the order quantities for cycles 1, 2, and 3.

Cycle	On Hand
1	42
2	8
3	103

32. A manager must set up inventory ordering systems for two new production items, P34 and P35. P34 can be ordered at any time, but P35 can be ordered only once every four weeks. The company operates 50 weeks a year, and the weekly usage rates for both items are normally distributed. The manager has gathered the following information about the items.

	Item P34	Item P35
Average weekly demand	60 units	70 units
Standard deviation	4 units per week	5 units per week
Unit cost	$15	$20
Annual holding cost	30%	30%
Ordering cost	$70	$30
Lead time	2 weeks	2 weeks
Acceptable stockout risk	2.5%	2.5%

 a. When should the manager reorder each item?

 b. Compute the order quantity for P34.

 c. Compute the order quantity for P35 if 110 units are on hand at the time the order is placed.

33. Given the following list of items,

 a. Classify the items as A, B, or C.

 b. Determine the economic order quantity for each item (round to the nearest whole unit).

Item	Estimated Annual Demand	Ordering Cost	Holding Cost (%)	Unit Price
H4-010	20,000	50	20	2.50
H5-201	60,200	60	20	4.00
P6-400	9,800	80	30	28.50
P6-401	14,500	50	30	12.00
P7-100	6,250	50	30	9.00
P9-103	7,500	50	40	22.00
TS-300	21,000	40	25	45.00
TS-400	45,000	40	25	40.00
TS-041	800	40	25	20.00
V1-001	33,100	25	35	4.00

34. Demand for jelly doughnuts on Saturdays at Don's Doughnut Shoppe is shown in the following table. Determine the optimal number of doughnuts, in dozens, to stock if labor, materials, and overhead are estimated to be $3.20 per dozen, doughnuts are sold for $4.80 per dozen, and leftover doughnuts at the end of each day are sold the next day at half price. What is the *resulting* service level?

Demand (dozens)	Relative Frequency	Demand (dozens)	Relative Frequency
19	.01	25	.10
20	.05	26	.11
21	.12	27	.10
22	.18	28	.04
23	.13	29	.02
24	.14		

35. A public utility intends to buy a turbine as part of an expansion plan and must now decide on the number of spare parts to order. One part, no. X135, can be purchased for $100 each. Carrying and disposal costs are estimated to be 145 percent of the purchase price over the life of the turbine. A stockout would cost roughly $88,000 due to downtime, ordering, and "special purchase" factors. Historical records based on the performance of similar equipment operating under similar conditions suggest that demand for spare parts will tend to approximate a Poisson distribution with a mean of 3.2 parts for the useful life of the turbine.

    a. What is the optimal number of spares to order?

    b. Carrying no spare parts would be the best strategy for what range of shortage cost?

36. Skinner's Fish Market buys fresh Boston bluefish daily for $4.20 per pound and sells it for $5.70 per pound. At the end of each business day, any remaining bluefish is sold to a producer of cat food for $2.40 per pound. Daily demand can be approximated by a normal distribution with a mean of 80 pounds and a standard deviation of 10 pounds. What is the optimal stocking level?

37. A small grocery store sells fresh produce, which it obtains from a local farmer. During the strawberry season, demand for fresh strawberries can be reasonably approximated using a normal distribution with a mean of 40 quarts per day and a standard deviation of 6 quarts per day. Excess costs run 35 cents per quart. The grocer orders 49 quarts per day.

    a. What is the implied cost of shortage per quart?

    b. Why might this be a reasonable figure?

38. Demand for devil's food whipped-cream layer cake at a local pastry shop can be approximated using a Poisson distribution with a mean of six per day. The manager estimates it costs $9 to prepare each cake. Fresh cakes sell for $12. Day-old cakes sell for $9 each. What stocking level is appropriate if one-half of the day-old cakes are sold and the rest thrown out?

39. Burger Prince buys top-grade ground beef for $1.00 per pound. A large sign over the entrance guarantees that the meat is fresh daily. Any leftover meat is sold to the local high school cafeteria for 80 cents per pound. Four hamburgers can be prepared from each pound of meat. Burgers sell for 60 cents each. Labor, overhead, meat, buns, and condiments cost 50 cents per burger. Demand is normally distributed with a mean of 400 pounds per day and a standard deviation of 50 pounds per day. What daily order quantity is optimal? (*Hint:* Shortage cost must be in dollars per pound.)

40. Demand for rug-cleaning machines at Clyde's U-Rent-It is shown in the following table. Machines are rented by the day only. Profit on the rug cleaners is $10 per day. Clyde has four rug-cleaning machines.

Demand	Frequency
0	.30
1	.20
2	.20
3	.15
4	.10
5	.05
	1.00

    a. Assuming that Clyde's stocking decision is optimal, what is the implied range of excess cost per machine?

    b. Your answer from part *a* has been presented to Clyde, who protests that the amount is too low. Does this suggest an increase or a decrease in the number of rug machines he stocks? Explain.

    c. Suppose now that the $10 mentioned as profit is instead the excess cost per day for each machine and that the shortage cost is unknown. Assuming that the optimal number of machines is four, what is the implied range of shortage cost per machine?

41. A manager is going to purchase new processing equipment and must decide on the number of spare parts to order with the new equipment. The spares cost $200 each, and any unused spares will have an expected salvage value of $50 each. The probability of usage can be described by this distribution:

Number	0	1	2	3
Probability	.10	.50	.25	.15

If a part fails and a spare is not available, two days will be needed to obtain a replacement and install it. The cost for idle equipment is $500 per day. What quantity of spares should be ordered?

a. Use the ratio method.

b. Use the tabular method (see Table 13.3).

42. A Las Vegas supermarket bakery must decide how many wedding cakes to prepare for the upcoming weekend. Cakes cost $33 each to make, and they sell for $60 each. Unsold cakes are reduced to half-price on Monday, and typically one-third of those are sold. Any that remain are donated to a nearby senior center. Analysis of recent demand resulted in the following table:

Demand	0	1	2	3
Probability	.15	.35	.30	.20

How many cakes should be prepared to maximize expected profit?

a. Use the ratio method.

b. Use the tabular method (see Table 13.3).

43. Offwego Airlines has a daily flight from Chicago to Las Vegas. On average, 18 ticket holders cancel their reservations, so the company intentionally overbooks the flight. Cancellations can be described by a normal distribution with a mean of 18 passengers and a standard deviation of 4.55 passengers. Profit per passenger is $99. If a passenger arrives but cannot board due to overbooking, the company policy is to provide a cash payment of $200. How many tickets should be overbooked to maximize expected profit?

CASE   UPD MANUFACTURING

UPD Manufacturing produces a range of health care appliances for hospital as well as for home use. The company has experienced a steady demand for its products, which are highly regarded in the health care field. Recently the company has undertaken a review of its inventory ordering procedures as part of a larger effort to reduce costs.

One of the company's products is a blood pressure testing kit. UPD manufactures all of the components for the kit in-house except for the digital display unit. The display units are ordered at six-week intervals from the supplier. This ordering system began about five years ago, because the supplier insisted on it. However, that supplier was bought out by another supplier about a year ago, and the six-week ordering requirement is no longer in place. Nonetheless, UPD has continued to use the six-week ordering policy. According to purchasing manager Tom Chambers, "Unless somebody can give me a reason for changing, I'm going to stick with what we've been doing. I don't have time to reinvent the wheel."

Further discussions with Tom revealed a cost of $32 to order and receive a shipment of display units from the supplier. The company assembles 89 kits a week. Also, information from Sara James, in Accounting, indicated a weekly carrying cost of $.08 for each display unit.

The supplier has been quite reliable with deliveries; orders are received five working days after they are faxed to the supplier. Tom indicated that as far as he was concerned, lead-time variability is virtually nonexistent.

Questions

1. Would using an order interval other than every six weeks reduce costs? If so, what order interval would be best, and what order size would that involve?

2. Would you recommend changing to the optimal order interval? Explain.

CASE   HARVEY INDUSTRIES

Background

Harvey Industries, a Wisconsin company, specializes in the assembly of highpressure washer systems and in the sale of repair parts for these systems. The products range from small portable high-pressure washers to large industrial installations for snow removal from vehicles stored outdoors during the winter months. Typical uses for high-pressure water cleaning include:

Automobiles	Airplanes
Building maintenance	Barns
Engines	Ice cream plants
Lift trucks	Machinery
Swimming pools	

Industrial customers include General Motors, Ford, Chrysler, Delta Airlines, United Parcel Service, and Shell Oil Company.

Although the industrial applications are a significant part of its sales, Harvey Industries is primarily an assembler of equipment for coin operated self-service car wash systems. The typical car wash is of concrete block construction with an equipment room in the center, flanked on either side by a number of bays. The cars are driven into the bays where the owner can wash and wax the car, utilizing high-pressure hot water and liquid wax. A dollar bill changer is available to provide change for the use of the equipment and the purchase of various products from dispensers. The products include towels, tire cleaner, and upholstery cleaner.

Current Inventory Control System

The current inventory control "system" consists of orders for stock replenishment being made by the stockroom foreman, the purchasing manager, or the manufacturing manager whenever one of them notices that the inventory is low. An order for replenishment of inventory is also placed whenever someone (either a customer or an employee in the assembly area) wants an item and it is not in stock.

Some inventory is needed for the assembly of the high-pressure equipment for the car wash and industrial applications. There are current and accurate bills of material for these assemblies. The material needs to support the assembly schedule are generally known well in advance of the build schedule.

The majority of inventory transactions are for repair parts and for supplies used by the car washes, such as paper towels, detergent, and wax concentrate. Because of the constant and rugged use of the car wash equipment, there is a steady demand for the various repair parts.

The stockroom is well organized, with parts stored in locations according to each vendor. The number of vendors is relatively limited, with each vendor generally supplying many different parts. For example, the repair parts from Allen Bradley, a manufacturer of electrical motors, are stocked in the same location. These repair parts will be used to provide service for the many electrical motors that are part of the high-pressure pump and motor assembly used by all of the car washes.

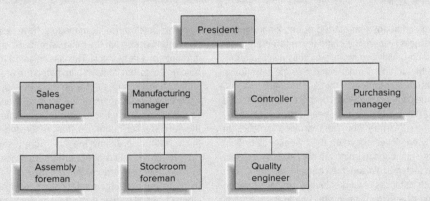

In recent years Harvey Industries has been in financial difficulty. The company has lost money for three of the last four years, with the last year's loss being $17,174 on sales of $1,238,674. Inventory levels have been steadily increasing to their present levels of $124,324.

The company employs 23 people with the management team consisting of the following key employees: president, sales manager, manufacturing manager, controller, and purchasing manager. The abbreviated organization chart reflects the reporting relationship of the key employees and the three individuals who report directly to the manufacturing manager.

Because of the heavy sales volume of repair parts, there are generally two employees working in the stockroom—a stockroom foreman who reports to the manufacturing manager and an assistant to the foreman. One of these two employees will handle customer orders. Many customers stop by and order the parts and supplies they need. Telephone orders are also received and are shipped by United Parcel Service the same day.

The assembly area has some inventory stored on the shop floor. This inventory consists of low-value items that are used every day, such as nuts, bolts, screws, and washers. These purchased items do not amount to very much dollar volume throughout the year.

(continued)

602   **Chapter Thirteen**   Inventory Management

(*concluded*)

Unfortunately, oftentimes the assembly area is out of one of these basic items and this causes a significant amount of downtime for the assembly lines.

Paperwork is kept to a minimum. A sales slip listing the part numbers and quantities sold to a customer is generally made out for each sale. If the assembly department needs items that are not stocked on the assembly floor, someone from that department will enter the stockroom and withdraw the necessary material. There is no paperwork made out for the items needed on the assembly floor.

There were 973 different part numbers purchased for stock last year and those purchases amounted to $314,673. An analysis of inventory records shows that $220,684 was spent on just 179 of the part numbers.

Fortunately for Harvey Industries, most of the items they purchase are stocked by either the manufacturer or by a wholesaler. When it is discovered that the company is out of stock on an item, it generally takes only two or three days to replenish the stock.

Due to the company's recent losses, its auditing firm became concerned about the company's ability to continue in business. Recently the company sold off excess vacant land adjoining its manufacturing facility to generate cash to meet its financial obligations.

New President

Because of the recent death of the owner, the trust department of a Milwaukee bank (as trustee for the state) has taken over the company's affairs and has appointed a new company president. The new president has identified many problem areas—one of which is improper inventory control. He has retained you as a consultant to make specific recommendations concerning a revised inventory control system. What are your recommendations and their rationale?

Source: Case "Harvey Industries" by Donald Condit presented at Midwest Case Writer's Association Workshop, 1984. Copyright © 1984 Donald Condit. Reprinted by permission.

CASE  **GRILL RITE**

Grill Rite is an old-line company that started out making wooden matches. As that business waned, the company entered the electric barbecue grill market, with five models of grills it sells nationally. For many years the company maintained a single warehouse from which it supplied its distributors.

The plant where the company produces barbecue sets is located in a small town, and many workers have been with the company for many years. During the transition from wooden matches to barbecue grills, many employees gave up their weekends to help with changing over the plant and learning the new skills they would need, without pay. In fact, Mac Wilson, the company president, can reel off a string of such instances of worker loyalty. He has vowed to never lay off any workers, and to maintain a full employment, steady rate of output. "Yes, I know demand for these babies (barbecue grills) is seasonal, but the inventory boys will just have to deal with it. On an annual basis, our output matches sales."

Inventory is handled by a system of four warehouses. There is a central warehouse located near the plant that supplies some customers directly, and the three regional warehouses.

The vice president for sales, Julie Berry, is becoming increasingly frustrated with the inventory system that she says "is antiquated and unresponsive." She points to increasing complaints from regional sales managers about poor customer service, saying customer orders go unfilled or are late, apparently due to shortages at the regional warehouse. Regional warehouse managers, stung by complaints from sales managers, have responded by increasing their order sizes from the main warehouse, and maintaining larger amounts of safety stock. This has resulted in increased inventory holding costs, but it hasn't eliminated the problem. Complaints are still coming in from salespeople about shortages and lost sales. According to managers of the regional warehouses, their orders to the main warehouse aren't being shipped, or when they are, they are smaller quantities than requested. The manager of the main warehouse, Jimmy Joe ("JJ") Sorely, says his policy is to give preference to "filling direct orders from actual customers, rather than warehouse orders that might simply reflect warehouses trying to replenish their safety stock. And besides, I never know when I'll get hit with an order from one of the regional warehouses. I guess they think we've got an unlimited supply." Then he adds, "I thought when we added the warehouses, we could just divide our inventory among the warehouses, and everything would be okay."

When informed of the "actual customers" remark, a regional warehouse manager exclaimed, "We're their biggest customer!"

Julie Berry also mentioned that on more than one occasion she has found that items that were out of stock at one regional warehouse were in ample supply in at least one other regional warehouse.

Take the position of a consultant called in by president Mac Wilson. What recommendations can you make to alleviate the problems the company is encountering?

CASE   FARMERS RESTAURANT

SARAH LUBBERS AND CHRIS RUSCHE, GRAND VALLEY STATE UNIVERSITY

Farmers Restaurant is a full service restaurant offering a variety of breakfast, lunch, and dinner items. Currently, Kristin Davis is the general manager for the Farmers Restaurant located in the Grand Rapids/ Wyoming metro area of Michigan. Since becoming manager, Kristin has faced some difficulties with ordering the right amounts of food items for the restaurant. Because of this, there are some weeks the restaurant has a surplus of menu items that are no longer fresh, and must be discarded. At other times, the restaurant has experienced shortages of some items. The fact that inventory accounts for an average cost of 26 percent of the restaurant's total revenues underscores the importance of managing inventory. Kristin would like to find a way to ensure that she is maintaining the proper amount of inventory. Customer counts at Kristin's restaurant have been declining recently, so one of Kristin's greatest focuses is to keep current customers and attract new customers. She believes that a key aspect of this is having all of the items on the menu in stock.

The restaurant industry is competitive. In the Grand Rapids/ Wyoming metro area alone there are over 1,600 restaurants. Some of Farmers Restaurant's most serious competitors are IHOP, Applebee's, and Big Boy, all of which are located within 20 miles of the Farmers Restaurant, so customers have many alternatives from which to choose.

Online inventory systems are used to assist restaurant managers in determining on-hand inventory and gauging how well the restaurant is controlling food costs. The fiscal week for Farmers Restaurant starts on Thursday and ends on Wednesday of the following week. Each Wednesday, the manager physically counts the inventory on hand and enters the data into the online inventory system. The computer software system then compares the on-hand inventory for that week, the amount of food ordered, and the inventory on hand for the end of the previous week with the sales for the current week. By doing so, it is able to determine a total food cost. The manager compares this cost with the benchmark cost to see how well the restaurant has been managing its inventory. This is one of the most important numbers to managers at the Farmers Restaurant because it accounts for approximately 30 percent of total costs in terms of a store's cost structure.

The computer software system also compares the total cost of food on hand with the total amount of sales for that week and computes a percentage of on-hand inventories. As a guideline, the company has set a standard of having between 29 and 36 percent for its on-hand inventory level. The company feels that this level of inventory is an appropriate average to ensure quality food that is fresh and within expiration. Lastly, it is better to keep the inventory

at a minimum level to ensure the accuracy and ease of inventory counts.

The Farmers Restaurant Kristin manages has been running above average in terms of food costs. For this reason, her boss has become concerned with the performance of the ordering system she is using at her restaurant. Kristin has been using her intuition to decide how much product to order despite the fact that the product order sheets provide a moving average usage of each product. Kristin bases her inventory management on her intuition because she does not understand how to utilize the moving average forecasting technique when placing orders. An additional complication with ordering inventory is that each item is packed in multiple quantities, so she cannot order the exact amount that she needs. Her boss requested that she create a more accurate way of ordering food and to report back to him in one month. Kristin is worried that if she cuts inventory levels too low she will run out of products, which may result in a decrease in customer counts.

After Kristin met with her boss, she began to think about what changes she could make. She knows that inventory has been a weak point for her, but she remembers one of her employees talking about inventory management from one of his college courses. Kristin decides to ask the employee if he would be willing to help her try and come up with a better way for her to order products. Kristin tells him how the ordering system works, shows him the ordering form, and relates the given information.

Suppose you have been asked to work with Kristin to improve inventory ordering.

Questions

1. Describe the importance of inventory management as it relates to the Farmers Restaurant.
2. What ordering system would be best for this situation?
3. Given the following information, provide an example of how much of Farmers Sausage Gravy Mix should be ordered. You are doing the order for Thursday. Also, Kristin would like a service level of 95 percent, and you have found that there is a standard deviation of 3.5 units per week, and a moving average weekly demand of 35 servings. The gravy mix comes in packs of two servings. There are currently three packs in inventory.
4. Given the above information and an on-hand inventory of 12, determine the risk of stock out at the end of initial lead time and at the end of the second lead time. The lead time is 2 days and orders are placed once a week.
5. The supplier Kristin uses is located in Ohio. Why might Kristin consider dealing with a nearby supplier instead of the one in Ohio? What reasons might there be for not switching suppliers?

OPERATIONS TOUR   BRUEGGER'S BAGEL BAKERY

Bruegger's Bagel Bakery makes and sells a variety of bagels, including plain, onion, poppyseed, and cinnamon raisin, as well as assorted flavors of cream cheese. Bagels are the major source of revenue for the company.

The bagel business is a $3 billion industry. Bagels are very popular with consumers. Not only are they relatively low in fat, they are filling, and they taste good! Investors like the bagel industry because it can be highly profitable: it only costs about $.10 to make a bagel, and they can be sold for $.50 each or more. Although some bagel companies have done poorly in recent years, due mainly to poor management, Bruegger's business is booming; it is number one nationally, with over 450 shops that sell bagels, coffee, and bagel sandwiches for takeout or onpremise consumption. Many stores in the Bruegger's chain generate an average of $800,000 in sales annually.

Production of bagels is done in batches, according to flavor, with each flavor being produced on a daily basis. Production of bagels at Bruegger's begins at a processing plant, where the basic ingredients of flour, water, yeast, and flavorings are combined in a special mixing machine. After the dough has been thoroughly mixed, it is transferred to another machine that shapes the dough into individual bagels. Once the bagels have been formed, they are loaded onto refrigerated trucks for shipping to individual stores. When the bagels reach a store, they are unloaded from the trucks and temporarily stored while they rise. The final two steps of processing involve boiling the bagels in a kettle of water and malt for one minute, and then baking the bagels in an oven for approximately 15 minutes.

The process is depicted in the figure.

Quality is an important feature of a successful business. Customers judge the quality of bagels by their appearance (size, shape, and shine), taste, and consistency. Customers are also sensitive to the service they receive when they make their purchases. Bruegger's devotes careful attention to quality at every stage of operation, from choosing suppliers of ingredients, careful monitoring of ingredients, and keeping equipment in good operating condition to monitoring

output at each step in the process. At the stores, employees are instructed to watch for deformed bagels and to remove them when they find them. (Deformed bagels are returned to a processing plant where they are sliced into bagel chips, packaged, and then taken back to the stores for sale, thereby reducing the scrap rate.) Employees who work in the stores are carefully chosen and then trained so that they are competent to operate the necessary equipment in the stores and to provide the desired level of service to customers.

The company operates with minimal inventories of raw materials and inventories of partially completed bagels at the plant and very little inventory of bagels at the stores. One reason for this is to maintain a high degree of freshness in the final product by continually supplying fresh product to the stores. A second reason is to keep costs down; minimal inventories mean less space is needed for storage.

Questions

1. Bruegger's maintains relatively little inventory at either its plants or its retail stores. List the benefits and risks of this policy.
2. Quality is very important to Bruegger's.
   a. What features of bagels do customers look at to judge their quality?
   b. At what points in the production process do workers check bagel quality?
   c. List the steps in the production process, beginning with purchasing ingredients, and ending with the sale, and state how quality can be positively affected at each step.
3. Which inventory models could be used for ordering the ingredients for bagels? Which model do you think would be most appropriate for deciding how many bagels to make in a given batch?
4. Bruegger's has bagel-making machines at its plants. Another possibility would be to have a bagel-making machine at each store. What advantages does each alternative have?

Processing plant   A retail store

PSC designs and produces a variety of laser bar code scanning devices. The products include handheld bar code readers, high-speed fixedposition industrial scanners, and retail checkout scanners as well as a full line of accessories, software, and supplies to support its products. Headquartered in Eugene, Oregon, the company has manufacturing facilities in Eugene and Paris, France, with roughly 1,200 employees worldwide.

Products

Bar code scanners are designed for a variety of situations that can involve long-range scanning, reading small bar codes, and performing high-speed scans. They are used extensively in industry, business, and government to manage and control the entire supply chain, which includes suppliers, production, warehousing, distribution, retail sales, and service. Examples of bar code readers include the familiar point-of-sale scanners encountered at supermarkets and other retail stores. They come in a variety of forms, ranging from handheld to built-in models. High-speed, unattended scanners are used for automated material handling and sorting. Typical installations include highvolume distribution centers such as JC Penney's catalog operation and airport baggage handling systems. The company also produces "reader engines" that it supplies to other companies for use in their products. These may be as small as 1.2 cubic inches. One application for an "engine product" is found in lottery ticket validation machines. Use of bar code readers has greatly increased the speed and accuracy of data collection, resulting in increased productivity, improved production and inventory tracking and control, and improved market information.

Operations

Forecasting

Forecasting is not a significant activity at PSC due to several factors. There is high standardization of scanner components, which creates stability in usage requirements. Supplier lead times are relatively short, often only a few days. Orders are typically small; 70 percent of all orders are for 10 units or less. There is a fair degree of production flexibility, particularly in terms of product customization. As a result of these factors, the company relies mainly on short-term, moving average forecasts.

Product Design

PSC has developed a robust design in many of its products, enabling them to perform effectively under a broad range of operating conditions. For example, many of its handheld scanners can operate at temperatures ranging from −22° F to 120° F, and can withstand drops onto concrete surfaces from heights up to six feet and still function. This has enabled the company to offer warranties ranging from 24 to 36 months, far exceeding the industry standard of 3 to 12 months.

Layout

PSC has developed an efficient production layout that consists of assembly lines and work centers. The assembly lines handle standardized production and subassemblies and the work centers handle final assembly and customization of products. Assembly lines are U-shaped to facilitate communication among workers. The work centers are designed for production flexibility; they can be reconfigured in about four hours. Work centers are staffed by teams of three to six cross-trained workers who are responsible for an order from start to finish.

The Production Process

Production involves a combination of assembly line and batch processing that provides high volume and flexibility to customized individual orders. Because of the high standardization among the internal components of different scanners, many of the subassemblies can be produced on assembly lines. Customization is done primarily on the external portion of various products according to customer specification.

The production process for scanner engines is depicted in the process flowchart shown in the figure. The process begins when an order is received from a customer. The order is then configured according to customer specifications. Next it is entered into the computer to obtain a bill of materials (BOM), and the order is transmitted to production control so that it can be scheduled for production. A "traveler" packet containing product specifications and the BOM is created. It will accompany the order throughout the process.

The traveler is sent to the "kitting" area where standard parts and any customized parts are obtained and placed into a bin ("kit") and then placed in a flow rack until the assigned work center is ready for the job (i.e., a pull system).

The next phase of the process transforms unprogrammed, panelized circuit boards into programmed boards. The boards first pass through a screen printer which uses a stencil to coat the boards with a solder paste. Next the boards pass through a chip mounter which enters values for the smaller, passive components of the circuit board at a rate of 25,000 parts per hour. A second mounter enters values for the larger, programmable components at a rate of 7,000 parts per hour. The slower rate for the larger components is offset by the fact that there are fewer of those components. The process ends up being balanced, and no bottlenecks occur.

The programmed boards move by conveyor to a station for visual inspection. Rejects are returned to the chip mounter area, and boards that pass are sent through an oven to solidify the solder, making the programming permanent. The circuit boards are then removed from the panels and placed into the kit. The kits are then taken to designated work centers for customization and placement in scanner engines.

Work centers typically have builders, computer operators, and a tester. A builder mounts the laser diodes on the circuit board and passes it to a computer operator who downloads the customer specifications into the microprocessor of the scan engine. The operator also mounts the optical components and adjusts them

(continued)

PSC Inc. Scanner Engine Production Process Flowchart

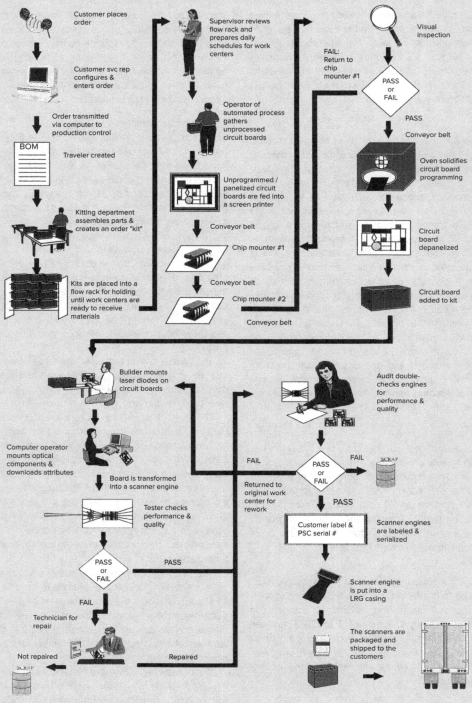

(continued)

(concluded)

for the design of the scanner (e.g., long-range scanning). Next, the engine goes to the tester, who checks to make sure that the scanner is capable of reading bar codes and laser characteristics. Engines that fail are sent for repair and later retested. If the engine fails a second time, it is either returned for further repair or scrapped. Engines which pass are placed in an electrostatic bag which protects them from static electricity that could damage the programming.

Engines are then sent to Audit for another check for performance quality.

Engines that pass are incorporated into the final product, a serial number is added, along with a label, and the product is sent to the packing area and then shipped to the customer.

Inventory

The company uses a variety of methods for inventory management, and it attempts to minimize the amount of inventory. A computer determines component requirements and generates purchase orders for the components for each order, and then appropriate orders for various components from vendors are prepared. However, the company maintains a stock of standard components that are replenished using a reorder point system. The company has adopted point-of-use replenishment for some areas of operations, having deliveries come directly to the production floor. Finished products are immediately shipped to the customer, which enhances the company's delivery performance and avoids finished goods inventory.

Suppliers

Approximately 40 vendors supply parts and materials to PSC, each of which has been subjected to a multiple-step supplier certification program that includes the supplier's completing a self-evaluation questionnaire; an on-site visit of supplier facilities by a team from PSC made up of people from engineering, purchasing, and operations; a probation period; and rating of products using government MIL-STD 105 specifications. Vendor performance is tracked on product quality, delivery, and service.

When an item is removed from inventory, it is scanned into the computer, and this information is transmitted directly to suppliers, along with purchase orders to restock components.

Quality

Quality is strongly emphasized at PSC. Employees are trained in quality concepts and the use of quality tools. Training is incorporated on-the-job so that employees can see the practical applications of what they are learning. Employees are responsible for performing in-process quality checks (quality at the source), and to report any defects they discover to their supervisor. Defects are assigned to one of three categories for problem solving:

- Operator/training error. The supervisor notifies a trainer who then provides appropriate retraining.
- Process/equipment problem. The supervisor notifies the manufacturing engineer who is then responsible for diagnosing the cause and correcting the problem.
- Parts/material problem. The supervisor notifies quality assurance, who then notifies the vendor to correct the problem. Defective parts are either scrapped or returned to the vendor.

Lean Production

PSC strives to operate on lean production principles. In addition to emphasizing high levels of quality, production flexibility, low levels of inventories, and having some deliveries come right to the production floor, its organization structure is fairly flat, and it uses a team approach. Still another feature of lean production is that many of PSC's workers are multiskilled. The company encourages employees to master new skills through a pay-for-skill program, and bases hourly pay rates on the number of skills a worker can perform.

Business Strategy

The company has developed what it believes is a strong strategy for success. Strategic initiatives include anticipating customer demand for miniaturization and the ability to customize products; expanding its proprietary technology; and expanding internationally into Western Europe (now accounts for about 35 percent of sales) and the Pacific Rim (now accounts for about 10 percent of sales). Several plants or groups are ISO certified, which has been important for European sales. The company intends to continue to expand its product lines through acquisition of other companies.

Hopp, Wallace J., and Mark L. Spearman. *Factory Physics*, 3rd ed. New York: Irwin/McGraw–Hill, 2007.

Muller, Max. *Essentials of Inventory Management*, 2nd ed. New York: Amacom Books, 2011.

Piasecki, David J. *Inventory Management Explained: A Focus on Forecasting, Lot Sizing, Safety Stock, and Ordering*. Kenosha, WI: Ops Publishing. 2009.

RFID Journal. www.rfidjournal.com

SELECTED BIBLIOGRAPHY AND FURTHER READINGS

14 JIT and Lean Operations

LEARNING OBJECTIVES

After completing this chapter, you should be able to:

LO14.1 Explain the terms *lean operations* and *JIT*.

LO14.2 Describe the main characteristics of lean systems.

LO14.3 List the five principles of the way lean systems function.

LO14.4 List some of the benefits and some of the risks of lean operation.

LO14.5 Describe the Toyota Production System (TPS).

LO14.6 List the three goals of a lean system and explain the importance of each.

LO14.7 List the eight wastes according to lean philosophy.

LO14.8 Identify and briefly discuss the four building blocks of a lean production system.

LO14.9 Describe key lean improvement tools.

LO14.10 Outline considerations for successful conversion from a traditional system to a lean system.

LO14.11 Describe some of the obstacles to lean success.

CHAPTER OUTLINE

14.1 Introduction, *610*
  Characteristics of Lean Systems, *610*
  Benefits and Risks of Lean Systems, *611*
  The Toyota Approach, *611*

14.2 Supporting Goals, *613*

14.3 Building Blocks, *614*
  Product Design, *614*
  Process Design, *615*
  Personnel/Organizational Elements, *620*

Manufacturing Planning and Control, *622*

14.4 Lean Tools, *631*
  Value Stream Mapping, *631*
  Process Improvement Using 5W2H, *632*
  Lean and Six Sigma, *632*
  JIT Deliveries and the Supply Chain, *632*
  Lean and ERP, *633*

14.5 Transitioning to a Lean System, *633*

Planning a Successful Conversion, *633*
  Obstacles to Conversion, *633*
  A Cooperative Spirit, *634*

14.6 Lean Services, *634*

14.7 JIT II, 633, *637*

14.8 Operations Strategy, *637*
  Case: Level Operations, *641*
  Operations Tour: Boeing, *642*
  Supplement: Maintenance, *644*

© Lennox McLendon/AP Images

As business organizations strive to maintain competitiveness in an ever-changing global economy, they are increasingly seeking new and better ways of operating. For some, this means changing from the traditional ways of operating to what is now referred to as lean operation. A **lean operation** is a flexible system of operation that uses considerably fewer resources (i.e., activities, people, inventory, and floor space) than a traditional system. Moreover, lean systems tend to achieve greater productivity, lower costs, shorter cycle times, and higher quality than nonlean systems.

Lean operation A flexible system that uses minimal resources and produces highquality goods or services.

Lean systems are sometimes referred to as **just-in-time (JIT)** systems owing to their highly coordinated activities and delivery of goods that occur just as they are needed. The lean approach was pioneered by Toyota's founder, Taiichi Ohno, and Shigeo Shingo as a much faster and less costly way of producing automobiles. Following its success, today the lean approach is being applied in a wide range of manufacturing and service operations.

Just-in-time (JIT) A highly coordinated processing system in which goods move through the system, and services are performed, just as they are needed.

Lean is both a philosophy and a methodology that focuses on eliminating waste (non-value-added activities) and streamlining operations by closely coordinating all activities. Lean systems have three basic elements: They are demand driven, are focused on waste reduction, and have a culture that is dedicated to excellence and continuous improvement.

This chapter describes the lean production approach, including the basic elements of these systems and what it takes to make them work effectively. It also points out the benefits of these systems and the potential obstacles that companies may encounter when they attempt to convert from a traditional system to a lean production system.

14.1 INTRODUCTION

LO14.1 Explain the terms *lean operations* and *JIT*.

Lean operations began as lean manufacturing in the mid-1900s. It was developed by the Japanese automobile manufacturer Toyota. The development in Japan was influenced by the limited resources available at the time. Not surprisingly, the Japanese were very sensitive to waste and inefficiency. Widespread interest in lean manufacturing occurred after a book about automobile production, *The Machine That Changed the World,* by James Womack, Daniel Jones, and Daniel Roos, was published in 1990. As described in the book, Toyota's focus was on the elimination of all waste from every aspect of the process. Waste was defined as anything that interfered with, or did not add value to, the process of producing automobiles.

A stunning example of the potential of lean manufacturing was illustrated by the successful adoption of lean methods in the mid-1980s in a Fremont, California, auto plant. The plant was originally operated by General Motors (GM). However, GM closed the plant in 1982 because of its low productivity and high absenteeism. A few years later the plant was reopened as a joint venture of Toyota and GM, called NUMMI (New United Motor Manufacturing, Inc.). About 80 percent of the former plant workers were rehired, but the white-collar jobs were shifted from directing to supporting workers, and small teams were formed and trained to design, measure, and improve their performance. The result? By 1985 productivity and quality improved dramatically, exceeding all other GM plants, and absenteeism was negligible.

As other North American companies attempted to adopt the lean approach, they began to realize that in order to be successful, they needed to make major organizational and cultural changes. They also recognized that mass production, which emphasizes the efficiency of individual operations and leads to unbalanced systems and large inventories, was outmoded. Instead, they discovered that lean methods involve demand-based operations, flexible operations with rapid changeover capability, effective worker behaviors, and continuous improvement efforts.

Characteristics of Lean Systems

LO14.2 Describe the main characteristics of lean systems.

There are a number of characteristics that are commonly found in lean systems. An overview of these will provide a better understanding of lean systems.

Waste reduction —A hallmark of lean systems

Continuous improvement—Another hallmark; never-ending efforts to improve

Use of teams—Cross-functional teams, especially for process improvement

Work cells—Along with cellular layouts allow for better communication and use of people

Visual controls—Simple signals that enable efficient flow and quick assessment of operations

High quality—In processes and in output

Minimal inventory—Excess inventory is viewed as a waste

Output only to match demand—Throughout the entire system; referred to a "demand pull"

Quick changeovers—Enables equipment flexibility and output variety without disruption

Small lot sizes—Enables variety for batch production

Lean culture—The entire organization embraces lean concepts and strives to achieve them

Five principles embody the way lean systems function. Note the connections to the preceding characteristics.

LO14.3 List the five principles of the way lean systems function.

Identify customer values.

Focus on processes that create value.

Eliminate waste to create "flow."

Produce only according to customer demand.

Strive for perfection.

Benefits and Risks of Lean Systems

There are numerous benefits of lean systems, as well as some risks. The key benefits include:

LO14.4 List some of the benefits and some of the risks of lean operation.

Reduced waste due to emphasis on waste reduction.

Lower costs due to reduced waste and lower inventories.

Increased quality motivated by customer focus and the need for high-quality processes.

Reduced cycle time due to elimination of non-value-added operations.

Increased flexibility due to quick changeovers and small lot sizes.

Increased productivity due to elimination of non-value-added processes.

There are also certain risks that often accompany lean operations, such as:

Increased stress on workers due to increased responsibilities for equipment changeovers, problem solving, and process and quality improvement.

Fewer resources (e.g., inventory, people, time) available if problems occur.

Supply chain disruptions can halt operations due to minimal inventory or time buffers.

John Deere, the well-known tractor supply company, bolstered profits during a recession by using a JIT approach to reduce inventory levels. However, when demand picked up as the economy strengthened, a shortage of parts led to stretched-out delivery dates. Long lead times to replenish parts meant that in some cases harvesting equipment farmers wanted wouldn't be available until *after* harvest time! As a result, some farmers turned to Deere competitors to purchase needed equipment.

The Toyota Approach

Many of the methods that are common to lean operations were developed as part of Japanese car maker Toyota's approach to manufacturing. Toyota's approach came to be known as the Toyota Production System (TPS), and it has served as a model for many implementations of lean systems, particularly in manufacturing. Many of the terms Toyota used are now commonly used in conjunction with lean operations, especially the following:

LO14.5 Describe the Toyota Production System (TPS).

- **Muda:** Waste and inefficiency. Perhaps the driving philosophy. Waste and inefficiency can be minimized by using the following tactics.

  Muda Waste and inefficiency.

- **Kanban:** A manual system used for controlling the movement of parts and materials that responds to *signals* of the need (i.e., demand) for delivery of parts or materials. This applies both to delivery to the factory and delivery to each workstation. The result is the delivery of a steady stream of containers of parts throughout the workday. Each container holds a small supply of parts or materials. New containers are delivered to replace empty containers.

  Kanban A manual system that signals the need for parts or materials.

- **Heijunka:** Variations in production volume lead to waste. The workload must be leveled; volume and variety must be averaged to achieve a steady flow of work.

  Heijunka Workload leveling.

- **Kaizen:** Continuous improvement of the system. There is always room for improvement, so this effort must be ongoing.

  Kaizen Continuous improvement of the system.

- **Jidoka:** Quality at the source. A machine automatically stops when it detects a bad part. A worker then stops the line. Also known as *autonomation.*

  Jidoka Quality at the source (autonomation).

In some respects, the just-in-time concept was operational over 60 years ago at Henry Ford's great industrial complex in River Rouge, Michigan.

Toyota learned a great deal from studying Ford's operations and based its lean approach on what it saw. However, Toyota was able to accomplish something that Ford couldn't—a system that could handle some variety.

A widely held view of JIT/lean production is that it is simply a system for scheduling production that results in low levels of work-in-process and inventory. But in its truest sense, JIT/lean production represents a *philosophy* that encompasses every aspect of the process, from

READING   TOYOTA RECALLS

In recent years Toyota has been plagued by more than a few recalls of its popular vehicles. This was somewhat surprising, given Toyota's reputation as a world leader in quality and lean production. Various news reports pointed to the following as possible causes: overdoing its quest for cost reduction; failure to heed early reports of problems and address them, possibly due to a refusal to admit there were problems; and increased difficulty in overseeing the entire system from Japan as overseas sales expanded.

In the mid-1920s, the Ford assembly plant in River Rouge, Michigan, was a state-of-the-art industrial complex employing over 75,000 workers. In 1982, Eiji Toyoda, head of the Toyota Company, toasted Ford's then-president Philip Caldwell, saying, "There is no secret to how we learned to do what we do—we learned it at the Rouge."

Courtesy of Ford Motor Company

FIGURE 14.1
An overview of the goals and building blocks of lean production systems

Source: Adapted from Thomas E. Vollmann, William L. Berry, and D. Clay Whybark, *Manufacturing Planning and Control Systems,* 5th ed. Copyright 2005 Irwin/ McGraw-Hill Companies, Inc. Used with permission.

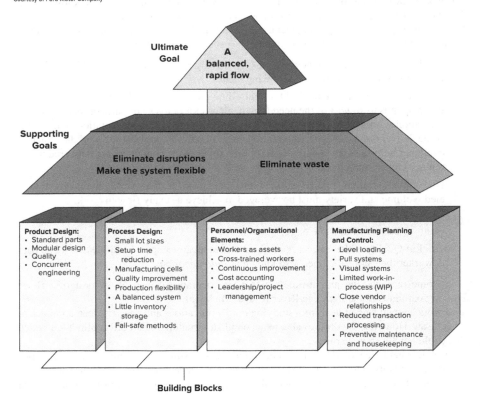

design to after the sale of a product. The philosophy is to pursue a system that functions well with minimal levels of inventories, minimal waste, minimal space, and minimal transactions. Truly, a *lean* system. As such, it must be a system that is not prone to disruptions and is flexible in terms of the product variety and range of volume that it can handle.

In lean systems, quality is ingrained in both the product and the process. Companies that use lean operations have achieved a level of quality that enables them to function with small batch sizes and tight schedules. Lean systems have high reliability; major sources of inefficiency and disruption have been eliminated, and workers have been trained not only to function in the system but also to continuously improve it.

The ultimate goal of a lean operation is to achieve a system that matches supply to customer demand; supply is synchronized to meet customer demand in a smooth, uninterrupted flow. Figure 14.1 provides an overview of the goals and building blocks of a lean production system. The following pages provide more details about the supporting goals and building blocks.

14.2 SUPPORTING GOALS

The ultimate goal of lean is a *balanced* system, that is, one that achieves a smooth, rapid flow of materials and/or work through the system. The idea is to make the process time as short as possible by using resources in the best possible way. The degree to which the overall goal is achieved depends on how well certain supporting goals are achieved. Those goals are to:

> **LO14.6** List the three goals of a lean system and explain the importance of each.

1. Eliminate disruptions
2. Make the system flexible
3. Eliminate waste, especially excess inventory

Disruptions have a negative influence on the system by upsetting the smooth flow of products through the system, and they should be eliminated. Disruptions are caused by a variety of factors, such as poor quality, equipment breakdowns, changes to the schedule, and late deliveries. Quality problems are particularly disruptive because in lean systems there is no extra inventory that can be used to replace defective items. All disruptions should be eliminated where possible. This will reduce the uncertainty that the system must deal with.

A *flexible system* is one that is robust enough to handle a mix of products, often on a daily basis, and to handle changes in the level of output while still maintaining balance and throughput speed. This enables the system to deal with some uncertainty. Long setup times and long lead times negatively impact the flexibility of the system. Hence, reduction of setup and lead times is very important in a lean system.

Waste represents unproductive resources; eliminating waste can free up resources and enhance production. *Inventory* is an idle resource, taking up space and adding cost to the system. It should be minimized as much as possible. In the lean philosophy, there are eight wastes:

1. **Excess inventory**—Beyond minimal quantities, an idle resource takes up floor space and adds to cost

> **LO14.7** List the eight wastes according to lean philosophy.

2. **Overproduction**—Involves excessive use of manufacturing resources
3. **Waiting time**—Requires space, adds no value.
4. **Unnecessary transporting** —Increases handling, increases work-in-process inventory
5. **Processing waste**—Makes unnecessary production steps, scrap
6. **Inefficient work methods**—Reduce productivity, increase scrap, increase work-in-process inventory
7. **Product defects**—Require rework costs and possible lost sales due to customer dissatisfaction
8. **Underused people**—Relates to mental and creative abilities as well as physical abilities

The existence of these wastes is an indication that improvement is possible. The list of wastes also can identify potential targets for continuous improvement efforts.

The *kaizen* philosophy for eliminating waste is based on the following tenets:[1]

1. Waste is the enemy, and to eliminate waste it is necessary to get the hands dirty.
2. Improvement should be done gradually and continuously; the goal is not big improvements done intermittently.
3. Everyone should be involved—top managers, middle managers, and workers.
4. *Kaizen* is built on a cheap strategy, and it does not require spending great sums on technology or consultants.
5. It can be applied anywhere.
6. It is supported by a visual system: a total transparency of procedures, processes, and values, making problems and wastes visible to all.
7. It focuses attention where value is created.
8. It is process oriented.
9. It stresses that the main effort of improvement should come from new thinking and a new work style.
10. The essence of organizational learning is to learn while doing.

14.3 BUILDING BLOCKS

LO14.8 Identify and briefly discuss the four building blocks of a lean production system.

The design and operation of a lean system provide the foundation for accomplishing the aforementioned goals. As shown in Figure 14.1, the building blocks are:

1. Product design
2. Process design
3. Personnel/organizational elements
4. Manufacturing planning and control

Speed and simplicity are two common threads that run through these building blocks.

Product Design

Four elements of product design are important for a lean production system:

1. Standard parts
2. Modular design
3. Highly capable production systems with quality built in
4. Concurrent engineering

The first two elements relate to speed and simplicity.

The use of *standard parts* means that workers have fewer parts to deal with, and training times and costs are reduced. Purchasing, handling, and checking quality are more routine and lend themselves to continual improvement. Another important benefit is the ability to use standard processing.

Modular design is an extension of standard parts. Modules are clusters of parts treated as a single unit. This greatly reduces the number of parts to deal with, simplifying assembly, purchasing, handling, training, and so on. Standardization has the added benefit of reducing the number of different parts contained in the bill of materials for various products, thereby simplifying the bill of materials.

---

[1]Adapted from Jorge Nascimento Rodrigues with Masaaki Imai, "Masaaki Imai: The Father of Kaizen," www.gurusonline.tv/uk/conteudos/imai.asp.

Lean requires highly capable production systems. Quality is the sine qua non ("without which not") of lean. It is crucial to lean systems because poor quality can create major disruptions. Quality must be embedded in goods and processes. The systems are geared to a smooth flow of work; the occurrence of problems due to poor quality creates disruption in this flow. Because of small lot sizes and the absence of buffer stock, production must cease when problems occur, and it cannot resume until the problems have been resolved. Obviously, shutting down an entire process is costly and cuts into planned output levels, so it becomes imperative to try to avoid shutdowns and to quickly resolve problems when they do appear.

Lean systems use a comprehensive approach to quality. Quality is designed into the product and the production process. High quality levels can occur because lean systems produce standardized products that lead to standardized job methods, employ workers who are very familiar with their jobs, and use standardized equipment. Moreover, the cost of product design quality (i.e., building quality in at the *design* stage) can be spread over many units, yielding a low cost per unit. It is also important to choose appropriate quality levels in terms of the final customer and of manufacturing capability. Thus, product design and process design must go hand in hand.

Engineering changes can be very disruptive to smooth operations. Concurrent engineering practices (described in Chapter 4) can substantially reduce these disruptions.

Process Design

Eight aspects of process design are particularly important for lean production systems:

1. Small lot sizes
2. Setup time reduction
3. Manufacturing cells
4. Quality improvement
5. Production flexibility
6. A balanced system
7. Little inventory storage
8. Fail-safe methods

Small Lot Sizes. In the lean philosophy, the ideal lot size is one unit, a quantity that may not always be realistic owing to practical considerations requiring minimum lot sizes (e.g., machines that process multiple items simultaneously, heat-treating equipment that processes multiple items simultaneously, and machines with very long setup times). Nevertheless, the goal is still to reduce the lot size as much as possible. Small lot sizes in both the production process and deliveries from suppliers yield a number of benefits that enable lean systems to operate effectively. First, with small lots moving through the system, in-process inventory is considerably less than it is with large lots. This reduces carrying costs, space requirements, and clutter in the workplace. Second, inspection and rework costs are less when problems with quality occur, because there are fewer items in a lot to inspect and rework.

Small lots also permit greater flexibility in scheduling. Repetitive systems typically produce a small variety of products. In traditional systems, this usually means long production runs of each product, one after the other. Although this spreads the setup cost for a run over many items, it also results in long cycles over the entire range of products. For instance, suppose a firm has three product versions, A, B, and C. In a traditional system, there would be a long run of version A (e.g., covering two or three days or more), then a long run of version B, followed by a long run of version C before the sequence would repeat. In contrast, a lean system, using small lots, would frequently shift from producing A to producing B and C. This flexibility enables lean systems to respond more quickly to changing customer demands for output: lean systems can produce just what is needed, when it is needed. The contrast between small and large lot sizes is illustrated in Figure 14.2. A summary of the benefits of small lot sizes is presented in Table 14.1.

FIGURE 14.2
Small versus large-lot run sizes

A = units of product A
B = units of product B
C = units of product C

Small-lot approach

AAA   BBBBBBB   CC   AAA   BBBBBBB   CC   AAA   BBBBBBB   CC   AAA   BBBBBBB   CC

Time ⟶

Large-lot approach

AAAAAAAAAAA   BBBBBBBBBBBBBBBBBBBBBBBBBBB   CCCCCCCCC   AAAAAAAAAA

Time ⟶

TABLE 14.1
Benefits of small lot sizes

Reduced inventory, lower carrying costs
Less space required to store inventory
Less rework if defects occur
Less inventory to "work off" before implementing product improvements
Increased visibility of problems
Increased production flexibility
Increased ease of balancing operations

It is important to note that the use of small lot sizes is not in conflict with the economic order quantity (EOQ) approach. Space is at a premium in Japan, making warehousing costs and the cost of space to store extra inventory near manufacturing very high. Also, on-site inventory increases the space between operations, which decreases communications, increases cycle time, and reduces visibility. All of these add to the burden of carrying inventory. So in an EOQ computation, using higher carrying cost, with carrying cost in the denominator, lot sizes naturally end up being smaller, and in some cases, much smaller.

Setup Time Reduction. Small lots and changing product mixes require frequent setups. Unless these are quick and relatively inexpensive, the time and cost to accomplish them can be prohibitive. Moreover, long setup times require holding more inventory than with short setup times. Hence, there is strong emphasis on reducing setup times. In JIT, workers are often trained to do their own setups. Moreover, programs to reduce setup time and cost are used to achieve the desired results; a deliberate effort is required, and workers are usually a valuable part of the process.

Shigeo Shingo made a very significant contribution to lean operation with the development of what is called the **single-minute exchange of die (SMED)** system for reducing change-over time. It involves first categorizing changeover activities as either "internal" or "external" activities. Internal activities are those that can only be done while a machine is stopped (i.e., not running). Hence, they contribute to long changeover times. External activities are those that do not involve stopping the machine; they can be done before or after the changeover.

Hence, they do not affect changeover time. After activities have been categorized, a simple approach to achieving quick changeovers is to convert as many internal activities as possible to external activities and then streamline the remaining internal activities.

The potential benefits that can be achieved using the SMED system were impressively illustrated in 1982 at Toyota, when the changeover time for a machine was reduced from 100 minutes to 3 minutes! The principles of the SMED system can be applied to any changeover operation.

Setup tools and equipment and setup procedures must be simple and standardized. Multi-purpose equipment or attachments can help to reduce setup time. For instance, a machine with multiple spindles that can easily be rotated into place for different job requirements can drastically reduce job changeover time. Moreover, *group technology* (described in Chapter 6) may be used to reduce setup cost and time by capitalizing on similarities in recurring operations. For instance, parts that are similar in shape, materials, and so on, may require very similar

Single-minute exchange of die (SMED) A system for reducing changeover time.

READING

GENERAL MILLS TURNS TO NASCAR TO REDUCE CHANGEOVER TIME

KAREN MILLS

MINNEAPOLIS—When General Mills wanted to cut the time it takes to make a product changeover at a Betty Crocker plant, it turned to NASCAR for help. The food company sent a team to work with a pit crew "because nobody can change over a car faster than these guys can," said Randy Darcy, senior vice president of General Mills' supply chain operations.

After studying the NASCAR crew, General Mills cut to 12 minutes—from as long as 4½ hours—the time it takes to switch production lines from one Betty Crocker meal to another. One thing the mechanics learned from working with the NASCAR pit crew was to videotape each of the changeovers, then critique everything that happened.

Source: Excerpted from Karen Mills, "General Mills Looks Outside the Box for Innovation." Copyright © The Associated Press. Used with permission.

setups. Processing them in sequence on the same equipment can reduce the need to completely change a setup; only minor adjustment may be necessary.

Manufacturing Cells. One characteristic of lean production systems is multiple *manufacturing cells.* The cells contain the machines and tools needed to process families of parts having similar processing requirements. In essence, the cells are highly specialized and efficient production centers. Among the important benefits of manufacturing cells are reduced changeover times, high utilization of equipment, and ease of cross-training operators.

Quality Improvement. The occurrence of quality defects during the process can disrupt the orderly flow of work. Consequently, problem solving is important when defects occur. Moreover, there is a never-ending quest for *quality improvement,* which often focuses on finding and eliminating the causes of problems so they do not continually crop up.

Lean production systems sometimes minimize defects through the use of **autonomation** (note the extra syllable *on* in the middle of the word). Also referred to as *jidoka,* it involves the automatic detection of defects during production. It can be used with machines or manual operations. It consists of two mechanisms: one for detecting defects when they occur and another for a human stopping production to correct the cause of the defects. Thus, the halting of production forces immediate attention to the problem, after which an investigation of the problem is conducted, and corrective action is taken to resolve the problem.

Autonomation Automatic detection of defects during production.

A worker is assembling a Louis Vuitton handbag at the company's fine leather goods factory in the Normany town of Ducey in France. To keep its brand exclusive and contain costs, the company monitors growth and incorporates lean production processes.

© LOIC VENANCE/AFP/Getty Images

TABLE 14.2
Guidelines for increasing
production flexibility

1. Reduce downtime due to changeovers by reducing changeover time.
2. Use preventive maintenance on key equipment to reduce breakdowns and downtime.
3. Cross-train workers so they can help when bottlenecks occur or other workers are absent. Train workers to handle equipment adjustments and minor repairs.
4. Use many small units of capacity; many small cells make it easier to shift capacity temporarily and to add or subtract capacity than a few units of large capacity.
5. Use offline buffers. Store infrequently used safety stock away from the production area to decrease congestion and to avoid continually turning it over.
6. Reserve capacity for important customers.

Source: Adapted from Edward M. Knod Jr. and Richard J. Schonberger, Operations Management: Meeting Customers' Demands, 7th ed. (New York: McGraw-Hill, 2001)

Work Flexibility. The overall goal of a lean system is to achieve the ability to process a mix of products or services in a smooth flow. One potential obstacle to this goal is bottlenecks that occur when portions of the system become overloaded. The existence of bottlenecks reflects inflexibilities in a system. Process design can increase *production flexibility* and reduce bottlenecks in a variety of ways. Table 14.2 lists some of the techniques used for this purpose.

A Balanced System. Line balancing of production lines (i.e., distributing the workload evenly among workstations) helps to achieve a rapid flow of work through the system. Time needed for work assigned to each workstation must be less than or equal to the cycle time. The cycle time is set equal to what is referred to as the *takt time*. (*Takt* is the German word for musical meter.) *Takt* time is the cycle time needed in a production system to match the pace of production to the demand rate. It is sometimes said to be the heartbeat of a lean production system.

Takt time is often set for a work shift. The procedure for obtaining the *takt* time is:

Takt time The cycle time needed to match customer demand for final product.

1. Determine the net time available per shift by subtracting any nonproductive time from total shift time.

2. If there is more than one shift per day, multiply the net time per shift by the number of shifts to obtain the net available time per day.

3. Compute *takt* time by dividing the net available time by demand.

EXAMPLE 1

mhhe.com/stevenson13e

Computing *Takt* Time

Given the following information, compute the *takt* time: Total time per shift is 480 minutes per day, and there are two shifts per day. There are two 20-minute rest breaks and a 30-minute lunch break per shift. Daily demand is 80 units.

SOLUTION

1. Compute net time available per shift:

Total time	480 minutes
Rest breaks	–40 minutes
Lunch	–30 minutes
	410 minutes per shift

2. Compute the net time available per day:

410 minutes per shift
× 2 shifts/day
820 minutes per day

3. Compute the *takt* time:

$$\text{Takt time} = \frac{\text{Net time available per day}}{\text{Daily demand}} = \frac{820 \text{ minutes per day}}{80 \text{ units per day}} \qquad (14\text{–}1)$$

$$= 10.25 \text{ minutes per cycle}$$

FIGURE 14.3 Large rocks (problems) are hidden by a high water level (inventory) in (A). Lower water level (B) reveals rocks (problems such as bottlenecks, waste, poor timing). Once the large rocks are removed, the water level (inventory) can be lowered (C). This process would be done repeatedly in the spirit of continuous improvement, achieving additional improvements with each iteration.

A

B

C

Once the *takt* time for the system has been determined, it can be used to determine the time that should be allotted to each workstation in the production process. Using the *takt* time results in minimizing work-in-process (WIP) inventory in instances where demand is stable and the system capacity matches demand. For unstable demand, additional inventory is needed to offset demand variability.

Inventory Storage. Lean systems are designed to *minimize* inventory storage. Recall that in the lean philosophy, inventory storage is a waste. Inventories are buffers that tend to cover up recurring problems that are never resolved, partly because they aren't obvious and partly because the presence of inventory makes them seem less serious. When a machine breaks down, it won't disrupt the system if there is a sufficient inventory of the machine's output to feed into the next workstation. The use of inventory as the "solution" can lead to increasing amounts of inventory if breakdowns increase. A better solution is to investigate the *causes* of machine breakdowns and focus on eliminating them. Similar problems with quality, unreliable vendors, and scheduling also can be solved by having ample inventories to fall back on. However, carrying all that extra inventory creates a tremendous burden in cost and space and allows problems to go unresolved.

The lean approach is to pare down inventories gradually in order to uncover the problems. Once they are uncovered and solved, the system removes more inventory, finds and solves additional problems, and so on. A useful analogy is a boat on a pond that has large, hidden rocks. (See Figure 14.3.) The rocks represent problems that can hinder production (the boat). The water in the pond

© Marcos Issa/Bloomberg via Getty

A worker attaches wheels and hubcaps to a GM Montana Sport pick-up truck on an assembly line in Brazil.

that covers the rocks is the inventory in the system. As the water level is slowly lowered, the largest rocks are the first to appear (those problems are the first to be identified). At that point, efforts are undertaken to remove these rocks from the water (resolve these problems). Once that has been accomplished, additional water is removed from the pond, revealing the next layer of rocks, which are then worked on. As more rocks are removed, the need for water to cover them diminishes. Likewise, as more of the major production problems are solved, there is less need to rely on inventory or other buffers.

Low inventories are the result of a *process* of successful problem solving, one that has occurred over time. Furthermore, because it is unlikely that all problems will be found and resolved, it is necessary to be able to deal quickly with problems when they do occur. Hence, there is a continuing need to identify and solve problems within a short time span to prevent new problems from disrupting the smooth flow of work through the system.

One way to minimize inventory storage in a lean system is to have deliveries from suppliers go directly to the production floor, which completely eliminates the need to store incoming parts and materials. At the other end of the process, completed units are shipped out as soon as they are ready, which minimizes storage of finished goods. Coupled with low work-in-process inventory, these features result in systems that operate with very little inventory.

Among the advantages of lower inventory are less carrying cost, less space needed, less tendency to rely on buffers, less rework if defects occur, and less need to "work off" current inventory before implementing design improvements. But carrying less inventory also has some risks: The primary one is that if problems arise, there is no safety net. Another is missed opportunities if the system is unable to respond quickly to them.

Fail-Safe Methods. Failsafing refers to building safeguards into a process to reduce or eliminate the potential for errors during a process. The term that was used initially was *baka-yoke*, which meant "foolproofing." However, due to its offensive connotation, the term was changed to *poka-yoke*, which means "mistake proofing." Some examples of failsafing include an alarm that sounds if the weight of a packaged item is too low, indicating missing components; putting assembly components in "egg cartons" to ensure that no parts are left out; and designing parts that can only be attached in the correct position. There are several everyday examples in vehicles, including signals that warn that the key is still in the ignition if the car door is opened, warn if a door is ajar, warn if seatbelts are not fastened, or warn if the fuel level is low. Other examples include an ATM signal if a card is left in a machine, detectors at department stores that signal if a monitoring tag hasn't been removed from an item, electrical fuses and circuit breakers that interrupt electrical supply if a circuit is overloaded, computers and other devices that won't operate if an incorrect password is used, and so on. Much of the credit for *poka-yoke* thinking is attributed to the work of Shigeo Shingo, who extensively promoted the use of failsafing in operations.

Poka-yoke Safeguards built into a process to reduce the possibility of errors.

Personnel/Organizational Elements

There are five elements of personnel and organization that are particularly important for lean systems:

1. Workers as assets
2. Cross-trained workers
3. Continuous improvement
4. Cost accounting
5. Leadership/project management

Workers as Assets. A fundamental tenet of the lean philosophy is that *workers are assets.* Well-trained and motivated workers are the heart of a lean system. They are given more authority to make decisions than their counterparts in more traditional systems, but they are also expected to do more.

"PEOPLE" FIRMS BOOST PROFITS, STUDY SHOWS

Companies that treat employees as valuable assets, invest in training programs and use innovative workplace practices are more profitable than those that don't, a study found.

The two-year look at the workplace strategies of American companies was conducted by the management consulting firm Ernst & Young LLP for the Labor Department.

For the study, researchers at Harvard and Wharton business schools in partnership with the Ernst & Young Center for Business Innovation, reviewed over 100 papers examining business practices of thousands of U.S. companies.

The report focused on the economic benefits to companies of such Japanese-inspired concepts of labor-management cooperation as Just-In-Time inventory, which moves components to factories only as they are needed.

Among the findings:

- Economic benefits to companies were greatest when they successfully integrated innovations in management and technology with the appropriate employee training and "empowerment" programs.
- Companies investing in employee development enjoy significantly higher market values on average than their industry peers.
- Companies that were first among their competitors in implementing new management practices reaped the largest rewards.

According to the study, Motorola, Inc. estimates it earns $30 for every $1 invested in employee training, while Xerox Corp. found that in cooperation with its employee union it has reduced manufacturing costs by 30 percent and halved the time needed to develop new products.

Cross-Trained Workers. Workers are *cross-trained* to perform several parts of a process and operate a variety of machines. This adds to system flexibility because workers are able to help one another when bottlenecks occur or when a coworker is absent. It also helps line balancing.

Continuous Improvement. Workers in a lean system have greater responsibility for quality than workers in traditional systems, and they are expected to be involved in problem solving and *continuous improvement*. Lean system workers receive extensive training in statistical process control, quality improvement, and problem solving.

Problem solving is a cornerstone of any lean system. Of interest are problems that interrupt, or have the potential to interrupt, the smooth flow of work through the system. When such problems surface, it becomes important to resolve them quickly. This may entail increasing inventory levels *temporarily* while the problem is investigated, but the intent of problem solving is to eliminate the problem, or at least greatly reduce the chances of it recurring.

The Andon board in the GM Powertrain Engine facility is a visual communication tool. It advises employees of the realtime status of each machine within the manufacturing lines, enabling the production system to be run more effectively.

Andon System of lights used at each workstation to signal problems or slowdowns.

Problems that occur during production must be dealt with quickly. Some companies use a light system to signal problems; in Japan, such a system is called *andon*. Each workstation is equipped with a set of three lights. A green light means no problems, an amber light means a worker is falling a little bit behind, and a red light indicates a serious problem. The purpose of the light system is to keep others in the system informed and to enable workers and supervisors to immediately see when and where problems are occurring.

Japanese companies have been very successful in forming teams composed of workers and managers who routinely work on problems. Moreover, workers are encouraged to report problems and potential problems to the teams.

It is important that all levels of management actively support and become involved in problem solving. This includes a willingness to provide financial support and to recognize achievements. It is desirable to formulate goals with the help of workers, publicize the goals, and carefully document accomplishments. Goals give workers something tangible to strive for; recognition can help maintain worker interest and morale.

A central theme of a true lean approach is to work toward continual improvement of the system—reducing inventories, reducing setup cost and time, improving quality, increasing the output rate, and generally cutting waste and inefficiency. Toward that end, problem solving becomes a way of life—a "culture" that must be assimilated into the thinking of management and workers alike. It becomes a never-ending quest for improving operations as all members of the organization strive to improve the system.

One challenge to continuous improvement is that once the "easy" improvements have been made, it becomes more difficult to keep workers motivated to continue to look for further improvements.

Workers in lean systems have more stress than their counterparts in more traditional systems. Stress comes not only from their added authority and responsibility but also from the high-paced system they work in, where there is little slack and a continual push to improve.

Activity-based costing Allocation of overhead to specific jobs based on their percentage of activities.

Cost Accounting. Another feature of some lean systems is the method of allocating overhead. Traditional accounting methods sometimes distort overhead allocation because they allocate it on the basis of direct labor hours. However, that approach does not always accurately reflect the consumption of overhead by different jobs. In addition, the number of direct labor hours in some industries has declined significantly over the years and now frequently accounts for a relatively small portion of the total cost. Conversely, other costs now represent a major portion of the total cost. Therefore, labor-intensive jobs (i.e., those that use relatively large proportions of direct labor) may be assigned a disproportionate share of overhead, one that does not truly reflect actual costs. That in turn can cause managers to make poor decisions. Furthermore, the need to track direct labor hours can itself involve considerable effort. One alternative method of allocating overhead is **activity-based costing**. This method is designed to more closely reflect the actual amount of overhead consumed by a particular job or activity. Activity-based costing first identifies traceable costs and then assigns those costs to various types of activities such as machine setups, inspection, machine hours, direct labor hours, and movement of materials. Specific jobs are then assigned overhead based on the percentage of activities they consume.

Leadership/Project Management. Another feature of lean systems relates to *leadership*. Managers are expected to be leaders and facilitators, not order givers. Lean encourages two-way communication between workers and managers.

Manufacturing Planning and Control

Seven elements of manufacturing planning and control are particularly important for lean systems:

1. Level loading
2. Pull systems
3. Visual systems

4.   Limited work-in-process (WIP)
5.   Close vendor relationships
6.   Reduced transaction processing
7.   Preventive maintenance and housekeeping

Level Loading. Lean systems place a strong emphasis on achieving stable, level daily mix schedules. Toward that end, the master production schedule is developed to provide *level capacity loading.* That may entail a rate-based production schedule instead of the more familiar quantity-based schedule. Moreover, once established, production schedules are relatively fixed over a short time horizon, and this provides certainty to the system. Even so, some adjustments may be needed in day-to-day schedules to achieve level capacity requirements. Suppliers like level loading because it means smooth demand for them.

A level production schedule requires smooth production. When a company produces different products or product models, it is desirable to produce in small lots (to minimize work-in-process inventory and to maintain flexibility) and to spread the production of the different products throughout the day to achieve smooth production. The extreme case would be to produce one unit of one product, then one of another, then one of another, and so on. While this approach would allow for maximum smoothness, it would generally not be practical because it would generate excessive setup costs.

Mixed-model sequencing begins with daily production requirements of each product or model. For instance, suppose a department produces three models, A, B, and C, with these daily requirements:

Three issues then need to be resolved. One is which sequence to use (C-B-A, A-C-B, etc.), another is how many times (i.e., cycles) the sequence should be repeated daily, and the third is how many units of each model to produce in each cycle.

Model	Daily Quantity
A	10
B	15
C	5

The choice of sequence can depend on several factors, but the key one is usually the setup time or cost, which may vary depending on the sequence used. For instance, if two of the models, say A and C, are quite similar, the sequences A-C and C-A may involve only minimal setup changes, whereas the setup for model B may be more extensive. Choosing a sequence that has A-C or C-A will result in about 20 percent fewer setups over time than having B produced between A and C on every cycle.

The number of cycles per day depends on the daily production quantities. If every model is to be produced in every cycle, which is often the goal, determining the smallest integer that can be evenly divided into each model's daily quantity will indicate the number of cycles. This will be the fewest number of cycles that will contain one unit of the model with the lowest quantity requirements. For models A, B, and C shown in the preceding table, there should be five cycles (five can be evenly divided into each quantity). High setup costs may cause a manager to use fewer cycles, trading off savings in setup costs and level production. If dividing by the smallest daily quantity does not yield an integer value for each model, a manager may opt for using the smallest production quantity to select a number of cycles, but then produce more of some items in some cycles to make up the difference.

Sometimes a manager determines the number of units of each model in each cycle by dividing each model's daily production quantity by the number of cycles. Using five cycles per day would yield the following:

Model	Daily Quantity	Units per Cycle
A	10	10/5 = 2
B	15	15/5 = 3
C	5	5/5 = 1

These quantities may be unworkable due to restrictions on lot sizes. For example, model B may be packed four to a carton, so producing three units per cycle would mean that at times finished units (inventory) would have to wait until sufficient quantities were available to fill a crate. Similarly, there may be standard production lot sizes for some operations. A heat-treating process might involve a furnace that can handle six units at a time. If the different models require different furnace temperatures, they could not be grouped. What would be necessary here is an analysis of the trade-off between furnace lot size and the advantages of level production.

EXAMPLE 2

Developing a Production Plan

Determine a production plan for these three models using the sequence A-B-C.

Model	Daily Quantity
A	7
B	16
C	5

SOLUTION

The smallest daily quantity is five, but dividing the other two quantities by five does not yield integers. The manager might still decide to use five cycles. Producing one unit of models A and C and three units of model B in each of the five cycles would leave the manager short two units of model A and one unit of model B. The manager might decide to intersperse those units like this to achieve nearly level production:

Cycle	1	2	3	4	5
Pattern	A B(3) C	A(2) B(3) C	A B(4) C	A(2) B(3) C	A B(3) C
Extra unit(s)		A	B	A	

If the requirement for model A had been eight units a day instead of seven, the manager might decide to use the following pattern:

Cycle	1	2	3	4	5
Pattern	A(2) B(3) C	A B(3) C	A(2) B(4) C	A B(3) C	A(2) B(3) C
Extra unit(s)	A		AB		A

Push system Work is pushed to the next station as it is completed.

Pull system A workstation pulls output from the preceding station as it is needed.

Pull Systems. The terms *push* and *pull* are used to describe two different systems for moving work through a production process. In traditional production environments, a **push system** is used: When work is finished at a workstation, the output is *pushed* to the next station; or, in the case of the final operation, it is pushed on to final inventory. Conversely, in a **pull system**, control of moving the work rests with the following operation; each workstation *pulls* the output from the preceding station as it is needed; output of the final operation is pulled by customer demand or the master schedule. Thus, in a pull system, work moves on in response to demand from the next stage in the process, whereas in a push system, work moves on as it is completed, without regard to the next station's readiness for the work. Consequently, work may pile up at workstations that fall behind schedule because of equipment failure or the detection of a problem with quality.

Communication moves backward through the system from station to station. Each workstation (i.e., customer) communicates its need for more work to the preceding workstation (i.e., supplier), thereby assuring that supply equals demand. Work moves "just in time" for the next operation; the flow of work is thereby coordinated, and the accumulation of excessive inventories between operations is avoided. Of course, some inventory is usually present because operations are not instantaneous. If a workstation waited until it received a request from the next workstation before starting its work, the next station would have to wait for the preceding station to perform its work. Therefore, by design, each workstation produces just enough output to meet the (anticipated) demand of the next station. This can be accomplished by having the succeeding workstation communicate its need for input sufficiently ahead of time to allow the preceding station to do the work. Or there can be a small buffer of stock between stations; when the buffer decreases to a certain level, this signals the preceding station to produce enough output to replenish the buffer supply. The size of the buffer supply depends on the cycle time at the preceding workstation. If the cycle time is short, the station will need little or no buffer; if the cycle time is long, it will need a considerable amount of buffer. However, production occurs only in response to *usage* of the succeeding station; work is still pulled by the demand generated by the next operation.

Pull systems aren't necessarily appropriate for all manufacturing operations because they require a fairly steady flow of repetitive work. Large variations in volume, product mix, or product design will undermine the system.

Visual Systems. In a pull system work flow is dictated by "next-step demand." A system can communicate such demand in a variety of ways, including a shout or a wave, but by far the most commonly used device is the *kanban* card. *Kanban* is a Japanese word meaning "signal" or "visible record." When a worker needs materials or work from the preceding station, he or she uses a kanban card. In effect, the kanban card is the *authorization* to move or work on parts. In kanban systems, no part or lot can be moved or worked on without one of these cards.

Kanban Card or other device that communicates demand for work or materials from the preceding station.

There are two main types of kanbans:

1. **Production kanban (p-kanban):** signals the need to produce parts.
2. **Conveyance kanban (c-kanban):** signals the need to deliver parts to the next work center.

The system works this way: A kanban card is affixed to each container. When a workstation needs to replenish its supply of parts, a worker goes to the area where these parts are stored and withdraws one container of parts. Each container holds a predetermined quantity. The worker removes the kanban card from the container and posts it in a designated spot where

Tri State Industries, footage courtesy of Mac Lean Media, Inc.

At TriState Industries, a kanban system is in effect to move work through the production system. Shown here, a kanban card provides the authorization to move or work on parts.

Tri State Industries, footage courtesy of Mac Lean Media, Inc.

Special carts were designed that, when filled, act as a visual signal that they are ready to be moved to the next work cell. An empty cart indicates that it is time to produce, in order to refill the cart.

it will be clearly visible, and the worker moves the container to the workstation. The posted kanban is then picked up by a stock person who replenishes the stock with another container, and so on down the line. Demand for parts triggers a replenishment, and parts are supplied as usage dictates. Similar withdrawals and replenishments—all controlled by kan-bans—occur all the way up and down the line from vendors to finished-goods inventories. If supervisors decide the system is too loose because inventories are building up, they may decide to tighten the system and withdraw some kanbans. Conversely, if the system seems too tight, they may introduce additional kanbans to bring the system into balance. Vendors also can influence the number of containers. Moreover, trip times can affect the number: Longer trip times may lead to fewer but larger containers, while shorter trip times may involve a greater number of small containers.

It is apparent that the number of kanban cards in use is an important variable. One can compute the ideal number of kanban cards using this formula:

$$N = \frac{D(T)(1 + X)}{C} \tag{14–2}$$

where

N = Total number of containers (1 card per container)

D = Planned usage rate of using work center

T = Average waiting time for replenishment of parts plus average production time for a container of parts

X = Policy variable set by management that reflects possible inefficiency in the system (the closer to 0, the more efficient the system)

C = Capacity of a standard container (should be no more than 10 percent of daily usage of the part)

Note that D and T must use the same units (e.g., minutes, days).

EXAMPLE 3   **Determining the Number of Kanban Cards Needed**

Usage at a work center is 300 parts per day, and a standard container holds 25 parts. It takes an average of .12 day for a container to complete a circuit from the time a kanban card is received until the container is returned empty. Compute the number of kanban cards (containers) needed if $X = .20$.

SOLUTION

$N = ?$

$D = 300$ parts per day

$T = .12$ day

$C = 25$ parts per container

$X = .20$

$N = \dfrac{300(.12)(1 + .20)}{25} = 1.728$; round to 2 containers

Note: Rounding up will cause the system to be looser, and rounding down will cause it to be tighter. Usually, rounding up is used.

Although the goals of MRP and kanban are essentially the same (i.e., to improve customer service, reduce inventories, and increase productivity), their approaches are different. Neither MRP nor kanban is a standalone system—each exists within a larger framework. MRP is a computerized system; kanban is a manual system that may be part of a lean system, although lean can exist without kanban.

Kanban is essentially a two-bin type of inventory: Supplies are replenished semiautomatically when they reach a predetermined level. MRP is more concerned with projecting requirements and with planning and scheduling operations.

A major benefit of the kanban system is its simplicity; a major benefit of MRP is its ability to handle complex planning and scheduling. In addition, MRP II enables management to answer what-if questions for capacity planning.

The philosophies that underlie kanban systems are quite different from those traditionally held by manufacturers. Nonetheless, both approaches have their merits, so it probably would not make sense in most instances to switch from one method of operation to the other. Moreover, to do so would require a tremendous effort. It is noteworthy that at the same time that Western manufacturers are studying kanban systems, some Japanese manufacturers are studying MRP systems. This suggests the possibility that either system could be improved by incorporating selected elements of the other. That would take careful analysis to determine which elements to incorporate as well as careful implementation of selected elements, and close monitoring to assure that intended results were achieved.

Whether manufacturers should adopt the kanban method is debatable. Some form of it may be useful, but kanban is merely an information system; by itself it offers little in terms of helping manufacturers become more competitive or productive. By the same token, MRP alone will not achieve those results either. Instead, it is the overall approach to manufacturing that is crucial; it is the commitment and support of top management and the continuing efforts of all levels of management to find new ways to improve their manufacturing planning and control techniques, and to adapt those techniques to fit their particular circumstances, that will determine the degree of success.

Comment The use of either kanban or MRP does not preclude the use of the other. In fact, it is not unusual to find the two systems used in the same production facility. Some Japanese manufacturers, for example, are turning to MRP systems to help them plan production. Both approaches have their advantages and limitations. MRP systems provide the capability to explode the bill of materials to project timing and material requirements that can then be used to plan production. But the MRP assumption of fixed lead times and infinite capacity can often result in significant problems. At the shop floor level, the discipline of a kanban system, with materials pull, can be very effective. But kanban works best when there is a uniform flow through the shop; a variable flow requires buffers, and this reduces the advantage of a pull system.

In effect, some situations are more conducive to a visual approach, others to an MRP approach. Still others can benefit from a hybrid of the two. Hybrid systems like kanban/MRP can be successful if MRP is used for planning and kanban is used as the execution system.

Limited Work-in-Process (WIP). Movement of materials and WIP in a lean system is carefully coordinated, so that they arrive at each step in a process just as they are needed. Controlling the amount of WIP in a production system can yield substantial benefits. One is lower carrying costs due to lower WIP inventory. Another is the increased flexibility that would be lost if there were large amounts of WIP in the system. In addition, low WIP aids scheduling and saves costs of rework and scrapping if there are design changes.

Controlling WIP also results in low cycle-time variability. WIP is determined by cycle time and the arrival rate of jobs. According to Little's law, WIP = Cycle time × Arrival rate. If both WIP and the arrival rate of jobs are held constant, the cycle time will also be constant. In a push system, the arrival rate of jobs is not held constant, so there is the possibility of large WIP buildups, which results in high variability in cycle times. This forces companies to quote longer lead times to customers to allow for variable cycle times.

There are two general approaches to controlling WIP; one is kanban and the other is constant work-in-process (CONWIP). Kanban's control of WIP focuses on individual workstations, while CONWIP'S focus is on the system as a whole. With CONWIP, when a job exits the system, a new job is allowed to enter. This results in a constant level of work-in-process.

Kanban works best in an environment that is stable and predictable. CONWIP offers an advantage if there is variability in a line, perhaps due to a breakdown in an operation or a quality problem. With kanban, upstream work is blocked and processing will stop fairly quickly, while with CONWIP upstream stations can continue to operate for a somewhat longer time. Then, after the reason for stoppage has been corrected, there will be less need to make up lost production than if the entire line had been shut down, as it would be under kanban. Also, in a mixed product environment, CONWIP can be easier than kanban because kanban focuses on specific part numbers whereas CONWIP does not.

Close Vendor Relationships. Lean systems typically have *close relationships with vendors,* who are expected to provide frequent small deliveries of high-quality goods. Traditionally, buyers have assumed the role of monitoring the quality of purchased goods, inspecting shipments for quality and quantity, and returning poor-quality goods to the vendor for rework. JIT systems have little slack, so poor-quality goods cause a disruption in the smooth flow of work. Moreover, the inspection of incoming goods is viewed as inefficient because it does not add value to the product. For these reasons, the burden of ensuring quality shifts to the vendor. Buyers work with vendors to help them achieve the desired quality levels and to impress upon them the importance of consistent, high-quality goods. The ultimate goal of the buyer is to be able to *certify* a vendor as a producer of high-quality goods. The implication of certification is that a vendor can be relied on to deliver high-quality goods without the need for buyer inspection.

Suppliers also must be willing and able to ship in small lots on a regular basis. Ideally, suppliers themselves will be operating under JIT systems. Buyers can often help suppliers convert to JIT production based on their own experiences. In effect, the supplier becomes part of an extended JIT system that integrates the facilities of buyer and supplier. Integration is easier when a supplier is dedicated to only one or a few buyers. In practice, a supplier is likely to have many different buyers, some using traditional systems and others using JIT. Consequently, compromises may have to be made by both buyers and suppliers.

Traditionally, a spirit of cooperation between buyer and seller has not been present; buyers and vendors have had a somewhat adversarial relationship. Buyers have generally regarded price as a major determinant in sourcing, and they have typically used *multiple-source* purchasing, which means having a list of potential vendors and buying from several to avoid getting locked into a sole source. In this way, buyers play vendors off against each other to get better pricing arrangements or other concessions. The downside is that vendors cannot rely on a long-term relationship with a buyer, and they feel no loyalty to a particular buyer. Furthermore, vendors have often sought to protect themselves from losing a buyer by increasing the number of buyers they supply.

Under JIT purchasing, good vendor relationships are very important. Buyers take measures to reduce their lists of suppliers, concentrating on maintaining close working relationships with a few good ones. Because of the need for frequent, small deliveries, many buyers attempt to find local vendors to shorten the lead time for deliveries and to reduce lead time variability. An added advantage of having vendors nearby is quick response when problems arise.

JIT purchasing is enhanced by long-term relationships between buyers and vendors. Vendors are more willing to commit resources to the job of shipping according to a buyer's JIT system given a long-term relationship. Moreover, price often becomes secondary to other aspects of the relationship (e.g., consistent high quality, flexibility, frequent small deliveries, and quick response to problems).

Supplier Tiers A key feature of many lean production systems is the relatively small number of suppliers used. In traditional production, companies often deal with hundreds or even thousands of suppliers in a highly centralized arrangement not unlike a giant wheel with many spokes. The company is at the hub of the wheel, and the spokes radiate out to suppliers, each of whom must deal directly with the company. In traditional systems, a supplier does not know the other suppliers or what they are doing. Each supplier works to specifications provided by the buyer. Suppliers have very little basis (or motivation) for suggesting improvements. Moreover, as companies play one supplier off against others, the sharing of information is more risky than rewarding. In contrast, lean production companies may employ a tiered approach for suppliers: They use relatively few first-tier suppliers who work directly with the company or who supply major subassemblies. The first-tier suppliers are responsible for dealing with second-tier suppliers who provide components for the subassemblies, thereby relieving the final buyer from dealing with large numbers of suppliers.

The automotive industry provides a good example of this situation. Suppose a certain car model has an electric seat. The seat and motor together might entail 250 separate parts. A traditional producer might use more than 30 suppliers for the electric seat, but a lean producer might use a single (first-tier) supplier who has the responsibility for the entire seat unit. The company would provide specifications for the overall unit, but leave to the supplier the details of the motor, springs, and so on. The first-tier supplier, in turn, might subcontract the motor to a second-tier supplier, the track to another second-tier supplier, and the cushions and fabric to still another. The second-tier suppliers might subcontract some of their work to third-tier suppliers, and so on. Each tier has only to deal with those just above it or just below it. Suppliers on each level are encouraged to work with each other, and they are motivated to do so because that increases the probability that the resulting item (the seat) will meet or exceed the final buyer's expectations. In this "team of suppliers" approach, all suppliers benefit from a successful product, and each supplier bears full responsibility for the quality of its portion of the product. Figure 14.4 illustrates the difference between the traditional approach and the tiered approach.

Reduced Transaction Processing. Traditional manufacturing systems often have many built-in transactions that do not add value. In their classic article, "The Hidden Factory," [2] Jeffrey G. Miller and Thomas Vollmann identify a laundry list of transaction processing that comprises a "hidden factory" in traditional manufacturing planning and control systems, and point out the tremendous cost burden that results. The transactions can be classified as logistical, balancing, quality, or change transactions.

Logistical transactions include ordering, execution, and confirmation of materials transported from one location to another. Related costs cover shipping and receiving personnel, expediting orders, data entry, and data processing.

Balancing transactions include forecasting, production planning, production control, procurement, scheduling, and order processing. Associated costs relate to the personnel involved in these and supporting activities.

Quality transactions include determining and communicating specifications, monitoring, recording, and follow-up activities. Costs relate to appraisal, prevention, internal failures (e.g., scrap, rework, retesting, delays, administration activities) and external failures (e.g., warranty costs, product liability, returns, potential loss of future business).

FIGURE 14.4 Traditional supplier network compared to supplier tiers

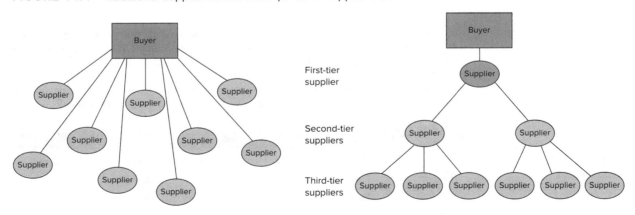

[2]Excerpted from Jeffrey Miller and Thomas Vollmann, "The Hidden Factory," *Harvard Business Review,* September/October 1985, pp. 141–50. Copyright © 1985 by the Harvard Business School Publishing Corporation. All rights reserved.

Change transactions primarily involve engineering changes and the ensuing changes generated in specifications, bills of material, scheduling, processing instructions, and so on. Engineering changes are among the most costly of all transactions.

Lean systems cut transaction costs by reducing the number and frequency of transactions. For example, suppliers deliver goods directly to the production floor, bypassing the storeroom entirely, thereby avoiding the transactions related to receiving the shipment into inventory storage and later moving the materials to the production floor. In addition, vendors are certified for quality, eliminating the need to inspect incoming shipments for quality. The unending quest for quality improvement that pervades lean systems eliminates many of the previously mentioned quality transactions and their related costs. The use of bar coding (not exclusive to lean systems) can reduce data entry transactions and increase data accuracy.

Preventive Maintenance and Housekeeping. Because lean systems have very little in-process inventory, equipment breakdowns can be extremely disruptive. To minimize breakdowns, companies use **preventive maintenance** programs, which emphasize maintaining equipment in good operating condition and replacing parts that have a tendency to fail before they fail. Workers are often responsible for maintaining their own equipment.

Even with preventive maintenance, occasional equipment failures will occur. Companies must be prepared for this, so they can quickly return equipment to working order. This may mean maintaining supplies of critical spare parts and making other provisions for emergency situations, perhaps maintaining a small force of repair people or training workers to do certain repairs themselves. Note that when breakdowns do occur, they indicate potential opportunities to be exploited in a lean environment.

Housekeeping involves keeping the workplace clean as well as keeping it free of any materials that are not needed for production, because those materials take up space and may cause disruptions to the work flow.

Housekeeping is part of what is often referred to as the five S's, which are five behaviors intended to make the workplace effective:

1. **Sort.** Decide which items are needed to accomplish the work, and keep only those items.
2. **Straighten.** Organize the workplace so that the needed items can be accessed quickly and easily.
3. **Sweep.** Keep the workplace clean and ready for work. Perform equipment maintenance regularly.
4. **Standardize.** Use standard instructions and procedures for all work.
5. **Self-discipline.** Make sure that employees understand the need for an uncluttered workplace.

Among the benefits of the five S's are increased productivity, improved employee morale, decreased risk of accidents, and improved appearance for visitors. Employees and managers must appreciate the rationale for the five S's. Otherwise, they may view them as unnecessary and a waste of effort.

Lean systems have been described and compared with traditional manufacturing systems in the preceding pages. Table 14.3 provides a brief overview of those comparisons.

Preventive maintenance Proactive approach; reducing breakdowns through a program of lubrication, adjustment, cleaning, inspection, and replacement of worn parts.

Housekeeping Maintaining a workplace that is clean and free of unnecessary materials.

TABLE 14.3
Comparison of lean and traditional production philosophies

Factor	Traditional	Lean
Inventory	Much, to offset forecast errors, late deliveries	Minimal necessary to operate
Deliveries	Few, large	Many, small
Lot sizes	Large	Small
Setups, runs	Few, long runs	Many, short runs
Vendors	Long-term relationships are unusual	Partners
Workers	Necessary to do the work	Assets

14.4 LEAN TOOLS

This section describes several tools that are used for process improvement in lean systems.

LO14.9 Describe key lean improvement tools.

Value Stream Mapping

Value stream mapping is a visual tool to systematically examine the flow of materials and information involved in bringing a product or service to a consumer. The technique originated at Toyota, where it is referred to as "Material and Information Flow Mapping."

The map is a sketch of an entire process that typically ranges from incoming goods from suppliers to shipment of a product or delivery of a service to the customer. The map shows all processes in the value stream, from arrivals of supplies to the shipping of the product. The objective is to increase value to the customer, where value is typically defined in terms of quality, time, cost, or flexibility (e.g., rapid response or agility). Data collected during the mapping process might include times (e.g., cycle time, setup time, changeover time, touch time, lead time), distances traveled (e.g., by parts, workers, paperwork), mistakes (e.g., product defects, data entry errors), inefficient work methods (e.g., extra motions, excessive lifting or moving, repositioning), and waiting lines (e.g., workers waiting for parts or equipment repairs, orders waiting to be processed). Information flows are also included in the mapping process.

You can get a sense of value stream mapping from the following tips for developing an effective mapping of a value stream:[3]

1. Map the value stream in person.
2. Begin with a quick walkthrough of the system from beginning to end to get a sense of the system.
3. Then do a more thorough walkthrough following the actual pathway to collect current information on material or information flow.
4. Record elements of the system such as cycle times, scrap rates, amounts of inventory, downtimes, number of operators, distances between processes, and transfer times.

Value improvement for a product or a service embodies the five lean principles described earlier and repeated here. It begins by specifying value from the customer's standpoint. You can see where value stream mapping can help process improvement:

1. Specify value from the standpoint of the end customer.
2. Identify all the steps in the value stream and create a visual (map) of the value stream.
3. Eliminate steps that do not create value to create flow.
4. Use next-customer-in-the-process demand to pull from each preceding process as needed to control the flow.
5. Repeat this process as long as waste exists in the system.

Once a value stream map is completed, data analysis can uncover improvement opportunities by asking key questions, such as:

Where are the process bottlenecks?

Where do errors occur?

Which processes have to deal with the most variation?

Where does waste occur?

All business organizations, whether they are primarily engaged in service or manufacturing, can benefit by applying lean principles to their office operations. This includes purchasing, accounting, order entry, and other office functions. Office wastes might include:

1. **Excess inventory**—excess supplies and equipment
2. **Overprocessing**—excess paperwork and redundant approvals

Value stream mapping A visual tool to systematically examine the flow of materials and information.

[3] Adapted from Rother, Mike, and John Shook. *Learning to See.* Cambridge, MA: Lean Enterprise Institute, 2009.

3. **Waiting times**—orders waiting to be processed, requests for information awaiting answers

4. **Unnecessary transportation**—inefficient routing

5. **Processing waste**—using more resources than necessary to accomplish a task

6. **Inefficient work methods**—poor layout design, unnecessary steps, inadequate training

7. **Mistakes**—order entry errors, lost files, miscommunications

8. **Underused people**—not tapping all of the mental and creative capabilities of workers

Process Improvement Using 5W2H

5W2H approach A method of asking questions about a process that includes what, why, where, when, who, how, and how much.

Asking certain questions about a process can lead to cost and waste reduction. The **5W2H approach** (five questions that begin with *w*, and two questions that begin with *h*) is outlined in Table 14.4. This approach can be used by itself or in conjunction with value stream mapping.

Lean and Six Sigma

Some believe that lean and Six Sigma are two alternate approaches for process improvement. However, another view is that the two approaches are complementary and, when used together, can lead to superior results.

Lean strives to eliminate non-value-added activities, using simple tools to find and eliminate them. It focuses on maximizing process velocity, and it employs tools to analyze and improve process flow. However, variation exists in all processes. Understanding and reducing variation are important for quality improvement. Lean principles alone cannot achieve statistical process control, and Six Sigma alone cannot achieve improved process speed and flow. Using the two approaches in combination integrates lean principles and Six Sigma statistical tools for variation reduction to achieve a system that has both a balanced flow and quality.

JIT Deliveries and the Supply Chain

Direct suppliers must be able to support frequent just-in-time deliveries of small batches of parts. That may lead to an increase in transportation costs if trucks carry partial loads, and perhaps to congestion at loading docks. Moreover, the JIT delivery requirement may extend to other portions of the supply chain, in which case close coordination among supply chain partners is critical. Also, JIT delivery results in pressure for on-time deliveries to avoid production interruptions due to stockouts.

TABLE 14.4
The 5W2H approach

Category	5W2H	Typical Questions	Goal
Subject	What?	What is being done?	Identify the focus of analysis.
Purpose	Why?	Why is this necessary?	Eliminate unnecessary tasks.
Location	Where?	Where is it being done? Why is it done there? Would it be better to do it someplace else?	Improve the location.
Sequence	When?	When is it done? Would it be better to do it at another time?	Improve the sequence.
People	Who?	Who is doing it? Could someone else do it better?	Improve the sequence or output.
Method	How?	How is it being done? Is there a better way?	Simplify tasks, improve output.
Cost	How much?	How much does it cost now? What would the new cost be?	Select an improved method.

Source: Adapted from Alan Robinson, ed., *Continuous Improvement in Operations: A Systematic Approach to Waste Reduction*, p. 246. Copyright © 1991 Productivity Press. www.productivitypress.com.

READING   NEARBY SUPPLIERS MATCH FORD'S MIX

Ford Motor Company took a page out of Toyota's just-in-time book at its Chicago plant by having some of its suppliers locate very close to its assembly plant. It leased production facilities on its 155 acres to about 10 key suppliers. Suppliers' parts and components feed directly into Ford's assembly operation, carefully coordinated to match the sequence of vehicles Ford is producing, which can range from small cars to SUVs. Not only are suppliers nearby in case problems arise, the shortened travel distance and lead times yield tremendous savings in the pipeline inventories of parts and materials.

Lean and ERP

Lean systems focus on pacing production and synchronizing delivery of incoming supply. SAP's Lean Planning and Operations module extends ERP to lean operation by providing lean planning and scheduling capability linked to customer demand. It enables leveling of schedules and synchronization of supply chain activities with paced company operations.

14.5 TRANSITIONING TO A LEAN SYSTEM

> **LO14.10** Outline considerations for successful conversion from a traditional system to a lean system.

The success of lean systems in Japan and the United States has attracted keen interest among other traditional manufacturers.

Planning a Successful Conversion

To increase the probability of successful transition, companies should adopt a carefully planned approach that includes the following elements:

1. Make sure top management is committed to the conversion and that they know what will be required. Make sure that management is involved in the process and knows what it will cost, how long it will take to complete the conversion, and what results can be expected.

2. Study the operations carefully; decide which parts will need the most effort to convert.

3. Obtain the support and cooperation of workers. Prepare training programs that include sessions in setups, maintenance of equipment, cross-training for multiple tasks, cooperation, and problem solving. Make sure workers are fully informed about what lean is and why it is desirable. Reassure workers that their jobs are secure.

4. Begin by trying to reduce setup times while maintaining the current system. Enlist the aid of workers in identifying and eliminating existing problems (e.g., bottlenecks, poor quality).

5. Gradually convert operations, beginning at the *end* of the process and working *backward*. At each stage, make sure the conversion has been relatively successful before moving on. Do not begin to reduce inventories until major problems have been resolved.

6. As one of the last steps, convert suppliers to JIT and be prepared to work closely with them. Start by narrowing the list of vendors, identifying those who are willing to embrace the lean philosophy. Give preference to vendors who have long-term track records of reliability. Use vendors located nearby if quick response time is important. Establish long-term commitments with vendors. Insist on high standards of quality and adherence to strict delivery schedules.

7. Be prepared to encounter obstacles to conversion.

Obstacles to Conversion

> **LO14.11** Describe some of the obstacles to lean success.

Converting from a traditional system to a lean system may not be smooth. For example, *cultures* vary from organization to organization. Some cultures relate better to the lean philosophy than others. If a culture doesn't relate, it can be difficult for an organization to change its culture within a short time. Also, manufacturers that operate with large amounts of inventory to handle varying customer demand may have difficulty acclimating themselves to less inventory.

Some other obstacles include the following:

1. Management may not be totally committed or may be unwilling to devote the necessary resources to conversion. This is perhaps the most serious impediment because the conversion is probably doomed without serious commitment.

2. Workers and/or management may not display a cooperative spirit. The system is predicated on cooperation. Managers may resist because lean shifts some of the responsibility from management to workers and gives workers more control over the work. Workers may resist because of the increased responsibility and stress.

3. It can be very difficult to change the culture of the organization to one consistent with the lean philosophy.

4. Suppliers may resist for several reasons:

    a. Buyers may not be willing to commit the resources necessary to help them adapt to the lean systems.

    b. They may be uneasy about long-term commitments to a buyer.

    c. Frequent, small deliveries may be difficult, especially if the supplier has other buyers who use traditional systems.

    d. The burden of quality control will shift to the supplier.

    e. Frequent engineering changes may result from continuing lean improvements by the buyer.

A Cooperative Spirit

Lean systems require a cooperative spirit among workers, management, and vendors. Unless that is present, it is doubtful that a truly effective lean system can be achieved. The Japanese have been very successful in this regard, partly because respect and cooperation are ingrained in the Japanese culture. In Western cultures, workers, managers, and vendors have historically been strongly at odds with each other. Consequently, a major consideration in converting to a lean system is whether a spirit of mutual respect and cooperation can be achieved. This requires an appreciation of the importance of cooperation and a tenacious effort by management to instill and maintain that spirit.

Finally, it should be noted that not all organizations lend themselves to a lean approach. Lean is best used for repetitive operations under fairly stable demand.

Despite the many advantages of lean production systems, an organization must take into account a number of other considerations when planning a conversion.

The key considerations are the time and cost requirements for successful conversion, which can be substantial. But it is absolutely essential to eliminate the major sources of disruption in the system. Management must be prepared to commit the resources necessary to achieve a high level of quality and to function on a tight schedule. That means attention to even the smallest of details during the design phase and substantial efforts to debug the system to the point where it runs smoothly. Beyond that, management must be capable of responding quickly when problems arise, and both management and workers must be committed to the continuous improvement of the system. Although each case is different, a general estimate of the time required for conversion is one to three years.

14.6 LEAN SERVICES

The discussion of lean systems has focused on manufacturing simply because that is where it was developed, and where it has been used most often. It is important to recognize that the full spectrum of lean benefits are more difficult to achieve in service operations. Nonetheless, services can and do benefit from many lean concepts. When just-in-time is used in the context of services, the focus is often on the time needed to perform a service—because speed is often an important order winner for services. Some services do have inventories of some sort, so inventory reduction is another aspect of lean that can apply to services. Examples of

Chapter Fourteen   JIT and Lean Operations   **635**

The Pyxis® ProcedureStation™ system provides rapid access to inventory in the operating room, cath and cardiac labs, and other specialty departments. Usage, inventory, and replenishment information are transmitted electronically, creating an efficient supply management and workflow process.

Courtesy © Becton, Dickinson and Company

speedy delivery ("available when requested") are Domino's Pizza, FedEx and Express Mail, fast-food restaurants, and emergency services. Other examples include just-in-time publishing and work cells at fast-food restaurants.

In addition to speed, lean services emphasize consistent, high-quality, standard work methods; flexible workers; and close supplier relationships.

Process improvement and problem solving can contribute to streamlining a system, resulting in increased customer satisfaction and higher productivity. The following are the ways lean benefits can be achieved in services:

- **Eliminate disruptions.** For example, try to avoid having workers who are servicing customers also answer telephones.
- **Make the system flexible.** This can cause problems unless approached carefully. Often, it is desirable to standardize work because that can yield high productivity. On the other hand, being able to deal with variety in task requirements can be a competitive advantage. One approach might be to train workers so that they can handle more variety. Another might be to assign work according to specialties, with certain workers handling different types of work according to their specialty.
- **Reduce setup times and processing times.** Have frequently used tools and spare parts readily available. Additionally, for service calls, try to estimate what parts and supplies might be needed so they will be on hand, and avoid carrying huge inventories.
- **Eliminate waste.** This includes errors and duplicate work. Keep the emphasis on quality and uniform service.
- **Minimize work-in-process.** Examples include orders waiting to be processed, calls waiting to be answered, packages waiting to be delivered, trucks waiting to be unloaded or loaded, applications waiting to be processed.
- **Simplify the process.** This works especially when customers are part of the system (self-service systems including retail operations, ATMs and vending machines, service stations, etc.).

TO BUILD A BETTER HOSPITAL, VIRGINIA MASON TAKES LESSONS FROM TOYOTA PLANTS

When you think of a hospital, what comes to mind? Patients, emergency rooms, technology, and medical advancements. Making the sick and injured well again.

When officials at Virginia Mason think of hospitals, they think of cars. A car manufacturing plant, to be exact.

Beginning in 2000 the hospital's leaders looked at their infrastructure and saw it was designed around them, not the patient, said Dr. Gary Kaplan, Virginia Mason's chairman and chief executive officer.

For example, you hurry up and be on time, only to wait for the physician to see you.

They began looking for a better way to improve quality, safety and patient satisfaction. After two years of searching, they discovered the Toyota Production System, also known as lean manufacturing. Developed in part by Japanese businessman Taiichi Ohno, the idea is to eliminate waste and defects in production. Virginia Mason has tailored the Japanese model to fit health care.

Kaplan and other Virginia Mason managers took their first trip to Japan in 2002 where they visited manufacturing plants such as Toyota and Yamaha. Nearly 200 employees have toured plants in Japan and a ninth trip is planned for this summer. While Virginia Mason couldn't say exactly how much they paid over the years to send the staff overseas, officials liken it to leadership training other companies pay for their employees. They say the benefits offset the costs.

"People are not cars is very common for me to hear," Kaplan said. "We get so wrapped up in the seriousness and specialness of health care, but we also have to open our eyes to other industries—we're way behind in information specialists and taking waste out of our process. Toyota is obsessed with the customer and customer satisfaction . . . all those things Toyota was about was what we wanted."

So what does that mean?

There are seven wastes, according to the production system. One is wasting time, such as patients waiting for a doctor or for test results to come back. Others are inventory waste—having more materials and information than is necessary—and overproduction waste, producing more than is necessary.

Take, for example, stockpiling brochures and pamphlets in storage closets. They take up space. There is wasted cost to make so many pamphlets that aren't needed.

The hospital and all of its campuses in the Seattle area implemented a Kanban system, which signals the need to restock. Kanban, which means "visual card" in Japanese, uses exactly that—a card put near the bottom of a pile of tongue dispensers, gauze strips, or brochures, for example. When a nurse or physician sees the card, he or she knows it's time to refill. Supplies don't run out, but they also aren't over-ordered.

The hospital created standardized instrument trays for surgeries and procedures, which saved several hundred dollars by no longer setting out extra instruments no one used. Unused but opened instruments have to be thrown away.

It takes a series of simple steps to make improvements, said Janine Wentworth, an administrative director who returned from a two-week trip to Japan last month. One example is the development of a flip chart showing the level of mobility in physical therapy patients. The chart shows the appropriate picture of what the patient can do, and each nurse or physician who comes in the room doesn't have to waste time searching charts or asking questions.

Wentworth also wants to implement a production plan to hire more staff before a shortage exists based on turnover rates on any given hospital floor.

Another adaptation from the Toyota model is a patient safety alert system. At the manufacturing plant, if there's a problem, the whole line is stopped and the problem is fixed immediately. Virginia Mason's practice had been to identify and fix problems after the fact, perhaps leading to mistakes recurring many times before a solution was found. The alert system allows nurses and physicians to signal a problem when it happens and fix it immediately. Virginia Mason's Kirkland site has about 10 alerts each day.

The Kirkland campus implemented the Toyota model in 2003. They've reduced appointment and telephone delays by having medical assistants handle incoming calls, instead of medically untrained operators.

Also, instead of doctors waiting until the end of the day to go through a stack of patient records, they now write comments and recommendations immediately after seeing the patient before going to see the next one. The time saved increases the time a physician can spend with a patient. Dr. Kim Pittenger, medical director at Virginia Mason Kirkland, said most of the cost of medical care involves clogs in the flow of information—paper forms, lab results, phone messages, often leading to irritated patients. Working the backlog down costs more than if you never let things pile up in the first place, he said.

He said not everyone has agreed with the new system and a few physicians have left Virginia Mason because of it.

"To some it seems like obsessive-compulsive disorder run amok, but it's part of a solution that eliminates mistakes," Pittenger said.

Other hospitals, including Swedish Medical Center, have incorporated the lean system into parts of their operation.

Virginia Mason said overall benefits include an 85 percent reduction in how long patients wait to get lab results back, and lowering inventory costs by $1 million. They've redesigned facilities to make patient and staff work flow more productive. The hospital reduced overtime and temporary labor expenses by $500,000 in one year and increased productivity by 93 percent. While direct cost savings aren't passed on to patients with the new system, less waiting, increased safety, and more efficient care are.

Kaplan's vision is to have patients start their appointment in the parking garage with a smart card that triggers their entire appointment process. No more waiting rooms, just move directly from the garage to an examination room.

Total flow—no waiting, no waste, and it's all about the patient.

"We have more than enough resources in health care," Kaplan said. "We just need to stop wasting it and only do what's appropriate and value-added and we'd save billions."

Source: Cherie Black, "To Build a Better Hospital, Virginia Mason Takes Lessons from Toyota Plant," *Seattle Post-Intelligencer,* March 15, 2008. Copyright © 2008. Used with permission.

JIT service can be a major competitive advantage for companies that can achieve it. An important key to JIT service is the ability to provide service when it is needed. That requires flexibility on the part of the provider, which generally means short setup times, and it requires clear communication on the part of the requester. If a requester can determine when it will need a particular service, a JIT server can schedule deliveries to correspond to those needs, eliminating the need for continual requests, and reducing the need for provider flexibility—and therefore probably reducing the cost of the JIT service.

Although lean concepts are applicable to service organizations, the challenge of implementing lean in service is that there are still relatively few lean service applications that service companies can reference to see how to apply the underlying lean principles. Consequently, it can be difficult to build a strong commitment among workers to achieve a lean service system.

14.7 JIT II

In some instances, companies allow *suppliers* to manage restocking of inventory obtained from the suppliers. A supplier representative works right in the company's plant, making sure there is an appropriate supply on hand. The term *JIT II* is used to refer to this practice. JIT II was popularized by the Bose Corporation. It is often referred to as *vendor-managed inventory (VMI)*. You can also read more about vendor-managed inventories in the supply chain management chapter (Chapter 15).

14.8 OPERATIONS STRATEGY

The lean operation offers new perspectives on operations that must be given serious consideration by managers in repetitive and batch systems who wish to be competitive.

Potential adopters should carefully study the requirements and benefits of lean production systems, as well as the difficulties and strengths of their current systems, before making a decision on whether to convert. Careful estimates of time and cost to convert, and an assessment of how likely workers, managers, and suppliers are to cooperate in such an approach, are essential.

The decision to convert can be sequential, giving management an opportunity to gain first-hand experience with portions of lean operations without wholly committing themselves. For instance, improving vendor relations, reducing setup times, improving quality, and reducing waste and inefficiency are desirable goals in themselves. Moreover, a level production schedule is a necessary element of a lean system, and achieving that will also be useful under a traditional system of operation.

It is prudent to carefully weigh the risks and benefits of a just-in-time approach to inventories. A just-in-time approach can make companies and even countries vulnerable to disruptions in their supply chains. For example, low stockpiles of flu vaccine at hospitals lower their costs but leave the health system at risk if there is a flu outbreak. Also, severe weather such as hurricanes, floods, and tornadoes, and other natural disasters caused by earthquakes can cut off supply routes, leaving community services as well as companies desperately in need of supplies.

Supplier management is critical to a JIT operation. Generally, suppliers are located nearby to facilitate delivery on a daily or even hourly basis. Moreover, suppliers at every stage must gauge the ability of their production facilities to meet demand requirements that are subject to change.

Finally, the success of a lean system relies heavily on leadership commitment, involvement, and support, achieving a lean thinking "culture" that includes everyone in the organization, and having effective teamwork. Without these three elements, the full benefits of lean are not likely to be realized.

638   **Chapter Fourteen**   JIT and Lean Operations

SUMMARY

Lean operation is an alternative to traditional operation that an increasing number of organizations are adopting. The ultimate goal of a lean system is to achieve a balanced, smooth flow of operations. Supporting goals include eliminating disruptions to the system, making the system flexible, and eliminating waste. The building blocks of a lean production system are product design, process design, personnel and organization, and manufacturing planning and control.

Lean systems require the elimination of sources of potential disruption to the even flow of work. High quality is essential because problems with quality can disrupt the process. Quick, low-cost setups, special layouts, allowing work to be pulled through the system rather than pushed through, and a spirit of cooperation are important features of lean systems. So, too, are problem solving aimed at reducing disruptions and making the system more efficient, and an attitude of working toward continual improvement.

Key benefits of lean systems are reduced inventory levels, high quality, flexibility, reduced lead times, increased productivity and equipment utilization, reduced amounts of scrap and rework, and reduced space requirements. The risks stem from the absence of buffers, such as extra personnel and inventory stockpiles to fall back on if something goes wrong. The possible results of risks include lost sales and lost customers.

Just-in-time (JIT) is a system of lean production used mainly in repetitive operations, in which goods move through the system and tasks are completed just in time to maintain the schedule. JIT systems require very little inventory because successive operations are closely coordinated. Careful planning and much effort are needed to achieve a smoothly functioning system in which all resources needed for production come together at precisely the right time throughout the process. Raw materials and purchased parts must arrive when needed, fabricated parts and subassemblies must be ready when needed for final assembly, and finished goods must be delivered to customers when needed. Special attention must be given to reducing the risk of disruptions to the system as well as rapid response to resolving any disruptions that do occur. Usually, a firm must redesign its facilities and rework labor contracts to implement lean operation. Teamwork and cooperation are important at all levels, as are problem-solving abilities of workers and an attitude of continuous improvement.

Table 14.5 provides an overview of lean.

TABLE 14.5
Overview of lean.

Lean systems are designed to operate with fewer resources than
   traditional systems.
Elements of lean operation include:
   Smooth flow of work (the ultimate goal)
   Elimination of waste
   Continuous improvement
   Elimination of anything that does not add value
   Simple systems that are easy to manage
   Use of product layouts that minimize time spent moving materials
      and parts
   Quality at the source: Each worker is responsible for the quality of his
      or her output
   Poka-yoke: fail-safe tools and methods to prevent mistakes
   Preventive maintenance to reduce the risk of equipment breakdown
   Good housekeeping: an orderly and clean workplace
   Setup time reduction
   Cross-trained workers
   A pull system
There are eight types of waste:
   Inventory
   Overproduction
   Waiting time
   Excess transportation
   Processing waste
   Inefficient work methods
   Product or service defects
   Underused people

1. Lean systems produce high-quality goods or services using fewer resources than traditional operations systems.

2. Lean thinking helps business organizations to become more productive, reduce costs, and be more market-responsive.

3. Lean operations are designed to eliminate waste (value stream mapping), minimize inventory (JIT deliveries), maximize work flow (small batches with quick changeovers), make only what is needed (demand pull), empower work teams, do it right the first time (quality at the source), and continually improve.

KEY POINTS

activity-based costing, 622	just-in-time (JIT), 609	pull system, 624
andon, 622	*kaizen*, 611	push system, 624
autonomation, 617	*kanban*, 611, 625	single-minute exchange of die
5W2H approach, 632	lean operation, 609	(SMED), 616
heijunka, 611	*muda*, 611	*takt* time, 618
housekeeping, 630	*poka-yoke*, 620	value stream mapping, 631
jidoka, 611	preventive maintenance, 630	

KEY TERMS

SOLVED PROBLEMS

Determine the number of containers needed for a workstation that uses 100 parts per hour if the time for a container to complete a cycle (move, wait, empty, return, fill) is 90 minutes and a standard container holds 84 parts. An inefficiency factor of .10 is currently being used.

Problem 1

$N = ?$

$D = 100$ parts per hour

$T = 90$ minutes (1.5 hours)

$C = 84$ parts

$X = .10$

$$N = \frac{D(T)(1 + X)}{C} = \frac{100(1.5)(1 + .10)}{84} = 1.96; \text{ round to 2 containers}$$

Solution

Determine the number of cycles per day and the production quantity per cycle for this set of products. The department operates five days a week. Assume the sequence A-B-C-D will be used.

Problem 2

Product	Weekly Quantity
A	20
B	40
C	30
D	15

Convert weekly quantities to daily quantities. The smallest *daily* quantity is 3 units. Producing in multiples of 3 units leaves A and B a few units short:

Solution

Product	Daily Quantity = Weekly Quantity ÷ 5	Units Short Using 3 Cycles
A	20 ÷ 5 = 4	1
B	40 ÷ 5 = 8	2
C	30 ÷ 5 = 6	—
D	15 ÷ 5 = 3	—

Use three cycles, producing all four products in every cycle. Produce units that are short by adding units to some cycles. Disperse the additional units as evenly as possible. There are several possibilities. One is as follows.

Cycle	1	2	3
Pattern	A B(3) C(2) D	A B(3) C(2) D	A(2) B(2) C(2) D
Extra unit(s)	B	B	A

640   **Chapter Fourteen**   JIT and Lean Operations

1. Some key elements of production systems are listed in Table 14.3. Explain briefly how lean systems differ from traditional production systems for each of those elements.
2. What is the ultimate goal of a lean system? What are the supporting goals? What are the building blocks?
3. Describe the philosophy that underlies JIT (i.e., what is JIT intended to accomplish?).
4. What are some of the main obstacles that must be overcome in converting from a traditional system to lean?
5. Briefly discuss vendor relations in lean systems in terms of the following issues:
   a. Why are they important?
   b. How do they tend to differ from the more adversarial relations of the past?
   c. Why might suppliers be hesitant about JIT purchasing?
6. Certain Japanese have claimed that Henry Ford's assembly line provided some of the rationale for lean. What features of assembly lines are common to lean systems?
7. What is the kanban aspect of JIT?
8. Contrast push and pull methods of moving goods and materials through production systems.
9. What are the main benefits of a lean system?
10. What are the benefits and risks of small lot sizes?

TAKING STOCK

1. What trade-offs are involved in shifting from a traditional operations system to a lean system for a manufacturing firm? For a service firm?
2. Who in the organization is affected by a decision to shift from a traditional operations system to a lean system?
3. To what extent has technology had an impact on lean systems?

**CRITICAL THINKING
EXERCISES**

1. In operations management, as in life, a balanced approach is often the best policy. One of the best examples of the benefits of this in operations management is the lean approach. Explain the basic factors that must be in place in order to achieve a balanced lean system.
2. Give three examples of unethical behavior involving lean operations, and state the relevant ethical principle that would be violated.

PROBLEMS

1. A manager wants to determine the number of containers to use for incoming parts for a kanban system to be installed next month. The process will have a usage rate of 80 pieces per hour. Because the process is new, the manager has assigned an inefficiency factor of .35. Each container holds 45 pieces, and it takes an average of 75 minutes to complete a cycle. How many containers should be used? As the system improves, will more or fewer containers be required? Why?
2. A JIT system uses kanban cards to authorize movement of incoming parts. In one portion of the system, a work center uses an average of 100 parts per hour while running. The manager has assigned an inefficiency factor of .20 to the center. Standard containers are designed to hold six dozen parts each. The cycle time for parts containers is about 105 minutes. How many containers are needed?
3. A machine cell uses 200 pounds of a certain material each day. Material is transported in vats that hold 20 pounds each. Cycle time for the vats is about two hours. The manager has assigned an inefficiency factor of .08 to the cell. The plant operates on an eight-hour day. How many vats will be used?
4. Determine the number of cycles per day and the production quantity per cycle for this set of vehicles:

Product	Daily Quantity
A	21
B	12
C	3
D	15

Chapter Fourteen   JIT and Lean Operations   **641**

Use the sequence A-B-C-D.

5. Given this set of daily service operations, and assuming a processing order of A-B-C-D-E:

  a. Give one reason that each arrangement might be preferred over the other.

  b. Determine the number of repetitions for each service if four cycles are used.

  c. Determine the number of repetitions for each service if two cycles are used.

Service Operation	Number of Daily Reps
A	22
B	12
C	4
D	18
E	8

6. Determine the number of cycles per day and a production quantity per cycle for this set of products that achieves fairly level production:

Product	Daily Quantity
F	9
G	8
H	5
K	6

Assume the production sequence will be F-G-H-K.

7. Compute the *takt* time for a system where the total time per shift is 480 minutes, there is one shift, and workers are given two 15-minute breaks and 45 minutes for lunch. Daily demand is 300 units.

8. What cycle time would match capacity and demand if demand is 120 units a day, there are two shifts of 480 minutes each, and workers are given three half-hour breaks during each shift, one of which is for lunch or dinner?

9. Compute the *takt* time for a service system that intended to perform a standardized service. The system will have a total work time of 440 minutes per day, two 10-minute breaks, and an hour for lunch. The service system must process 90 jobs a day.

CASE  LEVEL OPERATIONS

Level Operations is a small company located in eastern Pennsylvania. It produces a variety of security devices and safes. The safes come in several different designs. Recently, a number of new customers have placed orders, and the production facility has been enlarged to accommodate increased demand for safes. Production manager Stephanie Coles is currently working on a production plan for the safes. She needs a plan for each day of the week. She has obtained the following information from the marketing department on projected demand for the next five weeks.

The department operates five days a week. One complexity is that partially completed safes are not permitted; each cycle must turn out finished units.

After discussions with engineering, Stephanie determined that the best production sequence for each cycle is S7-S8-S9-S1-S2.

Question

What might Stephanie determine as the best production quantity per cycle for each day of the week?

Model	S1	S2	S7	S8	S9
Weekly Quantity	120	102	48	90	25

OPERATIONS TOUR   BOEING

The Boeing Company, headquartered in Chicago, Illinois, is one of the two major producers of aircraft in the global market. The other major producer is European Airbus.

Boeing produces three models in Everett, Washington: 747s, 767s, and 777s. The planes are all produced in the same building. At any one time, there may be as many as six planes in various stages of production. Obviously the building has to be fairly large to accommodate such a huge undertaking. In fact, the building is so large that it covers over 98 acres and it is four stories high, making it the largest building by volume in the world. It is so large that all of Disneyland would fit inside, and still leave about 15 acres for indoor parking! The windowless building has six huge doors along one side, each about 100 yards wide and 40 yards high (the size of a football field)—large enough to allow a completed airplane to pass through.

Boeing sells airplanes to airlines and countries around the globe. There isn't a set price for the planes; the actual price depends on what features the customer wants. Once the details have been settled and an order submitted, the customer requirements are sent to the design department.

Design

Designers formerly had to construct a mock-up to determine the exact dimensions of the plane and to identify any assembly problems that might occur. That required time, materials, labor, and space. Now they use computers (CAD) to design airplanes, avoiding the cost of the mockups and shortening the development time.

The Production Process

Once designs have been completed and approved by the customer, production of the plane is scheduled, and parts and materials are ordered. Parts come to the plant by rail, airplane, and truck, and are delivered to the major assembly area of the plane they will be used for. The parts are scheduled so they arrive at the plant just prior to when they will be used in assembly, and immediately moved to storage areas close to where they will be used. Time-phasing shipments to arrive as parts are needed helps to keep inventory investment low and avoids having to devote space to store parts that won't be used immediately. There is a tradeoff, though, because if any parts are missing or damaged and have to be reordered, that could cause production delays. When missing or defective parts are discovered, they are assigned priorities according to how critical the part is in terms of disruption of the flow of work. The parts with the highest priorities are assigned to expediters who determine the best way to replace the part. The expediters keep track of the progress of the parts and deliver them to the appropriate location as soon as they arrive. In the meantime, a portion of the work remains unfinished, awaiting the replacement parts, and workers complete other portions of the assembly. If the supplier is unable to replace the part in a time frame that will not seriously delay assembly, as a last resort, Boeing has a machine shop that can make the necessary part.

The partially assembled portions of the plane, and in later stages, the plane itself, move from station to station as the work progresses, staying about five days at each station. Giant overhead cranes are used to move large sections from one station to the next, although once the wheel assemblies have been installed, the plane is towed to the remaining stations.

Finished planes are painted in one of two separate buildings. Painting usually adds 400 to 600 pounds to the weight of a plane. The painting process involves giving the airplane a negative charge and the paint a positive charge so that the paint will be attracted to the airplane.

Testing and Quality Control

Boeing has extensive quality control measures in place throughout the entire design and production process. Not only are there quality inspectors, individual employees inspect their own work and the work previously done by others on the plane. Buyers inspectors also check on the quality of the work.

There are 60 test pilots who fly the planes. Formerly planes were tested to evaluate their flight worthiness in a wind tunnel, which required expensive testing and added considerably to product development time. Now new designs are tested using a computerized wind tunnel before production even begins, greatly reducing both time and cost. And in case you're wondering, the wings are fairly flexible; a typical wing can flap by as much as 22 feet before it will fracture.

Re-engineering

Boeing is re-engineering its business systems. A top priority is to upgrade its computer systems. This will provide better links to suppliers, provide more up-to-date information for materials management, and enable company representatives who are at customer sites to create a customized aircraft design on their laptop computer.

Another aspect of the re-engineering involves a shift to lean production. Key goals are to reduce production time and reduce inventory.

Boeing wants to reduce the time that a plane spends at each work station from 5 days to 3 days, a reduction of 40 percent. Not only will that mean that customers can get their planes much sooner, it will also reduce labor costs and inventory costs, and improve cash flow. One part of this will be accomplished by moving toward late-stage customization, or delayed differentiation. That would mean standardizing the assembly of planes as long as possible before adding custom features. This, and other time-saving steps, will speed up production considerably, giving it a major competitive advantage. It also wants to reduce the tremendous amount of inventory it carries (a 747 jumbo jet has about 6 million parts, including 3 million rivets). One part of the plan is to have suppliers do more predelivery work by assembling the parts into kits that are delivered directly to the staging area where they will be installed on the aircraft instead of delivering separate parts to inventory. That would cut down on inventory carrying costs and save time.

Boeing is also hoping to reduce the number of suppliers it has, and to establish better links and cooperation from suppliers. Currently Boeing has about 3,500 suppliers. Compare that with GM's roughly 2,500 suppliers, and you get an idea of how large this number is.

Chapter Fourteen JIT and Lean Operations

643

Chalice, Robert. *Improving Healthcare Using Toyota Lean Production Methods: 46 Steps for Improvement,* 2nd ed. Milwaukee: ASQ Quality Press, 2007.

El-Haik, Basem, and David M. Roy. *Service Design for Six Sigma: A Roadmap for Excellence.* New York: Wiley-Interscience, 2005.

Hariharan, Arun. "CEO's Guide to Six Sigma Success." *ASQ Six Sigma Forum Magazine,* May 2006, pp. 16–25.

Hopp, Wallace J., and Mark Spearman. *Factory Physics: Foundations of Manufacturing Management,* 3rd ed. New York: Irwin/McGraw-Hill, 2007.

Jacobs, F. Robert, William L. Berry, D. Clay Whybark, and Thomas E. Vollmann. *Manufacturing Planning and Control Systems for Supply Chain Management,* 6th ed. New York: Irwin/McGraw-Hill, 2011.

Liker, Jeffrey. *The Toyota Way: 14 Management Principles from the World's Greatest Manufacturer.* New York: McGraw-Hill, 2004.

Liker, Jeffery K., and Gary Convis. *The Toyota Way to Lean Leadership: Achieving and Sustaining Excellence through Leadership Development.* New York: McGraw-Hill, 2011.

Mann, David. *Creating a Lean Culture: Tools to Sustain Lean Conversions.* New York: Productivity Press, 2005.

Monden, Yasuhiro. "What Makes the Toyota Production System Really Tick?" *Industrial Engineering* 13, no. 1 (January 1981), pp. 38–46.

Rich, Nick, Nicola Bateman, Ann Esain, Lynn Massey, and Donna Samuel. *Lean Evolution: Lessons from the Workplace.* New York: Cambridge University Press, 2006.

Rother, Mike, and John Shook. *Learning to See.* Cambridge, MA: The Lean Institute, 2009.

Shingo, Shigeo. *Non-Stock Production: The Shingo System for Continuous Improvement.* New York: Productivity Press, 2006.

Spear, Steven, and H. Kent Bowen. "Decoding the DNA of the Toyota Production System." *Harvard Business Review,* 77, no. 5, (Sept. – Oct, 1999).

Swank, Cynthia Karen. "The Lean Service Machine." *Harvard Business Review,* October 2003, pp. 123–129.

Taghizadegan, Salman. *Essentials of Lean Six Sigma.* Burlington, MA: Butterworth-Heinemann, 2006.

Womack, James P., and Daniel T. Jones. *Lean Thinking: Banish Waste and Create Wealth in Your Corporation.* New York: Free Press, 2003.

Womack, James P., Daniel T. Jones, and Daniel Roos. *The Machine that Changed the World.* New York: Simon & Schuster, 1991, 2007.

SELECTED BIBLIOGRAPHY AND FURTHER READINGS

15 Supply Chain Management

LEARNING OBJECTIVES

After completing this chapter, you should be able to:

LO15.1   Explain the terms *supply chain* and *logistics*.

LO15.2   Name the key aspects of supply chain management.

LO15.3   List, and briefly explain, current trends in supply chain management.

LO15.4   Outline the benefits and risks related to outsourcing.

LO15.5   Explain what the main supply chain risks are and what businesses can do to minimize those risks.

LO15.6   Describe some of the complexities related to global supply chains.

LO15.7   Briefly describe ethical issues in supply chains and the key steps companies can take to avoid ethical problems.

LO15.8   Describe the three concerns of small businesses related to the supply chain and suggest ways to manage those concerns.

LO15.9   List several strategic, tactical, and operational responsibilities related to managing the supply chain.

LO15.10   Discuss procurement in terms of the purchasing interfaces, the purchasing cycle, ethics, and centralized versus decentralized decision making.

LO15.11   Briefly describe the key aspects of supplier management.

LO15.12   Discuss the logistics aspects of supply chain management, including RFID technology.

LO15.13   Discuss the issues involved in managing returns.

LO15.14   Describe some of the challenges in creating an effective supply chain and some of the trade-offs involved.

CHAPTER OUTLINE

15.1   Introduction *654*

15.2   Trends in Supply Chain Management *655*

Risk Management and Resiliency *657*

Shortening the Supply Chain *659*

15.3   Global Supply Chains *659*

15.4   ERP and Supply Chain Management *659*

15.5   Ethics and the Supply Chain *660*

15.6   Small Business *660*

15.7   Management Responsibilities *661*

Strategic Responsibilities *662*

Key Tactical and Operational Responsibilities *662*

15.8   Procurement *662*

© Mick Tsikas/Reuters

Purchasing Interfaces *663*
The Purchasing Cycle *664*
Centralized versus
Decentralized Purchasing *665*
Ethics in Purchasing *665*

15.9 E-Business *666*

15.10 Supplier Management *669*
Choosing Suppliers *669*
Supplier Audits *669*
Supplier Certification *670*

Supplier Relationship
Management *670*
Supplier Partnerships *670*
Strategic Partnering *671*

15.11 Inventory Management *672*

15.12 Order Fulfillment *673*

15.13 Logistics *674*
Movement within a Facility *674*
Operations Tour: Wegmans'
Shipping System *675*

Incoming and Outgoing
Shipments *676*
Tracking Goods: RFID *676*
Evaluating Shipping
Alternatives *677*
3-PL *679*

**15.14 Creating an Effective Supply
Chain** *680*
Managing Returns *681*
Challenges *683*

15.15 STRATEGY *684*

The Wegmans supermarket chain (see the Wegmans Operations Tour in Chapter 1) is often mentioned as being one of the best-run supermarket chains in the United States. It's now being mentioned for its leadership in supply chain management in the grocery industry. When a Wegmans spokesperson was asked how many of its people work in its supply chain, the spokesperson essentially said all of them.

The fact of the matter is that most if not all of the people who work in any business organization are somehow involved with the supply chain. And no matter where your career takes you, in every job you do, you'll be involved in one (or more) supply chain(s).

In this chapter you will learn about recent trends in supply chain management, key supply chain processes and management responsibilities, procurement, logistics, managing returns, managing risks, and creating an effective supply chain. You can get an indication of the importance of supply chains from this statistic: According to one estimate, the value of inventories in supply chains of U.S. companies is over a trillion dollars.[1]

[1]"What in the World is the Global Supply Chain?" Video, Council of Supply Chain Management Professionals, 2005.

15.1 INTRODUCTION

LO15.1 Explain the terms *supply chain* and *logistics*.

Supply chain A sequence of organizations—their facilities, functions, and activities—that are involved in producing and delivering a product or service

Supply chain management The strategic coordination of the supply chain for the purpose of *integrating* supply and demand management.

Logistics The movement of goods, services, cash, and information in a supply chain.

A **supply chain** is the sequence of organizations—their facilities, functions, and activities—that are involved in producing and delivering a product or service. The sequence begins with basic suppliers of raw materials and extends all the way to the final customer. Facilities include warehouses, factories, processing centers, distribution centers, retail outlets, and offices. Functions and activities include forecasting, purchasing, inventory management, information management, quality assurance, scheduling, production, distribution, delivery, and customer service.

Supply chain management is the strategic coordination of business functions within a business organization and throughout its supply chain for the purpose of *integrating* supply and demand management. Supply chain managers are people at various levels of the organization who are responsible for managing supply and demand both within and across business organizations. They are involved with planning and coordinating activities that include sourcing and procurement of materials and services, transformation activities, and logistics.

Logistics is the part of a supply chain involved with the forward and reverse flow of goods, services, cash, and information. Logistics management includes management of inbound and outbound transportation, material handling, warehousing, inventory, order fulfillment and distribution, third-party logistics, and reverse logistics (the return of goods from customers).

Every business organization is part of at least one supply chain, and many are part of multiple supply chains. Often the number and type of organizations in a supply chain are determined by whether the supply chain is manufacturing or service oriented. Figure 15.1 illustrates several perspectives of supply chains. Figure 15.2 shows a more detailed version of the farm-to-market supply chain that was shown in Chapter 1, with key suppliers at each stage included.

Supply chains are sometimes referred to as *value chains,* a term that reflects the concept that value is added as goods and services progress through the chain. Supply or value chains typically comprise separate business organizations, rather than just a single organization. Moreover, the supply or value chain has two components for each organization—a supply component and a demand component. The supply component starts at the beginning of the chain and ends with the internal operations of the organization. The demand component of the chain starts at the point where the organization's output is delivered to its immediate customer and ends with the final customer in the chain. The *demand chain* is the sales and distribution portion of the value chain. The length of each component depends on where a particular organization is in the chain; the closer the organization is to the final customer, the shorter its demand component and the longer its supply component.

Supply chains are the lifeblood of any business organization. They connect suppliers, producers, and final customers in a network that is essential to the creation and delivery of goods and services. Managing the supply chain is the process of planning, implementing, and controlling supply chain operations. The basic components are strategy, procurement, supply management, demand management, and logistics. The goal of supply chain management is to match supply to demand as effectively and efficiently as possible. Key aspects relate to:

LO15.2 Name the key aspects of supply chain management.

1. Determining the appropriate level of outsourcing
2. Managing procurement
3. Managing suppliers
4. Managing customer relationships
5. Being able to quickly identify problems and respond to them

An important aspect of supply chain management is *flow management.* The three types of flow that need to be managed are product and service flow, information flow, and financial flow. Product and service flow involves the movement of goods or services from suppliers to customers as well as handling customer service needs and product returns. Information flow involves sharing forecast and sales data, transmitting orders, tracking shipments, and updating order status. Financial flow involves credit terms, payments, and consignment and

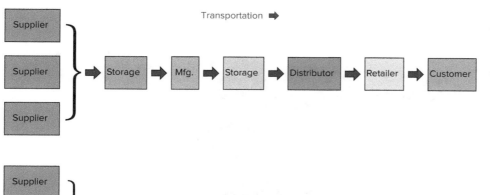

FIGURE 15.1
Typical supply chains

a. A typical manufacturing supply chain.

b. A typical service supply chain.

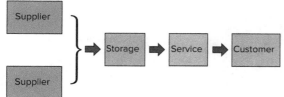

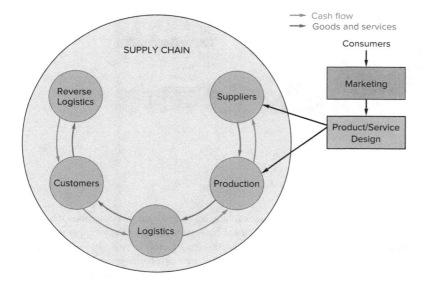

c. Goods and services flow clockwise in this diagram, and cash flows counterclockwise. Information flows in both directions.

d. A supply chain (network) is analogous to a tree with branches that have side branches.

title ownership arrangements. Technological advances have greatly enhanced the ability to effectively manage these flows. A dramatic decrease in the cost of transmitting and receiving information and the increased ease and speed of communication have facilitated the ability to coordinate supply chain activities and make timely decisions. In effect, a supply chain is a complex supply network.

15.2 TRENDS IN SUPPLY CHAIN MANAGEMENT

Although different industries and different businesses vary widely in terms of where they are in the evolution of their supply chain management, many businesses emphasize the following:

- Measuring supply chain ROI
- "Greening" the supply chain
- Reevaluating outsourcing

LO15.3 List, and briefly explain, current trends in supply change management.

FIGURE 15.2
A farm-to-market supply chain

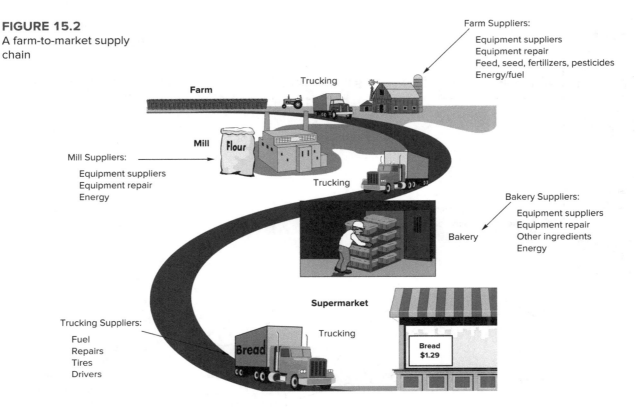

- Integrating IT
- Managing risks
- Adopting lean principles
- Being agile

Measuring supply chain ROI enables managers to incorporate economics into outsourcing and other decisions, giving them a rational basis for managing their supply chains.

Greening the supply chain is generating interest for a variety of reasons, including corporate responsibility, regulations, and public pressure. This may involve redesigning products and services; reducing packaging; near-sourcing to reduce pollution from transportation (one estimate is that marine shipping alone causes about 60,000 premature deaths annually worldwide due to lung cancer and cardiopulmonary disease);[2] choosing "green" suppliers; managing returns; and implementing end-of-life programs, particularly for appliances and electronic equipment.

Reevaluating outsourcing. Companies are taking a second look at outsourcing, especially global suppliers. Business organizations outsource for a variety of reasons. Often decisions to outsource have been based on lower prices resulting from lower labor costs. Other potential benefits include: the ability to focus on core strengths, converting fixed costs to variable costs, freeing up capital to devote to other needs, shifting some risks to suppliers, taking advantage of supplier expertise, and ease of expansion outside the home country. Some potential difficulties, depending on the nature of what is outsourced and the length of the supply chain, include inflexibility due to longer lead times for delivery of goods with distant suppliers, increased transportation costs, language and cultural differences, loss of jobs, loss of control, lower productivity, loss of ability to do the work internally and loss of business knowledge,

> **LO15.4** Outline the benefits and risks related to outsourcing.

[2]James J. Corbett, James J. Winebrake, Erin H. Green, Prasad Kasibhatla, Veronika Eyring, and Axel Lauer, "Mortality from Ship Emissions: A Global Assessment," *Environmental Science & Technology* 41, no. 24 (December 15, 2007), pp. 8512–8518.

© Danish Siddiqui/Reuters`

Supply chain disruptions can reduce revenue and threaten production and distribution. A risk from accidents is shown here with containers falling from the deck of a damaged cargo ship off the Mumbai coast after a collision between two cargo ships

knowledge transfer, concerns about intellectual property security, and increased effort needed to manage the supply chain.

One example of where this is getting increased attention is the clothing industry. Rising wages in China and other countries where suppliers make most of the clothing for retail sales provide less of a cost benefit than previously, and long lead times eliminate agility in an industry where the market rewards it. Add in instances of late deliveries and substandard quality, and events like factory fires and building collapses, and the decision to back-shore becomes easier to consider.

Integrating IT produces real-time data that can enhance strategic planning and help businesses to control costs, measure quality and productivity, respond quickly to problems, and improve supply chain operations. This is why ERP systems are so important for supply chain management.

Managing risks. For some businesses, the supply chain is a major source of risk, so it is essential to adopt procedures for managing risks. According to a Deloitte survey,[3] 45 percent of supply chain leaders lack confidence in their risk management. The following section discusses sources of risk and actions businesses can take to reduce risks.

Many businesses are turning to **lean principles** to improve the performance of their supply chains. In too many instances, traditional supply chains are a collection of loosely connected steps, and business processes are not linked to suppliers' or customers' needs. Applying lean principles to supply chains can overcome this weakness by eliminating non-value-added processes; improving product flow by using pull systems rather than push systems; using fewer suppliers and supplier certification programs, which can nearly eliminate the need for inspection of incoming goods; and adopting the lean attitude of never ceasing to improve the system.

Being agile. Being agile means that a supply chain is flexible enough to be able to respond fairly quickly to unpredictable changes or circumstances, such as supplier production or quality issues, weather disruptions, changing demand (volume of demand or customer preferences), transporting issues, and political issues.

As a result of these current and possible future trends, organizations are likely to give serious thought to reconfiguring their supply chains to reduce risks, improve flow, increase profits, and generally increase customer satisfaction.

Risk Management and Resiliency

Risk management involves identifying risks, assessing their likelihood of occurring and their potential impact, and then developing strategies for addressing those risks. Strategies can pertain to risk avoidance, risk reduction, and risk sharing with supply chain partners. Risk

> **LO15.5** Explain what the main supply chain risks are and what businesses can do to minimize those risks.

[3]Deloitte Survey: "Executives Face Growing Threats to Their Supply Chains." New York: Press release, February 7, 2013.

Resiliency   The ability of a business to recover from an event that negatively impacts the supply chain.

avoidance may mean not dealing with suppliers in a certain area, risk reduction can mean replacing unreliable suppliers, and risk sharing can mean contractual arrangements with supply chain partners that spread the risk. **Resiliency** is the ability of a business to recover from an event that negatively impacts the supply chain. Recovery is a function of the severity of the impact and the plans that are in place to cope with the event. Businesses can reduce, but not eliminate, the need for resiliency by managing risks.

The first step in risk management is to identify potential risks. Supply chain risks fall into several categories. One is disruptions, which can come from natural disasters such as fires, flooding, hurricanes and the like that either disrupt shipping or that affect suppliers directly (by damaging production or storage facilities) or indirectly (by impacting access to facilities or impacting employees in other ways). Other disruptions can occur as a result of supplier issues such as labor strife, production problems, and issues with their suppliers, including bankruptcy. Another source of risk is quality issues, which can disrupt supplies and may lead to product recalls, liability claims, and negative publicity. Still another risk is the potential for suppliers divulging sensitive information to competitors that weakens a competitive advantage.

Key elements of successful risk management include:

Know your suppliers. Mapping the supply chain can be helpful in grasping the scope of the supply chain, identifying suppliers, and seeing if there are any supplier concentrations in first or second tiers of suppliers, which can greatly amplify risk. This might also lead to the desirability of simplifying (shortening) the supply chain.

Supply chain visibility   A major trading partner can connect to its supply chain to access data in real time.

Event-response capability   The ability to detect and respond to unplanned events.

Provide supply chain visibility. **Supply chain visibility** means that a major trading partner can connect to any part of its supply chain to access data in real time on inventory levels, shipment status, and similar key information. This requires data sharing.

Develop event-response capability. **Event-response capability** is the ability to detect and respond to unplanned events such as delayed shipment or a warehouse running low on a certain item. An event management system should have four capabilities: monitoring the system; notifying when certain planned or unplanned events occur; simulating potential solutions when an unplanned event occurs; and measuring the long-term performance of suppliers, transporters, and other supply chain partners.

Event response can mean identifying alternate sources of supply. It should also be somewhat general to be able to deal with the possibility of unknown disruptions, which are events

READING   **AT 3M, A LONG ROAD BECAME A SHORTER ROAD**

One of 3M's many products is a plastic hook. Production occurred at several widely scattered locations in the Midwest. The process started in a Springfield, Missouri, plant that made adhesives, which were then shipped about 550 miles to a plant in Hartford City, Indiana, where the adhesive was applied to foam. Next, the foam was shipped another 600 miles to a plant near Minneapolis, Minnesota, where the foam was cut into individual pieces and imprinted with the 3M logo. Finally the foam pieces were shipped to a plant in central Wisconsin, another 200 miles or so, where they were bundled with the hooks and packages for sale. This entire process took over a hundred days and over 1,000 miles to complete.

3M eventually consolidated operations in a single plant in Hutchinson, Minnesota, where a number of other 3M products are made. That eliminated all the travel and reduced the process time by two-thirds.

Situations like this can arise when businesses acquire other companies and then elect to maintain their processing operations in their current locations.

Questions

1. Businesses sometimes acquire widely dispersed processing facilities through a number of mergers or acquisitions. What trade-offs might they face in considering consolidation?
2. This reading offers one possible reason for the existence of a long supply process. Can you think of some other possible reasons for long supply processes?

Based on: "3M Begins Untangling Their Hairballs." *The Wall Street Journal*, May 17, 2012.

that cannot generally be predicted, but which can, if they do occur, have an impact on the supply chain. Because these are unknowns, the severity and length of a disruption are impossible to predict. Consequently, it is important to recognize that unforeseen events could occur, and to have a plan for addressing them should they occur.

Simplify (shorten) the supply chain if need be. The following section discusses this important topic.

Shortening the Supply Chain

As businesses search for ways to reduce transportation time and cost, some are placing more emphasis on using nearby suppliers, storage facilities, and processing centers. Others are finding savings by consolidating their supply chains, as described in the preceding reading.

15.3 GLOBAL SUPPLY CHAINS

> **LO15.6** Describe some of the complexities related to global supply chains.

As businesses increasingly make use of outsourcing and pursue opportunities beyond their domestic markets, their supply chains are becoming increasingly global. For example, product design often uses inputs from around the world, and products are sold globally.

As businesses recognize the strategic importance of effective supply chain management, they are also discovering that global supply chains have additional complexities that were either negligible or nonexistent in domestic operations. These complexities include language and cultural differences, currency fluctuations, armed conflicts, increased transportation costs and lead times, and the increased need for trust and cooperation among supply chain partners. Furthermore, managers must be able to identify and analyze factors that differ from country to country, which can affect the success of the supply chain, including local capabilities; financial, transportation, and communication infrastructures; governmental, environmental, and regulatory issues; and political issues.

These and other factors have made risk management an important aspect of global supply chain management. To compensate for this, some firms have increased the amount of inventory at various points in their supply chains, thereby losing some of the benefits of global sourcing.

Risks can relate to supply (e.g., supplier failure, quality issues, sustainability issues, transportation issues, pirates, terrorism), costs (e.g., increasing commodity costs), and demand (e.g., decreasing demand, demand volatility, and transportation issues). Still other risks can involve intellectual rights issues, contract compliance issues, competitive pressure, forecasting errors, and inventory management.

A positive factor of globalization has been the set of technological advances in communications: the ability to link operations around the world with real-time information exchange. Consequently, information technology has a key role in integrating operations across global supply chains.

15.4 ERP AND SUPPLY CHAIN MANAGEMENT

Supply chain management that integrates ERP is a formal approach to effectively plan and manage all the resources of a business enterprise. Implementation of ERP involves establishing operating systems and operating performance measurements to enable them to manage business operations and meet business and financial objectives. ERP encompasses supply chain management activities such as planning for demand and managing supply, inventory replenishment, production, warehousing, and transportation. ERP software also plays a key role in centralizing transaction data.

ERP software provides the ability to coordinate, monitor, and manage a supply chain. It is an integrated system that provides for systemwide visibility of key activities and events in areas such as supplier relationships, performance management, sales and order fulfillment, and customer relationships.

Supplier Relationship Management ERP integrates purchasing, receiving, information about vendor ratings and performance, lead times, quality, electronic funds disbursements, simplifying processes, and enabling analysis of those processes.

Performance Management This aspect of ERP pulls together information on costs and profits, productivity, quality performance, and customer satisfaction.

Sales and Order Fulfillment ERP includes the ability to provide inventory and quality management, track returns, and schedule and monitor production, packaging, and distribution. Reports can provide information on order and inventory status, delivery dates, and logistics performance.

Customer Relationship Management An ERP system not only centralizes basic contact information, details on contracts, payment terms, credit history, and shipping preferences, it also provides information on purchasing patterns, service, and returns.

15.5 ETHICS AND THE SUPPLY CHAIN

LO15.7 Briefly describe ethical issues in supply chains and the key steps companies can take to avoid ethical problems.

There are many examples of unethical behavior involving supply chains. They include bribing government or company officials to secure permits or favorable status; "exporting smoke-stacks" to developing countries; claiming a "green" supply chain when in reality the level of "green" is only minimal; ignoring health, safety, and environmental standards; violating basic rights of workers (e.g., paying substandard wages; using sweatshops, forced labor, or child labor); mislabeling country of origin; and selling goods abroad that are banned at home.

Every company should develop an ethical supply chain code to guide behavior. A code should cover behaviors that involve customers, suppliers, suppliers' behaviors, contract negotiation, recruiting, and the environmental issues.

A major risk of unethical behavior is that when such behavior is exposed in the media, consumers tend to blame the major company or brand in the supply chain associated with the ethical infractions that were actually committed by legally independent companies in the supply chain. The problem is particularly difficult to manage when supply chains are global, as they often are in manufacturing operations. Unfortunately, many companies lack the ability to quickly contact most or all of the companies in their supply chain, and communicate with suppliers on critical issues of ethics and compliance. Although monitoring of supply chain activities is essential, it is only one aspect of maintaining an ethical supply chain. With global manufacturing and distribution, supply chain scrutiny should include all supply chain activities from purchasing, manufacturing, assembly, and transportation, to service and repair operations, and eventually to proper disposal of products at the end of their useful life.

Key steps companies can take to reduce the risk of damages due to unethical supplier behavior are to choose those that have a reputation for good ethical behavior; incorporate compliance with labor standards in supplier contracts; develop direct, long-term relationships with ethical suppliers; and address quickly any problems that occur.

15.6 SMALL BUSINESSES

LO15.8 Describe the three concerns of small businesses related to the supply chain and suggest ways to manage those concerns.

Small businesses do not always give adequate attention to their supply chains. However, there are many benefits to be had for small businesses by actively managing their supply chains, including increased efficiencies, reduced costs, reduced risks, and increased profits. And size can actually be a competitive advantage for small businesses because they often are more agile than larger companies, enabling them to make decisions and changes more quickly when the need arises.

Three aspects of supply chain management that are often of concern to small businesses are:

- Inventory management
- Reducing risks
- International trade

Inventories can be an issue for small businesses. They may carry extra inventory as a way to avoid shortages due to supply chain interruptions. However, that can tie up capital and take up space. An alternative is to have backup suppliers for critical items. Similarly, having backups for delivery from suppliers and deliveries to customers can help overcome disruptions. Because it can take a fair amount of time to set up accounts, it is prudent to have these systems in place before they are needed to maintain operations.

Another area that often needs attention is risk management. The key to reducing risks is managing suppliers. Important steps are:

- Use only reliable suppliers
- Determine which suppliers are critical; get to know them, and any challenges they have
- Measure supplier performance (e.g., quality, reliability, flexibility)
- Recognize warning signs of supplier issues (e.g., late deliveries, incomplete orders, quality problems)
- Have plans in place to manage supply chain problems

Exporting can offer opportunities for small business producers to greatly expand their businesses, although they typically lack the knowledge to do so, which can cause unforeseen problems. For instance, exporting nonconforming goods or packaging can result in shipments being held up at a port of entry, which can be costly and time-consuming, and can lead to dissatisfied customers.

Importing can have benefits for small businesses. The Small Business Administration has some tips for using foreign suppliers:[4]

- Work with someone who has expertise to help oversee foreign suppliers, preferably someone who spends a good deal of time in that country. Also, a licensed customs broker can help with laws and regulations, necessary documents, and working with importers and exporters.
- Describe your buying patterns and schedules to set expectations for demand and timing.
- Don't rely on a single supplier; a backup supplier can reduce risk and provide bargaining leverage.
- Building goodwill can have benefits in negotiations and resolving problems when they arise.
- Consider using domestic suppliers if the risks or other issues with foreign suppliers are formidable. Advantages can involve lower shipping times and costs, closer interactions with suppliers, and increased agility.

15.7 MANAGEMENT RESPONSIBILITIES

Generally speaking, corporate management responsibilities have legal, economic, and ethical aspects. Legal responsibilities include being knowledgeable about laws and regulations of the countries where supply chains exist, obeying the laws, and operating to conform to regulations. Economic responsibilities include supplying products and services to meet demand as

---

[4]U.S. Small Business Administration, "5 Tips for Managing an Efficient Global Supply Chain," *Small Business Operations,* March 12, 2013.

SOME SUPPLY CHAIN STRATEGIES

There are many different strategies a business organization can choose from. Here is a sample of some of those strategies:

Responsive/agile. A flexible supply chain that has the ability to quickly respond to changes in product requirements or volume of demand as well as adapt to supply chain disruptions.

Lean supply chain. Focused on eliminating non-value-added activities to create an efficient, low-cost supply chain.

Near-sourcing. Using nearby suppliers shortens the supply chain, reducing transportation time and cost, reducing supply chain inventory, reducing the risk of disruptions, and increasing responsiveness.

---

efficiently as possible. Ethical responsibilities include conducting business in ways that are consistent with the moral standards of society.

More specific areas of responsibility relate to organizational strategy, tactics, and operations.

Strategic Responsibilities

LO15.9 List several strategic, tactical, and operational responsibilities related to managing the supply chain.

Top management has certain strategic responsibilities that have a major impact on the success not only of supply chain management but also of the business itself. These strategies include:

Supply chain strategy alignment: Aligning supply and distribution strategies with organizational strategy and deciding on the degree to which outsourcing will be employed.

Network configuration: Determining the number and location of suppliers, warehouses, production/operations facilities, and distribution centers.

Information technology: Integrating systems and processes throughout the supply chain to share information, including forecasts, inventory status, tracking of shipments, and events.

Products and services: Making decisions on new product and services selection and design.

Capacity planning: Assessing long-term capacity needs, including when and how much will be needed and the degree of flexibility to incorporate.

Strategic partnerships: Partnership choices, level of partnering, and degree of formality.

Distribution strategy: Deciding whether to use centralized or decentralized distribution, and deciding whether to use the organization's own facilities and equipment for distribution or to use third-party logistics providers.

Uncertainty and risk reduction: Identifying potential sources of risk and deciding the amount of risk that is acceptable.

Key Tactical and Operational Responsibilities

The key tactical and operational responsibilities are outlined in Table 15.1.

15.8 PROCUREMENT

LO15.10 Discuss procurement in terms of the purchasing interfaces, the purchasing cycle, ethics, and centralized versus decentralized decision making.

The purchasing department of an organization is responsible for obtaining the materials, parts, supplies, and services needed to produce a product or provide a service. You can get some idea of the importance of purchasing when you consider that, in manufacturing, upwards of 60 percent of the cost of finished goods comes from purchased parts and materials. Furthermore, the percentages for purchased inventories are even higher for retail and wholesale companies, sometimes exceeding 90 percent. Nonetheless, the importance of purchasing is more than just the cost of goods purchased; other important factors include the *quality* of goods and services and the *timing* of deliveries of goods or services, both of which can have a significant impact on operations.

Tactical Responsibilities
  Forecasting: Prepare and evaluate forecasts.
  Sourcing: Choose suppliers and some make-or-buy decisions.
  Operations planning: Coordinate the external supply chain and internal operations.
  Managing inventory: Decide where in the supply chain to store the various types of inventory (raw
    materials, semifinished goods, finished goods).
  Transportation planning: Match capacity with demand.
  Collaborating: Work with supply chain partners to coordinate plans.

Operational Responsibilities
  Scheduling: Short-term scheduling of operations and distribution.
  Receiving: Management of inbound deliveries from suppliers.
  Transforming: Conversion of inputs into outputs.
  Order fulfilling: Linking production resources and/or inventory to specific customer orders.
  Managing inventory: Maintenance and replenishment activities.
  Shipping: Management of outbound deliveries to distribution centers and/or customers.
  Information sharing: Exchange of information with supply chain partners.
  Controlling: Control of quality, inventory, and other key variables and implementing corrective action,
    including variation reduction, when necessary.

TABLE 15.1
Key tactical and
operational responsibilities

Among the duties of purchasing are identifying sources of supply, negotiating contracts, maintaining a database of suppliers, obtaining goods and services that meet or exceed operations requirements in a timely and cost-efficient manner, and managing suppliers.

Purchasing Interfaces

Purchasing has interfaces with a number of other functional areas, as well as with outside suppliers. It is the connecting link between the organization and its suppliers. In this capacity, it exchanges information with suppliers and functional areas. The interactions between purchasing and these other areas are briefly summarized in the following paragraphs.

Operations constitute the main source of requests for purchased materials, and close cooperation between these units and the purchasing department is vital if quality, quantity, and delivery goals are to be met. Cancellations, changes in specifications, or changes in quantity or delivery times must be communicated immediately for purchasing to be effective.

The purchasing department may require the assistance of the *legal* department in contract negotiations, in drawing up bid specifications for nonroutine purchases, and in helping interpret legislation on pricing, product liability, and contracts with suppliers.

Accounting is responsible for handling payments to suppliers and must be notified promptly when goods are received in order to take advantage of possible discounts. In many firms, *data processing* is handled by the accounting department, which keeps inventory records, checks invoices, and monitors vendor performance.

Design and engineering usually prepare material specifications, which must be communicated to purchasing. Because of its contacts with suppliers, purchasing is often in a position to pass information about new products and materials improvements on to design personnel. Also, design and purchasing people may work closely to determine whether changes in specifications, design, or materials can reduce the cost of purchased items (see the following section on value analysis).

Receiving checks incoming shipments of purchased items to determine whether quality, quantity, and timing objectives have been met, and it moves the goods to temporary storage. Purchasing must be notified when shipments are late; accounting must be notified when shipments are received so that payments can be made; and both purchasing and accounting must be apprised of current information on continuing vendor evaluation.

Suppliers or vendors work closely with purchasing to learn what materials will be purchased and what kinds of specifications will be required in terms of quality, quantity, and deliveries. Purchasing must rate vendors on cost, reliability, and so on (see the later section on

664   **Chapter Fifteen**   Supply Chain Management

FIGURE 15.3
Purchasing interfaces

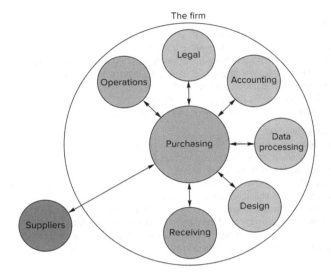

vendor analysis). Good supplier relations can be important on rush orders and changes, and vendors provide a good source of information on product and material improvements.

Figure 15.3 depicts the purchasing interfaces.

The Purchasing Cycle

Purchasing cycle Series of steps that begin with a request for purchase and end with notification of ship-ment received in satisfactory condition.

The **purchasing cycle** begins with a request from within the organization to purchase mate-rial, equipment, supplies, or other items from outside the organization, and the cycle ends when the purchasing department is notified that a shipment has been received in satisfactory condition. The main steps in the cycle are these:

1. **Purchasing receives the requisition.** The requisition includes (*a*) a description of the item or material desired, (*b*) the quantity and quality necessary, (*c*) desired delivery dates, and (*d*) who is requesting the purchase.

2. **Purchasing selects a supplier.** The purchasing department must identify suppliers who have the capability of supplying the desired goods. If no suppliers are currently listed in the files, new ones must be sought. Vendor ratings may be referred to in choosing among vendors, or perhaps rating information can be relayed to the vendor with the thought of upgrading future performance.

3. **Purchasing places the order with a vendor.** If the order involves a large expenditure, par-ticularly for a one-time purchase of equipment, for example, vendors will usually be asked to bid on the job, and operating and design personnel may be asked to assist in negotiations with a vendor. Large-volume, continuous-usage items may be covered by blanket purchase orders, which often involve annual negotiation of prices with deliveries subject to request throughout the year. Moderate-volume items may also have blanket purchase orders, or they may be handled on an individual basis. Small purchases may be handled directly between the operating unit requesting a purchased item and the supplier, although some control should be exercised over those purchases so they don't get out of hand.

4. **Monitoring orders.** Routine follow-up on orders, especially large orders or those with lengthy lead times, allows the purchasing department to project potential delays and relay that information to the operating units. Conversely, the purchasing department must communicate changes in quantities and delivery needs of the operating units to suppliers to allow them time to change their plans.

5. **Receiving orders.** Receiving must check incoming shipments for quality and quantity. It must notify purchasing, accounting, and the operating unit that requested the goods.

If the goods are not satisfactory, they may have to be returned to the supplier or subjected to further inspection.

Centralized versus Decentralized Purchasing

Purchasing can be centralized or decentralized. Centralized purchasing means that purchasing is handled by one special department. Decentralized purchasing means that individual departments or separate locations handle their own purchasing requirements.

Centralized purchasing may be able to obtain lower prices than decentralized units if the higher volume created by combining orders enables it to take advantage of quantity discounts offered on large orders. Centralized purchasing may also be able to obtain better service and closer attention from suppliers. In addition, centralized purchasing often enables companies to assign certain categories of items to specialists, who tend to be more efficient because they are able to concentrate their efforts on relatively few items instead of spreading themselves across many items.

Centralized purchasing
Purchasing is handled by one special department.

Decentralized purchasing has the advantage of awareness of differing "local" needs and being better able to respond to those needs. Decentralized purchasing usually can offer quicker response than centralized purchasing. Where locations are widely scattered, decentralized purchasing may be able to save on transportation costs by buying locally, which has the added attraction of creating goodwill in the community.

Decentralized purchasing
Individual departments or separate locations handle their own purchasing requirements.

Some organizations manage to take advantage of both centralization and decentralization by permitting individual units to handle certain items while centralizing purchases of other items. For example, small orders and rush orders may be handled locally or by departments, while centralized purchases would be used for high-volume, high-value items for which discounts are applicable or specialists can provide better service than local buyers or departments.

Ethics in Purchasing

Ethical behavior is important in all aspects of business. This is certainly true in purchasing, where the temptations for unethical behavior can be enormous. Buyers often hold great power, and salespeople are often eager to make a sale. Unless both parties act in an ethical manner, the potential for abuse is very real. Furthermore, with increased globalization, the

READING   IBM'S SUPPLY CHAIN SOCIAL RESPONSIBILITY

From its inception almost a century ago, IBM has been based on a set of fundamental values. IBM's values shape and define our company and permeate all of our relationships—between our company's people and our shareholders, our clients, the communities where our people live and work, and among our network of suppliers.

Within our supply chain relationships, we know that our company's sizable purchasing power is a unique resource that we must manage responsibly, and we do. IBM spends nearly $2 billion a year with diverse suppliers, for example, greater than any other technology company. Yet more than managing our spending, we have a responsibility to hold ourselves—and our suppliers—to high standards of behavior. This means complying with all applicable laws and regulations. But it goes beyond that. It entails a strong commitment to work with suppliers to encourage sound practices and develop sound global markets.

We have always maintained an open channel of communications with suppliers to set expectations. Today, in an increasingly interconnected world market, the expectations for all players across the entire supply chain go up. Therefore, we are both reaffirming our existing policies and instituting some new practices, which are spelled out in the following Supplier Conduct Principles. These principles establish for our suppliers the minimum standards we expect from them as a condition of doing business with IBM. IBM will have the right to take action with suppliers that fail to comply with these principles, including terminating our relationship with them.

666   **Chapter Fifteen**   Supply Chain Management

TABLE 15.2
Guidelines for ethical behavior in purchasing

> **PRINCIPLES**
> **Integrity in Your Decisions and Actions**
> **Value for Your Employer**
> **Loyalty to Your Profession**
>
> **STANDARDS**
> 1. **Perceived Impropriety.** Prevent the intent and appearance of unethical or compromising conduct in relationships, actions, and communications.
> 2. **Conflicts of Interest.** Ensure that any personal, business, or other activity does not conflict with the lawful interests of your employer.
> 3. **Issues of Influence.** Avoid behaviors or actions that may negatively influence, or appear to influence, supply management decisions.
> 4. **Responsibilities to Your Employer.** Uphold fiduciary and other responsibilities using reasonable care and granted authority to deliver value to your employer.
> 5. **Supplier and Customer Relationships.** Promote positive supplier and customer relationships.
> 6. **Sustainability and Social Responsibility.** Champion social responsibility and sustainability practices in supply management.
> 7. **Confidential and Proprietary Information.** Protect confidential and proprietary information.
> 8. **Reciprocity.** Avoid improper reciprocal agreements.
> 9. **Applicable Laws, Regulations, and Trade Agreements.** Know and obey the letter and spirit of laws, regulations, and trade agreements applicable to supply management.
> 10. **Professional Competence.** Develop skills, expand knowledge, and conduct business that demonstrates competence and promotes the supply management profession.

Reprinted with permission from the publisher. The Institute for Supply Management™, *Principles and Standards of Ethical Supply Management Conduct*. Adopted January 2012.

challenges are particularly great because a behavior regarded as customary in one country might be regarded as unethical in another country.

The National Association of Purchasing Management has established a set of guidelines for ethical behavior. (See Table 15.2.) As you read through the list, you gain insight into the scope of ethics issues in purchasing.

15.9 E-BUSINESS

E-business The use of electronic technology to facilitate business transactions.

The commercial blossoming of the Internet has led to an explosion of Internet-related activities, many of which have a direct impact on organizations' supply chains, even if those organizations aren't themselves users of the Internet. **E-business** refers to the use of electronic technology to facilitate business transactions. E-business, or e-commerce, involves the interaction of different business organizations as well as the interaction of individuals with business organizations. Applications include Internet buying and selling, e-mail, order and shipment tracking, and electronic data interchange. In addition, companies use e-business to promote their products or services, and to provide information about them. Delivery firms have seen the demand for their services increase dramatically due to e-business. Among them are giants UPS and FedEx.

Table 15.3 lists some of the numerous advantages of e-business.

There are two essential features of e-business: the website and order fulfillment. Companies may invest considerable time and effort in front-end design (the website), but the back end (order fulfillment) is at least as important. It involves order processing, billing, inventory management, warehousing, packing, shipping, and delivery.

Many of the problems that occur with Internet selling are supply related. The ability to order quickly creates an expectation in customers that the remainder of the process will proceed smoothly and quickly. But the same capability that enables quick ordering also enables demand fluctuations that can inject a certain amount of chaos into the system, almost guaranteeing that there won't be a smooth or quick delivery. Oftentimes the rate at which orders come in via the Internet greatly exceeds an organization's ability to fulfill them. Not too long

Companies and publishers have a global presence and the customer has global choices and easy access to information.

Companies can improve competitiveness and quality of service by allowing access to their services any place, any time. Companies also have the ability to monitor customers choices and requests electronically.

Companies can analyze the interest in various products based on the number of hits and requests for information.

Companies can collect detailed information about clients preferences, which enables mass customization and personalized products. An example is the purchase of PCs over the Web, where the buyer specifies the final configuration.

Supply chain response times are shortened. The biggest impact is on products that can be delivered directly on the Web, such as forms of publishing and software distribution.

The roles of the intermediary and sometimes the traditional retailer or service provider are reduced or eliminated entirely in a process called *disintermediation*. This process reduces costs and adds alternative purchasing options.

Substantial cost savings and substantial price reductions related to the reduction of transaction costs can be realized. Companies that provide purchasing and support through the Web can save significant personnel costs.

E-commerce allows the creation of virtual companies that distribute only through the Web, thus reducing costs. Amazon.com and other net vendors can afford to sell for a lower price because they do not need to maintain retail stores and, in many cases, warehouse space.

The playing field is leveled for small companies that lack significant resources to invest in infrastructure and marketing.

TABLE 15.3
Advantages of e-business

Source: Reprinted by permission from David Simchi-Levi, Philip Kaminsky, and Edith Simchi-Levi, *Designing and Managing the Supply Chain: Concepts, Strategies, and Case Studies* (New York: Irwin/McGraw-Hill, 2000), p. 235.

ago, Toys"R"Us had that experience during the busy Christmas season; it ended up offering thousands of disappointed customers a $100 coupon to make up for it.

In the early days of Internet selling, many organizations thought they could avoid bearing the costs of holding inventories by acting solely as intermediaries, having their suppliers ship directly to their customers. Although this approach worked for some companies, it failed for others, usually because suppliers ran out of certain items. This led some companies to rethink the strategy. Industry giants such as Amazon.com and Barnesandnoble.com built huge warehouses around the country so they could maintain greater control over their inventories. Still others are outsourcing fulfillment, turning over that portion of their business to third-party fulfillment operators such as former catalog fulfillment company Fingerhut, now a unit of Federated Department Stores.

Using third-party fulfillment means losing control over fulfillment. It might also result in fulfillers substituting their standards for the company they are serving, and using the fulfiller's shipping price structure. On the other hand, an e-commerce company may not have the resources or infrastructure to do the job itself. Another alternative might be to form a strategic partnership with a bricks-and-mortar company. This can be a quick way to jumpstart an e-commerce business. In any case, somewhere in the supply chain there has to be a bricks-and-mortar facility.

A growing portion of e-business involves business-to-business (B2B) commerce rather than business-to-consumer commerce. To facilitate business-to-business commerce, B2B marketplaces are created. Table 15.4 describes B2B marketplace enablers.

B2B exchanges can improve supply chain visibility to trading partners from a single point of access, facilitating the development of common standards and data formats for schedules,

Type	Description
Financial	Provide financial and other resources for Web-enhanced commerce.
Technology	Provide software, applications, and expertise necessary to create B2B marketplace.

TABLE 15.4
B2B marketplace enablers

Source: Adapted from *Forbes,* July 2000.

READING      E-PROCUREMENT AT IBM

"In 1999, IBM did what would seem to be a near impossible task. It began doing business with 12,000 suppliers over the Internet—sending purchase orders, receiving invoices and paying suppliers, all using the World Wide Web as its transaction-processing network."

Setting up 12,000 suppliers to do business on the Internet was relatively easy compared to the resistance of suppliers to link to IBM via EDI (electronic data interchange). Suppliers who didn't have large contracts with IBM balked at EDI because of the expense of special software and a VAN (value-added network) that were needed to do EDI. No such problem with using the Internet: Suppliers don't need special software or a costly VAN to do business with IBM.

The Internet's simplicity reduces costs for IBM and its suppliers. IBM estimated that it saved $500 million in 1999 by moving procurement to the Web, and believes that is only the tip of the iceberg. Much of the savings came from eliminating intermediaries. IBM uses the Web to manage multiple tiers of suppliers and as a tool to work with suppliers to improve quality and reduce costs.

But cost reduction was not the only reason IBM switched to Internet procurement. Web-based procurement is a key part of its supplier management strategy: IBM sees great value in using the Internet to collaborate with suppliers and tap into their expertise much more rapidly than previously. "The Internet will also allow IBM to collaborate with suppliers over scheduling issues. If the company wants to increase production of a certain product it will be able to check with component suppliers and determine if suppliers can support the increase. If there are schedule cutbacks, [it] will be able to notify suppliers almost instantaneously and excess inventory can be avoided."

And although supply chains are viewed as sequential, IBM doesn't necessarily want to manage them that way. Rather, it wants to use the Internet to manage multiple tiers of suppliers simultaneously. An example of this is how it deals with CMs (contract manufacturers). The company sends forecasts and purchase orders to the CMs for the printed circuit boards they supply. It also gives all the component manufacturers the requirements and they ship parts directly to the CM. The company estimates it saved in excess of $150 million in 1999. "The savings were the difference between contract manufacturers price for components used on the boards and IBM's price that it had negotiated with component suppliers."

Because the Internet is becoming crucial to IBM's supplier-management strategies, IBM is trying to make it easier for

suppliers to do business over the Web. The company has developed a Web-based portal to provide a single entry point to IBM. As is the case with most large companies, IBM has multiple interfaces with its suppliers, including engineering, quality, as well as purchasing, and typically suppliers have to connect to separate URLs (universal resource locators) in a company. IBM's portal provides a single point of entry for suppliers, making it easier for suppliers to do business with IBM and increasing the speed of the supply chain. Speed is vitally important in the electronics industry due to very short product life cycles. If products don't get to the market quickly, most of the profit opportunity is lost.

Still another benefit envisioned by IBM will be the ability to form strategic alliances with some of its suppliers. In the past, the fact that many suppliers used by IBM for its production processes were as far as 12,000 miles away made it difficult to build strategic alliances with them. IBM believes that using the Internet will strengthen relations and enable it to develop alliances.

"The Internet also will play an important role in IBM's general procurement . . . IBM was doing EDI with core production suppliers, but not with . . . other forms of general procurement. Purchasers were still faxing and phoning orders, which is timely and costly."

Additional cost savings come from small volume, one-of-a-kind special purchases, because of the speed and ease of using the Internet.

Web-based procurement will eliminate mistakes that occur during the procurement process due to having to type or enter prices and other figures on paper documents.

Questions

1. How did IBM achieve cost reductions by using the Internet for procurement?
2. What advantage did IBM's use of the Internet have for small suppliers?
3. Aside from cost reduction, what major value does IBM envision for its interaction with suppliers?
4. How does use of the Internet for procurement reduce mistakes? Indicate how using the Internet made that benefit possible.
5. How does having a Web-based portal help IBM's suppliers?

Source: Based on James Carbone, "E-Procurement at IBM: POs Are Just the Beginning," *Purchasing* 128, no. 4 (March 23, 2000), p. S50.

product codes, location codes, and performance criteria. And e-businesses focusing on transportation services can benefit from having an efficient hub for collaboration between shippers and transportation providers, helping to translate customer shipment forecasts into more predictable demand for equipment, and enabling carriers to deploy their equipment more effectively.

15.10 SUPPLIER MANAGEMENT

Reliable and trustworthy suppliers are a vital link in an effective supply chain. Timely deliveries of goods or services and high quality are just two of the ways that suppliers can contribute to effective operations. A purchasing manager may function as an "external operations manager," working with suppliers to coordinate supplier operations and buyer needs.

In this section, various aspects of supplier management are described, including supplier audits, supplier certification, and supplier partnering. The section starts with an aspect that can have important ramifications for the entire organization: choosing suppliers.

LO15.11 Briefly describe the key aspects of supplier management.

Choosing Suppliers

In many respects, choosing a vendor involves taking into account many of the same factors associated with making a major purchase (e.g., a car or stereo system). A company considers price, quality, the supplier's reputation, past experience with the supplier, and service after the sale. The main difference is that a company, because of the quantities it orders and operations requirements, often provides suppliers with detailed specifications of the materials or parts it wants instead of buying items off the shelf, although most organizations buy standard items that way. The main factors a company takes into account when it selects a vendor are outlined in Table 15.5.

Because different factors are important for different situations, purchasing must decide, with the help of operations, the importance of each factor (i.e., how much weight to give to each factor), and then rate potential vendors according to how well they can be expected to perform against this list. This process is called **vendor analysis**, and it is conducted periodically, or whenever there is a significant change in the weighting assigned to the various factors.

Vendor analysis Evaluating the sources of supply in terms of price, quality, reputation, and service.

Supplier Audits

Periodic audits of suppliers are a means of keeping current on suppliers' production (or service) capabilities, quality and delivery problems and resolutions, and suppliers' performance on other criteria. If an audit reveals problem areas, a buyer can attempt to find a solution before more serious problems develop. Among the factors typically covered by a supplier audit are management style, quality assurance, materials management, the design process used, process improvement policies, and procedures for corrective action and follow-up.

Supplier audits are also an important first step in supplier certification programs.

TABLE 15.5
Choosing a supplier

Factor	Typical Questions
Quality and quality assurance	What procedures does the supplier have for quality control and quality assurance? Are quality problems and corrective actions documented?
Flexibility	How flexible is the supplier in handling changes in delivery schedules, quantity, and product or service changes?
Location	Is the supplier nearby?
Price	Are prices reasonable given the entire package the supplier will provide? Is the supplier willing to negotiate prices? Is the supplier willing to cooperate to reduce costs?
Product or service changes	How much advance notification does the supplier require for product or service changes?
Reputation and financial stability	What is the reputation of the supplier? How financially stable is the supplier?
Lead times and on-time delivery	What lead times can the supplier provide? What procedures does the supplier have for assuring on-time deliveries? What procedures does the supplier have for documenting and correcting problems?
Other accounts	Is the supplier heavily dependent on other customers, causing a risk of giving priority to those needs over ours?

Supplier Certification

Supplier certification is a detailed examination of the policies and capabilities of a supplier. The certification process verifies that a supplier meets or exceeds the requirements of a buyer. This is generally important in supplier relationships, but it is particularly important when buyers are seeking to establish a long-term relationship with suppliers. Certified suppliers are sometimes referred to as *world class* suppliers. One advantage of using certified suppliers is that the buyer can eliminate much or all of the inspection and testing of delivered goods. And although problems with supplier goods or services might not be totally eliminated, there is much less risk than with noncertified suppliers.

Rather than develop their own certification programs, some companies rely on standard industry certifications such as ISO 9000, perhaps the most widely used international certification.

Supplier Relationship Management

Purchasing has the ultimate responsibility for establishing and maintaining good supplier relationships. The type of relationship is often related to the length of a contract between buyers and sellers. Short-term contracts involve competitive bidding. Companies post specifications and potential suppliers bid on the contracts. Suppliers are kept at arm's length, and the relationship is minimal. Business may be conducted through computerized interaction. Medium-term contracts often involve ongoing relationships. Long-term contracts often evolve into partnerships, with buyers and sellers cooperating on various issues that tend to benefit both parties. Increasingly, business organizations are establishing long-term relationships with suppliers in certain situations that are based on *strategic* considerations.

Some business organizations use *supplier forums* to educate potential suppliers about the organization's policies and requirements and to enhance opportunities for receiving contracts. Others use supplier forums to share information, strengthen cooperation, and encourage joint thinking. And some organizations use a *supplier code of conduct* that requires suppliers to maintain safe working conditions, treat workers with respect and dignity, and have production processes that do not harm workers, customers, or the environment.

Business organizations are becoming increasingly aware of the importance of building good relationships with their suppliers. In the past, too many firms regarded their suppliers as adversaries and dealt with them on that basis. One lesson learned from the Japanese is that numerous benefits derive from good supplier relations, including supplier flexibility in terms of accepting changes in delivery schedules, quality, and quantities. Moreover, suppliers can often help identify problems and offer suggestions for solving them. Thus, simply choosing and switching suppliers on the basis of price is a very shortsighted approach to handling an ongoing need.

Keeping good relations with suppliers is increasingly recognized as an important factor in maintaining a competitive edge. Many companies are adopting a view of suppliers as partners. This viewpoint stresses a stable relationship with relatively few reliable suppliers who can provide high-quality supplies, maintain precise delivery schedules, and remain flexible relative to changes in productive specifications and delivery schedules. A comparison of the contrasting views of suppliers is provided in Table 15.6.

Supplier Partnerships

More and more business organizations are seeking to establish partnerships with other organizations in their supply chains. This implies fewer suppliers, longer-term relationships, sharing of information (forecasts, sales data, problem alerts), and cooperation in planning. Among the possible benefits are higher quality, increased delivery speed and reliability, lower inventories, lower costs, higher profits, and, in general, improved operations.

There are a number of obstacles to supplier partnerships, not the least of which is that because many of the benefits go to the buyer, suppliers may be hesitant to enter into such relationships. Suppliers may have to increase their investment in equipment, which might put a strain on cash flow. Another possibility is that the cultures of the buyer and supplier might be quite different and not lend themselves to such an arrangement.

Aspect	Adversary	Partner
Number of suppliers	Many; play one off against the others	One or a few
Length of relationship	May be brief	Long-term
Low price	Major consideration	Moderately important
Reliability	May not be high	High
Openness	Low	High
Quality	May be unreliable; buyer inspects	At the source; vendor certified
Volume of business	May be low due to many suppliers	High
Flexibility	Relatively low	Relatively high
Location	Widely dispersed	Nearness is important for short lead times and quick service

TABLE 15.6
Supplier as adversary versus supplier as partner

Strategic Partnering

Strategic partnering occurs when two or more business organizations that have complementary products or services that would *strategically* benefit the others agree to join so that each may realize a strategic benefit. One way this occurs is when a supplier agrees to hold inventory for a customer, thereby reducing the customer's cost of holding the inventory, in exchange for the customer's agreeing to a long-term commitment, thereby relieving the supplier of the costs that would be needed to continually find new customers, negotiate prices and services, and so on.

Collaborative planning, forecasting, and replenishment (CPFR) is a contractual agreement used to achieve supply chain integration by cooperative management of inventory in the supply chain by major supply chain partners. It involves information sharing, forecasting, and joint decision making. If done well, it can lead to cost savings on inventory, logistics, and merchandising for the partners.

Strategic partnering Two or more business organizations that have complementary products or services join so that each may realize a strategic benefit.

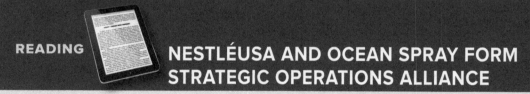

READING

NESTLÉUSA AND OCEAN SPRAY FORM STRATEGIC OPERATIONS ALLIANCE

Glendale, CA—01/25/02—The NestléUSA—Beverage Division and Ocean Spray Cranberries, Inc., announced today that they have formed a long-term strategic operations alliance that will enable both companies to significantly increase manufacturing and supply chain efficiency, while maintaining high quality products for their respective juice businesses.

"Ocean Spray shares many of our same business values, in particular their commitment to high quality manufacturing standards," said Mike Mitchell, President and General Manager of NestléUSA—Beverage Division. "By capitalizing upon each other's best practices, we feel both Nestlé and Ocean Spray will be better equipped to grow in this highly aggressive juice category in which we compete."

Within the strategic operations alliance, Nestlé will transition over time its manufacturing of Libby's Juicy Juice and Libby's Kerns Nectars to Ocean Spray facilities. The companies will also pursue collaborative procurement of common raw and packaging materials, and common operating supplies, as well as shared logistics to increase process efficiency across the supply chain.

"This alliance between two great companies creates a powerful synergy," said Ocean Spray President and Chief Operating Officer Randy Papadellis. "By bringing Nestlé juice production into our plants and joining forces with them on purchasing and distribution, we will establish an economy of scale that will boost the profitability of both companies."

With Ocean Spray leading the category of shelf stable juices and Libby's Juicy Juice being the leader in 100 percent juice for kids, the operations alliance is expected to create added value of mutual benefit. The strategic operations alliance will be governed by a leadership team and an executive operating committee, both comprised of members from each company.

Source: www.Nestleusa.com, www.NestleNewsroom.com.

672   **Chapter Fifteen**   Supply Chain Management

15.11 INVENTORY MANAGEMENT

Inventories are a key component of supply chains. Although inventory management is discussed in more detail in several other chapters, certain aspects of inventory management are particularly important for supply chain management. They relate to the location of inventories in the supply chain, the speed at which inventory moves through the supply chain, and dealing with the effect of demand variability on inventories.

The location of inventories is an important factor for effective material flow through the chain and for order fulfillment. Often trade-offs must be made. One approach is to use centralized inventories, which generally results in lower overall inventory than there would be if decentralized inventories were used, because with decentralized inventories, one location may be understocked while another location is overstocked. Conversely, decentralized locations can provide faster delivery and generally lower shipping costs.

Inventory velocity The speed at which goods move through a supply chain.

The rate at which material moves through a supply chain is referred to as **inventory velocity**. The greater the velocity, the lower the inventory holding costs and the faster orders are filled and goods are turned into cash.

Without careful management, demand variations can easily cause inventory fluctuations to get out of control. Variations in demand at the consumer end of a supply chain tend to ripple backwards through the chain. Moreover, periodic ordering and reaction to shortages can magnify variations, causing inventories to oscillate in increasingly larger swings. This is known as the **bullwhip effect**, because the pattern of demand variation is analogous to the motion of a bullwhip in response to a slight jerking of the handle. Consequently, shortages and surpluses occur throughout the chain, resulting in higher costs and lower customer satisfaction, unless preventive action is taken. The bullwhip effect is illustrated in Figure 15.4.

Bullwhip effect Inventory oscillations become progressively larger looking backward through the supply chain.

The causes of inventory variability can be not only demand variability but also factors such as quality problems, labor problems, unusual weather conditions, and delays in shipments of goods. Adding to this can be communication delays, incomplete communications, and lack of coordination of activities among organizations in the supply chain.

Still other factors can contribute to the bullwhip effect. They include forecast inaccuracies, overreaction to stockouts (customers often order more than they need after experiencing a shortage), order batching to save on ordering and transportation costs (e.g., full truckloads, economic lot sizes), sales incentives and promotions, and service and product mix changes, which can create uneven demand patterns, and liberal return policies.

Good supply chain management can overcome the bullwhip effect by *strategic buffering* of inventory, information sharing, and inventory replenishment based on needs. An example of strategic buffering would be holding the bulk of retail inventory at a distribution center rather than at retail outlets. That way, inventories of specific retail outlets can be replenished as needed based on point-of-sale information from retail outlets as well as information on retail outlet inventories.

Vendor-managed inventory (VMI) Vendors monitor goods and replenish retail inventories when supplies are low.

This is sometimes accomplished using **vendor-managed inventory (VMI)**. Vendors track goods shipped to distributors and retail outlets, and monitor retail supplies, enabling

FIGURE 15.4

The bullwhip effect: demand variations begin at the customer end of the chain and become increasingly large as they radiate backward through the chain

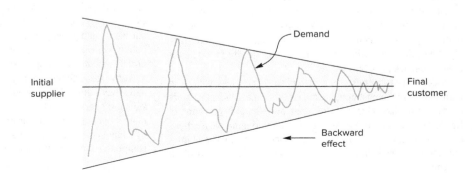

Employees assemble Boeing 777 airplanes on a moving production line at the company's facility in Everett, Washington. Airplanes move slowly but at a steady pace toward completion and the hangar door. If there is a production problem along the route, the line stops, responsible teams are alerted, and the issue is addressed until it is resolved.

© Mike Kane/Bloomberg via Getty

the vendors to replenish inventories when supplies are low. The practice is common in the retail sector, and is also used in other phases of supply chains. VMI lets companies reduce overhead by shifting responsibility for owning, managing, and replenishing inventory to vendors. Not only do assets decrease, the amount of working capital needed to operate a business also decreases.

15.12 ORDER FULFILLMENT

Order fulfillment refers to the processes involved in responding to customer orders. Fulfillment time can be an important criterion for customers. It is often a function of the degree of customization required. Here are some common approaches:

- **Engineer-to-Order (ETO).** With this approach, products are designed and built according to customer specifications. This approach is frequently used for large-scale construction projects, custom homebuilding, home remodeling, and for products made in job shops. The fulfillment time can be relatively lengthy because of the nature of the project, as well as the presence of other jobs ahead of the new one.
- **Make-to-Order (MTO).** With this approach, a standard product design is used, but production of the final product is linked to the final customer's specifications. This approach is used by aircraft manufacturers such as Boeing. Fulfillment time is generally less than with ETO fulfillment, but still fairly long.
- **Assemble-to-Order (ATO).** With this approach, products are assembled to customer specifications from a stock of standard and modular components. Computer manufacturers such as Dell operate using this approach. Fulfillment times are fairly short, often a week or less.
- **Make-to-Stock (MTS).** With this approach, production is based on a forecast, and products are sold to the customer from finished goods stock. This approach is used in department stores and supermarkets. The order fulfillment time is immediate. A variation of this is e-commerce; although goods have already been produced, there is a lag in fulfillment to allow for shipping.

Order fulfillment The processes involved in responding to customer orders.

15.13 LOGISTICS

LO15.12 Discuss the logistics aspects of supply chain management, including RFID technology.

Logistics The movement of materials, services, cash, and information in a supply chain.

Logistics refers to the movement of materials, services, cash, and information in a supply chain. Materials include all of the physical items used in a production process. In addition to raw materials and work in process, there are support items such as fuels, equipment, parts, tools, lubricants, office supplies, and more. Logistics includes movement within a facility, overseeing incoming and outgoing shipments of goods and materials, and information flow throughout the supply chain.

Movement within a Facility

Movement of goods within a manufacturing facility is part of production control. Figure 15.5 shows the many steps where materials move within a manufacturing facility:

1. From incoming vehicles to receiving
2. From receiving to storage
3. From storage to the point of use (e.g., a work center)
4. From one work center to the next or to temporary storage
5. From the last operation to final storage
6. From storage to packaging/shipping
7. From shipping to outgoing vehicles

In some instances, the goods being moved are supplies; in other instances, the goods are actual products or partially completed products; and in still other instances, the goods are raw materials or purchased parts.

FIGURE 15.15
Movement within a facility

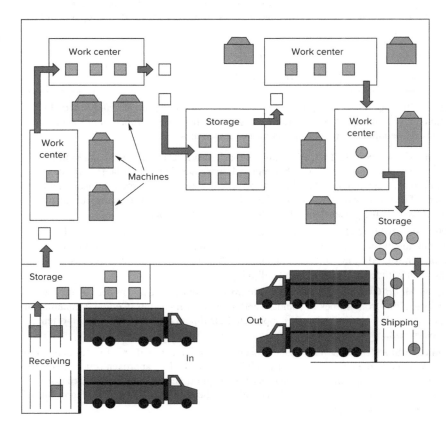

Movement of materials must be coordinated to arrive at the appropriate destinations at appropriate times. Workers and supervisors must take care so that items are not lost, stolen, or damaged during movement.

OPERATIONS TOUR  **WEGMANS' SHIPPING SYSTEM**

The Wegmans supermarket chain (see the Wegmans Operations Tour at the end of Chapter 1) has been cited as a leader in supply chain management in the grocery industry. Its distribution system provides a number of examples of strategies and tactics that contribute to its success in managing its supply chain.

Wegmans operates a number of warehouses that are used to supply its stores. Some warehouses stock grocery items, while others stock frozen foods, and still others stock bakery products, seasonal items, and/or produce. Even though all stores and warehouses are owned by Wegmans, the warehouses service the stores on a B2B basis.

Distribution

Individual stores' orders are generated automatically on a daily basis. These are directed to the appropriate warehouses. Order fulfillment begins when a warehouse downloads a store's order to its information system. There are a variety of methods used to replenish stores' inventories. Several of these avoid the need for warehouse storage, saving the company storage and handling costs. Those methods are:

1. **Cross-dock:** A full inbound pallet is redirected to an outbound shipment.
2. **Cross-distribution:** An inbound pallet is broken down into cases right on the dock, and then the cases are immediately distributed to outbound pallets.
3. **Vendor-managed inventory:** Vendors of some non–store brand items such as bread and soft drinks handle replenishment, and those items come directly from the vendor's warehouse to the stores.

Warehoused replenishment items are handled as full pallets, or broken down into cases, depending on quantities ordered:

1. **Block pick:** An entire pallet of goods in the warehouse is placed on an outbound truck.
2. **Case pick:** Individual cases or packages are pulled from inventory, placed on pallets and shrink wrapped, and then placed on outbound trucks.

Computerized information on incoming orders is checked against incoming shipments of stocks to determine which items can be filled using cross-docking or cross-distribution right in the loading area. These items are then subtracted from a store's order. The remaining items are filled from warehouse supplies.

Warehoused Items

Here is a brief description of retrieval of warehoused items in a dry goods (canned, boxed, etc.) warehouse: The system is semiautomated, and only a few workers are needed to process orders and monitor the system.

Warehoused items are classified for either conveyor belt or non–conveyor belt handling. Items are designated for conveyor belt handling based on their packaging and volume. If volume is low and packaging can withstand the conveyor belt, it will be assigned to the conveyor belt. If the packaging cannot withstand the conveyor belt, the items will be individually case-picked. Non-conveyor belt items that are high volume are automatically moved in bulk from their

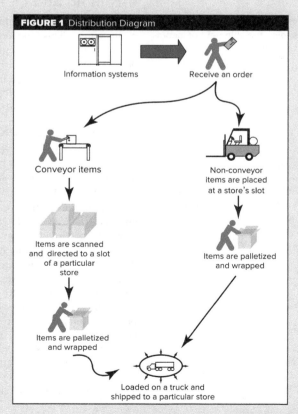

FIGURE 1 Distribution Diagram

Information systems → Receive an order

Conveyor items

Items are scanned and directed to a slot of a particular store

Items are palletized and wrapped

Non-conveyor items are placed at a store's slot

Items are palletized and wrapped

Loaded on a truck and shipped to a particular store

(continued)

(*concluded*)

warehouse locations to a staging area to await loading onto an outbound truck.

When orders for conveyor belt items are received, a worker is given bar code labels that contain the number of the ordering store. The worker then goes to the section where an item is stored, affixes the appropriate store bar code, and places the item on the conveyor belt. As items move along the conveyer, their bar codes are scanned and they are sorted according to store number. After scanning and sorting, items move to staging areas where they are placed on pallets and shrink wrapped, and then placed in a slot designated for the appropriate store. The figure illustrates the handling of low-volume items.

Collaboration with Vendors

A desire to improve conveyer belt transporting has led Wegmans to collaborate with vendors in an effort to improve packaging design. Occasionally goods will fall off the belt, and those items have to be inspected to see if they have been damaged. Damaged goods not only are costly, but they are also lost from inventory and must be replaced. Improved packaging also increases the number of goods that can be handled with the conveyer system.

Forecasting

Wegmans implemented a program of consistent low pricing. This program reduced the number of promotional and sale items, reduced much of the volatility in demand, and made forecasting and inventory planning easier.

New Approaches

Wegmans is now using RFID tags. The tags are very small micro chips, no bigger than a grain of salt. The tags are somewhat similar to bar codes, but offer greater potential for supply chain management because they can be more quickly read (e.g., multiple items can be scanned at once and, unlike bar codes, no line-of-sight is required for a reading), and scanning devices can be placed in warehouses and even on supermarket shelves that would warn when stocks of individual items are running low. The tags initially cost about $1 each, and currently cost about five cents each, making them cost effective for tracking shipments and bulk quantities of items, but still too costly to use on individual store items. However, they hold great promise for increasing supply chain visibility and event management capabilities.

Incoming and Outgoing Shipments

Traffic management Overseeing the shipment of incoming and outgoing goods.

Overseeing the shipment of incoming and outgoing goods comes under the heading of **traffic management**. This function handles schedules and decisions on shipping method and times, taking into account costs of various alternatives, government regulations, the needs of the organization relative to quantities and timing, and external factors such as potential shipping delays or disruptions (e.g., highway construction, truckers' strikes).

Computer tracking of shipments often helps to maintain knowledge of the current status of shipments as well as to provide other up-to-date information on costs and schedules.

Tracking Goods: RFID

Radio frequency identification (RFID) A technology that uses radio waves to identify objects, such as goods in supply chains.

Advances in technology are revolutionizing the way businesses track goods in their supply chains. **Radio frequency identification (RFID)** is a technology that uses radio waves to identify objects, such as goods in supply chains. This is done through the use of an RFID tag that is attached to an object. The tag has an integrated circuit and an antenna that project information or other data to network-connected RFID readers using radio waves. RFID tags can be attached to pallets, cases, or individual items. They provide unique identification, enabling businesses to identify, track, monitor, or locate practically any object in the supply chain that is within range of a tag reader. These tags are similar to bar codes,

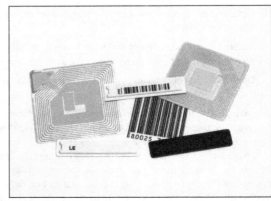

READING   SPRINGDALE FARM

The Springdale Farm is a demonstration farm located near Rochester, New York. One area of the farm is dedicated to advances in dairy cow management that involves a unique application of RFID technology. The farm has a milking parlor that features a robotic milking system that has been "trained" on a cow-by-cow basis so that it automatically adapts to the physical aspects of each particular cow. When a cow enters the milking parlor, it is immediately identified by its RFID tag, and the milking machine adjusts itself and then attaches itself to the cow for milking. The system includes a self-cleaning, laser-guided robot plus an automatic feeder, all managed by a software program tied into RFID

tags worn by the cows. The accompanying software keeps track of data regarding the cow's health, history, milk production, and milk quality. It also allows the cows to be milked whenever they want, without human intervention, freeing workers to focus on other aspects of the operation of the farm. When a cow enters the milking parlor, it is bathed, and then the milking equipment automatically attaches itself to the cow and begins milking. Meanwhile, the cow is given a snack especially formulated for that cow. When the milking is complete, the machine detaches from the cow, the snack is withdrawn, the front door swings open, and the cow exits.

but they have the advantage of conveying much more information, and they do not require a line-of-sight for reading that bar codes require. And unlike bar codes, which must be scanned individually and usually manually, multiple RFID tags can be read simultaneously and automatically. Furthermore, an RFID tag provides more precise information than a bar code: Tags contain detailed information on each object, whereas bar codes convey only an object's classification, such as its stockkeeping unit (SKU). This enables management to know where every object is in the supply chain. RFID has the potential to fundamentally change the way companies track inventory and share information, and to dramatically improve the management of supply chains. This technology increases supply chain visibility, improves inventory management, improves quality control, and enhances relationships with suppliers and customers.

RFID eliminates the need for manual counting and bar-code scanning of goods at receiving docks, in warehouses, and on retail shelves. This eliminates errors and greatly speeds up the process. Tags could reduce employee and customer theft by placing readers at building exits and in parking lots. Still other advantages include increased accuracy in warehouse "picking" of items for shipping or for use in assembly operations, increased accuracy in dispensing drugs to patients in hospitals, and reduced surgical errors.

RFID may enable small, agile businesses to compete with larger, more bureaucratic businesses that may be slow to adopt this new technology. Conversely, large businesses may be better able to afford the costs involved. These include the costs of the tags themselves as well as the cost of affixing individual tags, the cost of readers, and the cost of computer hardware and software to transmit and analyze the data generated.

The potential benefits for supply chain management are huge, and widespread adoption of RFID technology by retailers and manufacturers is predicted. In order to take advantage of RFID technology, businesses must first assess the capabilities of their existing information systems, then identify where RFID can have the greatest impact, estimate the time and resources that will be needed to implement the new system, estimate the risks and rewards of early versus late adoption, and then decide the best course of action. Important concerns at the retail level relate to privacy concerns if tags are not deactivated after items have been purchased and placement of tags so they do not hide important customer information on products.

The following reading provides an explanation of how an RFID system would work.

Evaluating Shipping Alternatives

Evaluation of shipping alternatives is an important component of supply chain management. Considerations include not only shipping costs, but also coordination of shipments with other

READING   RFID TAGS: KEEPING THE SHELVES STOCKED

The supply chain of the consumer packaged goods industry works well when sales are steady, but it often breaks down when confronted by a sudden surge in demand. RFID tags could change that by providing real-time information about what's happening on store shelves. Here's how the system would work:

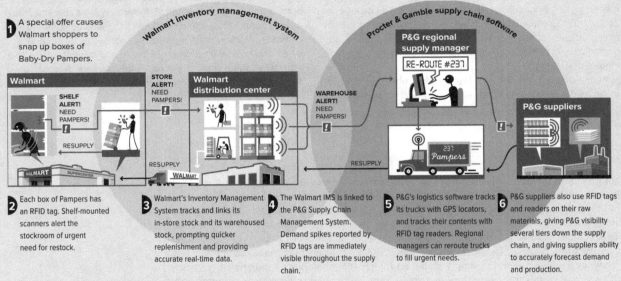

1. A special offer causes Walmart shoppers to snap up boxes of Baby-Dry Pampers.

2. Each box of Pampers has an RFID tag. Shelf-mounted scanners alert the stockroom of urgent need for restock.

3. Walmart's Inventory Management System tracks and links its in-store stock and its warehoused stock, prompting quicker replenishment and providing accurate real-time data.

4. The Walmart IMS is linked to the P&G Supply Chain Management System. Demand spikes reported by RFID tags are immediately visible throughout the supply chain.

5. P&G's logistics software tracks its trucks with GPS locators, and tracks their contents with RFID tag readers. Regional managers can reroute trucks to fill urgent needs.

6. P&G suppliers also use RFID tags and readers on their raw materials, giving P&G visibility several tiers down the supply chain, and giving suppliers ability to accurately forecast demand and production.

Source: As seen in *Business 2.0* Copyright © 2002, Xplane Corp. Used with permission.

READING   ACTIVE RFID VS. PASSIVE RFID

Allan Griebenow

RFID tag technology falls into two broad categories—passive or active. Active RFID has an on-board power supply (e.g., a battery) while passive relies on capturing and "re-using" a small portion of the wake-up signal's energy to transmit its RFID tag I.D. back to the receiver. This is a "good news, bad news" situation. The "good news" is that passive tags can be manufactured and sold at a much lower price point today than active tags. This is a critical element in many RFID supply chain applications requiring the tagging of millions of units. The "bad news" is that passive tags often struggle to provide reliable reads given the performance limitations of a technology using only a small amount of power to push its signal off metal surfaces, through layers of palletized products, etc. Also, passive tags sometimes struggle to provide a highly reliable signal when supply chain goods are in motion. Active tags therefore have an innate performance advantage over passive tags when it comes to providing a consistently robust, penetrating signal. So higher value "things" at the pallet level and above often require active tags. Considering the total cost of ownership, an active tag's higher cost is offset by a lower cost reader and processor infrastructure making the cost justification easier. Containers, trucks, and trailers are the best examples of high value items that require active tags.

In summary, passive and active RFID capabilities are related, but they are distinctly different technologies which should be matched to the application's technical and economic requirements. Automatically identifying personnel, assets, and vehicles are "active" applications and the cornerstones of automated visibility, security, and quality improvements in the enterprise. In the supply chain, for example, total visibility, security and quality can only be attained by utilizing both.

Source: Excerpted from: www.rfidsb.com/index.php?page=rfidsb&c_ID=156. Copyright © 2008 Axcess International, Inc. Used with permission.

supply chain activities, flexibility, speed, and environmental issues. Shipping options can involve trains, trucks, planes, and boats. Relevant factors include cost, time, availability, materials being shipped, and sometimes environmental considerations. At times options may be limited due to one or more of these factors. For example, heavy materials such as coal and iron ore would not be shipped by plane. High costs in some cases may rule out certain options. Also, time–cost trade-offs can be important. Organizations using a low-cost strategy often opt for slower, lower cost options, whereas organizations using a responsive strategy more often opt for quicker, higher cost options.

A situation that often arises in some businesses is the need to make a choice between rapid (but more expensive) shipping alternatives such as overnight or second-day air and slower (but less expensive) alternatives. In some instances, an overriding factor justifies sending a shipment by the quickest means possible, so there is little or no choice involved. However, in other instances, urgency is not the primary consideration, so there is a choice. The decision in such cases often focuses on the cost savings of slower alternatives versus the incremental holding cost (here, the annual dollar amount that could be earned by the revenue from the item being shipped) that would result from using the slower alternative. An important assumption is that the seller gets paid upon receipt of the goods by the buyer (e.g., through electronic data interchange).

The incremental holding cost incurred by using the slower alternative is computed as

$$\text{Incremental holding cost} = \frac{H(d)}{365}$$ (15–1)

where

H = Annual earning potential of shipped item

d = Difference (in days) between shipping alternatives

Comparing Costs of Shipping Alternatives   **EXAMPLE 1**

Determine which shipping alternative, one day or three days, is best when the holding cost of an item is $1,000 per year, the one-day shipping cost is $40, and the three-day shipping cost is:

a. $35

b. $30

SOLUTION

H = $1,000 per year
Time savings = 2 days using 1-day shipping
Holding cost for additional 2 days = $1,000 × (2/365) = $5.48

a. Cost savings = $5. Because the actual savings of $5 is less than the holding cost ($5.48), use the one-day alternative.

b. Cost savings = $10. Because the actual savings of $10 exceeds the savings in holding cost of $5.48, use the three-day alternative.

3-PL

Third-party logistics (3-PL) is the term used to describe the outsourcing of logistics management. According to the website of the Council of Supply Chain Management Professionals, the legal definition of a 3PL is "A person who solely receives, holds, or otherwise transports a consumer product in the ordinary course of business but who does not take title to the product."

This might involve part or even all of the logistics function. For example, some companies use third-party providers just for shipping, others include warehousing and distribution, and still others rely on third-party companies to manage most or all of their supply chains. Companies are turning over warehousing and distribution to companies that specialize in these

Third-party logistics (3-PL) The outsourcing of logistics management.

areas. Among the potential benefits of this are taking advantage of specialists' knowledge, their well-developed information system, and their ability to obtain more favorable shipping rates, and enabling the company to focus more on its core business.

15.14 CREATING AN EFFECTIVE SUPPLY CHAIN

Strategic sourcing Analyzing the procurement process to lower costs by reducing waste and non-value-added activities, increase profits, reduce risks, and improve supplier performance.

Creating an effective supply chain requires a thorough analysis of all aspects of the supply chain. Strategic sourcing is a term that is sometimes used to describe the process. **Strategic sourcing** is a systematic process for analyzing the purchase of products and services to reduce costs by reducing waste and non-value-added activities, increase profits, reduce risks, and improve supplier performance. Strategic sourcing differs from more traditional sourcing in that it emphasizes total cost rather than purchase price. Total cost includes storage costs, repair costs, disposal costs, and sustainability costs in addition to purchase price. It also seeks to consolidate purchasing power to achieve lower prices, relies on fewer suppliers and collaborative relationships, works to eliminate redundancies, and employs cross-functional teams to help overcome traditional organizational barriers.

Strategic sourcing looks at current procurement in terms of what is bought, where and from what suppliers it is bought, and what other sources of supply are available; a sourcing strategy then is designed to minimize a combination of costs and risks. The goal is to have a cooperative relationship among supply chain partners that will facilitate planning and coordination of activities. It is essential for major trading partners to trust each other and to feel confident that partners share similar goals and will take actions that are mutually beneficial. The process is repeated periodically. A system for tracking results and making changes when needed is also established.

The SCOR® (Supply Chain Operations Reference) model (www.supply-chain.org/SCOR) provides steps that can be used to create an effective supply chain:

1. **Plan.** Develop a strategy for managing all the resources that go into meeting expected customer demand for a product or service, including a set of metrics to monitor the supply chain.

2. **Source.** Select suppliers that will provide the goods and services needed to create products or support services. Also, develop a system for delivery, receiving, and verifying shipments or services. Structure payment along with metrics for monitoring and, if necessary, improving relationships.

3. **Make.** Design the processes necessary for providing services or producing, testing, and packaging goods. Monitor quality, service levels or production output, and worker productivity.

4. **Deliver.** Establish systems for coordinating receipt of shipments from vendors; develop a network of warehouses; select carriers to transport goods to customers; set up an invoicing system to receive payments; and devise a communication system for two-way flow of information among supply chain partners.

5. **Manage returns.** Create a responsive and flexible network for receiving defective and excess products from customers.

Achieving an effective supply chain requires integration of all aspects of the supply chain. Three important aspects of this are effective communication, the speed with which information moves through the supply chain, and having performance metrics.

Effective communication. Effective supply chain communication requires integrated technology and standardized ways and means of communicating among partners.

Information velocity The speed at which information is communicated in a supply chain.

Information velocity. Information velocity is important; the faster information flows (two-way), the better.

Performance metrics. Performance metrics are necessary to confirm that the supply chain is functioning as expected, or that there are problems that must be addressed.

 ## CLICKS OR BRICKS, OR BOTH?

The term "clicks-or-bricks" refers to a business model in which a company has either an online (clicks) or an offline (bricks) presence. Many companies have both. Sometimes that business model is referred to as "clicks-and-mortar" or "clicks-and-bricks." In one version, a chain store may allow a customer to order goods online and pick them up at a local store. In another version, large items such as appliances or furniture may be viewed at a local store and then ordered electronically for home delivery. In both instances, the "bricks" portion necessitates a location decision.

Even companies that are seemingly pure "clicks," selling electronic products such as computers, still have warehousing and delivery facilities behind businesses that trade in material goods. Again, location decisions are necessary.

The choice of which business model to use requires taking into account the costs of having a physical presence and what the balance between the two should be. Of course, customer preferences and shopping patterns are important. For example, some reasons people shop online include ease of price comparison, convenience, availability of hard-to-find items, research recommendations, and elimination of the need to travel. Reasons for offline shopping include immediate possession of an item, ease of returns, the security risks of online shopping, the need to use a credit card, the burden of logistics for returns, and ability to "kick the tires" (e.g., try on clothing or footwear, judge quality).

Questions

1. Retail outlets that do not have an Internet presence often complain that consumers come in to "kick the tires" but then buy online from a competitor. Can you suggest some ways outlets can overcome that?

2. Some customers of Internet businesses can avoid paying state sales taxes on purchases if the Internet businesses don't have a physical presence in their state. However, more states are enacting laws to collect taxes. What impact might this have on the clicks, bricks, or both choices?

Financial	Operations	Order fulfillment
Return on assets	Productivity	Order accuracy
Cost	Quality	Time to fill orders
Cash flow		Percentage of incomplete orders shipped
Profits		Percentage of orders delivered on time
Suppliers	**Inventory**	**Customers**
Quality	Average value	Customer satisfaction
On-time delivery	Turnover	Percentage of customer complaints
Cooperation	Weeks of	
Flexibility	supply	

TABLE 15.7
Supply chain performance measures

There are a variety of measures that can be used, which relate to such things as late deliveries, inventory turnover, response time, quality issues, and so on. In the retail sector, the **fill rate** (the percentage of demand filled from stock on hand) is often very important.

Table 15.7 lists some other key performance measures.

Fill rate The percentage of demand filled from stock on hand.

Managing Returns

Products are returned to companies or third-party handlers for a variety of reasons, and in a variety of conditions. Among them are the following:

LO15.13 Discuss the issues involved in managing returns.

- Defective products
- Recalled products
- Obsolete products
- Unsold products returned from retailers.
- Parts replaced in the field
- Items for recycling
- Waste

The importance of returns is underscored by the fact that in the United States, the annual value of returns is estimated to be in the neighborhood of $100 billion. In the past, most

An Amazon.com employee inspects returned products at a distribution warehouse in Nevada. The returned goods are inspected for restocking if in pristine condition, forwarded to a repair center if necessary, inventoried, and examined for potential product, process, or packaging improvements if they are defective.

© Mark Richard/PhotoEdit

items—except unsold products—were typically discarded. More recently, companies are recognizing that substantial value can be reclaimed from returned items. For example, defective parts can be repaired or replaced, and products can be resold as reconditioned. Obsolete products may have usable parts or subassemblies, or they may have value in other markets. Parts replaced in the field may in fact not be defective at all; it is estimated that about a third of such parts are not defective and may be reusable as "reconditioned" replacement parts. Recyclable items can be sold to recyclers and might be usable for energy production; other waste and unusable products and parts might require disposal according to sometimes stringent guidelines. For example, governments, particularly in Europe, are increasingly enacting legislation making original manufacturers responsible for acquiring and disposing of their products at the end of their products' useful lives.

To make a determination as to the appropriate disposition of returned items, the items must be sorted, inspected, or tested and directed to the appropriate destination for repair and reuse, recycling, or disposal. Often, transportation is required. **Reverse logistics** is the process of physically transporting returned items. This involves either retrieving items from the field or moving items from the point of return to a facility where they will be inspected and sorted and then transporting to their final destination.

Two key elements of managing returns are *gatekeeping* and *avoidance*. **Gatekeeping** oversees the acceptance of returned goods with the intent of reducing the cost of returns by screening returns at the point of entry into the system and refusing to accept goods that should not be returned or goods that are returned to the wrong destination. Effective gatekeeping enables organizations to control the rate of returns without negatively impacting customer service. **Avoidance** refers to finding ways to minimize the number of items that are returned. It can involve product design and quality assurance. It may also involve monitoring forecasts during promotional programs to avoid overestimating demand to minimize returns of unsold product.

The condition of returned products as well as the timing of returns may vary, making it difficult to plan for the reverse flow. On the other hand, returns can provide valuable information, such as how and why failures occurred, which can improve product quality and/or

Reverse logistics   The process of transporting returned items.

Gatekeeping   Screening returned goods to prevent incorrect acceptance of goods.

Avoidance   Finding ways to minimize the number of items that are returned.

product design and minimize future returns for that reason. They can also help identify some sources of customer dissatisfaction, which can have design benefits.

It is likely that the importance of this aspect of supply chain management will grow due to shortened product life cycles, increasing returns from increasing Internet commerce sales from dissatisfied customers, replacement of consumer electronics that are in working order as newer models become available, pressures on manufacturers to reduce costs, and increasing consumer and government environmental concerns. The term **closed-loop supply chain** is used to describe a situation where a manufacturer controls both the forward and reverse logistics.

Closed-loop supply chain A manufacturer controls both the forward and reverse shipment of product.

Challenges

The often dynamic supply chain environment and the complexity of supply chains can make managing them very challenging.

Barriers to Integration of Separate Organizations. Organizations, and their functional areas, have traditionally had an inward focus. They set up buffers between themselves and their suppliers. Changing that attitude can be difficult. The objective of supply chain management is to be efficient across the entire supply chain.

LO15.14 Describe some of the challenges in creating an effective supply chain and some of the trade-offs involved.

One difficulty in achieving this objective is that different components of the supply chain often have conflicting objectives. For example, to reduce their inventory holding costs, some companies opt for frequent small deliveries of supplies. This can result in increased holding costs for suppliers, so the cost is merely transferred to suppliers. Similarly, within an organization, functional areas often make decisions with a narrow focus, doing things that "optimize" results under their control; in so doing, however, they may suboptimize results for the overall organization. To be effective, organizations must adopt a *systems approach* to both the internal and external portions of their supply chains, being careful to make decisions that are consistent with optimizing the supply chain.

Another difficulty is that for supply chain management to be successful, organizations in the chain must allow other organizations access to their data. There is a natural reluctance to do this in many cases. One reason can be lack of trust; another can be unwillingness to share proprietary information in general; and another can be that an organization, as a member of multiple chains, fears exposure of proprietary information to competitors.

Getting CEOs, Boards of Directors, Managers, and Employees "Onboard." CEOs and boards of directors need to be convinced of the potential payoffs from supply chain management. And because much of supply chain management involves a change in the way business has been practiced for an extended period of time, getting managers and workers to adopt new attitudes and practices that are consistent with effective supply chain operations poses a real challenge.

Making the Supply Chain More Efficient.

1. **Large vs. small lot sizes.** Compare the benefits and costs of large lots (quantity discounts and lower setup costs, but larger carrying costs) with the benefits and risks of small lots (agility, the possibility of shorter lead times from not needing to wait for production of larger lot quantities, and lower carrying costs, but increased risk of stockouts). Note, too, that use of large lots can contribute to the bullwhip effect.

2. **Saving cost and time by using cross-docking.** **Cross-docking** is a technique whereby goods arriving at a warehouse from a supplier are unloaded from the supplier's truck and immediately loaded on one or more outbound trucks, thereby avoiding storage at the warehouse completely. Walmart is among the companies that have used this technique successfully to reduce inventory holding costs and lead times.

Cross-docking A technique whereby goods arriving at a warehouse from a supplier are unloaded from the supplier's truck and loaded onto outbound trucks, thereby avoiding warehouse storage.

Delayed differentiation Production of standard components and subassemblies, which are held until late in the process to add differentiating features.

3. **Increase the perception of variety while taking advantage of the benefits of low variety by using delayed differentiation.** Delayed differentiation involves producing standard components and subassemblies, then delaying until late in the process to add differentiating features. For example, an automobile producer may allow dealers to add (or subtract) certain features for customers, increasing the appeal of vehicles while reducing the need to maintain large inventories of vehicles to be able to satisfy different customer wants. Similarly, a bakery can produce "standard" cakes which can be decorated (e.g., Happy Birthday Baby!) according to a customer's specifications.

4. **Ship directly to the customer to reduce waiting time.** One approach to reducing the time customers must wait for their orders is to ship directly from a warehouse to the customer, bypassing a retail outlet. Reducing one or more steps in a supply chain by cutting out one or more intermediaries is referred to as **disintermediation**. Aside from reducing waiting time, storage costs are avoided, although delivery costs are higher. Allowing store pickups can reduce transportation costs.

Disintermediation Reducing one or more steps in a supply chain by cutting out one or more intermediaries.

Small Businesses. Small businesses may be reluctant to embrace supply chain management because it can involve specialized, complicated software as well as sharing sensitive information with outside companies. Nonetheless, in order for them to survive, they may have to do so.

Variability and Uncertainty. Variations create uncertainty, thereby causing inefficiencies in a supply chain. Variations occur in incoming shipments from suppliers, internal operations, deliveries of products or services to customers, and customer demands. Increases in product and service *variety* add to uncertainty, because organizations have to deal with a broader range and frequent changes in operations. Hence, when deciding to increase variety, organizations should consider this trade-off.

Although variations exist throughout most supply chains, decision makers often treat the uncertainties as if they were certainties and make decisions on that basis. In fact, systems are often designed on the basis of certainty, so they may not be able to cope with uncertainty. Unfortunately, uncertainties are detrimental to effective management of supply chains because they result in various undesirable occurrences, such as inventory buildups, bottleneck delays, missed delivery dates, and frustration for employees and customers at all stages of a supply chain.

Response Time. Response time is an important issue in supply chain management. Long lead times impair the ability of a supply chain to quickly respond to changing conditions, such as changes in the quantity or timing of demand, changes in product or service design, and quality or logistics problems. Therefore, it is important to work to reduce long product lead times and long collaborative lead times, and a plan should be in place to deal with problems when they arise.

15.15 STRATEGY

Effective supply chains are critical to the success of business organizations. Development of supply chains should be accorded strategic importance. Achieving an effective supply chain requires integration of all aspects of the chain. Supplier relationships are a critical component of supply chain management. Collaboration and joint planning and coordination are keys to supply chain success. In that regard, a systems view of the supply chain is essential.

Many businesses are employing principles of lean operations and six sigma methodology to improve supply chain performance. However, lean supply chains can increase supply chain risk and may necessitate increased inventories to offset those risks.

SUMMARY

A supply chain consists of all of the organizations, facilities, functions, and activities involved in producing a product or providing a service. The chapter provides a list of strategic, tactical, and operational responsibilities related to supply chain management. The chapter covers key issues, recent trends, procurement, ethical behavior, e-business, supplier management, inventory management, returns management, and risk management.

The basic components of supply chain management are strategy formulation, procurement, supply management, demand management, and logistics management. The key issues in supply chain management relate to determining the appropriate level of outsourcing, managing procurement, managing suppliers, managing customer relationships, being able to quickly identify problems and respond to them, and managing risk.

The goal of supply chain management is to match supply and demand as effectively and efficiently as possible. Because supply chains are made up of multiple organizations, cooperation and collaboration among supply chain partners is very important. Supply chain functioning benefits from mutual trust, information sharing, and collaborative forecasting and planning.

Recent trends in supply chain management relate to managing risk, reevaluating outsourcing, managing inventories, and applying lean principles to improve supply chain performance.

KEY POINTS

1. Supply chains are a vital part of every business organization and need to be managed effectively to achieve a balance of supply and demand.
2. Among important trends in supply chain management are measuring ROI, "greening" the supply chain, reevaluating outsourcing, integrating IT, managing risks, and adopting lean principles.
3. It is important for businesses to encourage their supply chain partners to act ethically.
4. Effective supply chains involve trust, communication, a rapid two-way flow of information, visibility, and event-response capability.

KEY TERMS

avoidance 682
bullwhip effect 672
centralized purchasing 665
closed-loop supply chain 683
cross-docking 683
decentralized purchasing 665
delayed differentiation 684
disintermediation 684
e-business 666
event-response capability 658
fill rate 681

gatekeeping 682
information velocity 680
inventory velocity 672
logistics 654, 674
order fulfillment 673
purchasing cycle 664
reverse logistics 682
radio frequency identification (RFID) 676
resiliency 658
strategic partnering 671

strategic sourcing 680
supply chain 654
supply chain management 654
supply chain visibility 658
third-party logistics (3-PL) 679
traffic management 676
vendor analysis 669
vendor-managed inventory (VMI) 672

DISCUSSION AND REVIEW QUESTIONS

1. What is a supply chain?
2. What are some recent trends in supply chain management?
3. What are the elements of supply chain management?
4. What are the strategic, tactical, and operations responsibilities in supply chain management?
5. What is the bullwhip effect, and why does it occur? How can it be overcome?
6. Explain the increasing importance of the procurement function.
7. What is meant by the term *inventory velocity* and why is this important? What is *information velocity,* and why is it important?
8. Explain strategic partnering.
9. What impact has e-business had on supply chain management?
10. What are some of the advantages of e-business?
11. What are some of the trade-offs that might be factors in designing a supply chain?
12. Why is managing returns important?
13. Explain the importance of supply chain visibility.
14. Describe what purchasing managers do.

15. Describe how purchasing interacts with two other functional areas of an organization.
16. Discuss the importance of RFID for supply chain management.
17. Discuss centralization versus decentralization in purchasing. What are the advantages of each?
18. Describe vendor analysis.
19. Describe supplier certification and explain why it can be important.
20. Compare viewing suppliers as adversaries with viewing them as partners.
21. Explain the benefit of cross-docking.

TAKING STOCK

1. What trade-offs are involved in (*a*) sharing information with other organizations in a supply chain and (*b*) the acquisition of information-processing technology?
2. Who needs to be involved in (*a*) decisions on technology acquisition for supply chain management and (*b*) supply chain management?
3. Name three different ways that technology has improved the ability to manage supply chains.

CRITICAL THINKING EXERCISES

1. Explain why each of these is critical for a successful supply chain operation:
   a. Integrated technology
   b. Information sharing
   c. Trust among trading partners
   d. Real-time information availability
   e. Event-response capability
   f. Procurement
   g. Risk management
2. Given the complexities and risks involved with supply chains, might it make sense for a business organization to vertically integrate and be its own supply chain?
3. From a systems viewpoint, what are some of the environmental issues involved in a decision by a company to outsource manufacturing operations to a foreign country?
4. Select three of the examples of unethical behavior in section 15.5, other than those that violate basic human rights, and indicate which principle in Table 15.2 would be violated.

PROBLEMS

1. A manager at Strateline Manufacturing must choose between two shipping alternatives: two-day freight and five-day freight. Using five-day freight would cost $135 less than using two-day freight. The primary consideration is holding cost, which is $10 per unit a year. Two thousand items are to be shipped. Which alternative would you recommend? Explain.
2. Determine which shipping alternative would be most economical to ship 80 boxes of parts when each box has a price of $200 and holding costs are 30 percent of price, given this shipping information: overnight, $300, two-day, $260, six-day, $180.
3. A manager must make a decision on shipping. There are two shippers, A and B. Both offer a two-day rate: A for $500 and B for $525. In addition, A offers a three-day rate of $460 and a nine-day rate of $400, and B offers a four-day rate of $450 and a seven-day rate of $410. Annual holding costs are 35 percent of unit price. Three hundred boxes are to be shipped, and each box has a price of $140. Which shipping alternative would you recommend? Explain.

CASE — MASTERTAG

Nicole Foster, Grand Valley State University

When MasterTag was founded in 1949, its founder, Ludwig Schmidt, set out to be a manufacturer of plastic fishing bobbers. Then, in 1950, Mr. Schmidt was approached by a local greenhouse owner and was asked if he could produce a line of horticultural labels for plants. At the time, these labels were made of wood. Mr. Schmidt adapted his machines to produce these labels and has been manufacturing the plastic "tags" for plants ever since. Over the years, the labels have increased in quality and now feature full-color pictures of the plants along with the name and planting and care instructions.

Many of MasterTag's largest customers are seed companies that sell the seeds to commercial growers. The large seed companies typically place one or two large orders with MasterTag at the beginning of the growing season. The seed companies then sell their seeds and the labels to their customers who grow the plants and sell them to the end consumer. For various reasons, the seed companies do not like ordering tags, but do so because their customers demand labels with their seeds.

However, there are several problems with this ordering process. The main issue stems from the fact that the exact quantities of tags that will be needed is difficult to predict due to possible crop failures and the introduction of new items. To avoid a shortage of tags, seed companies order and ship a large quantity of tags to their customers. Tags are ordered early to allow for the time needed to incorporate the tags with the seeds. Seed companies usually end up each year with huge numbers of leftover tags. In fact, MasterTag's largest customers often end up with millions of leftover tags.

When MasterTag's management became aware of all the unused labels and unhappy customers, they decided they must come up with a better solution for achieving a match between supply and demand of the tags. One possible solution would be to make an initial, fairly large batch, which would be produced and shipped directly to the growers instead of the seed companies, as is now being done. Later, when the grower results became available, a second batch would be produced using information from growers on how many additional tags are needed. The second batch would then be made and shipped to the growers. (See figure for Before and After.)

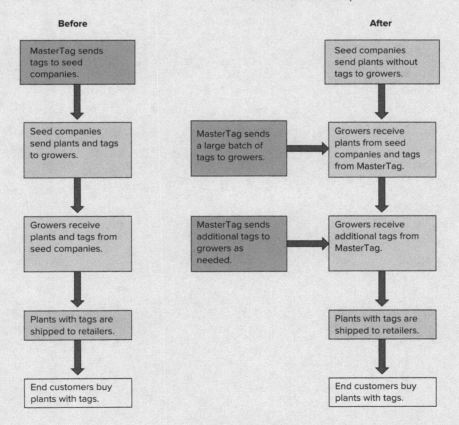

Questions

1. Explain the key benefit of the revised approach, and the reason for the benefit.

2. MasterTag has not yet decided to implement this plan. List the pros and cons you think should be considered.

SELECTED BIBLIOGRAPHY AND FURTHER READINGS

Benton, W. C. *Purchasing and Supply Chain Management,* 2nd ed. New York: McGraw-Hill, 2010.

Blanchard, David. *Supply Chain Management: Best Practices,* 2nd ed. New York: Wiley, 2011.

Bowersox, Donald J., David J. Closs, and M. Bixby Cooper. *Supply Chain Logistics Management,* 3rd ed. New York: Irwin/McGraw-Hill, 2010.

Chopra, Sunil, and Peter Meidl. *Supply Chain Management: Strategy, Planning, and Operation,* 5th ed. New York: Pearson, 2012.

Guide, V. Daniel R., Jr., and Luk N. Van Wassenhove. "The Reverse Supply Chain." *Harvard Business Review* 80, (2), pp. 25–26, 2002.

Handfield, Robert B., and Ernest L. Nichols Jr. *Introduction to Supply Chain Management.* Upper Saddle River, NJ: Prentice Hall, 1999.

Johnson, P. Fraser, Michiel R. Leenders, and Anna E. Flynn. *Purchasing and Supply Management,* 14th ed. New York: McGraw-Hill/Irwin, 2011.

Lee, Hau L. "The Triple-A Supply Chain." *Harvard Business Review,* October 2004.

Monczka, Robert M., Robert H. Handfield, Larry Guinipero, and James Patterson. *Purchasing and Supply Chain Management,* 5th ed. Stamford, CT: South-Western - Cengage Learning, 2011.

RFID Journal.com

Simchi-Levi, David, Philip Kaminsky, and Edith Simchi-Levi. *Designing and Managing the Supply Chain: Concepts, Strategies, and Case Studies.* New York: Irwin/McGraw-Hill, 2000.

Webster, Scott. *Principles and Tools for Supply Chain Management.* New York: McGraw-Hill, 2008.

16 Scheduling

LEARNING OBJECTIVES

After completing this chapter, you should be able to:

LO16.1   Explain what scheduling involves and the importance of good scheduling.

LO16.2   Compare product and service scheduling hierarchies.

LO16.3   Describe scheduling needs in high-volume systems.

LO16.4   Describe scheduling needs in intermediate-volume systems.

LO16.5   Describe scheduling needs in job shops.

LO16.6   Use and interpret Gantt charts.

LO16.7   Use the assignment method for loading.

LO16.8   Give examples of commonly used priority rules.

LO16.9   Discuss the theory of constraints and that approach to scheduling.

LO16.10   Summarize some of the unique problems encountered in service systems, and describe some of the approaches used for scheduling service systems.

CHAPTER OUTLINE

16.1 Scheduling Operations, *692*
   Scheduling in High-Volume Systems, *692*
   Scheduling in Intermediate-Volume Systems, *694*

16.2 Scheduling in Low-Volume Systems, *695*
   Loading, *695*
   Sequencing, *702*
   Sequencing Jobs through Two Work Centers, *709*

Sequencing Jobs When Setup Times Are Sequence-Dependent, *711*
Why Scheduling Can Be Difficult, *711*
Minimizing Scheduling Difficulties, *712*
The Theory of Constraints, *712*

16.3 Scheduling Services, *713*
   Appointment Systems, *714*
   Reservation Systems, *714*

Yield Management, *714*
Scheduling the Workforce, *715*
Cyclical Scheduling, *715*
Scheduling Multiple Resources, *716*

16.4 Operations Strategy, *717*
   Case: Hi-Ho, Yo-Yo, Inc., *729*

© U. Baumgarten via Getty

Within an organization, **scheduling** pertains to establishing the timing of the use of specific resources of that organization. It relates to the use of equipment, facilities, and human activities. Scheduling occurs in every organization, regardless of the nature of its activities. For example, manufacturers must schedule production, which means developing schedules for workers, equipment, purchases, maintenance, and so on. Hospitals must schedule admissions, surgery, nursing assignments, and support services such as meal preparation, security, maintenance, and cleaning. Educational institutions must schedule classrooms, instruction, and students. And lawyers, doctors, dentists, hairdressers, and auto repair shops must schedule appointments.

In the decision-making hierarchy, scheduling decisions are the final step in the transformation process before actual output occurs. Many decisions about system design and operation have been made long before scheduling decisions. They include the capacity of the system, product or service design, equipment selection, selection and training of workers, and aggregate planning and master scheduling. Consequently, scheduling decisions must be made within the constraints established by many other decisions, making them fairly narrow in scope and latitude. Figure 16.1 depicts scheduling hierarchies for manufacturing and service scheduling.

Effective scheduling can yield cost savings, increases in productivity, and other benefits. For example, in hospitals, effective scheduling can save lives and improve patient care. In educational institutions, it can reduce the need for expansion of facilities. In competitive environments, effective scheduling can give a company a competitive advantage in terms of customer service (shorter wait time for their orders) if its competitors are less effective with their scheduling.

Generally, the objectives of scheduling are to achieve trade-offs among conflicting goals, which include efficient utilization of staff, equipment, and facilities, and minimization of customer waiting time, inventories, and process times.

This chapter covers scheduling in both manufacturing and service environments. Although the two environments have many similarities, some basic differences are important.

Airline travel can be difficult when flights are delayed or canceled due to weather problems. And even though it may be clear and dry in some areas, flights in those places can still be affected by weather in other areas. Because of all the interdependencies, a problem in one area, especially around major hub airports like Chicago, Atlanta, and New York, has a cascading effect with impacts throughout the nation. This results in massive scheduling problems. Flight arrivals and departures have to be rescheduled, which then means flight crews, terminal gates, connections, and baggage and freight also must be rescheduled. Airline and air traffic control software scheduling systems include and optimize thousands of variables.

LO16.1 Explain what scheduling involves and the importance of good scheduling.

Scheduling Establishing the timing of the use of equipment, facilities, and human activities in an organization.

FIGURE 16.1
Scheduling hierarchies

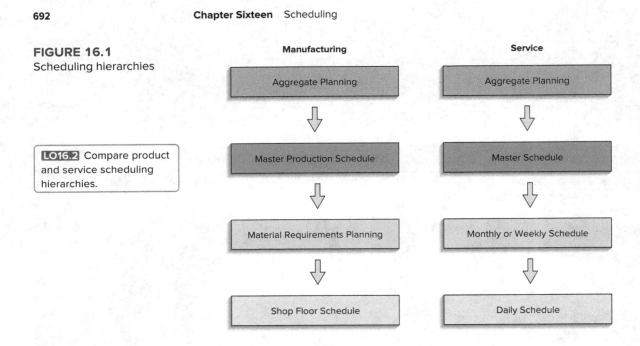

Manufacturing	Service
Aggregate Planning	Aggregate Planning
Master Production Schedule	Master Schedule
Material Requirements Planning	Monthly or Weekly Schedule
Shop Floor Schedule	Daily Schedule

LO16.2 Compare product and service scheduling hierarchies.

16.1 SCHEDULING OPERATIONS

LO16.3 Describe scheduling needs in high-volume systems.

Scheduling tasks are largely a function of the volume of system output. High-volume systems require approaches substantially different from those required by job shops, and project scheduling requires still different approaches. In this chapter, we will consider scheduling for high-volume systems, intermediate-volume systems, and low-volume (job shop) scheduling. Project scheduling is discussed in Chapter 17.

Scheduling in High-Volume Systems

Scheduling encompasses allocating workloads to specific work centers and determining the sequence in which operations are to be performed. High-volume systems are characterized by standardized equipment and activities that provide identical or highly similar operations on customers or products as they pass through the system. The goal is to obtain a smooth rate of flow of goods or customers through the system in order to get a high utilization of labor and equipment. High-volume systems, where jobs follow the same sequence, are often referred to as **flow systems**; scheduling in these systems is referred to as **flow-shop scheduling**, although flow-shop scheduling also can be used in medium-volume systems. Examples of high-volume products include autos, smartphones, radios and televisions, office supplies, toys, and appliances. In process industries, examples include petroleum refining, sugar refining, mining, waste treatment, and the manufacturing of fertilizers. Examples of services include cafeteria lines, news broadcasts, and mass inoculations. Because of the highly repetitive nature of these systems, many of the loading and sequence decisions are determined during the design of the system. The use of highly specialized tools and equipment, arrangement of equipment, use of specialized material-handling equipment, and division of labor are all designed to enhance the flow of work through the system, since all items follow virtually the same sequence of operations.

A major aspect in the design of flow systems is *line balancing,* which concerns allocating the required tasks to workstations so that they satisfy technical (sequencing) constraints and

Flow system High–volume system in which jobs all follow the same sequence.

Flow-shop scheduling Scheduling for flow systems.

are balanced with respect to equal work times among stations. Highly balanced systems result in the maximum utilization of equipment and personnel as well as the highest possible rate of output. Line balancing is discussed in Chapter 6.

In setting up flow systems, designers must consider the potential discontent of workers in connection with the specialization of job tasks in these systems; high work rates are often achieved by dividing the work into a series of relatively simple tasks assigned to different workers. The resulting jobs tend to be boring and monotonous and may give rise to fatigue, absenteeism, turnover, and other problems, all of which tend to reduce productivity

Courtesy Rexam PLC.

At the Wakefield, U.K. factory, Rexam produces 5,000 cans per minute and delivers them to its main customer, Coca-Cola Bottling. To meet Coke's lean manufacturing requirements, Rexam needed to spray cans the same every single time. They added a spray monitor system to immediately identify spray malfunctions. The early diagnostics of the spray monitor system can save Rexam from coating hundreds of cans improperly. The objectives in upgrading were to improve quality, reduce variation, and reduce costs.

and disrupt the smooth flow of work. These problems and potential solutions are elaborated on in Chapter 7, which deals with the design of work systems.

In spite of the built-in attributes of flow systems related to scheduling, a number of scheduling problems remain. One stems from the fact that few flow systems are *completely* devoted to a single product or service; most must handle a variety of sizes and models. Thus, an automobile manufacturer will assemble many different combinations of cars—two-door and four-door models, some with air-conditioning and some not, some with deluxe trim and others with standard trim, some with CD players, some with tinted glass, and so on. The same can be said for producers of appliances, electronic equipment, and toys. Each change involves slightly different inputs of parts, materials, and processing requirements that must be scheduled into the line. If the line is to operate smoothly, a supervisor must coordinate the flow of materials and the work, which includes the inputs, processing, and outputs, as well as purchases. In addition to achieving a smooth flow, it is important to avoid excessive buildup of inventories. Again, each variation in size or model will tend to have somewhat different inventory requirements, so that additional scheduling efforts will be needed.

One source of scheduling concern is possible disruptions in the system that result in less than the desired output. These can be caused by equipment failures, material shortages, accidents, and absences. In practice, it is usually impossible to increase the rate of output to compensate for these factors, mainly because flow systems are designed to operate at a given rate. Instead, strategies involving subcontracting or overtime are often required, although subcontracting on short notice is not always feasible. Sometimes work that is partly completed can be made up off the line.

The reverse situation can also impose scheduling problems although these are less severe. This happens when the desired output is less than the usual rate. However, instead of slowing the ensuing rate of output, it is usually necessary to operate the system at the usual rate, but for fewer hours. For instance, a production line might operate temporarily for seven hours a day instead of eight.

High-volume systems usually require automated or specialized equipment for processing and handling. Moreover, they perform best with a high, uniform output. Shutdowns and start-ups are generally costly, and especially costly in process industries. Consequently, the following factors often determine the success of such a system:

- **Process and product design.** Here, cost and manufacturability are important, as is achieving a smooth flow through the system.

- **Preventive maintenance.** Keeping equipment in good operating order can minimize breakdowns that would disrupt the flow of work.
- **Rapid repair when breakdowns occur.** This can require specialists as well as stocks of critical spare parts.
- **Optimal product mixes.** Techniques such as linear programming can be used to determine optimal blends of inputs to achieve desired outputs at minimal costs. This is particularly true in the manufacture of fertilizers, animal feeds, and diet foods.
- **Minimization of quality problems.** Quality problems can be extremely disruptive, requiring shutdowns while problems are resolved. Moreover, when output fails to meet quality standards, not only is there the loss of output but also a waste of the labor, material, time, and other resources that went into it.
- **Reliability and timing of supplies.** Shortages of supplies are an obvious source of disruption and must be avoided. On the other hand, if the solution is to stockpile supplies, that can lead to high carrying costs. Shortening supply lead times, developing reliable supply schedules, and carefully projecting needs are all useful.

Scheduling in Intermediate-Volume Systems

LO16.4 Describe scheduling needs in intermediate-volume systems.

Intermediate-volume system outputs fall between the standardized type of output of the high-volume systems and made-to-order output of job shops. Like the high-volume systems, intermediate-volume systems typically produce standard outputs. If manufacturing is involved, the products may be for stock rather than for special order. However, the volume of output in such cases is not large enough to justify continuous production. Instead, it is more economical to process these items *intermittently*. Thus, intermediate-volume work centers periodically shift from one job to another. In contrast to a job shop, the run (batch) sizes are relatively large. Examples of products made in these systems include canned foods, baked goods, paint, and cosmetics.

The three basic issues in these systems are the *run size* of jobs, the *timing* of jobs, and the *sequence* in which jobs should be processed.

Sometimes, the issue of run size can be determined by using a model such as the economic run size model discussed in Chapter 13 on inventory management. The run size that would minimize setup and inventory costs is

$$Q_p = \sqrt{\frac{2DS}{H}} \sqrt{\frac{p}{p-u}}, \text{ where } S = \text{Setup cost} \tag{16-1}$$

Setup cost may be an important consideration. Setup costs may depend on the order in which jobs are processed; similar jobs may require less setup change between them. For example, jobs in a print shop may be sequenced by ink color to reduce the number of setups needed. This opens up the possibility of reducing setup cost and time by taking processing sequence into account. It also makes sequencing more complex, and it requires estimating job setup costs for every sequence combination.

In another vein, companies are working to reduce setup times and, hence, experience less downtime for equipment changeover. Tactics include offline setups, snap-on parts, modular setups, and flexible equipment designed to handle a variety of processing requirements.

Another difficulty arises because usage is not always as smooth as assumed in the model. Some products will tend to be used up faster than expected and have to be replenished sooner. Also, because multiple products are to be processed, it is not always possible to schedule production to correspond with optimum run times.

Another approach frequently used is to base production on a master schedule developed from customer orders and forecasts of demand. Companies engaged in assembly operations would then use an MRP approach (described in Chapter 12) to determine the quantity and projected timing of jobs for components. The manager would then compare projected requirements with projected capacity and develop a feasible schedule from that information. Companies engaged in producing processed rather than assembled goods (e.g., food products, such as canned goods and beverages; publishing, such as magazines; paints and cleaning supplies) would use a somewhat different approach; the *time-phasing* information provided by MRP would not be an important factor.

16.2 SCHEDULING IN LOW-VOLUME SYSTEMS

LO16.5 Describe scheduling needs in job shops.

The characteristics of low-volume systems (job shops) are considerably different from those of high- and intermediate-volume systems. Products are made to order, and orders usually differ considerably in terms of processing requirements, materials needed, processing time, and processing sequence and setups. Because of these circumstances, **job-shop scheduling** is usually fairly complex. This is compounded by the impossibility of establishing firm schedules prior to receiving the actual job orders.

Job-shop scheduling Scheduling for low-volume systems with many variations in requirements.

Job-shop processing gives rise to two basic issues for schedulers: how to distribute the workload among work centers and what job processing sequence to use.

Loading

Loading refers to the assignment of jobs to processing (work) centers. Loading decisions involve assigning specific jobs to work centers and to various machines in the work centers. In cases where a job can be processed only by a specific center, loading presents little difficulty. However, problems arise when two or more jobs are to be processed and there are a number of work centers capable of performing the required work. In such cases, the operations manager needs some way of assigning jobs to the centers.

Loading The assignment of jobs to processing centers.

When making assignments, managers often seek an arrangement that will minimize processing and setup costs, minimize idle time among work centers, or minimize job completion time, depending on the situation.

Gantt Charts. Visual aids called **Gantt charts** are used for a variety of purposes related to loading and scheduling. They derive their name from Henry Gantt, who pioneered the use of charts for industrial scheduling in the early 1900s. Gantt charts can be used in a number of different ways, two of which are illustrated in Figure 16.2, which shows scheduling classrooms for a university and scheduling hospital operating rooms for a day.

Gantt charts Chart used as visual aid for loading and scheduling purposes.

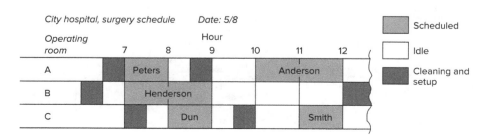

FIGURE 16.2
Examples of charts used for scheduling

LO16.6 Use and interpret Gantt charts..

The purpose of Gantt charts is to organize and visually display the actual or intended use of resources in a *time framework*. In most cases, a time scale is represented horizontally, and resources to be scheduled are listed vertically. The use and idle times of resources are reflected in the chart.

Managers may use the charts for trial-and-error schedule development to get an idea of what different arrangements would involve. Thus, a tentative surgery schedule might reveal insufficient allowance for surgery that takes longer than expected and can be revised accordingly. Use of the chart for classroom scheduling would help avoid assigning two different classes to the same room at the same time.

There are a number of different types of Gantt charts. Two of the most commonly used are the *load chart* and the *schedule chart*.

Load chart A Gantt chart that shows the loading and idle times for a group of machines or list of departments.

A **load chart** depicts the loading and idle times for a group of machines or a list of departments. Figure 16.3 illustrates a typical load chart. This chart indicates that work center 3 is completely loaded for the entire week, center 4 will be available from Tuesday to Friday, and the other two centers have idle time scattered throughout the week. This information can help a manager rework loading assignments to better utilize the centers. For instance, if all centers perform the same kind of work, the manager might want to free one center for a long job or a rush order. The chart also shows when certain jobs are scheduled to start and finish, and where to expect idle time.

FIGURE 16.3
A. Sample Gantt load chart.
B. The same Gantt chart using the Lekin software, developed at New York University, includes multiple scheduling routines along with graphics.

Source: © Pinedo and Feldman. Used with permission.

A.

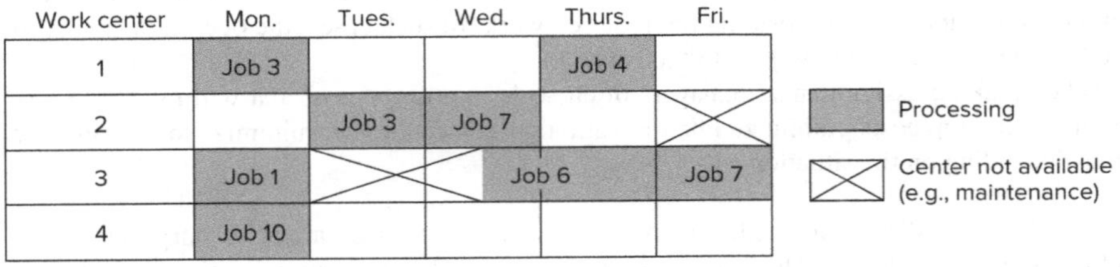

B.

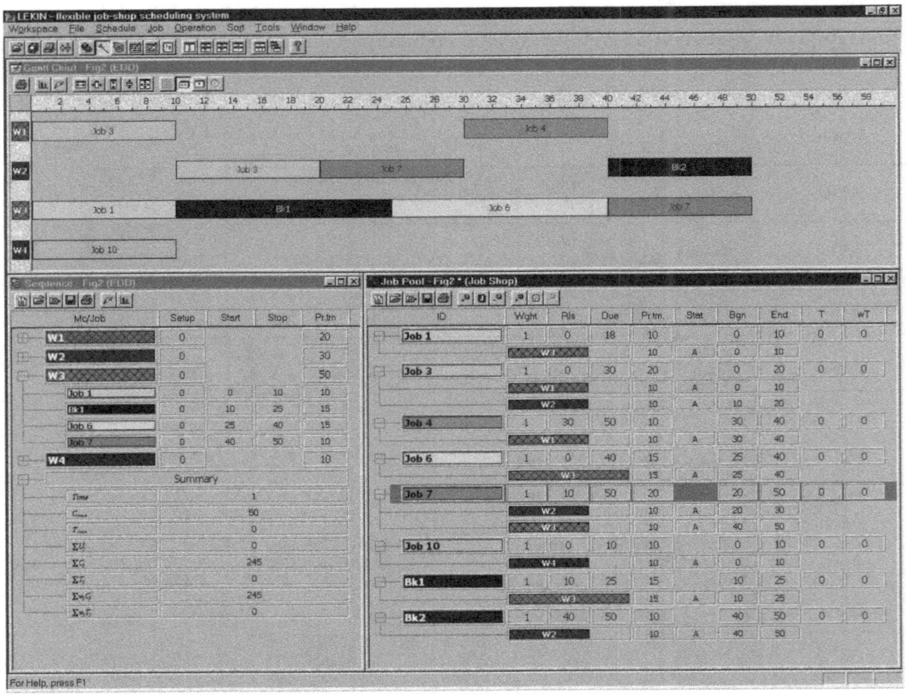

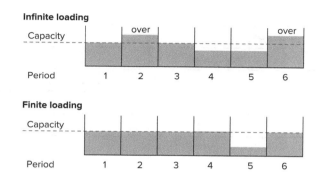

Two different approaches are used to load work centers: *infinite* loading and *finite* loading. **Infinite loading** assigns jobs to work centers without regard to the capacity of the work center. As you can see in the diagram that follows, this can lead to overloads in some time periods and underloads in others. The priority sequencing rules described in this chapter use infinite loading. One possible result of infinite loading is the formation of queues in some (or all) work centers. That requires a second step to correct the imbalance. **Finite loading** projects actual job starting and stopping times at each work center, taking into account the capacities of each work center and the processing times of jobs, so that capacity is not exceeded. One output of finite loading is a detailed projection of hours each work center will operate. Schedules based on finite loading may have to be updated often, perhaps daily, due to processing delays at work centers and the addition of new jobs or cancellation of current jobs. The following diagram illustrates these two approaches.

With infinite loading, a manager may need to make some response to overloaded work centers. Among the possible responses are shifting work to other periods or other centers, working overtime, or contracting out a portion of the work. Note that the last two options in effect increase capacity to meet the workload.

Finite loading may reflect a fixed upper limit on capacity. For example, a bus line will have only so many buses. Hence, the decision to place into service a particular number of buses fixes capacity. Similarly, a manufacturer might have one specialized machine that it operates around the clock. Thus, it is operated at the upper limit of its capacity, so finite loading would be called for.

There are two general approaches to scheduling—forward scheduling and backward scheduling. **Forward scheduling** means scheduling ahead from a point in time; **backward scheduling** means scheduling backward from a due date. Forward scheduling is used if the issue is "How long will it take to complete this job?" Backward scheduling would be used if the issue is "When is the latest the job can be started and still be completed by the due date?" Forward scheduling enables the scheduler to determine the earliest possible completion time for each job and, thus, the amount of lateness or the amount of slack can be determined. That information can be combined with information from other jobs in setting up a schedule for all current jobs.

A manager often uses a **schedule chart** to monitor the progress of jobs. The vertical axis on this type of Gantt chart shows the orders or jobs in progress, and the horizontal axis shows time. The chart indicates which jobs are on schedule and which are behind or ahead.

A typical schedule chart is illustrated in Figure 16.4. It shows the current status of a landscaping job with planned and actual starting and finishing times for the five stages of the job. The chart indicates that approval and the ordering of trees and shrubs was on schedule. The site preparation was a bit behind schedule. The trees were received earlier than expected, and planting is ahead of schedule. However, the shrubs have not yet been received. The chart indicates some slack between scheduled receipt of shrubs and shrub planting, so if the shrubs arrive by the end of the week, it appears the schedule can still be met.

Despite the obvious benefits of Gantt charts and the fact that they are widely used, they possess certain limitations, the chief one being the need to repeatedly update a chart to keep it

Infinite loading Jobs are assigned to work centers without regard to the capacity of the work center.

Finite loading Jobs are assigned to work centers taking into account the work center capacity and job processing times.

Forward scheduling Scheduling ahead from a point in time.

Backward scheduling Scheduling backward from a due date.

Schedule chart A Gantt chart that shows the orders or jobs in progress and whether they are on schedule.

FIGURE 16.4
Progress chart for
landscaping job

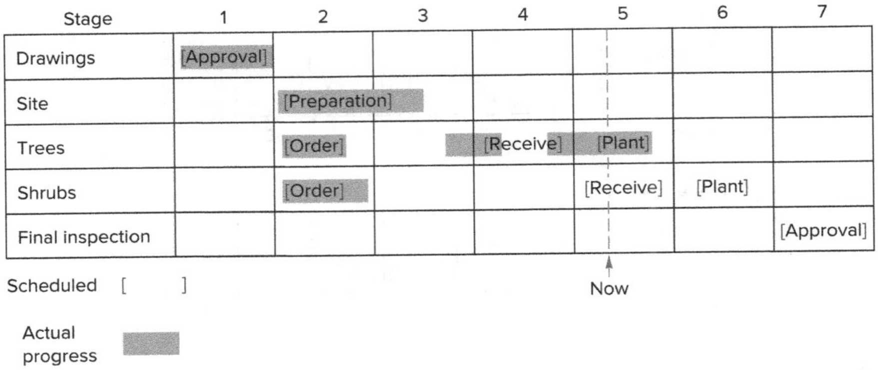

Stage	1	2	3	4	5	6	7
Drawings	[Approval]						
Site		[Preparation]					
Trees		[Order]		[Receive]	[Plant]		
Shrubs		[Order]			[Receive]	[Plant]	
Final inspection							[Approval]

Scheduled   [   ]   Now

Actual
progress

current. In addition, a chart does not directly reveal costs associated with alternative loadings. Finally, a job's processing time may vary depending on the work center; certain stations or work centers may be capable of processing some jobs faster than other stations. Again, that situation would increase the complexity of evaluating alternative schedules.

In addition to Gantt charts, managers often rely on input/output reports to manage work flow.

Input/output (I/O) control
Managing work flow and queues at work centers.

Input/Output Control. Input/output (I/O) control refers to monitoring the work flow and queue lengths at work centers. The purpose of I/O control is to manage work flow so that queues and waiting times are kept under control. Without I/O control, demand may exceed processing capacity, causing an overload at a center. Conversely, work may arrive slower than the rate a work center can handle, leaving the work center underutilized. Ideally, a balance can be struck between the input and output rates, thereby achieving effective use of work center capacities without experiencing excessive queues at the work centers. A simple example of I/O control is the use of stoplights on some expressway on-ramps. These regulate the flow of entering traffic according to the current volume of expressway traffic.

Figure 16.5 illustrates an input/output report for a work center. A key portion of the report is the backlog of work waiting to be processed. The report also reveals deviations-from-planned for both inputs and outputs, thereby enabling a manager to determine possible sources of problems.

The deviations in each period are determined by subtracting "planned" from "actual." For example, in the first period, subtracting the planned input of 100 hours from the actual input

FIGURE 16.5
A sample input/output report for a work center showing input and output in hours of processing time

Note: Figures represent standard hours of processing time.

*Given, not derived from the data.

		Period					
		1	2	3	4	5	6
Input	Planned	100	100	90	90	90	90
	Actual	120	95	80	88	93	94
	Deviation	+20	−5	−10	−2	+3	+4
	Cum. dev.	+20	+15	+5	+3	+6	+10

Output	Planned	110	110	100	100	100	95
	Actual	110	105	95	101	103	96
	Deviation	0	−5	−5	+1	+3	+1
	Cum. dev.	0	+5	+10	+9	+6	+5

Backlog	40*	50	40	25	12	2	0

of 120 hours produces a deviation of +20 hours. Similarly, in the first period, the planned and actual outputs are equal, producing a deviation of 0 hours.

The backlog for each period is determined by subtracting the "actual output" from the "actual input" and adjusting the backlog from the previous period by that amount. For example, in the second period actual output exceeds actual input by 10 hours. Hence, the previous backlog of 50 hours is reduced by 10 hours to 40 hours.

Another approach that can be used to assign jobs to resources is the *assignment method.*

Assignment Method of Linear Programming. The **assignment model** is a special-purpose linear programming model that is useful in situations that call for assigning tasks or other work requirements to resources. Typical examples include assigning jobs to machines or workers, territories to salespeople, and repair jobs to repair crews. The idea is to obtain an optimum *matching* of tasks and resources. Commonly used criteria include costs, profits, efficiency, and performance.

Table 16.1 illustrates a typical problem, where four jobs are to be assigned to four workers. The problem is arranged in a format that facilitates evaluation of assignments. The numbers in the body of the table represent the value or cost associated with each job-worker combination. In this case, the numbers represent costs. Thus, it would cost $8 for worker A to do job 1, $6 for worker B to do job 1, and so on. If the problem involved minimizing the cost for job 1 alone, it would clearly be assigned to worker C, since that combination has the lowest cost. However, that assignment does not take into account the other jobs and their costs, which is important since the lowest-cost assignment for any one job may not be consistent with a minimum-cost assignment when all jobs are considered.

If there are to be *n* matches, there are *n!* different possibilities. In this case, there are 4! = 24 different matches. One approach is to investigate each match and select the one with the lowest cost. However, if there are 12 jobs, there would be 479 million different matches! A much simpler approach is to use a procedure called the **Hungarian method** to identify the lowest-cost solution.

To be able to use the Hungarian method, a one-for-one matching is required. Each job, for example, must be assigned to only one worker. It is also assumed that every worker is capable of handling every job, and that the costs or values associated with each assignment combination are known and fixed (i.e., not subject to variation). The number of rows and columns must be the same. Solved Problem 1 at the end of the chapter shows what to do if they aren't the same.

Once the relevant cost information has been acquired and arranged in tabular form, the basic procedure of the Hungarian method is as follows:

1. Subtract the smallest number in each row from every number in the row. This is called a *row reduction.* Enter the results in a new table.

2. Subtract the smallest number in each column of the new table from every number in the column. This is called a *column reduction.* Enter the results in another table.

3. Test whether an optimum assignment can be made. You do this by determining the *minimum* number of lines (horizontal or vertical) needed to cross out (cover) all zeros. If the number of lines equals the number of rows, an optimum assignment is possible. In that case, go to step 6. Otherwise go on to step 4.

4. If the number of lines is less than the number of rows, modify the table in this way:
   a. Subtract the smallest uncovered number from every uncovered number in the table.
   b. Add the smallest uncovered number to the numbers at *intersections* of cross-out lines.
   c. Numbers crossed out but not at intersections of cross-out lines carry over to the next table.

5. Repeat steps 3 and 4 until an optimal table is obtained.

6. Make the assignments. Begin with rows or columns with only one zero. Match items that have zeros, using only one match for each row and each column. Eliminate both the row and the column after the match.

Assignment model A linear programming model for optimal assignment of tasks and resources.

LO16.7 Use the assignment method for loading.

SCREENCAM TUTORIAL

Hungarian method Method of assigning jobs by a one-for-one matching to identify the lowest-cost solution.

TABLE 16.1

A typical assignment problem showing job times for each job/ worker combination

		WORKER			
		A	B	C	D
	1	8	6	2	4
Job	2	6	7	11	10
	3	3	5	7	6
	4	5	10	12	9

EXAMPLE 1

*e**X**cel*

mhhe.com/stevenson13e

Using the Assignment Method to Make Job Assignments

Determine the optimum assignment of jobs to workers for the following data (from Table 16.1):

		WORKER				
		A	B	C	D	Row Minimum
Job	1	8	6	2	4	2
	2	6	7	11	10	6
	3	3	5	7	6	3
	4	5	10	12	9	5

SOLUTION

a. Subtract the smallest number in each row from every number in the row, and enter the results in a new table. The result of this row reduction is:

		WORKER			
		A	B	C	D
Job	1	6	4	0	2
	2	0	1	5	4
	3	0	2	4	3
	4	0	5	7	4
Column Minimum		0	1	0	2

b. Subtract the smallest number in each column from every number in the column, and enter the results in a new table. The result of this column reduction is:

		WORKER			
		A	B	C	D
Job	1	6	3	0	0
	2	0	0	5	2
	3	0	1	4	1
	4	0	4	7	2

c. Determine the *minimum* number of lines needed to cross out all zeros. (Try to cross out as many zeros as possible when drawing lines.)

		WORKER			
		A	B	C	D
Job	1	6	3	0	0
	2	0	0	5	2
	3	0	1	4	1
	4	0	4	7	2

d. Since only three lines are needed to cross out all zeros and the table has four rows, this is not the optimum. Note that the smallest uncovered value is 1.

e. Subtract the smallest uncovered value from every uncovered number that hasn't been crossed out, and add it to numbers that are at the intersections of covering lines. The results are as follows:

		WORKER			
		A	B	C	D
job	1	7	3	0	0
	2	1	0	5	2
	3	0	0	3	0
	4	0	3	6	1

f.   Determine the minimum number of lines needed to cross out all zeros (four). Since
this equals the number of rows, you can make the optimum assignment.

WORKER

		A	B	C	D
	1	7	3	0	0
Job	2	1	0	5	2
	3	0	0	3	0
	4	0	3	6	1

g.   Make assignments: Start with rows and columns with only one zero. Match jobs with
machines that have a zero cost.

WORKER

		A	B	C	D
	1	7	3	0	0
Job	2	1	0	5	2
	3	0	0	3	0
	4	0	3	6	1

Assignment	Cost
1-C	$ 2
2-B	7
3-D	6
4-A	5
	20

The assignment problem can also be solved using an Excel template, as seen in Table 16.2.
The ones in the solution matrix denote assignments (i.e., assign C to job 1), and the zeros
denote no assignment for a worker/machine and job combination.

TABLE 16.2   Excel solution to Example 1

Input Matrix:

Worker/Machine

	A	B	C	D	E	F	G	H	
1	8	6	2	4					1
2	6	7	11	10					1
3	3	5	7	6					1
4	5	10	12	9					1
5									0
6									0
7									0
8									0
	1	1	1	1	0	0	0	0	

Total Jobs = 4

Do not change or delete unshaded cells.   Total Workers/Machines = 4

Solution Matrix:

Worker/Machine

	A	B	C	D	E	F	G	H	
1	0	0	1	0	0	0	0	0	1
2	0	1	0	0	0	0	0	0	1
3	0	0	0	1	0	0	0	0	1
4	1	0	0	0	0	0	0	0	1
5	0	0	0	0	0	0	0	0	0
6	0	0	0	0	0	0	0	0	0
7	0	0	0	0	0	0	0	0	0
8	0	0	0	0	0	0	0	0	0
	1	1	1	1	0	0	0	0	

Total Cost = 20

As you can see, the process is relatively simple. The simplicity of the Hungarian method
belies its usefulness when the assumptions are met. Not only does it provide a rational method
for making assignments, it guarantees an optimal solution, often without the use of a computer, which is necessary only for fairly large problems. When profits instead of costs are

involved, the profits can be converted to *relative costs* by subtracting every number in the table from the largest number and then proceeding as in a minimization problem.

It is worth knowing that one extension of this technique can be used to prevent undesirable assignments. For example, union rules may prohibit one person's assignment to a particular job, or a manager might wish to avoid assigning an unqualified person to a job. Whatever the reason, specific combinations can be avoided by assigning a relatively high cost to that combination. In the previous example, if we wish to avoid combination 1-A, assigning a cost of $50 to that combination will achieve the desired effect, because $50 is much greater than the other costs.

Sequencing

Although loading decisions determine the machines or work centers that will be used to process specific jobs, they do not indicate the *order* in which the jobs waiting at a given work center are to be processed. **Sequencing** is concerned with determining job processing order. Sequencing decisions determine both the order in which jobs are processed at various work centers and the order in which jobs are processed at individual **workstations** *within* the work centers.

If work centers are lightly loaded and if jobs all require the same amount of processing time, sequencing presents no particular difficulties. However, for heavily loaded work centers, especially in situations where relatively lengthy jobs are involved, the order of processing can be very important in terms of costs associated with jobs waiting for processing and in terms of idle time at the work centers. In this section, we will examine some of the ways in which jobs are sequenced.

Typically, a number of jobs will be waiting for processing. **Priority rules** are simple heuristics used to select the order in which the jobs will be processed. Some of the most common are listed in Table 16.3. The rules generally rest on the assumption that job setup cost and time are *independent* of processing sequence. In using these rules, job processing times and due dates are important pieces of information. **Job time** usually includes setup and processing times. Jobs that require similar setups can lead to reduced setup times if the sequencing rule takes this into account (the rules described here do not). Due dates may be the result of delivery times promised to customers, material requirements planning (MRP) processing, or managerial decisions. They are subject to revision and must be kept current to give meaning to sequencing choices. Also, it should be noted that due dates associated with all rules except slack per operation (S/O) and critical ratio (CR) are for the operation about to be performed; due dates for S/O and CR are typically final due dates for orders rather than intermediate, departmental deadlines.

The priority rules can be classified as either *local* or *global*. **Local priority rules** take into account information pertaining only to a single workstation; **global priority rules** take into account information pertaining to multiple workstations. First come, first served (FCFS), shortest processing time (SPT), and earliest due date (EDD) are local rules; CR and S/O are global rules. Rush can be either local or global. As you might imagine, global rules require more effort than local rules. A major complication in global sequencing is that not all jobs

---

Sequencing Determining the order in which jobs at a work center will be processed.

Workstation An area where one or a few workers and/or machines perform similar work.

Priority rules Simple heuristics used to select the order in which jobs will be processed.

Job time Time needed for setup and processing of a job.

Local priority rules Focus on information pertaining to a single workstation when establishing a job sequence.

Global priority rules Incorporate information from multiple workstations when establishing a job sequence.

TABLE 16.3
Possible priority rules

LO16.8 Give examples of commonly used priority rules.

First come, first served (FCFS): Jobs are processed in the order in which they arrive at a machine or work center.

Shortest processing time (SPT): Jobs are processed according to processing time at a machine or work center, shortest job first.

Earliest due date (EDD): Jobs are processed according to due date, earliest due date first.

Critical ratio (CR): Jobs are processed according to smallest ratio of time remaining until due date to processing time remaining.

Slack per operation (S/O): Jobs are processed according to average slack time (time until due date minus remaining time to process). Compute by dividing slack time by number of remaining operations, including the current one.

Rush: Emergency or preferred customers first.

The set of jobs is known; no new jobs arrive after processing begins; and no jobs are canceled. Setup time is independent of processing sequence. Setup time is deterministic. Processing times are deterministic rather than variable. There will be no interruptions in processing such as machine breakdowns, accidents, or worker illness.

TABLE 16.4
Assumptions of priority rules

require the same processing or even the same order of processing. As a result, the set of jobs is different for different workstations. Local rules are particularly useful for bottleneck operations, but they are not limited to those situations.

A number of assumptions apply when using the priority rules; Table 16.4 lists them. In effect, the priority rules pertain to *static* sequencing: For simplicity, it is assumed that there is no variability in either setup or processing times, or in the set of jobs. The assumptions make the scheduling problem manageable. In practice, jobs may be delayed or canceled, and new jobs may arrive, requiring schedule revisions.

The effectiveness of any given sequence is frequently judged in terms of one or more *performance measures*. The most frequently used performance measures follow:

- **Job flow time** is the amount of time it takes from when a job arrives until it is complete. It includes not only actual processing time but also any time waiting to be processed, transportation time between operations, and any waiting time related to equipment breakdowns, unavailable parts, quality problems, and so on. The average flow time for a group of jobs is equal to the total flow time for the jobs divided by the number of jobs.

  Job flow time The amount of time from when a job arrives until it is finished.

- **Job lateness** is the amount of time the job completion date is expected to exceed the date the job was due or promised to a customer. It is the difference between the actual completion time and the due date. If only differences for jobs with completion times that exceed due dates are recorded, and zeros are assigned to jobs that are early, the term used is job *tardiness*.

  Job lateness The difference between the actual completion date and the due date.

- **Makespan** is the total time needed to complete a *group* of jobs. It is the length of time between the start of the first job in the group and the completion of the last job in the group. If processing involves only one work center, makespan will be the same regardless of the priority rule being used.

  Makespan Total time needed to complete a group of jobs from the beginning of the first job to the completion of the last job.

- **Average number of jobs.** Jobs that are in a shop are considered to be work-in-process inventory. The average work-in-process for a group of jobs can be computed using the following formula:

  Average number of jobs = Total flow time ÷ Makespan

  If the jobs represent equal amounts of inventory, the average number of jobs will also reflect the average work-in-process inventory.

Of the priority rules, rush scheduling is quite simple and needs no explanation. The other rules and performance measures are illustrated in the following two examples.

Determining Job Sequences Using Various Rules

Processing times (including setup times) and due dates for six jobs waiting to be processed at a work center are given in the following table. Determine the sequence of jobs, the average flow time, average tardiness, and average number of jobs at the work center, for each of these rules:

a. FCFS

b. SPT

E X A M P L E 2

mhhe.com/stevenson13e

c. EDD

d. CR

Job	Processing Time (days)	Due Date (days from present time)
A	2	7
B	8	16
C	4	4
D	10	17
E	5	15
F	12	18

Assume jobs arrived in the order shown.

SOLUTION

a. The FCFS sequence is simply A-B-C-D-E-F. The measures of effectiveness are as follows (see table):

(1) *Average flow time:* 120/6 = 20 days.

(2) *Average tardiness:* 54/6 = 9 days.

(3) The *makespan* is 41 days. *Average number of jobs at the work center:* 120/41 = 2.93.

Job Sequence	(1) Processing Time	(2) Flow Time	(3) Due Date	(2) − (3) Days Tardy [0 if negative]
A	2	2	7	0
B	8	10	16	0
C	4	14	4	10
D	10	24	17	7
E	5	29	15	14
F	12	41	18	23
	41	120		54

The flow time column indicates *cumulative* processing time, so summing these times and dividing by the total number of jobs processed indicates the average time each job spends at the work center. Similarly, find the average number of jobs at the center by summing the flow times and dividing by the total processing time.

The Excel solution is shown in Table 16.5.

b. Using the SPT rule, the job sequence is A-C-E-B-D-F (see the following table). The resulting values for the three measures of effectiveness are:

(1) *Average flow time:* 108/6 = 18 days.

(2) *Average tardiness:* 40/6 = 6.67 days.

(3) *Average number of jobs at the work center:* 108/41 = 2.63.

Job Sequence	(1) Processing Time	(2) Flow Time	(3) Due Date	(2) − (3) Days Tardy [0 if negative]
A	2	2	7	0
C	4	6	4	2
E	5	11	15	0
B	8	19	16	3
D	10	29	17	12
F	12	41	18	23
	41	108		40

TABLE 16.5   Excel solution for Example 2a

Job Sequencing
<Back   Notes | Clear | FCFS | SPT | DD | CR | S/O |

Current Date: 23

Job	Process. Time	Due Date	Remain Oper.	CR Sequence	Critical Ratio	Slack	S/O	Flow Time	Days Late
A	2	7		3		5		2	0
B	8	16		5		8		10	0
C	4	4		1		0		14	10
D	10	17		6		7		24	7
E	5	15		4		10		29	14
F	12	18		2		6		41	23
Totals	41		0			36		120	54

Method	FCFS
Average Flow Time	20.00
Average Tardiness	9.00
Average Number of Jobs	2.93

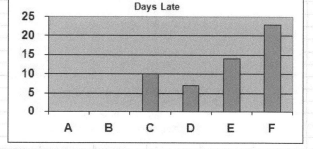

See notes below.

Notes:

1. Enter Job Name, Processing Time, and Due Date for each job.

2. For the FCFS, SPT, and DD rules, simply press the appropriate button.

3. For the CR rule, perform the following BEFORE pressing the CR button:
    a. Select job with lowest Critical Ratio
    b. Schedule that job next by entering next sequence number (start with 1) in the CR Sequence column.
    c. Add the processing time for that job to the current date.
    d. Repeat steps a, b, and c until all jobs have been scheduled (i.e. the CR Sequence column is filled in).
    e. Then press the CR button.

4. Fill in the Remaining Operations column and then press the S/O button.

c.   Using earliest due date as the selection criterion, the job sequence is C-A-E-B-D-F.
      The measures of effectiveness are as follows (see table):
      (1) *Average flow time:* 110/6 = 18.33 days.

      (2) *Average tardiness:* 38/6 = 6.33 days.

      (3) *Average number of jobs at the work center:* 110/41 = 2.68.

Job Sequence	(1) Processing Time	(2) Flow Time	(3) Due Date	(2) – (3) Days Tardy [0 if negative]
C	4	4	4	0
A	2	6	7	0
E	5	11	15	0
B	8	19	16	3
D	10	29	17	12
F	12	41	18	23
	41	110		38

d.   Using the critical ratio we find:

Job Sequence	Processing Time	Due Date	Critical Ratio Calculation
A	2	7	$(7 - 0)/2 = 3.5$
B	8	16	$(16 - 0)/8 = 2.0$
C	4	4	$(4 - 0)/4 = 1.0$ (lowest)
D	10	17	$(17 - 0)/10 = 1.7$
E	5	15	$(15 - 0)/5 = 3.0$
F	12	18	$(18 - 0)/12 = 1.5$

At day 4 [C completed], the critical ratios are

Job Sequence	Processing Time	Due Date	Critical Ratio Calculation
A	2	7	$(7 - 4)/2 = 1.5$
B	8	16	$(16 - 4)/8 = 1.5$
C	—	—	—
D	10	17	$(17 - 4)/10 = 1.3$
E	5	15	$(15 - 4)/5 = 2.2$
F	12	18	$(18 - 4)/12 = 1.17$ (lowest)

At day 16 [C and F completed], the critical ratios are

Job Sequence	Processing Time	Due Date	Critical Ratio Calculation
A	2	7	$(7 - 16)/2 = -4.5$ (lowest)
B	8	16	$(16 - 18)/8 = 0.0$
C	—	—	—
D	10	17	$(17 - 16)/10 = 0.1$
E	5	15	$(15 - 16)/5 = -0.2$
F	—	—	—

At day 18 [C, F, and A completed], the critical ratios are:

Job Sequence	Processing Time	Due Date	Critical Ratio Calculation
A	—	—	—
B	8	16	$(16 - 18)/8 = -0.25$
C	—	—	—
D	10	17	$(17 - 18)/10 = -0.10$
E	5	15	$(15 - 18)/5 = -0.60$ (lowest)
F	—	—	—

At day 23 [C, F, A, and E completed], the critical ratios are

Job Sequence	Processing Time	Due Date	Critical Ratio Calculation
A	—	—	—
B	8	16	$(16 - 23)/8 = -0.875$ (lowest)
C	—	—	—
D	10	17	$(17 - 23)/10 = -0.60$
E	—	—	—
F	—	—	—

The job sequence is C-F-A-E-B-D, and the resulting values for the measures of effectiveness are as follows:

(1) *Average flow time:* $133/6 = 22.17$ days.

(2) *Average tardiness:* $58/6 = 9.67$ days.

(3) *Average number of jobs at the work center:* $133/41 = 3.24$.

Sequence	(1) Processing Time	(2) Flow Time	(3) Due Date	(2) − (3) Days Tardy
C	4	4	4	0
F	12	16	18	0
A	2	18	7	11
E	5	23	15	8
B	8	31	16	15
D	10	41	17	24
	41	133		58

The results of these four rules are summarized in Table 16.6.

In Example 2, the SPT rule was the best according to two of the measures of effectiveness and a little worse than the EDD rule on average tardiness. The CR rule was the worst in every case. For a different set of numbers, the EDD rule (or perhaps another rule not mentioned here) might prove superior to SPT in terms of average job tardiness or some other measure of effectiveness. However, SPT is always superior in terms of minimizing flow time and, hence, in terms of minimizing the average number of jobs at the work center and completion time. This results in faster job completion, which has the potential to generate more revenue.

Generally speaking, the FCFS rule and the CR rule turn out to be the least effective of the rules.

The primary limitation of the FCFS rule is that long jobs will tend to delay other jobs. If a process consists of work on a number of machines, machine idle time for downstream work-stations will increase. However, for service systems in which customers are directly involved, the FCFS rule is by far the dominant priority rule, mainly because of the inherent fairness but also because of the inability to obtain realistic estimates of processing time for individual jobs. The FCFS rule also has the advantage of simplicity. If other measures are important when there is high customer contact, companies may adopt the strategy of moving processing to the "backroom" so they don't necessarily have to follow FCFS.

Because the SPT rule always results in the lowest (i.e., optimal) average completion (flow) time, it can result in lower in-process inventories. And because it often provides the lowest (optimal) average tardiness, it can result in better customer service levels. Finally, since it always involves a lower average number of jobs at the work center, there tends to be less congestion in the work area. SPT also minimizes downstream idle time. However, due dates are often uppermost in managers' minds, so they may not use SPT because it doesn't incorporate due dates.

The major disadvantage of the SPT rule is that it tends to make long jobs wait, perhaps for rather long times (especially if new, shorter jobs are continually added to the system). That can be troubling if long jobs are from the company's best customers. Various modifications may be used in an effort to avoid this. For example, after waiting for a given time period, any remaining jobs are automatically moved to the head of the line. This is known as the *truncated* SPT rule.

TABLE 16.6
Comparison of the four rules for Example 2

Rule	Average Flow Time (days)	Average Tardiness (days)	Average Number of Jobs at the Work Center
FCFS	20.00	9.00	2.93
SPT	18.00	6.67	2.63
EDD	18.33	6.33	2.68
CR	22.17	9.67	3.24

The EDD rule directly addresses due dates and minimizes lateness. Although it has intuitive appeal, its main limitation is that it does not take processing time into account. One possible consequence is that it can result in some jobs waiting a long time, which adds to both in-process inventories and shop congestion.

The CR rule is easy to use and has intuitive appeal. Although it had the poorest showing in Example 2 for all three measures, it usually does quite well in terms of minimizing job tardiness. Therefore, if job tardiness is important, the CR rule might be the best choice among the rules.

Let's take a look now at the S/O (slack per operation) rule.

EXAMPLE 3

eXcel
mhhe.com/stevenson13e

Scheduling Jobs Using the S/O Rule

Use the S/O rule to schedule the following jobs. Note that processing time includes the time remaining for the current and subsequent operations. In addition, you will need to know the number of operations remaining, including the current one.

Job	Remaining Processing Time	Due Date	Remaining Number of Operations
A	4	14	3
B	16	32	6
C	8	8	5
D	20	34	2
E	10	30	4
F	18	30	2

SOLUTION

Determine the difference between the due date and the processing time for each operation. Divide the difference by the number of remaining operations, and rank them from low to high. This yields the sequence of jobs:

	(1) Remaining Processing	(2) Due	(3) (2) − (1)	(4) Remaining Number of	(5) (3) ÷ (4)	(6)
Job	Time	Date	Slack	Operations	Ratio	Rank
A	4	14	10	3	3.33	3
B	16	32	16	6	2.67	2
C	8	8	0	5	0	1
D	20	34	14	2	7.00	6
E	10	30	20	4	5.00	4
F	18	30	12	2	6.00	5

The indicated sequence (see column 6) is C-B-A-E-F-D.

Using the S/O rule, the designated job sequence may change after any given operation, so if that happened, it would be necessary to reevaluate the sequence after each operation. Note that any of the previously mentioned priority rules could be used on a station-by-station basis for this situation; the only difference is that the S/O approach incorporates downstream information in arriving at a job sequence.

In reality, many priority rules are available to sequence jobs, and some other rule might provide superior results for a given set of circumstances. The purpose in examining these few rules is to provide insight into the nature of sequencing rules. Each shop or organization should consider carefully its own circumstances and the measures of effectiveness it feels are important, when selecting a rule to use.

The following section describes a special-purpose algorithm that can be used to sequence a set of jobs that must all be processed at the same two machines or work centers.

Sequencing Jobs through Two Work Centers[1]

Johnson's rule is a technique that managers can use to minimize the makespan for a group of jobs to be processed on two machines or at two successive work centers (sometimes referred to as a two-machine flow shop).[2] It also minimizes the total idle time at the work centers. For the technique to work, several conditions must be satisfied:

- Job time (including setup and processing) must be known and constant for each job at each work center.
- Job times must be independent of the job sequence.
- All jobs must follow the same two-step work sequence.
- A job must be completed at the first work center before the job moves on to the second work center.

Application of Johnson's rule begins with a listing of all jobs to be scheduled, and how much time will be required by each job at each workstation. The sequence is determined by following these steps:

1. Select the job with the shortest time. If the shortest time is at the first work center, schedule that job first; if the time is at the second work center, schedule the job last. Break ties arbitrarily.

2. Eliminate the job and its time from further consideration.

3. Repeat steps 1 and 2, working toward the center of the sequence, until all jobs have been scheduled.

Successful application of these steps identifies the sequence with the minimum makespan, or all work is completed as soon as possible. However, precisely *when* a certain job will be completed (its flow time) or when idle time will occur is not apparent by inspecting the sequence. To determine such detailed performance information, it is generally easiest to create a Gantt chart illustrating the finished sequence, as demonstrated in Example 4.

When significant idle time at the second work center occurs, job splitting at the first center just prior to the occurrence of idle time may alleviate some of it and also shorten throughput time. In Example 4, this is not a concern. The last solved problem at the end of this chapter illustrates the use of job splitting.

Johnson's rule Technique for minimizing makespan for a group of jobs to be processed on two machines or at two work centers.

Using Johnson's Rule to Sequence Jobs

EXAMPLE 4

mhhe.com/stevenson13e

A group of six jobs is to be processed through a two-machine flow shop. The first operation involves cleaning and the second involves painting. Determine a sequence that will minimize the total completion time for this group of jobs. Processing times are as follows:

	PROCESSING TIME (hours)	
Job	Work Center 1	Work Center 2
A	5	5
B	4	3
C	8	9
D	2	7
E	6	8
F	12	15

To employ Johnson's rule, create a "blank" sequence first, such as:

1st	2nd	3rd	4th	5th	6th

---

[1]For a description of a heuristic that can be used for the case where a set of jobs is to be processed through more than two work centers, see Thomas Vollmann et al., *Manufacturing Planning and Control Systems,* 5th ed. (New York: Irwin/McGraw-Hill, 2004).

[2]S. M. Johnson, "Optimal Two- and Three-Stage Production with Setup Times Included," *Naval Research Quarterly* 1 (March 1954), pp. 61–68.

SOLUTION

a. Select the job with the shortest processing time. It is job D, with a time of two hours.

b. Since the time is at the first center, schedule job D first. Eliminate job D from further consideration.

1st	2nd	3rd	4th	5th	6th
D					

c. Job B has the next shortest time. Since it is at the second work center, schedule it last and eliminate job B from further consideration. We now have

1st	2nd	3rd	4th	5th	6th
D					B

d. The remaining jobs and their times are

Job	1	2
A	5	5
C	8	9
E	6	8
F	12	15

Note that there is a tie for the shortest remaining time; job A has the same time at each work center. It makes no difference, then, whether we place it toward the beginning or the end of the sequence. Suppose it is placed arbitrarily toward the end. We now have

1st	2nd	3rd	4th	5th	6th
D				A	B

e. The shortest remaining time is six hours for job E at work center 1. Thus, schedule that job toward the beginning of the sequence (after job D):

1st	2nd	3rd	4th	5th	6th
D	E			A	B

f. Job C has the shorter time of the remaining two jobs. Since it is for the first work center, place it third in the sequence. Finally, assign the remaining job (F) to the fourth position and the result is

1st	2nd	3rd	4th	5th	6th
D	E	C	F	A	B

g. Construct a Gantt chart to reveal flow time and idle time information. Be very careful not to schedule the beginning of work at center 2 *before* work at center 1 has been completed for any given job. Traditionally, it is assumed that center 1 must finish and pass the job to center 2, which can cause idle time in center 2's schedule, such as in the case of job F as follows:

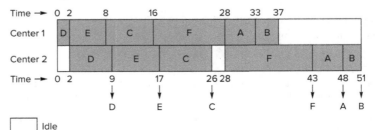

Idle

Thus, the group of jobs will take 51 hours to complete. The second work center will wait two hours for its first job and also wait two hours after finishing job C. Center 1 will be finished in 37 hours. Of course, idle periods at the beginning or end of the sequence could be used to do other jobs or for maintenance or setup/teardown activities.

Sequencing Jobs When Setup Times Are Sequence-Dependent

The preceding discussion and examples assumed that machine setup times are independent of processing order, but in many instances that assumption is not true. Consequently, a manager may want to schedule jobs at a workstation taking those dependencies into account. The goal is to minimize total setup time.

Consider the following table, which shows workstation machine setup times based on job processing order. For example, if job A is followed by job B, the setup time for B will be six hours. Furthermore, if job A is completed first, followed by job B, job C will then follow job B and have a setup time of four hours. If a job is done first, its setup time will be the amount shown in the setup time column to the right of the job. Thus, if job A is done first, its setup time will be three hours.

		Setup time (hrs.)	Resulting following job setup time (hrs.) is		
			A	B	C
If the	A	3	—	6	2
preceding	B	2	1	—	4
job is	C	2	5	3	—

The simplest way to determine which sequence will result in the lowest total setup time is to list each possible sequence and determine its total setup time. In general, the number of different alternatives is equal to $n!$, where n is the number of jobs. Here, n is 3, so $n! = 3 \times 2 \times 1 = 6$. The six alternatives and their total setup times are as follows:

Sequence	Setup Times	Total
A-B-C	$3 + 6 + 4 = 13$	
A-C-B	$3 + 2 + 3 = 8$	
B-A-C	$2 + 1 + 2 = 5$ (best)	
B-C-A	$2 + 4 + 5 = 11$	
C-A-B	$2 + 5 + 6 = 13$	
C-B-A	$2 + 3 + 1 = 6$	

Hence, to minimize total setup time, the manager would select sequence B-A-C.

This procedure is relatively simple to do manually when the number of jobs is two or three. However, as the number of jobs increases, the list of alternatives quickly becomes larger. For example, six jobs would have 720 alternatives. In such instances, a manager would employ a computer to generate the list and identify the best alternative(s). (Note that more than one alternative may be tied for the lowest setup time.)

Why Scheduling Can Be Difficult

Scheduling can be difficult for a number of reasons. One is that, in reality, an operation must deal with variability in setup times, processing times, interruptions, and changes in the set of

© Alex Mcaclean/The Image Bank/Getty Images

LO16.9 Discuss the theory of constraints and that approach to scheduling.

jobs. Another major reason is that, except for small job sets, there is no method for identifying the optimal schedule, and it would be virtually impossible to sort through the vast number of possible alternatives to obtain the best schedule. As a result, scheduling is far from an exact science and, in many instances, is an ongoing task for a manager.

Computer technology reduces the burden of scheduling and makes real-time scheduling possible.

Minimizing Scheduling Difficulties

There are a number of actions that managers can consider to minimize scheduling problems:

- Setting realistic due dates.
- Focusing on bottleneck operations: First, try to increase the capacity of the operations. If that is not possible or feasible, schedule the bottleneck operations first, and then schedule the nonbottleneck operations around the bottleneck operations.
- Considering lot splitting for large jobs. This usually works best when there are relatively large differences in job times. Note that this doesn't apply to single-unit jobs.

The Theory of Constraints

Another approach to scheduling was developed and promoted by Eli Goldratt.[3] He first described it in his book *The Goal*. Goldratt avoided much of the complexity often associated with scheduling problems by simply focusing on *bottleneck* operations (i.e., those for which there was insufficient capacity—in effect, a work center with zero idle time). He reasoned the output of the system was limited by the output of the bottleneck operation(s); therefore, it was essential to schedule the nonbottleneck operations in a way that minimized the idle time of the bottleneck operation(s). Thus, idle time of nonbottleneck operations was not a factor in overall productivity of the system, as long as the bottleneck operations were used effectively. These observations have been refined into a series of scheduling principles which include:

- An hour lost at a bottleneck operation is an hour lost by the system. The bottleneck operation determines the overall capacity of the system.
- Saving time through improvements of a nonbottleneck will not increase the ultimate output of the system.
- Activation of a resource is not the same as utilization of a resource. Because a nonbottleneck operation is active does not necessarily mean it is being useful.

These principles are also the foundation of a specific scheduling technique for intermittent production systems, one that many firms have found simpler and less time-consuming to use than traditional analytical techniques. This technique uses a *drum-buffer-rope* conceptualization to manage the system. The "drum" is the schedule; it sets the pace of production. The goal is to schedule to make maximum use of bottleneck resources. The "buffer" refers to potentially constraining resources outside of the bottleneck. The role of the buffer is to keep a small amount of inventory ahead of the bottleneck operation to minimize the risk of having it be idle. The "rope" represents the synchronizing of the sequence of operations to ensure effective use of the bottleneck operations. The goal is to avoid costly and time-consuming multiple setups, particularly of capacity-constrained resources, so they do not become bottlenecks too.

[3]Eli Goldratt, *The General Theory of Constraints* (New Haven, CT: Avraham Y. Institute, 1989).

The drum-buffer-rope approach provides a basis for developing a schedule that achieves maximum output and shorter lead times while avoiding carrying excess inventory. Use of the drum-buffer-rope approach generally results in operations capable of consistent on-time delivery, reduced inventory, and shorter lead times, as well as a reduction in disruptions that require expediting.

Goldratt also developed a system of varying batch sizes to achieve the greatest output of bottleneck operations. He used the term **process batch** to denote the basic lot size for a job and the term **transfer batch** to denote a portion of the basic lot that could be used during production to facilitate utilization of bottleneck operations. In effect, a lot could be split into two or more parts. Splitting a large lot at one or more operations preceding a bottleneck operation would reduce the waiting time of the bottleneck operation.

Traditional management has emphasized maximizing output of every operation. In contrast to that approach, the **theory of constraints** has as its goal maximizing flow through the entire system, which it does by emphasizing balancing the flow through the various operations. It begins with identifying the bottleneck operation. Next, there is a five-step procedure to improve the performance of the bottleneck operation:

1. Determine what is constraining the operation.
2. Exploit the constraint (i.e., make sure the constraining resource is used to its maximum).
3. Subordinate everything to the constraint (i.e., focus on the constraint).
4. Determine how to overcome (eliminate) the constraint.
5. Repeat the process for the next highest constraint.

(Note the similarity to the plan-do-study-act [PDSA] approach discussed in Chapter 9.)

The goal, of course, is to make *money*. The theory of constraints uses three metrics to assess the effectiveness of improvements:

- **Throughput:** The rate at which the system generates *money* through sales (i.e., the contribution margin, or sales revenue less variable costs; labor costs are considered to be part of operating expense)
- **Inventory:** Inventory represents *money* tied up in goods and materials used in a process
- **Operating expense:** All the *money* the system spends to convert inventory into throughput; this includes utilities, scrap, depreciation, and so on

Goldratt's ideas are applicable to both manufacturing and service environments.

Process batch The economical quantity to produce upon the activation of a given operation.

Transfer batch The quantity to be transported from one operation to another, assumed to be smaller than the first operation's process batch.

Theory of constraints Production planning approach that emphasizes balancing flow throughout a system, and pursues a perpetual five-step improvement process centered around the system's currently most restrictive constraint.

16.3 SCHEDULING SERVICES

LO16.10 Summarize some of the unique problems encountered in service systems, and describe some of the approaches used for scheduling service systems.

Scheduling service systems presents certain problems not generally encountered in manufacturing systems. This is due primarily to (1) the inability to store or inventory services and (2) the random nature of customer requests for service. In some situations, the second difficulty can be moderated by using appointment or reservation systems, but the inability to store services in most cases is a fact of life that managers must contend with.

The approach used to schedule services generally depends on whether customer contact is involved. In back-office operations, where there is little or no customer contact—such as processing mail-order requests, loan approvals, and tax preparation—the same priority rules described in the preceding pages are used. The goal is to maximize worker efficiency, and work is often processed in batches. A key factor can be the due date, say for rush orders, orders where the customer has paid a premium for faster than normal delivery. That is similar to the situation that occurs in front-office operations, where there is a high degree of customer contact, and efficiency may become secondary to keeping customer waiting times to reasonable levels, so scheduling the workforce to meet demand becomes a priority. Having too few workers causes waiting lines to form, but having more workers than needed increases labor costs, which can have a substantial impact on profits, particularly in service systems where labor is the major cost involved.

An ideal situation is one that has a smooth flow of customers through the system. This would occur if each new customer arrives at the precise instant that the preceding customer's service is completed, as in a physician's office, or in air travel if the demand just equals the number of available seats. In each of these situations customer waiting time would be minimized, and the service system staff and equipment would be fully utilized. Unfortunately, the random nature of customer requests for service that generally prevails in service systems makes it nearly impossible to provide service capability that matches demand. Moreover, if service times are subject to variability—say, because of differing processing requirements—the inefficiency of the system is compounded. The inefficiencies can be reduced if arrivals can be scheduled (e.g., appointments), as in the case of doctors and dentists. However, in many situations appointments are not possible (supermarkets, gas stations, theaters, hospital emergency rooms, repair of equipment breakdowns). Chapter 18, on waiting lines, focuses on those kinds of situations. There, the emphasis is on intermediate-term decisions related to service capacity. In this section, we will concern ourselves with short-term *scheduling*, in which much of the capacity of a system is essentially fixed, and the goal is to achieve a certain degree of customer service by efficient utilization of that capacity.

Scheduling in service systems may involve scheduling (1) customers, (2) the workforce, and (3) equipment. Scheduling customers often takes the form of appointment systems or reservation systems.

Appointment Systems

Appointment systems are intended to control the timing of customer arrivals in order to minimize customer waiting while achieving a high degree of capacity utilization. A doctor can use an appointment system to schedule patients' office visits during the afternoon, leaving the mornings free for hospital duties. Similarly, an attorney can schedule client meetings around court appearances. Even with appointments, however, problems can still arise due to lack of punctuality on the part of patients or clients, no-shows, and the inability to completely control the length of contact time (e.g., a dentist might run into complications in filling a tooth and have to spend additional time with a patient, thus backing up later appointments). Some of this can be avoided by trying to match the time reserved for a patient or client with the specific needs of that case rather than setting appointments at regular intervals. Even with the problems of late arrivals and no-shows, the appointment system is a tremendous improvement over random arrivals.

Reservation Systems

Reservation systems are designed to enable service systems to formulate a fairly accurate estimate of the demand on the system for a given time period and to minimize customer disappointment generated by excessive waiting or inability to obtain service. Reservation systems are widely used by resorts, hotels and motels, restaurants, and some modes of transportation (e.g., airlines, car rentals). In the case of restaurants, reservations enable management to spread out or group customers so that demand matches service capabilities. Late arrivals and no-shows can disrupt the system. One approach to the no-show problem is to use decision theory (described in the supplement to Chapter 5). The problem also can be viewed as a single-period inventory problem, as described in Chapter 13.

Yield Management

Many companies, especially in the travel and tourist industries, operate with fixed capacities. Examples include hotels and motels, which operate with a fixed number of rooms to rent each night; airlines, which operate with a fixed number of seats to sell on any given flight; and cruise lines, which operate with a fixed number of berths to sell for any given cruise. The number of rooms, seats, or berths can be thought of as perishable inventory. For example, unsold seats on a flight cannot be carried over to the next flight; they are lost. The same is true for hotel rooms and cruise berths. Of course that unsold inventory does not generate income, so companies with fixed capacities must develop strategies to deal with sales.

Yield management is the application of pricing strategies to allocate capacity among various categories of demand with the goal of maximizing the revenue generated by the fixed capacity. Demand for fixed capacity usually consists of customers who make advance reservations and walk-ins. Customers who make advance reservations are typically price-sensitive, while walk-ins are often price-insensitive. Companies must decide on the percentage of their limited inventory to allocate to reservations, trading off lower revenue per unit for increased certainty of sales, and how much to allocate to walk-ins, where demand is less certain but revenue per unit is higher.

© Mark Wilson/Getty

The basic yield management concept is applicable to railroads as well as airlines. Yield management is multidisciplinary because it blends elements of marketing, operations, and financial management.

The ability to predict demand is critical to the success of yield management, so forecasting plays a key role in the process. Seasonal variations are generally important, so forecasts must incorporate seasonality and plans must also be somewhat flexible to allow for ever-present random variations.

Yield management The application of pricing strategies to allocate capacity among various categories of demand.

Scheduling the Workforce

Scheduling customers is demand management. Scheduling the workforce is capacity management. This approach works best when demand can be predicted with reasonable accuracy. This is often true for restaurants, theaters, rush-hour traffic, and similar instances that have repeating patterns of intensity of customer arrivals. Scheduling hospital personnel, police, and telephone operators for catalog sales, credit card companies, and mutual fund companies also comes under this heading. An additional consideration is the extent to which variations in customer demands can be met with workforce flexibility. Thus, capacity can be adjusted by having cross-trained workers who can be temporarily assigned to help out on bottleneck operations during periods of peak demand.

Various constraints can affect workforce scheduling flexibility, including legal, behavioral, technical—such as workers' qualifications to perform certain operations—and budget constraints. Union or federal work rules and vacations can make scheduling more complicated.

Cyclical Scheduling

In many services (e.g., hospitals, police departments, fire departments, restaurants, and supermarkets) the scheduling requirements are fairly similar: Employees must be assigned to work shifts or time slots, and have days off, on a repeating or cyclical basis. Here is a method for determining both a schedule and the minimum number of workers needed.

Generally a basic work pattern is set (e.g., work five consecutive days, have two consecutive days off), and a list of staffing needs for the schedule cycle (usually one week) is given. For example:

Day	Mon	Tue	Wed	Thu	Fri	Sat	Sun
Staff needed	2	4	3	4	6	5	5

A fairly simple but effective approach for determining the minimum number of workers needed is the following: Begin by repeating the staff needs for worker 1. Then,

1.   Make the first worker's assignment such that the two days with the lowest need (i.e., lowest sum) are designated as days off. Here Mon–Tues has the two lowest consecutive requirements. Circle those days. (Note, in some instances, Sun–Mon might yield the two lowest days.) In case of a tie, pick the pair with the lowest adjacent requirement day to the left and day to the right. If there is still a tie, pick arbitrarily.

Day	Mon	Tue	Wed	Thu	Fri	Sat	Sun
Staff needed	2	4	3	4	6	5	5
Worker 1	(2	4)	3	4	6	5	5

2. Subtract one from each day's requirement, except for the circled days. Assign the next employee, again using the two lowest consecutive days as days off. Circle those days.

Day	Mon	Tue	Wed	Thu	Fri	Sat	Sun
Staff needed	2	4	3	4	6	5	5
Worker 1	(2	4)	3	4	6	5	5
Worker 2	2	4	(2	3)	5	4	4

3. Repeat the preceding step for each additional worker until all staffing requirements have been met. However, don't subtract from a value of zero. Note the tie for worker 3: Mon–Tue and Sun–Mon have the lowest consecutive requirements, 4. The Mon–Tue two adjacents are Sun = 3 and Wed = 2, for a total of 5, which is less than the two adjacents for Sun–Mon (Sat = 3 and Tue = 3 for a total of 6). So circle Mon–Tue requirements for worker 3. Worker 4 also has a tie, and adjacents Sat and Tue total 5, whereas Tue–Fri adjacents total 6, so circle Sun–Mon requirements.

Day	Mon	Tue	Wed	Thu	Fri	Sat	Sun	
Staff needed	2	4	3	4	6	5	5	
Worker 1	(2	4)	3	4	6	5	5	
Worker 2	2	4	(2	3)	5	4	4	
Worker 3	(1	3)	2	3	4	3	3	
Worker 4	(1)	3	1	2	3	2	(2)	(tie)
Worker 5	1	2	(0	1)	2	1	2	
Worker 6	(0	1)	0	1	1	0	1	(multiple ties)
Worker 7	0	1	(0	0)	0	0	0	(multiple ties)
No. working:	2	4	3	4	6	5	5	

For Worker 7, circle Wed and Thu 0 0.

To identify the days each worker is working, go across each worker's row to find the non-zero values that are not circled, signifying that the worker is assigned for those days. Similarly, to find the workers who are assigned to work for any particular day, go down that day's column to find the nonzero values that are not circled. *Note:* Worker 6 will only work three days, and worker 7 will only work one day.

Scheduling Multiple Resources

In some situations, it is necessary to coordinate the use of more than one resource. For example, hospitals must schedule surgeons, operating room staffs, recovery room staffs, admissions, special equipment, nursing staffs, and so on. Educational institutions must schedule faculty, classrooms, audiovisual equipment, and students. As you might guess, the greater the number of resources to be scheduled simultaneously, the greater the complexity and the less likely that an optimum schedule can be achieved. The problem is further complicated by the variable nature of such systems. For example, educational institutions frequently change their course offerings, student enrollments change, and students exhibit different course-selection patterns.

Some schools and hospitals are using computer software to assist them in devising acceptable schedules, although many appear to be using intuitive approaches with varying degrees of success.

Airlines are another example of service systems that require the scheduling of multiple resources. Flight crews, aircraft, baggage handling equipment, ticket counters, gate personnel, boarding ramps, food service, cleaning, and maintenance personnel all have to be coordinated. Furthermore, government regulations on the number of hours a pilot can spend flying place an additional restriction on the system. Another interesting variable is that, unlike most systems, the flight crews and the equipment do not remain in one location. Moreover, the crew and the equipment are not usually scheduled as a single unit. Flight crews are often scheduled so that they return to their base city every two days or more, and rest breaks must be considered. On the other hand, the aircraft may be in almost continuous use except for periodic maintenance and repairs. Consequently, flight crews commonly follow different trip patterns than that of the aircraft.

Service systems are prone to slowdowns when variability in demand for services causes bottlenecks. Part of the difficulty lies in predicting which operations will become bottlenecks. Moreover, bottlenecks may shift with the passage of time, so that different operations become bottleneck operations—further complicating the problem.

16.4 OPERATIONS STRATEGY

Scheduling can either help or hinder operations strategy. If scheduling is done well, goods or services can be made or delivered in a timely manner. Resources can be used to best advantage and customers will be satisfied. Scheduling not performed well will result in inefficient use of resources and possibly dissatisfied customers.

The implication is clear: Management should not overlook the important role that scheduling plays in the success of an organization and the supply chain, giving a competitive advantage if done well or disadvantage if done poorly. Time-based competition depends on good scheduling. Coordination of materials, equipment use, and employee time is an important function of operations management. It is not enough to have good design, superior quality, and the other elements of a well-run organization if scheduling is done poorly—just as it is not enough to own a well-designed and well-made car, with all the latest features for comfort and safety, if the owner doesn't know how to drive it!

SUMMARY

Scheduling involves the timing and coordination of operations. Such activities are fundamental to virtually every organization. Scheduling problems differ according to whether a system is designed for high volume, intermediate volume, or low volume. Scheduling problems are particularly complex for job shops (low volume) because of the variety of jobs these systems are required to process.

The two major problems in job-shop scheduling are assigning jobs to machines or work centers, and designating the sequence of job processing at a given machine or work center. Gantt load charts are frequently employed to help managers visualize workloads, and they are useful for describing and analyzing sequencing alternatives. In addition, both heuristic and optimizing methods are used to develop loading and sequencing plans. For the most part, the optimization techniques can be used only if certain assumptions can be made.

Customer requirements in service systems generally present very different circumstances than those encountered in manufacturing systems. Some services can use appointments and reservations for scheduling purposes, although not all systems are amenable to this. When multiple resources are involved, the task of balancing the system can be fairly complex.

KEY POINTS

1. Scheduling occurs in every business organization.
2. Scheduling decisions are made within constraints established by decisions on capacity, product or service design, process selection and layout, aggregate planning, and master scheduling.
3. Scheduling decisions occur just prior to the conversion of inputs into outputs.
4. Effective scheduling can reduce costs and increase productivity.

KEY TERMS			
	assignment model, 699	input/output (I/O) control, 698	priority rules, 702
	backward scheduling, 697	job flow time, 703	process batch, 713
	finite loading, 697	job lateness, 703	schedule chart, 697
	flow-shop scheduling, 692	job-shop scheduling, 695	scheduling, 691
	flow system, 692	job time, 702	sequencing, 702
	forward scheduling, 697	Johnson's rule, 709	theory of constraints, 713
	Gantt chart, 695	load chart, 696	transfer batch, 713
	global priority rules, 702	loading, 695	workstation, 702
	Hungarian method, 699	local priority rules, 702	yield management, 715
	infinite loading, 697	makespan, 703	

SOLVED PROBLEMS

Problem 1   *The assignment method.* The following table contains information on the cost to run three jobs on four available machines. Determine an assignment plan that will minimize costs.

		MACHINE			
		A	**B**	**C**	**D**
	1	12	16	14	10
Job	**2**	9	8	13	7
	3	15	12	9	11

Solution   In order for us to be able to use the assignment method, the numbers of jobs and machines must be equal. To remedy this situation, add a *dummy* job with costs of 0, and then solve as usual.

		MACHINE			
		A	**B**	**C**	**D**
	1	12	16	14	10
Job	**2**	9	8	13	7
	3	15	12	9	11
(dummy)	**4**	0	0	0	0

a. Subtract the smallest number from each row. The results are

		MACHINE			
		A	**B**	**C**	**D**
	1	2	6	4	0
Job	**2**	2	1	6	0
	3	6	3	0	2
	4	0	0	0	0

b. Subtract the smallest number in each column. (Because of the dummy zeros in each column, the resulting table will be unchanged.)

c. Determine the minimum number of lines needed to cross out the zeros. One possible way is as follows:

		MACHINE			
		A	**B**	**C**	**D**
	1	2	6	4	0
Job	**2**	2	1	6	0
	3	6	3	0	2
	4	0	0	0	0

d. Because the number of lines is less than the number of rows, modify the numbers.

  (1) Subtract the smallest uncovered number (1) from each uncovered number.

  (2) Add the smallest uncovered number to numbers at line intersections. The result is:

		MACHINE			
		A	**B**	**C**	**D**
	1	1	5	4	0
Job	**2**	1	0	6	0
	3	5	2	0	2
	4	0	0	1	1

e. Test for optimality:

		MACHINE			
		A	**B**	**C**	**D**
	1	1	5	4	0
Job	**2**	1	0	6	0
	3	5	2	0	2
	4	0	0	1	1

Because the minimum number of lines equals the number of rows, an optimum assignment can be made.

f. Assign jobs to machines. Start with rows 1 and 3, since they each have one zero, and columns A and C, also with one zero each. After each assignment, cross out all the numbers in that row *and* column. The result is:

		MACHINE			
		A	**B**	**C**	**D**
Job	**1**	1	5	4	0
	2	1	0	6	0
	3	5	2	0	2
	4	0	0	1	1

Notice that there is only one assignment in each row, and only one assignment in each column.

g. Compute total costs, referring to the original table.

1-D	$10
2-B	8
3-C	9
4-A	0
	$27

h. The implication of assignment 4-A is that machine A will not be assigned a job. It may remain idle or be used for another job.

Priority rules. Job times (including processing and setup) are shown in the following table for five jobs waiting to be processed at a work center.

Problem 2

Job	Job Time (hours)	Due Date (hours)
a	12	15
b	6	24
c	14	20
d	3	8
e	7	6

Determine the processing sequence that would result from each of these priority rules:

a. SPT   b. EDD

Solution   Assume job times are independent of processing sequence.

	a. SPT		b. EDD	
Job	Job Time	Processing Order	Hour Due	Processing Order
a	12	4	15	3
b	6	2	24	5
c	14	5	20	4
d	3	1	8	2
e	7	3	6	1

Problem 3   *Priority rules.* Using the job times and due dates from Solved Problem 2, determine each of the following performance measures for first-come, first-served processing order: Assume jobs listed in order of arrival.

a. Makespan

b. Average flow time

c. Average tardiness

d. Average number of jobs at the workstation

Solution

Job	Job Time	Flow Time	Hour Due	Hours Tardy
a	12	12	15	0
b	6	18	24	0
c	14	32	20	12
d	3	35	8	27
e	7	42	6	36
Total		139		75

a. Makespan = 42 hours

b. Average flow time $= \dfrac{\text{Total flow time}}{\text{Number of jobs}} = \dfrac{139}{5} = 27.80$ hours

c. Average tardiness $= \dfrac{\text{Total hours tardy}}{\text{Number of jobs}} = \dfrac{75}{5} = 15$ hours

d. $\dfrac{\text{Average number of}}{\text{jobs at workstation}} = \dfrac{\text{Total flow time}}{\text{Makespan}} = \dfrac{139}{42} = 3.31$

Problem 4   *S/O rule.* Using the following information, determine an order processing sequence using the S/O priority rule.

Order	Processing Time Remaining (days)	Due Date (days)	Number of Operations Remaining
A	20	30	2
B	11	18	5
C	10	6	2
D	16	23	4

Assume times are independent of processing sequence.   Solution

Order	(1) Remaining Processing Time	(2) Due Date	(3) (2) − (1) Slack	(4) Number of Operations	(5) Ratio	(6) Rank (sequence)
A	20	30	10	2	5.00	4
B	11	18	7	5	1.40	2
C	10	6	−4	2	−2.00	1
D	16	23	7	4	1.75	3

(Note that one ratio is negative. When negatives occur, assign the *lowest* rank to the *most negative* number.)

Sequencing jobs through two work centers. Use Johnson's rule to obtain the optimum sequence for processing the jobs shown through work centers A and B.   **Problem 5**

Job	JOB TIMES (hours)	
	Work Center A	**Work Center B**
a	2.50	4.20
b	3.80	1.50
c	2.20	3.00
d	5.80	4.00
e	4.50	2.00

a. Identify the smallest time: job b (1.50 hours at work center B). Because the time is for B, schedule this job last.   Solution

b. The next smallest time is job e (2.00 hours at B). Schedule job e next to last.

c. Identify the smallest remaining job time: job c (2.20 hours at center A). Since the time is in the A column, schedule job c first. At this point, we have:

c, _____, _____, e, b

d. The smallest time for the remaining jobs is 2.50 hours for job a at center A. Schedule this job after job c. The one remaining job (job d) fills the remaining slot. Thus, we have c-a-d-e-b.

For Solved Problem 5, determine what effect splitting jobs c, d, e, and b in work center A would have on the idle time of work center B and on the throughput time. Assume that each job can be split into two equal parts.   **Problem 6**

We assume that the processing sequence remains unchanged and proceed on that basis. The solution from the previous problem is shown in the following chart. The next chart shows reduced idle time at center B when splitting is used.   Solution

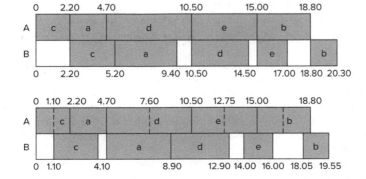

An inspection of these two figures reveals that throughput time has decreased from 20.30 hours to 19.55 hours. In addition, the original idle time was 5.6 hours. After splitting certain jobs, it was reduced to 4.85 hours, so some improvement was achieved. Note that processing times at B are generally less than at A for jobs toward the end of the sequence. As a result, jobs such as e and b at B were scheduled so that they were *centered* around the finishing times of e and b, respectively, at A, to avoid having to break the jobs due to waiting for the remainder of the split job from A. Thus, the greatest advantage from job splitting generally comes from splitting earlier jobs when Johnson's rule is used for sequencing.

DISCUSSION AND REVIEW QUESTIONS

1. Why is scheduling fairly simple for repetitive systems but fairly complex for job shops?
2. What are the main decision areas of job-shop scheduling?
3. What are Gantt charts? How are they used in scheduling? What are the advantages of using Gantt charts?
4. What are the basic assumptions of the assignment method of linear programming?
5. Briefly describe each of these priority rules:
   a. FCFS
   b. SPT
   c. EDD
   d. S/O
   e. Rush
6. Why are priority rules needed?
7. What problems not generally found in manufacturing systems do service systems present in terms of scheduling the use of resources?
8. Explain forward and backward schedulings and each one's advantage.
9. How are scheduling and productivity related?
10. What factors would you take into account in deciding whether to split a job?
11. Explain the term *makespan*.

TAKING STOCK

1. What general trade-offs are involved in sequencing decisions? In scheduling decisions?
2. Who needs to be involved in setting schedules?
3. How has technology had an impact on scheduling?

CRITICAL THINKING EXERCISES

1. One approach that can be effective in reducing the impact of production bottlenecks in a job shop or batch operations setting is to use smaller lot sizes.
   a. What is the impact of a production bottleneck?
   b. Explain how small lot sizes can reduce the impact of bottleneck operations.
   c. What are the key trade-offs in using small lot sizes for the purpose of reducing the bottleneck effect?
   d. In some cases, the location of a bottleneck will shift (i.e., sometimes it is at workstation 3, another time it is at workstation 12). Furthermore, there can be more than one bottleneck operation at the same time. How would these situations impact scheduling using small lot sizes?
2. Doctors' and dentists' offices frequently schedule patient visits at regularly spaced intervals. What problems can this create? Can you suggest an alternative approach to reduce these problems? Under what circumstances would regularly spaced appointments constitute a reasonable approach to patient scheduling?
3. Name three examples of unethical behavior involving scheduling and state the ethical principle each violates.

1. Use the assignment method to determine the best way to assign workers to jobs, given the following cost information. Compute the total cost for your assignment plan.

PROBLEMS

		JOB		
		A	B	C
Worker	1	5	8	6
	2	6	7	9
	3	4	5	3

2. Rework Problem 1, treating the numbers in the table as profits instead of costs. Compute the total profit.

3. Assign trucks to delivery routes so that total costs are minimized, given the cost data shown. What is the total cost?

		ROUTE				
		A	B	C	D	E
Truck	1	4	5	9	8	7
	2	6	4	8	3	5
	3	7	3	10	4	6
	4	5	2	5	5	8
	5	6	5	3	4	9

4. Develop an assignment plan that will minimize processing costs, given the information shown, and interpret your answer.

		WORKER		
		A	B	C
Job	1	12	8	11
	2	13	10	8
	3	14	9	14
	4	10	7	12

5. Use the assignment method to obtain a plan that will minimize the processing costs in the following table under these conditions:

   a. The combination 2-D is undesirable

   b. The combinations 1-A and 2-D are undesirable

		WORKER				
		A	B	C	D	E
Job	1	14	18	20	17	18
	2	14	15	19	16	17
	3	12	16	15	14	17
	4	11	13	14	12	14
	5	10	16	15	14	13

6. The following table contains information concerning four jobs that are awaiting processing at a work center.

Job	Job Time (days)	Due Date (days)
A	14	20
B	10	16
C	7	15
D	6	17

a. Sequence the jobs using (1) FCFS, (2) SPT, (3) EDD, and (4) CR. Assume the list is by order of arrival.

b. For each of the methods in part *a,* determine (1) the average job flow time, (2) the average tardiness, and (3) the average number of jobs at the work center.

c. Is one method superior to the others? Explain.

7. Using the information presented in the following table, identify the processing sequence that would result using (1) FCFS, (2) SPT, (3) EDD, and (4) CR. For each method, determine (1) average job flow time, (2) average job tardiness, and (3) average number of jobs in the system. Jobs are listed in order of arrival. (*Hint:* First determine the total job time for each job by computing the total processing time for the job and then adding in the setup time. All times and due dates are in hours.)

Job	Processing Time per Unit	Units per Job	Setup Time	Due Date
a	.14	45	0.7	4
b	.25	14	0.5	10
c	.10	18	0.2	12
d	.25	40	1.0	20
e	.10	75	0.5	15

8. The following table shows orders to be processed at a machine shop as of 8:00 a.m. Monday. The jobs have different operations they must go through. Processing times are in days. Jobs are listed in order of arrival.

a. Determine the processing sequence at the first work center using each of these rules: (1) FCFS, (2) S/O.

b. Compute the effectiveness of each rule using each of these measures: (1) average flow time, (2) average number of jobs at the work center.

Job	Processing Time (days)	Due Date (days)	Remaining Number of Operations
A	8	20	2
B	10	18	4
C	5	25	5
D	11	17	3
E	9	35	4

9. A wholesale grocery distribution center uses a two-step process to fill orders. Tomorrow's work will consist of filling the seven orders shown. Determine a job sequence that will minimize the time required to fill the orders.

	TIME (hours)	
Order	Step 1	Step 2
A	1.20	1.40
B	0.90	1.30
C	2.00	0.80
D	1.70	1.50
E	1.60	1.80
F	2.20	1.75
G	1.30	1.40

10. The times required to complete each of eight jobs in a two-machine flow shop are shown in the table that follows. Each job must follow the same sequence, beginning with machine A and moving to machine B.

a. Determine a sequence that will minimize makespan time.

b. Construct a chart of the resulting sequence, and find machine B's idle time.

c. For the sequence determined in part *a*, how much would machine B's idle time be reduced by splitting the last two jobs in half?

	TIME (hours)	
Job	**Machine A**	**Machine B**
a	16	5
b	3	13
c	9	6
d	8	7
e	2	14
f	12	4
g	18	14
h	20	11

11. Given the operation times provided:
    a. Develop a job sequence that minimizes idle time at the two work centers.
    b. Construct a chart of the activities at the two centers, and determine each one's idle time, assuming no other activities are involved.

	JOB TIMES (minutes)					
	A	**B**	**C**	**D**	**E**	**F**
Center 1	20	16	43	60	35	42
Center 2	27	30	51	12	28	24

12. A shoe repair operation uses a two-step sequence that all jobs in a certain category follow. All jobs can be split in half at both stations. For the group of jobs listed:
    a. Find the sequence that will minimize total completion time.
    b. Determine the amount of idle time for workstation B.
    c. What jobs are candidates for splitting? Why? If they were split, how much would idle time and makespan time be reduced?

	JOB TIMES (minutes)				
	A	**B**	**C**	**D**	**E**
Workstation A	27	18	70	26	15
Workstation B	45	33	30	24	10

13. The following schedule was prepared by the production manager of Marymount Metal Shop: Determine a schedule that will result in earliest completion of all jobs on this list.

	CUTTING		POLISHING	
Job	**Start**	**Finish**	**Start**	**Finish**
A	0	2	2	5
B	2	6	6	9
C	6	11	11	13
D	11	15	15	20
E	15	17	20	23
F	17	20	23	24
G	20	21	24	28

14. The production manager must determine the processing sequence for seven jobs through the grinding and deburring departments. The same sequence will be followed in both departments. The manager's goal is to move the jobs through the two departments as quickly as possible. The foreman of the deburring department wants the SPT rule to be used to minimize the work-in-process inventory in his department.

726   **Chapter Sixteen** Scheduling

PROCESSING TIME (hours)

Job	Grinding	Deburring
A	3	6
B	2	4
C	1	5
D	4	3
E	9	4
F	8	7
G	6	2

a. Prepare a schedule using SPT for the grinding department.
b. What is the flow time in the grinding department for the SPT sequence? What is the total time needed to process the seven jobs in both the grinding and deburring departments?
c. Determine a sequence that will minimize the total time needed to process the jobs in both departments. What flow time will result for the grinding department?
d. Discuss the trade-offs between the two alternative sequencing arrangements. At what point would the production manager be indifferent concerning the choice of sequences?

15. A foreman has determined processing times at a work center for a set of jobs and now wants to sequence them. Given the information shown, do the following:
a. Determine the processing sequence using (1) FCFS, (2) SPT, (3) EDD, and (4) CR. For each sequence, compute the average job tardiness, the average flow time, and the average number of jobs at the work center. The list is in FCFS order.
b. Using the results of your calculations in part a, show that the ratio of average flow time and the average number of jobs measures are equivalent for all four sequencing rules.
c. Determine the processing sequence that would result using the S/O rule.

Job	Job Time (days)	Due Date	Operations Remaining
a	4.5	10	3
b	6.0	17	4
c	5.2	12	3
d	1.6	27	5
e	2.8	18	3
f	3.3	19	1

16. Given the information in the following table, determine the processing sequence that would result using the S/O rule.

Job	Remaining Processing Time (days)	Due Date	Remaining Number of Operations
a	5	8	2
b	6	5	4
c	9	10	4
d	7	12	3
e	8	10	2

17. Given the following information on job times and due dates, determine the optimal processing sequence using (1) FCFS, (2) SPT, (3) EDD, and (4) CR. For each method, find the average job flow time and the average job tardiness. Jobs are listed in order of arrival.

Job	Job Time (hours)	Due Date (hours)
a	3.5	7
b	2.0	6
c	4.5	18
d	5.0	22
e	2.5	4
f	6.0	20

18. The Budd Gear Co. specializes in heat-treating gears for automobile companies. At 8:00 a.m., when Budd's shop opened today, five orders (listed in order of arrival) were waiting to be processed.

Order	Order Size (units)	Per Unit Time in Heat Treatment (minutes/unit)	Due Date (min. from now)
A	16	4	160
B	6	12	200
C	10	3	180
D	8	10	190
E	4	1	220

a. If the earliest due date rule is used, what sequence should be used?
b. What will be the average job tardiness?
c. What will be the average number of jobs in the system?
d. Would the SPT rule produce better results in terms of job tardiness?

19. The following table contains order-dependent setup times for three jobs. Which processing sequence will minimize the total setup time?

		Setup Time (hrs.)	Following Job's Setup Time (hrs.)		
			A	**B**	**C**
	A	2	—	3	5
Preceding Job	**B**	3	8	—	2
	C	2	4	3	—

20. The following table contains order-dependent setup times for three jobs. Which processing sequence will minimize the total setup time?

		Setup Time (hrs.)	Following Job's Setup Time (hrs.)		
			A	**B**	**C**
	A	2.4	—	1.8	2.2
Preceding Job	**B**	3.2	0.8	—	1.4
	C	2.0	2.6	1.3	—

21. The following table contains order-dependent setup times for four jobs. For safety reasons, job C cannot follow job A, nor can job A follow job C. Determine the processing sequence that will minimize the total setup time. (*Hint:* There are 12 alternatives.)

		Setup Time (hrs.)	Following Job's Setup Time (hrs.)			
			A	B	C	D
	A	2	—	5	×	4
Preceding job	B	1	7	—	3	2
	C	3	x	2	—	2
	D	2	4	3	6	—

22. Given this information on planned and actual inputs and outputs for a service center, determine the work backlog for each period. The beginning backlog is 12 hours of work. The figures shown are standard hours of work.

PERIOD

Input		1	2	3	4	5
	Planned	24	24	24	24	20
	Actual	25	27	20	22	24

Output		1	2	3	4	5
	Planned	24	24	24	24	23
	Actual	24	22	23	24	24

23. Given the following data on inputs and outputs at a work center, determine the cumulative deviation and the backlog for each time period. The beginning backlog is 7.

PERIOD

Input		1	2	3	4	5	6
	Planned	200	200	180	190	190	200
	Actual	210	200	179	195	193	194

PERIOD

Output		1	2	3	4	5	6
	Planned	200	200	180	190	190	200
	Actual	205	194	177	195	193	200

24. Determine the minimum number of workers needed, and a schedule for the following staffing requirements, giving workers two consecutive days off per cycle (not including Sunday).

Day	Mon	Tue	Wed	Thu	Fri	Sat
Staff needed	2	3	1	2	4	3

25. Determine the minimum number of workers needed, and a schedule for the following staffing requirements, giving workers two consecutive days off per cycle (not including Sunday).

Day	Mon	Tue	Wed	Thu	Fri	Sat
Staff needed	3	4	2	3	4	5

26. Determine the minimum number of workers needed, and a schedule for the following staffing requirements, giving workers two consecutive days off per cycle (not including Sunday).

Day	Mon	Tue	Wed	Thu	Fri	Sat
Staff needed	4	4	5	6	7	8

It was a little past 9:00 on a Monday morning when Jeff Baker walked into your office with a box of donuts.

"I've been talking with Anne about a problem we have with short-term capacity in our pad printing operation. You know, that's where we print the logo on the custom lines of yo-yos. We have received more orders than usual for July, and I want to release the orders to pad printing in a way that will enable us to meet our due date commitments in the best way possible. Would you have time to look at the order list (attached) and see what kind of schedule we should follow to do that? By the way, you have established quite a reputation in your short stay here. You have a talent for really explaining why your recommendations are the best approach in a way that all of us 'over-the-hill' managers can understand. Please be sure to do that for me, too. I want to understand why your recommendation is the best schedule and what the trade-offs are for other possible schedules—and none of that philosophical college mumbo-jumbo. Remember, I came up through the ranks. I don't have one of those sheepskins on my wall," he says with a laugh.

Since your schedule was back to normal after that MRP report you did for Anne, you agreed to look at the information. After that compliment, how could you say no? "Try to get back to me within a couple of days," Jeff said as he left your office.

After a few minutes with your old operations management text, you call the production control office to confirm the pad printing schedule. They confirm that pad printing runs one eight-hour shift per day. They tell you that due to a make-up day for flooding in June, pad printing will be running 23 days in July, beginning Friday, July 1 (they will work three Saturdays on July 9, 16, and 23, and take a one-day holiday for July 4).

You thank them for the information and then you begin to develop your plan.

Even though Jeff lacks a college degree, from what you have seen, he is very sharp. And obviously he knows good work when he sees it since he liked, and apparently understood, your past work. You resolve to cover all the bases but in a way that is as clear as possible.

PAD PRINTING ORDER LIST

Job	Date Order Received	Setup Time	Production Time	Due Date[1]
A	6/4	2 hrs.	6 days	11 July
B	6/7	4 hrs.	2 days	8 July
C	6/12	2 hrs.	8 days	25 July
D	6/14	4 hrs.	3 days	19 July
E	6/15	4 hrs.	9 days	29 July

[1]Jobs are due at the beginning of their respective due dates.

Note: Setup time is to set up the pad printer at the start of the job. Setup includes thoroughly cleaning the printing heads and ink reservoirs, installing the new pad(s) and ink supply, and carefully aligning the machine. Setup at the beginning of a new day with the same job is insignificant.

Examine the following rules and write a report to Jeff Baker summarizing your findings and advise him on which rule to use. Rules: FCFS, SPT, EDD, and CR.

Source: Victor E. Sower, "Hi-Ho, Yo-Yo, Inc." Copyright © 2006 Victor E. Sower, PhD, CDE.

SELECTED BIBLIOGRAPHY AND FURTHER READINGS

Goldratt, Eli, and Jeff Cox. *The Goal: A Process of Ongoing Improvement,* 3rd ed. Great Barrington, MA: North River Press, 2012.

Hopp, Wallace J., and Mark L. Spearman. *Factory Physics,* 3rd ed. New York: Irwin/McGraw-Hill, 2007.

Jacobs, F. Robert, William L. Berry, D. Clay Whybark, and Thomas E.Vollmann. *Manufacturing Planning and Control Systems,* 6th ed. New York: Irwin/McGraw-Hill, 2011.

Pinedo, Michael. *Planning and Scheduling in Manufacturing and Services.* New York: Springer, 2005.

B   Tables

A. Areas under the normal curve, 0 to z
B. Areas under the standardized normal curve
    1. From $-\infty$ to $-z$
    2. From $-\infty$ to $-z$
C. Cumulative Poisson probabilities

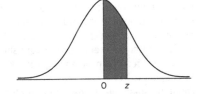

Table A   Areas under the normal curve, 0 to z

z	.00	.01	.02	.03	.04	.05	.06	.07	.08	.09
0.0	.0000	.0040	.0080	.0120	.0160	.0199	.0239	.0279	.0319	.0359
0.1	.0398	.0438	.0478	.0517	.0557	.0596	.0636	.0675	.0714	.0753
0.2	.0793	.0832	.0871	.0910	.0948	.0987	.1026	.1064	.1103	.1141
0.3	.1179	.1217	.1255	.1293	.1331	.1368	.1406	.1443	.1480	.1517
0.4	.1554	.1591	.1628	.1664	.1700	.1736	.1772	.1808	.1844	.1879
0.5	.1915	.1950	.1985	.2019	.2054	.2088	.2123	.2157	.2190	.2224
0.6	.2257	.2291	.2324	.2357	.2389	.2422	.2454	.2486	.2517	.2549
0.7	.2580	.2611	.2642	.2673	.2703	.2734	.2764	.2794	.2823	.2852
0.8	.2881	.2910	.2939	.2967	.2995	.3023	.3051	.3078	.3106	.3133
0.9	.3159	.3186	.3212	.3238	.3264	.3289	.3315	.3340	.3365	.3389
1.0	.3413	.3438	.3461	.3485	.3508	.3531	.3554	.3577	.3599	.3621
1.1	.3643	.3665	.3686	.3708	.3729	.3749	.3770	.3790	.3810	.3830
1.2	.3849	.3869	.3888	.3907	.3925	.3944	.3962	.3980	.3997	.4015
1.3	.4032	.4049	.4066	.4082	.4099	.4115	.4131	.4147	.4162	.4177
1.4	.4192	.4207	.4222	.4236	.4251	.4265	.4279	.4292	.4306	.4319
1.5	.4332	.4345	.4357	.4370	.4382	.4394	.4406	.4418	.4429	.4441
1.6	.4452	.4463	.4474	.4484	.4495	.4505	.4515	.4525	.4535	.4545
1.7	.4554	.4564	.4573	.4582	.4591	.4599	.4608	.4616	.4625	.4633
1.8	.4641	.4649	.4656	.4664	.4671	.4678	.4686	.4693	.4699	.4706
1.9	.4713	.4719	.4726	.4732	.4738	.4744	.4750	.4756	.4761	.4767
2.0	.4772	.4778	.4783	.4788	.4793	.4798	.4803	.4808	.4812	.4817
2.1	.4821	.4826	.4830	.4834	.4838	.4842	.4846	.4850	.4854	.4857
2.2	.4861	.4864	.4868	.4871	.4875	.4878	.4881	.4884	.4887	.4890
2.3	.4893	.4896	.4898	.4901	.4904	.4906	.4909	.4911	.4913	.4916
2.4	.4918	.4920	.4922	.4925	.4927	.4929	.4931	.4932	.4934	.4936
2.5	.4938	.4940	.4941	.4943	.4945	.4946	.4948	.4949	.4951	.4952
2.6	.4953	.4955	.4956	.4957	.4959	.4960	.4961	.4962	.4963	.4964
2.7	.4965	.4966	.4967	.4968	.4969	.4970	.4971	.4972	.4973	.4974
2.8	.4974	.4975	.4976	.4977	.4977	.4978	.4979	.4979	.4980	.4981
2.9	.4981	.4982	.4982	.4983	.4984	.4984	.4985	.4985	.4986	.4986
3.0	.4987	.4987	.4987	.4988	.4988	.4989	.4989	.4989	.4990	.4990

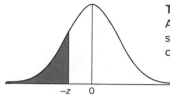

Table B.1
Areas under the standardized normal curve, from $-\infty$ to $-z$

.09	.08	.07	.06	.05	.04	.03	.02	.01	.00	z
.0002	.0003	.0003	.0003	.0003	.0003	.0003	.0003	.0003	.0003	−3.4
.0003	.0004	.0004	.0004	.0004	.0004	.0004	.0005	.0005	.0005	−3.3
.0005	.0005	.0005	.0006	.0006	.0006	.0006	.0006	.0007	.0007	−3.2
.0007	.0007	.0008	.0008	.0008	.0008	.0009	.0009	.0009	.0010	−3.1
.0010	.0010	.0011	.0011	.0011	.0012	.0012	.0013	.0013	.0013	−3.0
.0014	.0014	.0015	.0015	.0016	.0016	.0017	.0018	.0018	.0019	−2.9
.0019	.0020	.0021	.0021	.0022	.0023	.0023	.0024	.0025	.0026	−2.8
.0026	.0027	.0028	.0029	.0030	.0031	.0032	.0033	.0034	.0035	−2.7
.0036	.0037	.0038	.0039	.0040	.0041	.0043	.0044	.0045	.0047	−2.6
.0048	.0049	.0051	.0052	.0054	.0055	.0057	.0059	.0060	.0062	−2.5
.0064	.0066	.0068	.0069	.0071	.0073	.0075	.0078	.0080	.0082	−2.4
.0084	.0087	.0089	.0091	.0094	.0096	.0099	.0102	.0104	.0107	−2.3
.0110	.0113	.0116	.0119	.0122	.0125	.0129	.0132	.0136	.0139	−2.2
.0143	.0146	.0150	.0154	.0158	.0162	.0166	.0170	.0174	.0179	−2.1
.0183	.0188	.0192	.0197	.0202	.0207	.0212	.0217	.0222	.0228	−2.0
.0233	.0239	.0244	.0250	.0256	.0262	.0268	.0274	.0281	.0287	−1.9
.0294	.0301	.0307	.0314	.0322	.0329	.0336	.0344	.0351	.0359	−1.8
.0367	.0375	.0384	.0392	.0401	.0409	.0418	.0427	.0436	.0446	−1.7
.0455	.0465	.0475	.0485	.0495	.0505	.0516	.0526	.0537	.0548	−1.6
.0559	.0571	.0582	.0594	.0606	.0618	.0630	.0643	.0655	.0668	−1.5
.0681	.0694	.0708	.0721	.0735	.0749	.0764	.0778	.0793	.0808	−1.4
.0823	.0838	.0853	.0869	.0885	.0901	.0918	.0934	.0951	.0968	−1.3
.0985	.1003	.1020	.1038	.1056	.1075	.1093	.1112	.1131	.1151	−1.2
.1170	.1190	.1210	.1230	.1251	.1271	.1292	.1314	.1335	.1357	−1.1
.1379	.1401	.1423	.1446	.1469	.1492	.1515	.1539	.1562	.1587	−1.0
.1611	.1635	.1660	.1685	.1711	.1736	.1762	.1788	.1814	.1841	−0.9
.1867	.1894	.1922	.1949	.1977	.2005	.2033	.2061	.2090	.2119	−0.8
.2148	.2177	.2206	.2236	.2266	.2296	.2327	.2358	.2389	.2420	−0.7
.2451	.2483	.2514	.2546	.2578	.2611	.2643	.2676	.2709	.2743	−0.6
.2776	.2810	.2843	.2877	.2912	.2946	.2981	.3015	.3050	.3085	−0.5
.3121	.3156	.3192	.3228	.3264	.3300	.3336	.3372	.3409	.3446	−0.4
.3483	.3520	.3557	.3594	.3632	.3669	.3707	.3745	.3783	.3821	−0.3
.3859	.3897	.3936	.3974	.4013	.4052	.4090	.4129	.4168	.4207	−0.2
.4247	.4286	.4325	.4364	.4404	.4443	.4483	.4522	.4562	.4602	−0.1
.4641	.4681	.4721	.4761	.4801	.4840	.4880	.4920	.4960	.5000	−0.0

Table B.2
Areas under the standardized normal curve, from $-\infty$ to $+z$

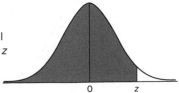

z	.00	.01	.02	.03	.04	.05	.06	.07	.08	.09
.0	.5000	.5040	.5080	.5120	.5160	.5199	.5239	.5279	.5319	.5359
.1	.5398	.5438	.5478	.5517	.5557	.5596	.5636	.5675	.5714	.5753
.2	.5793	.5832	.5871	.5910	.5948	.5987	.6026	.6064	.6103	.6141
.3	.6179	.6217	.6255	.6293	.6331	.6368	.6406	.6443	.6480	.6517
.4	.6554	.6591	.6628	.6664	.6700	.6736	.6772	.6808	.6844	.6879
.5	.6915	.6950	.6985	.7019	.7054	.7088	.7123	.7157	.7190	.7224
.6	.7257	.7291	.7324	.7357	.7389	.7422	.7454	.7486	.7517	.7549
.7	.7580	.7611	.7642	.7673	.7703	.7734	.7764	.7794	.7823	.7852
.8	.7881	.7910	.7939	.7967	.7995	.8023	.8051	.8078	.8106	.8133
.9	.8159	.8186	.8212	.8238	.8264	.8289	.8315	.8340	.8365	.8389
1.0	.8413	.8438	.8461	.8485	.8508	.8531	.8554	.8577	.8599	.8621
1.1	.8643	.8665	.8686	.8708	.8729	.8749	.8770	.8790	.8810	.8830
1.2	.8849	.8869	.8888	.8907	.8925	.8944	.8962	.8980	.8997	.9015
1.3	.9032	.9049	.9066	.9082	.9099	.9115	.9131	.9147	.9162	.9177
1.4	.9192	.9207	.9222	.9236	.9251	.9265	.9279	.9292	.9306	.9319
1.5	.9332	.9345	.9357	.9370	.9382	.9394	.9406	.9418	.9429	.9441
1.6	.9452	.9463	.9474	.9484	.9495	.9505	.9515	.9525	.9535	.9545
1.7	.9554	.9564	.9573	.9582	.9591	.9599	.9608	.9616	.9625	.9633
1.8	.9641	.9649	.9656	.9664	.9671	.9678	.9686	.9693	.9699	.9706
1.9	.9713	.9719	.9726	.9732	.9738	.9744	.9750	.9756	.9761	.9767
2.0	.9772	.9778	.9783	.9788	.9793	.9798	.9803	.9808	.9812	.9817
2.1	.9821	.9826	.9830	.9834	.9838	.9842	.9846	.9850	.9854	.9857
2.2	.9861	.9864	.9868	.9871	.9875	.9878	.9881	.9884	.9887	.9890
2.3	.9893	.9896	.9898	.9901	.9904	.9906	.9909	.9911	.9913	.9916
2.4	.9918	.9920	.9922	.9925	.9927	.9929	.9931	.9932	.9934	.9936
2.5	.9938	.9940	.9941	.9943	.9945	.9946	.9948	.9949	.9951	.9952
2.6	.9953	.9955	.9956	.9957	.9959	.9960	.9961	.9962	.9963	.9964
2.7	.9965	.9966	.9967	.9968	.9969	.9970	.9971	.9972	.9973	.9974
2.8	.9974	.9975	.9976	.9977	.9977	.9978	.9979	.9979	.9980	.9981
2.9	.9981	.9982	.9982	.9983	.9984	.9984	.9985	.9985	.9986	.9986
3.0	.9987	.9987	.9987	.9988	.9988	.9989	.9989	.9989	.9990	.9990
3.1	.9990	.9991	.9991	.9991	.9992	.9992	.9992	.9992	.9993	.9993
3.2	.9993	.9993	.9994	.9994	.9994	.9994	.9994	.9995	.9995	.9995
3.3	.9995	.9995	.9995	.9996	.9996	.9996	.9996	.9996	.9996	.9997
3.4	.9997	.9997	.9997	.9997	.9997	.9997	.9997	.9997	.9997	.9998

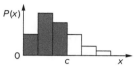

$$P(x \le c) = \sum_{x=0}^{x=c} \frac{\mu^x \cdot e^{-\mu}}{x!}$$

Table C
Cumulative Poisson
probabilities

μ\x	0	1	2	3	4	5	6	7	8	9
0.05	.951	.999	1.000							
0.10	.905	.995	1.000							
0.15	.861	.990	.999	1.000						
0.20	.819	.982	.999	1.000						
0.25	.779	.974	.998	1.000						
0.30	.741	.963	.996	1.000						
0.35	.705	.951	.994	1.000						
0.40	.670	.938	.992	.999	1.000					
0.45	.638	.925	.989	.999	1.000					
0.50	.607	.910	.986	.998	1.000					
0.55	.577	.894	.982	.998	1.000					
0.60	.549	.878	.977	.997	1.000					
0.65	.522	.861	.972	.996	.999	1.000				
0.70	.497	.844	.966	.994	.999	1.000				
0.75	.472	.827	.960	.993	.999	1.000				
0.80	.449	.809	.953	.991	.999	1.000				
0.85	.427	.791	.945	.989	.998	1.000				
0.90	.407	.772	.937	.987	.998	1.000				
0.95	.387	.754	.929	.984	.997	1.000				
1.0	.368	.736	.920	.981	.996	.999	1.000			
1.1	.333	.699	.900	.974	.995	.999	1.000			
1.2	.301	.663	.880	.966	.992	.998	1.000			
1.3	.273	.627	.857	.957	.989	.998	1.000			
1.4	.247	.592	.833	.946	.986	.997	.999	1.000		
1.5	.223	.558	.809	.934	.981	.996	.999	1.000		
1.6	.202	.525	.783	.921	.976	.994	.999	1.000		
1.7	.183	.493	.757	.907	.970	.992	.998	1.000		
1.8	.165	.463	.731	.891	.964	.990	.997	.999	1.000	
1.9	.150	.434	.704	.875	.956	.987	.997	.999	1.000	
2.0	.135	.406	.677	.857	.947	.983	.995	.999	1.000	
2.2	.111	.355	.623	.819	.928	.975	.993	.998	1.000	
2.4	.091	.308	.570	.779	.904	.964	.988	.997	.999	1.000
2.6	.074	.267	.518	.736	.877	.951	.983	.995	.999	1.000
2.8	.061	.231	.470	.692	.848	.935	.976	.992	.998	.999

Table C (concluded)

μ\x	0	1	2	3	4	5	6	7	8	9	10	11	12	13	14	15	16	17	18	19	20
3.0	.050	.199	.423	.647	.815	.916	.966	.988	.996	.999	1.000										
3.2	.041	.171	.380	.603	.781	.895	.955	.983	.994	.998	1.000										
3.4	.033	.147	.340	.558	.744	.871	.942	.977	.992	.997	.999	1.000									
3.6	.027	.126	.303	.515	.706	.844	.927	.969	.988	.996	.999	1.000									
3.8	.022	.107	.269	.474	.668	.816	.909	.960	.984	.994	.998	.999	1.000								
4.0	.018	.092	.238	.433	.629	.785	.889	.949	.979	.992	.997	.999	1.000								
4.2	.015	.078	.210	.395	.590	.753	.868	.936	.972	.989	.996	.999	1.000								
4.4	.012	.066	.185	.359	.551	.720	.844	.921	.964	.985	.994	.998	.999	1.000							
4.6	.010	.056	.163	.326	.513	.686	.818	.905	.955	.980	.992	.997	.999	1.000							
4.8	.008	.048	.143	.294	.476	.651	.791	.887	.944	.975	.990	.996	.999	1.000							
5.0	.007	.040	.125	.265	.441	.616	.762	.867	.932	.968	.986	.995	.998	.999	1.000						
5.2	.006	.034	.109	.238	.406	.581	.732	.845	.918	.960	.982	.993	.997	.999	1.000						
5.4	.005	.029	.095	.213	.373	.546	.702	.822	.903	.951	.978	.990	.996	.999	1.000						
5.6	.004	.024	.082	.191	.342	.512	.670	.797	.886	.941	.972	.988	.995	.998	.999	1.000					
5.8	.003	.021	.072	.170	.313	.478	.638	.771	.867	.929	.965	.984	.993	.997	.999	1.000					
6.0	.003	.017	.062	.151	.285	.446	.606	.744	.847	.916	.957	.980	.991	.996	.999	.999	1.000				
6.2	.002	.015	.054	.134	.259	.414	.574	.716	.826	.902	.949	.975	.989	.995	.998	.999	1.000				
6.4	.002	.012	.046	.119	.235	.384	.542	.687	.803	.886	.939	.969	.986	.994	.997	.999	1.000				
6.6	.001	.010	.040	.105	.213	.355	.511	.658	.780	.869	.927	.963	.982	.992	.997	.999	.999	1.000			
6.8	.001	.009	.034	.093	.192	.327	.480	.628	.755	.850	.915	.955	.978	.990	.996	.998	.999	1.000			
7.0	.001	.007	.030	.082	.173	.301	.450	.599	.729	.830	.901	.947	.973	.987	.994	.998	.999	1.000			
7.2	.001	.006	.025	.072	.156	.276	.420	.569	.703	.810	.887	.937	.967	.984	.993	.997	.999	1.000			
7.4	.001	.005	.022	.063	.140	.253	.392	.539	.676	.788	.871	.926	.961	.980	.991	.996	.998	.999	1.000		
7.6	.001	.004	.019	.055	.125	.231	.365	.510	.648	.765	.854	.915	.954	.976	.989	.995	.998	.999	1.000		
7.8	.000	.004	.016	.048	.112	.210	.338	.481	.620	.741	.835	.902	.945	.971	.986	.993	.997	.999	1.000		
8.0	.000	.003	.014	.042	.100	.191	.313	.453	.593	.717	.816	.888	.936	.966	.983	.992	.996	.998	.999	1.000	
8.2	.000	.003	.012	.037	.089	.174	.290	.425	.566	.692	.796	.873	.926	.960	.979	.990	.995	.998	.999	1.000	
8.4	.000	.002	.010	.032	.079	.157	.267	.400	.537	.666	.774	.857	.915	.952	.975	.987	.994	.997	.999	1.000	
8.6	.000	.002	.009	.030	.070	.142	.246	.373	.509	.640	.752	.849	.909	.949	.973	.986	.993	.997	.999	1.000	
8.8	.000	.002	.007	.024	.062	.128	.226	.348	.482	.614	.729	.822	.889	.935	.964	.981	.990	.995	.998	.999	1.000
9.0	.000	.001	.006	.021	.055	.116	.207	.324	.456	.587	.706	.803	.876	.926	.959	.978	.989	.995	.998	.999	1.000
9.5	.000	.001	.004	.015	.040	.089	.165	.269	.392	.522	.645	.752	.836	.898	.940	.967	.982	.991	.996	.998	.999

Subject Index

A-B-C approach, 558–560, 559*f*
  annual dollar value, 559
  cycle counting, 560
Above/below median runs, 438
Acceptance sampling, 417, 418*f*
Accidents, 303–304
Accounting department, 11
  forecasting and, 77
  purchasing and, 663
Active RFID, 678. *See also* Radio frequency
  identification (RFID)
Activities, 740–741
Activity-on-arrow (AOA), 740–742,
  744–748, 744*f*
Activity-on-node (AON), 740–741, 748–750,
  749*f*, 750*f*
Actual output, 192
Additive manufacturing. *See* 3D printing
Add value function, 6
Aggregate planning
  capacity strategies, 467
  concept of, 465–466
  demand options, 467–469
  disaggregating the plan, 483, 484*f*
  duplicate orders and excess capacity, 468
  explanation of, 463
  general procedure for, 474
  inputs to, 467, 467*t*
  intermediate planning, 464–465, 464*t*, 465*f*
  levels, 464*t*
  linear programming, 478–480, 479*t*–481*t*
  for manufacturing and services compared,
    482–483
  mathematical techniques for, 478–481
  mixed strategies, 467
  need for, 466
  overview of, 466–467
  services and, 481–483
  simulation models, 481, 481*t*
  supply chain and, 467
  supply options, 469–472
  trial-and-error techniques for, 474–478,
    475*t*, 481*t*
  uneven demand strategies, 471–473, 473*t*
  variations and, 466
Agility, 26, 657
Airlines
  aggregate planning and, 481
  scheduling, 716–717
Alpha risk, 427
American Society for Quality (ASQ), 12, 13, 375
Analytics, descriptive and predictive models in, 20
Andon system, 621–622
Annual dollar value, 559
APICS, the Association for Operations
  Management, 12, 13
Appointment (scheduling) systems, 714
Appointment systems, 714
Appraisal costs, 384–385, 385*t*

Areas under normal curve (table), 866
Areas under standardized normal curve (table),
  867–868
Arizona State University, 28
Assemble-to-Order (ATO), 673
Assembly diagram, 503, 504*f*
Assembly line, 258
Assembly (repetitive processing), 245–246, 246*t*,
  247*f*, 247*t*
Assets, workers as, 620
Assignable variation, 14, 424
Assignment model, 699–702, 699*t*, 701*t*
Associative forecasting techniques, 101–106,
  101*f*, 102*f*, 103*t*
Associative model, 82
Atkinson, Ron, 374
Attributes, 428, 433–437
Automation, 251–255, 252*t*
  computer-aided manufacturing (CAM), 252
  computer-integrated manufacturing (CIM), 254
  direct numerical control, 252
  explanation of, 251
  fixed, 252
  flexible, 253
  global location decisions and, 348
  integrating, 252
  numerically controlled machines, 252–253
  programmable, 252
  robots, 252–253
  in services, 269
Autonomation, 611, 617
Autonomous vehicles, 257
Availability
  of equipment, 180–181
  of inputs, 192
Available-to-promise (ATP) inventory, 486, 488*f*
Averaging techniques, 86–88, 86*f*–88*f*
Avoidance (of returns), 682

Baatz, E., 523
Bacal, Robert, 301
Backflushing, 516
Backlogs, 472
Backward pass, 747
Backward scheduling, 697
Balance delay, 273
The Balanced Scorecard (BSC), 54–56, 55*f*, 55*t*
Balancing transactions, 629
Baldrige, Malcolm, 387
Baldrige Award, 387, 388
Ball, Jeff, 384
Banks, GIS data and, 355
Bar codes, 556–557
Basic quality (Kano model), 160, 161
Batch processing, 245, 246*t*, 247*f*, 247*t*
Behavioral aspects, of project management,
  733–738
  behavior issues, 737
  key decisions, 735–736

  nature of projects, 734
  project champions, 737
  project manager, 736
Behavioral school, 297
Benchmarking, 405, 406
Beta distribution, 751, 751*f*
Bias, 108
Bill of materials (BOM), 503–506, 504*f*
Binding constraint, 837
Block pick, 675
Bonuses, 306
Bottleneck management, 211
Bottleneck operation, 201, 201*f*
Bottleneck process, 514
Brainstorming, 404, 764
Branding, 6
Breakdown maintenance, 645
Breakdown programs, 648
Break-even point (BEP), 206–208, 208*f*
B2B commerce, 667–668, 667*t*
Budgeting, 757
Buffer inventories, 648
Building blocks, in lean production
  process design, 615–620
  product design, 614–615
Bullwhip effect, 672, 672*f*
Business organizations, 4, 4*f*
Business plan, 464–465
Business-to-business (B2B) commerce, 667–668

Calkins, Patricia, 149
Capability analysis, 442–446, 443*f*, 444*f*
Capability index limitations, 446
Capacity costs, 785
Capacity cushion, 196
Capacity decisions, 464
Capacity load reports, 520
Capacity planning, 14, 662
  capacity "chunks," 202
  constraint management, 205
  defining/measuring capacity, 192–193, 192*t*
  determinants of effective capacity,
    193–195, 195*t*
  determining needed capacity, 198
  evaluating alternatives, 205–210
  expansion strategy, 204
  explanation of, 189
  flexibility and, 200
  forecasting capacity requirements, 196–198,
    197*f*, 197*t*
  identifying optimal operation level, 203, 203*f*
  importance of, 191
  in-house or outsourcing decisions, 199–200
  key questions, 190
  overview, 189–190
  processing requirements calculation, 197
  product or service life cycle and, 200–201
  restaurants and, 200
  seasonal variations and, 202–203

880   Subject Index

Capacity planning—*Cont.*
  for services, 198–199
  smoothing capacity requirements, 202–203, 203*f*
  strategy development, 200–204
  strategy formulation, 195–196
  systems approach to, 201
Capacity requirements planning, 518, 519–521, 520*f*
Capacity (resource) buffers, 761
Capacity utilization, 193
Capital intensity, 244
Capital productivity, 58*t*
Career opportunities, 12–13, 12*t*
Case pick, 675
Cases
  big bank, 820
  Chick-N-Gravy, 411–412
  DMD Enterprises, 546
  EGAD Bottling Company, 498
  Farmers Restaurant, 603
  Grill Rite, 602
  Harvey Industries, 601–602
  Hazel, 38, 69
  Highline Financial Services, Ltd., 135
  Hi-Ho, Yo-Yo, Inc., 729
  Home-Style Cookies, 68–69
  Level Operations, 641
  MasterTag, 686–687
  Mexican Crazy Quilt, 779–780
  M&L Manufacturing, 134
  outsourcing of hospital services, 213
  product recall, 341
  Promotional Novelties, 545
  Tiger Tools, 460
  Time, please, 781
  Tip Top Markets, 412–413
  Toys, Inc., 460
  UPD Manufacturing, 600
  Walmart, 370
Cash flow, 209
Causal regression models, 111*t*
Cause-and-effect diagram, 399*f*, 402–403, 402*f*
c-chart, 433*t*, 435
Cellular layouts
  cellular production, 263–265
  group technology, 265–266, 265*f*
  and process layouts compared, 264*f*, 265*t*
Cellular production, 263–265
Centered moving average, 98
Center of gravity method, 361–363, 362*f*, 363*f*
Centralized purchasing, 665
Central limit theorem, 424
Certainty, 825
Champion, of TQM, 391
Chance variations, 423
Change, speed of, 738
Changeovers, 610
Changeover time, 53
Changes (in MRP reports), 514
Change transactions, 630
Channel, 787
Chase demand strategy, 471–473, 472*f*, 473*t*
Cheaper by the Dozen, 23
Check sheet, 398, 399*f*, 400*f*

"Clever Little Bag" (Puma), 28
"Clicks-and-mortar," 681
"Clicks-or-bricks," 681
Closed-loop MRP, 518
Closed-loop supply chain, 683
Closing phase (project life cycle), 733
Clustering, 356
Coburn, Larry, 386
Codes of ethics, 29
Column reduction, 699
Combination layouts, 262–263
Common Good principle, 29
Common variability, 423
Communication, in supply chain management, 680
Community, and ethics, 30
Compensation
  individual incentive plans, 306
  knowledge-based, 306
  management, 306
  output-based (incentive) system, 304, 305*t*
  production of goods vs. services, 9
  time-based system, 304, 305*t*
  trends, 306
Competition
  in a global economy, 27
  pressures, 31
  time-based, 465
Competitive benchmarking, 391
Competitive edge, 26, 46
Competitiveness, 41, 42–43
  automation and, 251
  capacity decisions and, 191
  influence of marketing on, 42
Competitive strategy, flexibility as, 257
Complaints, response time for, 53
Computer-aided design (CAD), 163–164, 762
Computer-aided manufacturing (CAM), 252
Computer-integrated manufacturing, 254
Computerized numerical control (CNC), 252
Computing algorithm, 744–751
  activity-on-arrow, 744–748
  activity-on-node, 748–750, 749*f*, 750*f*
  rules for, 747
  slack times, 750, 751*t*
Concurrent engineering, 162–163
Conformance, quality of, 381–382
Constant work-in-process (CONWIP), 627–628
Constraint, 205
Constraint management, 205, 811
Constraints, 825, 826
  binding, 837
  explanation of, 824
  plotting, 828–831, 829*f*– 831*f*
Consumer Reports, 647
Consumer surveys, 83
Continuous improvement, 390, 391, 610, 621–622
Continuous processing, 245, 246, 246*t*, 247*f*, 247*t*
Continuous review system (inventory), 555
Contribution margin, 206
Control charts, 106, 107*f*, 110, 399*f*, 402, 402*f*, 404*f*, 426–437, 426*f*
  for attributes, 433–437
  c-chart, 433*t*, 435
  formulas summary, 448*t*

managerial considerations, 436–437
  mean charts, 428–430, 431*t*, 432, 432*f*
  p-chart, 433–434, 433*t*
  range charts, 430–431, 431*t*, 432*f*
  used with run tests, 441
  for variables, 428–433
Control limits, 106–110, 116*t*, 426, 427, 442
Conveyance kanban (c-kanban), 625
Cooperative decision making, 10
Core competencies, 46, 47
Corporate mergers and consolidations, 738
Correlation, 104
Cost accounting, 622
Cost-volume analysis, 206–209, 206*t*, 207*f*
Council of Supply Chain Management Professionals (CSCMP), 13
CPM (critical path method), 740–741
Cradle-to-grave assessment, 146
Craft production, 21
Crashing, 757–760, 757*t*, 759*f*
Critical activities, 741
Critical chain project management (CCPM), 761
Critical path method (CPM), 740–741, 758
Critical rate, 702, 707*t*, 708
Crosby, Philip B., 377, 377*t*, 385
Cross-distribution, 675
Cross-docking, 675, 683
Cross-functional teams, 162, 610
Cross-trained workers, 278, 621
Cultural differences, globalization and, 348
Cumulative lead time, 503
Cumulative Poisson probabilities, 869–870
Currency and exchange rate risk, 351
Customer contact, goods vs. services, 9
Customer relationship management, ERP and, 660
Customer satisfaction, 26, 390
Customer service
  Amazon.com, 45
  quality and, 383
Customer waiting costs, 785
Customer wants and needs, identifying, 42
Customization, mass customization, 154–155
Cyber-security, 27
Cycle counting, 560
Cycles, 84
  cyclical scheduling, 715–716
  forecasting and, 100
Cycle stock, 561
Cycle time, 270–271
Cycle-time variability, 627

Dantzig, George, 24
Darcy, Randy, 617
Darnell, Michael, 142
Database, in PIMS, 50
Data processing, 663
Decentralized purchasing, 665
Decision making, 18–20
  analysis of trade-offs, 19–20
  degree of customization, 20
  fact-based, 391
  hierarchy of, 45*f*
  maintenance and, 645
  models, 18–19
  performance metrics, 19

prioritizing, 20
project management and, 735–736
quantitative approaches, 19
scheduling, 691
systems approach, 20
Decision models, 23
Decision Sciences Institute, 13
Decision table approach, 583–584, 584t
Decision theory, 210
Decision variables, 824–826
Decline phase, life cycle, 201
Defect detection, 617
Delayed differentiation, 154–155, 684
Delivery time, 53
Dell, Michael, 50
Delphi method, 83–84
Demand fence, 519
Demand forecasting (DF) technologies, 113–114
Demand forecasts, 557
Demand management strategies, 199
Demand options (aggregate planning)
back orders, 468
new demand, 469
pricing, 468
promotion, 468
Demand pull, 610
Deming, W. Edwards, 23, 24, 374, 376, 376t, 377t, 387
Deming Prize, 376, 387
DemographicsNow, 357
Dependent demand, 501
Dependent-demand items, 551–552
Depth skills, 306
Descriptive models, 20
Design. See also Product and service design
quality, 381, 382
review, 162
Design and engineering, purchasing and, 663
Design capacity, 192. See also Capacity planning
Design for disassembly (DFD), 147
Design for recycling (DFR), 149
Deterministic time estimates, 743–744, 744f
Dewhurst, Nicholas P., 139
Differentiation, 44, 47t
Direct numerical control, 252
Diseconomies of scale, 203
Disintermediation, 684
Disruptions, 613
Distribution, 16, 32
Distribution resource planning (DRP), 520–521, 521f
Distribution strategy, 662
Divisibility, 825, 827
Division of labor, 23, 374
Dodge, H. F., 23, 24, 375
Drum-buffer-rope, 712–713
Dummy activity, 742
Dunn, Brian, 147
Duplicate orders, 468
Dynamic line balancing, 278

Earliest due date, 702, 707–708, 707t
E-business, 24–25, 666–668
advantages of, 667t
e-procurement at IBM, 668
supply chain management and, 31

E-commerce, 24–25, 526–527
Economic conditions, 27
Economic instability, 348
Economic order quantity (EOQ) model, 515, 561–565, 565f, 568, 569f, 616
annual carrying cost, 562–563, 563f
annual ordering cost, 563
assumptions, 561t
computing, 565
inventory cycle, 562f
Economic production quantity (EPQ) model, 565–568, 566f
Economies of scale, 203
Effective capacity, 192. See also Capacity planning
Efficiency, 62, 273
Efficiency school, 297
Elemental motions, 311, 313, 318
Emergency services, GIS data and, 356
Emerson, Harrington, 22
Employees. See Workers
Empowerment, 391
End-of-life programs, 146
Energy productivity, 58t
Engineer-to-Order (ETO), 673
Enterprise resource planning (ERP), 33, 732
big bang implementation, 526
business processes automation, 523–524
cost of, 524, 525–526
e-commerce and, 526–527
explained, 523
explanation of, 521
franchising strategy, 526
installing, 526
key connections, 522f
lean systems and, 633
mistakes common to, 527–529
operations strategy, 529
payback from, 525
project length, 524
reasons for using, 524
in services, 527
slam-dunk implementation, 526
software configuration, 525
software modules, 522t
supply chain management and, 659–660
Enumeration approach, 835
Environmental concerns, 27–29
diet and the environment, 29
ethical issues, 30
greening the supply chain, 656
Environmental scanning, 47, 48
Equation of a straight line, 828
Equipment availability, 180–181
Equivalent interest rate, 210
Ergonomics, 301
Erlang, A. K., 784
ERP. See Enterprise resource planning (ERP)
Ethics and ethical issues
ethical conduct, 29–30
financial statements and, 30
firing workers, 30
global markets and, 348
in location searches, 353
product safety, 30

product/service design and, 143–144
project management and, 736–737
quality management and, 386
supplier code of conduct, 670
working conditions and, 304–306
Ethisphere Institute, 30
European Quality Award, 387
European Union, 346
Event-response capability, 658
Events, 741
Exception reports, 514
Excess costs, 581
Excitement quality (Kano model), 160, 161
Executing phase (project life cycle), 732
Executive opinions, forecasting and, 83
Exponential distribution, 177, 177f
Exponential service times, 788
Exponential smoothing, 89–90, 90f, 95, 111t, 116t
External factors, capacity and, 195
External failures, 385, 385t
Extrusion, 255

Facilities
capacity and, 194
locating, 15
Facilities layout, 15, 257–269
cellular layouts, 263–266, 264f, 265t
combination layouts, 262–263
fixed-position layouts, 262
line balancing, 269–278
process layouts (nonrepetitive processing), 260–262, 261f, 264f, 265t
product layouts (repetitive processing), 258–260, 259f, 261f
service layouts, 266–269
Factor rating, 360–361
Fail-safing, 620
Failure, 43, 155–156
Failure costs, 385, 385t
Fairness Principle, 29
Fair Trade Certified label, 29
FastPass (Disney theme parks), 783
Feasibility analysis, 161–162
Feasible solution space, 824, 826, 831, 835, 837f
Feedback, 6, 16
Feeding (time) buffers, 761
Feigenbaum, Armand, 377, 377t
Fill rate, 577, 681
Finance department
forecasting and, 77
operations management and, 10
Financial analysis, 209–210
Financial statements, 30
Finite loading, 697
Finite-source queuing model, 805–811, 806t, 807t–809t
Finite-source situation, 786
Firing workers, 30
First-come, first-served, 789
First come, first served (FCFS) (job processing), 702, 707, 707t
Five forces model (Porter), 48
5W2H approach, 632, 632t
Fixed automation, 252
Fixed costs, 206

Fixed-order-interval (FOI) model, 577–580
    benefits and disadvantages, 580
    determining ordering amount, 578–580
    explanation of, 577
    fixed-quantity and fixed-interval
        comparisons, 578*f*
    reasons for using, 578
Fixed period ordering, 515–516
Fixed-position layouts, 262
Fixed-position service layout, 266
Flattening, 26
Flexibility, 42
    capacity planning and, 200
    as competitive strategy, 257
    general-purpose equipment and, 261
    in lean systems, 613
    process design and, 618
Flexible automation, 253
Flexible manufacturing system (FMS), 253
Flowchart, 398, 399*f*, 400*f*
Flow process chart, 308, 308*f*, 309*f*
Flow-shop scheduling, 692
Flow system, 692
Following capacity strategy, 195
Following tasks, 274
Follow-up evaluation, of product design, 162
Food and Agricultural Organization
    (FAO), 29
Ford, Henry, 22–24, 611
Forecast error, 80
    comparing errors, 90–91
    historical error performance, 82
    monitoring, 106–110, 106*f*, 107*f*
    sources of, 106
Forecasting, 14
    accuracy, 76, 79–82
    approaches, 82, 115*t*
    associative techniques, 101–106, 101*f*,
        102*f*, 103*t*
    choosing a technique, 110–111, 111*t*
    common features of forecasts, 77–78
    computer software, 112
    cycles, 100
    diffusion models, 91
    elements of a good forecast, 78
    expected level of demand and, 76
    factors, 111*t*
    focus forecasting, 91
    forecast explanation of, 75
    long-range forecasts, 75
    reactive and proactive approaches to, 112
    seasonality, 95–100, 96*t*, 97*f*, 98*f*
    steps in process of, 79
    supply chain and, 78–79
    time-series forecasts, 82, 84–100
    trend, analysis of, 91–94
    uses of, 77, 112
Forecast of demand, 555, 557
Forecasts, qualitative, 82–84
Forrester, Jay, 24
Forward pass, 747
Forward scheduling, 697
Foster, Nicole, 686
From-to charts, 279
Frozen phase, 485
Functional strategies, 45

Gantt, Henry, 22, 24
Gantt charts
    loading and, 695–696, 695*f*, 696*f*, 697
    project management and, 739–740, 740*f*
Gatekeeping, 682
General Agreement on Tariffs and Trade
    (GATT), 25, 346
General-purpose equipment, 261
Geographic information systems (GIS), 355–356
Gilbreth, Frank, 22–24, 301, 310, 311
Gilbreth, Lillian, 23, 24, 301, 311
Gispan, Jonathan, 738
Global competition, 24, 41
Globalization, 25
    benefits, 346–347
    capacity decisions and, 191
    disadvantages, 347
    managing global operations, 348
    risks, 347–348
    supply chain management and, 31
    virtual project teams and, 761–762
Global location decisions, 346–348
Global priority rules, 702
Global strategy, 50–51
Global supply chains, 659
Global warming, 29
Go, no-go gauge, 437
The Goal (Goldratt), 712
Goals, 44
Goldratt, Eli, 712–713
Goods, 4
    nonmanufactured, 8
    production of, vs. providing services,
        8–10, 10*t*
    variety of offerings, 14
Goods-service continuum, 6, 7*f*
Graphical linear programming, 826–838
    explanation of, 826
    graphical procedure outline, 826–828
    identifying feasible solution space,
        831, 831*f*
    minimization, 835–837
    plotting constraints, 828–831, 829*f*–831*f*
    plotting objective function line, 831–834,
        832*f*, 833*f*
    redundant constraints, 834–835, 835*f*
    slack and surplus, 837
    solutions and corner points, 835, 836*f*
Graphical tools, 403–404, 403*f*
Green initiatives, 28
Green products, 150
Griebenow, Allan, 678
Gross requirements, 507, 508
Group incentive plans, 304, 306
Group technology, 265, 616–617
Growth phase (life cycle), 200

Hamburger Stackers (Vlasic), 142–143
Harris, F. W., 23, 24
Health care, 303
Heijunka, 611
Hertzberg, Frederick, 23
Heuristic (intuitive) rules, 272, 275
"The Hidden Factory" (Miller and
    Vollmann), 629
High technology, 25, 250

High-volume system scheduling, 692–694
Hiring costs, 469
Hiring workers
    ethical issues, 30
    supply options, 469
Histogram, 398, 399*f*, 401*f*
Historical evolution, of operations management
    human relations movement, 23
    Industrial revolution, 21
    influence of Japanese manufacturers, 23–24
    scientific management, 21–23
Holding (carrying) costs, 557
Holland, Max, 67
Hoover Dam bridge, 731
Horizontal loading, 299
Horizontal skills, 306
Hospitals
    aggregate planning and, 481
    outsourcing of services, 213
    quality control and, 447
    room layouts, 267, 268
Housekeeping, 630
House of quality, 158, 158*f*–160*f*
Human factors, capacity and, 194
Human relations movement, 23
Human resources department, 11*f*, 12, 48, 77
Hungarian method, 699

Idle time percentage, 273
Ihlwan, Moon, 384
"Improved Product Design Practices Would
    Make U.S. Manufacturing More Cost
    Effective," 139
Incentive pay, 304–305, 305*t*
Independence assumption, 754
Independent contractors, 470
Independent-demand items, 551
Independent events, 174–175
Individual incentive plans, 306
Industrial engineering, 16
Industrial parks, 354
Industrial Revolution, 21, 374
Infinite loading, 697
Infinite-source queuing model, 790–805
    basic relationships, 791–793, 792*f*
    cost analysis, 799–801, 800*f*
    maximum line length, 801–802
    multiple priorities, 802–805, 803*t*
    multiple servers, 795–799, 795*t*, 796*t*–797*t*
    single server, constant service time, 794–795
    single server, exponential service time,
        793–794, 793*t*
    symbols, 791*t*
Infinite-source situation, 786
Information technology (IT), 24, 25, 250–251
    integrating, 657
    supply chains and, 662
Information velocity, 680
Initiating phase (project life cycle), 732
Innovation, 27, 42
    manufacturing as source of, 17
    as strategy, 54*t*
Input/output control (I/O), 698–699, 698*f*
Inputs, 6, 7*t*, 8*t*
    availability of, 192
    uniformity of, goods vs. services, 9

Inspection, 420*f*
    centralized vs. on-site, 422–423
    explanation of, 418
    points, 420–421, 421*t*
Institute for Operations Research and
    Management Sciences (INFORMS), 13
Institute for Supply Management (ISM), 12, 13
Institute of Industrial Engineers, 13
In Store Take Back (ISTB) (Best Buy), 147
Insurance companies, GIS data and, 355
Interchangeable parts, 22, 153
Intermediate-term capacity decisions, 464–465,
    464*t*, 465*f*
Intermediate-volume system scheduling,
    694–695
Intermittent processing, 261
Internal failures, 385, 385*t*
Internal rate of return (IRR), 210
International Ergonomics Association, 301
International Organization for Standardization
    (ISO), 387
Internet potential, 24. *See also* E-business
Introduction phase (life cycle), 200
Inventory, 32, 33
    available-to-promise (ATP), 486, 488*f*
    explanation of, 551
    finished-goods, 470–471
    functions of, 553–554
    goods vs. services, 9
    kanban cards and, 625–628
    minimal, in lean systems, 610, 613
    minimizing, 619
    nature and importance of, 552–555
    overly optimistic forecasts and, 80
    preventive maintenance and, 648
    projected-on-hand, 486, 487*f*, 488*f*, 507
    safety stock, 514–515, 554, 561, 573–574, 574*f*
    storage, 619
    vendor-managed (VMI), 637
    waste of, 636
    work-in-process (WIP) inventory, 619
Inventory counting systems
    periodic system, 555
    perpetual inventory system (continuous
        review), 555–556
    point-of-sale system, 556
    RFID tags, 557
    two-bin system, 556
    universal product code (UPC), 556
Inventory management, 15, 31, 42, 672–673
    cases, 600–603
    classification system, 558–560
    demand forecasts, 557
    economic order quantity (EOQ) model, 561–
        565, 561*t*, 562*f*, 565*f*, 568, 569*f*
    economic production quantity (EPQ) model,
        565–568, 566*f*
    effective, 555–560
    fixed-order-interval model, 577–580
    formulas summary, 586*t*
    inventory costs, 557–558
    lead-time information, 557
    objective of, 554–555
    operations strategy, 585
    ordering policies, 561
    overview, 551–552

quantity discounts, 568–572, 569*f*–572*f*
record keeping, 585
reorder point ordering, 573–577, 574*f*, 575*f*
single-period model (for perishables),
    580–585, 581*f*
Wegmans Food Markets and, 34
Inventory metric, in constraints theory, 713
Inventory records (in MRP), 506
Inventory turnover, 555
Inventory velocity, 672
iPod Shuffle, 392
Irregular variation, 84
Ishikawa, Kaoru, 24, 377, 377*t*
ISO 9000, 388
ISO 14000, 388
ISO 24700, 388

Japanese manufacturers, influence of, 23–24
Japanese-produced goods, 375
Jidoka, 611, 617
JIT II, 637
Job design. *See also* Work design
    behavioral approaches to, 298–299
    explanation of, 297
Job enlargement, 299
Job enrichment, 299
Job flow time, 703
Job lateness (job tardiness), 703
Job opportunities, 12–13, 12*t*
Job rotation, 299
Job shop, 243–244, 246*t*, 247*f*, 247*t*
Job time, 702
Johnson's rule, 709–710
Jones, Daniel, 610
Judgmental forecasts, 82
Juran, Joseph, 23, 24, 376–377, 377*t*, 385
Just-in-time (JIT) systems. *See also*
    Lean systems
    overview, 609–613, 638*t*
    as philosophy, 611, 613
    supplier management and, 637
    supply chain and JIT deliveries, 632, 633
    waiting lines and, 784

Kaizen, 391, 611, 614
Kanban, 611, 625–628
Kano, Noriaki, 160
Kano model, 160–161, 161*f*
Kaplan, Gary, 636
Kee, Suh Byung, 384
Kill Van Kull (Bayonne, New Jersey), 363
Knowledge-based pay systems, 306
Koch, Christopher, 523
Koo, Chung Mong, 384
Kowalski, Bill, 397

Labor content, of jobs, 9
Labor productivity, 57, 58*t*
Layout. *See* Facilities layout
Leadership, in lean systems, 622
Leading capacity strategy, 195
Lead time, 11
Lead time demand, 577, 577*f*
Lead-time information, 557
Lean culture, 610
Lean operation, 609

Lean principles, 657
Lean process design, 250
Lean production, 26–27
Lean services, 634–637
    JIT II, 637
    process improvement and problem solving,
        635–637
Lean systems, 26. *See also* Just-in-time (JIT)
    systems
    benefits and risks of, 611
    building blocks (*See* Building blocks, in lean
        production)
    characteristics of, 610
    cooperative spirit and, 634
    inventory management and, 585
    operations strategy and, 637
    overview, 638*t*
    personnel/organizational elements, 620–622
    principles embodying, 610
    supporting goals, 613–614
    Toyota approach, 611–613, 612*f*
    and traditional production compared, 630*t*
    transitioning to, 633–634
Lean tools
    process improvement using 5W2H,
        632, 632*t*
    Six Sigma and, 632
    value stream mapping, 631–632
Learning curves
    applications of, 334–336, 335*f*
    cautions and criticisms, 336–337, 337*f*
    coefficients, 333*t*
    concept of, 330–334, 331*f*
    doubling effect, 331–332
    operations strategy and, 336
    repetitions and unit time, 335–336
Least squares criterion, 101
Least squares line, 101
Legal department, 11, 11*f*
Level capacity loading, 623
Level capacity strategy, 471, 472*f*, 473*t*
Leveraged buyout (LBO), 67
Liability, and poor quality, 383
Linearity, 825
Linear programming
    for aggregate planning, 478–480, 479*t*–481*t*
    assignment method of, 699–702, 699*t*, 701*t*
    computer solutions, 838–841
    graphical (*See* Graphical linear programming)
    sensitivity analysis, 841–844
    simplex method, 838
    solving, using MS Excel, 838–841
Linear programming models, 824–826
    assumptions, 825
    components of, 824
    explained, 824–825
    formulation, 825–826
Linear regression, 116*t*
    analysis, 104–106
    correlation, 104
    determining a regression equation, 102–104
Linear trend equation, 92
Linear trend forecast, 92, 116*t*
Line balancing, 692–693
    balance delay, 273
    cycle time, 270–271

Line balancing—*Cont.*
  dynamic, 278
  efficiency, 273
  explanation of, 269
  guidelines, 274–277
  mixed model line, 278
  output constraints, 274
  precedence diagrams, 271–272, 272*f*
  sequential requirements, 272
  technical considerations, 277
  technological constraints, 274
  workstations, 270
Line functions, 10
Liquid phase, 485
Little's Law, 554, 627, 791
Livestock production, 29
Load chart, 696
Loading
  approaches, 697
  assignment model of linear programming,
    699–702, 699*t*, 701*t*
  Gantt charts, 695–696, 695*f*, 696*f*, 697
  input/output control (I/O), 698
  scheduling approaches, 697
Load reports, 519–520, 520*f*
Local priority rules, 702
Location, customers and, 42
Location cost-profit-volume analysis, 358–360
  center of gravity method, 361–363, 362*f*, 363*f*
  factor rating, 360–361
  transportation model, 360
Location planning
  climate considerations, 352
  decision procedures, 348–349
  general purpose plant strategy, 355
  geographic information systems (GIS),
    355–356
  global locations, 346–348
  identifying a community, 352–353
  identifying a country, 350–351
  identifying a location and site, 349–356
  identifying a region, 351–352
  identifying a site, 353–354, 354*t*
  labor factors, 352
  location options, 345–346
  market area plant strategy and, 354–355
  market locations, 351–352
  multiple plant manufacturing strategies,
    354–355
  need for, 343–344
  objectives of, 345
  process plant strategy, 355
  product plan strategy and, 354
  service and retail locations, 356–357, 357*t*
  strategic importance of, 344
  supply chain considerations, 345
  tax considerations, 352
Logistical transactions, 629
Logistics, 654, 674–675, 674*f*
  evaluating shipping alternatives, 677,
    679–680
  incoming/outgoing shipments, 676
  third-party logistics (3-PL), 679–680
  tracking goods with RFID, 676–678
Logistics companies, GIS data and, 355
Loma Linda University, 29

Long-range forecasts, 75
Long-term capacity decisions, 464, 464*t*
Long-term capacity needs, 196
Lot-for-lot ordering, 508, 509, 509*f*, 515
Lot-size ordering, 508, 511
Lower control limit (LCL), 427
Low-level coding, 506
Low price strategy, 47*t*, 54*t*
Low-volume system scheduling, 695–713
  loading, 695–702
  sequencing, 702–712, 702*t*, 703*t*, 705*t*
Lubbers, Sarah, 603

MacDonald, Jim, 140
Machine productivity, 57*t*, 58
The Machine That Changed the World (Womack,
  Jones, and Roos), 610
Maintenance, 16
  breakdown maintenance, 645
  breakdown programs, 648
  buildings and grounds, 644
  decision making and, 645
  equipment, 644
  explanation of, 644
  overview, 644–646
  preventive, 630, 645, 645*f*, 646–648, 694
  of production systems, 644–648
  replacement, 648
Maister, David H., 812
Makespan, 703
Make-to-Order (MTO), 673
Make-to-Stock (MTS), 673
Malpractice claims (medical), 383
Management informations systems (MIS),
  11*f*, 12, 77
Management science, 23
Manufacturability, 138
Manufacturing
  importance of, 17
  reasons for decline in, 17
Manufacturing cells, 617
Manufacturing planning and control, 622–630
  constant work-in-process
    (CONWIP), 627–628
  level loading, 623
  limited work-in-process (WIP), 627–628
  mixed-model sequencing, 623–624
  preventive maintenance and housekeeping, 630
  push and pull systems, 624–625
  reduced transaction processing, 629
  supplier tiers, 628–629, 629*f*
  vendor relationships and, 628
  visual systems, 625
Manufacturing resources planning (MRP II),
  517–518, 518*f*
Marketing
  forecasting and, 77
  influence on competitiveness, 42
  operations and finance departments and,
    10–11, 11*f*
  quality and, 382
Market test, 162
Markula Center for Applied Ethics, 29
Maslow, Abraham, 23
Mass customization, 154–155
Mass production, 22

Master production schedule (MPS), 483, 486,
  487*f*, 488*f*, 502–503, 503*f*
Master scheduling, 483–488, 483*f*
  inputs, 486
  master scheduler, 484
  outputs, 486, 486*f*
  process, 484–488, 485*f*
  time fences, 485, 485*f*
Material requirements planning (MRP)
  benefits, 516
  bill of materials (BOM), 503–506, 504*f*
  capacity requirements planning, 518,
    519–521, 520*f*
  closed-loop, 518
  distribution resource planning for supply
    chain, 520–521, 521*f*
  explanation of, 501
  information sources, 502–506, 502*f*
  inventory records, 506
  lot sizing, 515–516, 515*f*
  master schedule, 484, 502–503, 503*f*
  MRP II, 517–518, 518*f*
  outputs (primary and secondary reports),
    513–514
  overview, 501–502, 502*f*
  processing, 506–513, 507*f*, 509*f*, 510*f*,
    512*f*, 513*f*
  requirements of, 517
  safety stock, 514–515
  scheduling and, 694–695
  in services, 516
  spreadsheet terms, 507–508
  updating, 511–513
Mathematical models, 18
Matrix organization, 734
Maturity phase, life cycle, 201
Mayo, Elton, 23, 24
McGregor, Douglas, 23
McNulty, Steven, 142–143
Mean absolute deviation (MAD), 81–82, 115*t*
Mean absolute percent error (MAPE), 81–82, 115*t*
Mean (average), 14
Mean control charts, 428–430, 431*t*, 432
Mean squared error (MSE), 81–82, 115*t*
Mean time between failures (MTBF),
  176–177, 177*f*
Meczkowski, Frank, 142
Medical malpractice claims, 383
Meeker, David G., 139
Methods analysis, 306–310, 308*f*–310*f*
Methods Engineering Council, 318
Methods-time measurement (MTM), 318
Michigan International Speedway, 300
Microfactory, 353
Micromotion study, 311
Miller, Jeffrey G., 629
Mills, Karen, 617
Minneapolis-St. Paul International Airport layout
  changes, 257–258
Mission, 44
Mission statement, 44
Mistake proofing, 392
Mitchell, William E., 390
Mixed model line, 278
Mixed-model sequencing, 623–624
Models, 18–19

Modular design, 154–155, 614
Monitoring and controlling phase (project life cycle), 732
Most likely time, 751
Motion study
    micromotion study, 311
    principles, 310–311, 311*t*
    simo chart, 311, 312*f*
Motivation, 299
Motivational theories, 23
Moving average, 86–90, 87*f*–88*f*, 90*f*, 111*t*, 115*t*
MS Excel
    determining range of feasibility, 843–844
    sensitivity analysis and, 841–842
    solving LP models using, 838–841, 839*f*, 840*f*
Muda, 611
Mulholland overpass demolition, 758
Multifactor productivity, 58
Multiple-channel system, 787, 787*f*
Multiple-priority model, 802–805, 803*t*
Multiple regression analysis, 106
Multiple-server system, 795–799, 795*t*, 796*t*–797*t*
Muther, Richard, 281
Muther grid, 281, 281*f*

Naive forecast, 84–85
Near-sourcing, 662
Negative errors, 80
Negative exponential distribution, 788–789, 788*f*, 789*f*
Negotiated purchasing, 334–335
Net-change system, 512–513
Net material requirements, 508
Net requirements (netting), 508
Network configuration, 662
Network conventions, 742, 743*t*
Network (precedence) diagram, 740–742, 741*f*, 742
Newness strategy, 54*t*
New product development, 758
Newsboy problem. *See* Single-period model
Nichols, Karen, 738
Nonlinear regression analysis, 106
Nonmanufactured goods, 8
Nonnegativity constraints, 825, 827, 828*f*
Nonrandomness
    detecting, 106
    examples, 107*f*
Nonrandom variation, 424, 427, 441
Nonrepetitive jobs, analysis of, 319
Nonrepetitive processing, 260–262, 261*f*, 264*f*, 265*t*
Non-value-added occurrences, 783
Normal distribution, 871–876
    tables of, 873–876
    z values, 872–873
Normal operating conditions, 156
Normal time, 315
North American Free Trade Agreement (NAFTA), 25, 346

Objective function, 824, 825
Observed time, 315
Occupational health care, 303
Occupational Safety and Health Act (1970), 304

Occupational Safety and Health Administration (OSHA), 304
Office layouts, 268
Office operations, lean principles and, 631–632
Ohno, Taiichi, 24, 377, 377*t*, 636
Olympic Games, 731
Operating expense metric, in constraints theory, 713
Operational decisions, 16
Operational factors, capacity and, 195
Operational processes, 13
Operations
    function, 6*f*
    purchasing and, 663
    study, work design and measurement, 322–323
Operations management
    decision making and, 18–20
    defined, 4
    finance and marketing departments and, 10–11, 11*f*
    forecasting and, 77 (*See also* Forecasting)
    historical evolution of, 21–24
    importance of, 10–12
    interfaces with supporting functions, 11–12, 11*f*
    key issues, 27–33
    in present, 24–27
    quality and time strategies, 53
    scope of, 14–17
    strategic decision areas, 52–53, 52*t*
Operations strategy, 25, 51–53, 52*t*
    capacity planning, 211
    enterprise resource planning, 529
    explanation of, 51
    forecasts and, 112
    inventory management, 585
    lean systems and, 637
    learning curves, 336
    product and service design and, 169
    project management and, 763
    quality control and, 446–447
    quality management and, 406
    scheduling and, 717
    waiting lines, 812–813
Operations tours
    Boeing, 642
    Bruegger's Bagel Bakery, 604–607
    facilities layout, 248–249
    High Acres Landfill, 173
    inventory management, 604–607
    lean operations, 642
    Morton Salt, 248–249
    operations management, 33–35
    operations strategy, 546–549
    product and service design, 173
    productivity, 70–73
    PSC, Inc., 605–607
    Stickley Furniture, 546–547
    supply chain management, 675–676, 675*f*
    U.S. Postal Service (USPS), 70–73
    Wegmans Food Markets, 33–35, 675–676, 675*f*
Optimistic time, 751
Order fulfillment, 660, 673
Ordering costs, 558
Order qualifiers, 48

Order releases, 514
Order winners, 48
Organizational elements, of lean systems, 620–622
Organizational strategies, 45
Organization culture, 633
Organization strategies, 54, 54*t*
Ouchi, William, 23
Output-based (incentive) compensation, 304, 305*t*
Outputs, 6, 7*t*, 8*t*
Outsourcing
    decline in manufacturing and, 17
    vs. redesign, 139
    reevaluation of, 656–657
    supply chain management and, 31
Overhead, 622
"Over-the-wall" approach, 162
Overtime, 469–470

Packaging
    quality and, 382
    sustainability and, 148, 149–150
Parameter design, 157
Parameters, 824
Pareto analysis, 398, 399*f*, 401, 401*f*
Pareto charts, 404*f*
Pareto effect, 396
Pareto phenomenon, 20, 648
Part families, 265
Part-period model, 516
Part-time workers, 470
Passive RFID, 678. *See also* Radio frequency identification (RFID)
Patents, 9
Path, 741
Path probabilities, determining, 754–756, 754*f*
Pay. *See* Compensation
Payback time, 210
p-chart, 433–434, 433*t*
Pegging, 511
Perceived quality, 378
Performance-control reports, 514
Performance management, 660
Performance metrics, 19, 680, 681*t*
Performance quality (Kano model), 160, 161
Periodic system (inventory), 555
Perishables inventory, 580–585
Perpetual inventory system, 555–556
Personnel department, 11*f*, 12
Personnel elements, of lean systems, 620–622
PERT (program evaluation and review technique), 740–741, 763
    advantages of, and potential errors, 760–761
    network (precedence) diagram, 740–742, 741*f*
Pessimistic time, 751
Phases, in queuing systems, 787
Physical models, 18
Pipes, Kerry, 357
Pittenger, Kim, 636
Plan-do-study-act (PDSA) cycle, 394–395, 395*f*
Planned-order receipts, 507, 508
Planned-order releases, 508, 520
Planned orders, 514
Planning
    forecasting and, 75
    hierarchy of, 45*f*

Planning fence, 519

Planning phase (project life cycle), 732

Planning reports, 514

Planning time, 53

Plotting the data, 110

Point-of-sale (POS) systems, 556

Poisson distribution, 197, 584, 788–789, 788*f*, 789*f*

Poka-yoke, 620

Policy factors, capacity and, 195

Political instability and unrest, 347

Porter, Michael, 48

Porter's five forces model, 48

Port of Singapore, 349

Positional weight, for a task, 274

Positive errors, 80

Powell, David, 357

Practitioner certification exam, 13

Precedence diagrams, 271–272, 272*f*

Preceding tasks, 274

Predictive maintenance, 647

Predictive models, 20

Predictor variables, 101

Present value, 209

Present value (PV) method, 210

Prevention costs, 385, 385*t*

Preventive maintenance, 630, 645, 645*f*,
     646–648, 694
     and breakdown maintenance costs compared,
         646–647
     periodic nature of, 646
     predictive, 647
     repetitive processing and, 259
     total quality management (TQM) and, 647

The Principles of Scientific Management
     (Taylor), 21

Prioritizing, 20

Priority rules, 702, 702*t*

Proactive maintenance, 645

Probabilistic time estimates, 743, 751–753,
     751*f*, 753*f*

Problem solving, in lean systems, 621

Process
     defined, 13
     managing, to meet demand, 13–14, 13*f*
     variation, 14

Process analysis and improvement, 26

Process batch, 713

Process capability, 441–446, 449*t*
     determining, 443–444
     improving, 445–446, 446*t*
     index, 444–445
     limits of capability indexes, 446
     process variability and, 443
     Taguchi loss function, 446

Process design
     balanced system, 618–619
     fail-safe methods, 620
     in lean production, 615–620, 619*f*
     manufacturing cells, 617
     quality improvement, 617
     setup time reduction, 616
     small lot sizes, 615–616, 616*f*, 616*t*
     work flexibility, 618, 618*t*

Process factors, capacity and, 194

Process flexibility, 244

Process improvement, 26, 394–395, 395*t*

Processing, 8*t*, 32

Processing time, 53

Process layouts, 260–262, 264*f*, 265*t*
     and cellular layouts compared, 264*f*, 265*t*
     closeness ratings, 281–282
     designing, 278–282, 278*f*
     effectiveness measures, 279
     information requirements, 279
     intermittent processing, 261
     minimizing transportation costs/distances,
         279–281, 280*t*, 281*f*
     and product layouts compared, 261*f*
     in service environments, 261

Process management, 13–14

Process selection, 243–250
     drones, 256
     lean process design, 250
     process types, 244–249
     product and service profiling, 249–250
     sustainable production, 250
     technology and, 250–257
     3D printing, 255–256, 256*t*

Process specifications, 162

Process strategy, 244, 257

Process technology, 25, 250

Process types
     batch, 245, 246*t*, 247*f*, 247*t*
     continuous, 245, 246, 246*t*, 247*f*, 247*t*
     job shop, 243–244, 246*t*, 247*f*, 247*t*
     project, 247, 247*t*
     repetitive, 245–246, 246*t*, 247*f*, 247*t*

Process variability, 423–424, 442

Procurement, 662–666, 663*t*
     e-procurement at IBM, 668
     purchasing interfaces, 663–664, 664*f*
     quality and, 382

Product and service design. *See also* Product
     design; Service design
     cultural factors, 145
     degree of newness, 157
     design as business strategy, 138
     human factors, 144–145
     idea generation, 140–143
     importance of, 137
     Kano model, 160–161, 161*f*
     key questions, 138
     legal and ethical considerations, 143–144
     mass customization, 154–155
     operations strategy, 169
     overview, 138
     quality function deployment, 157–160,
         158*f*, 159*f*
     reasons for, 139–140
     redesign, 139–140
     robust design, 156–157
     standardization and, 153, 153*t*
     strategies for life cycle stages, 151–152, 151*f*
     sustainability, 146–150

Product and service technology, 25

Product bundle, 165

Product design, 42. *See also* Product and service
     design
     capacity and, 194
     computer-aided design (CAD), 163–164
     designing for production, 162–165
     forecasting and, 77

     in lean production, 614–615
     phases in, 161–162, 162*t*
     time-based strategy, 53

Product introduction, 162

Production
     computer-aided design (CAD), 163–164
     concurrent engineering, 162–163
     designing for, 162–165
     supply chain management, 32

The Production and Operations Management
     Society (POMS), 13

Production flow analysis, 266

Production kanban (p-kanban), 625

Production line, 258

Production/operations, quality and, 382

Production supervisor, 12*t*

Productivity, 41, 42, 56–62
     computing, 57–59, 57*t*, 58*t*, 63–64
     decline in manufacturing and, 17
     Dutch tomato growers' advantage in, 60
     explanation of, 56
     factors affecting, 60–61
     goods vs. services, 9
     importance of, 59
     improving, 61–62
     quality and, 384
     in the service sector, 59–60
     time-based strategies and, 53

Productivity growth, 56–57

Productivity paradox, 65

Product layouts, 258–260, 259*f*, 261*f*
     line balancing, 269–278
     U-shaped layouts, 260, 260*f*

Product liability, 143

Product life cycle management (PLM), 152–153

Product packages, 6

Product profiling, 249–250

Product quality, 378, 378*t*

Product recall, 341

Product safety, 30

Product-service package, 516

Product specifications, 162

Product structure tree, 503

Product variety, 54*t*

Professional societies, 12–13

Profit Impact of Market Strategy (PIMS), 49–50

Programmable automation, 252

Project champions, 737

Projected on hand, 507

Project management
     behavioral aspects of, 733–738
     budget control, 757
     certification, 737
     computing algorithm, 744–751
     crashing, 757–760, 757*t*, 759*f*
     critical chain (CCPM), 761
     deterministic time estimates, 743–744, 744*f*
     ethical issues, 736–737
     Gantt charts and, 739–740, 740*f*
     in lean systems, 622
     multiple projects and, 762
     network conventions, 742, 743*t*
     operations strategy, 763
     overview, 732, 733*t*
     path probabilities, 754–756, 754*f*
     PERT and CPM, 740–743, 760–761, 763

probabilistic time estimates, 743, 751–753, 751f, 753f
project life cycle, 732–733, 734f
risk management, 763–764, 763f, 764f
simulation, 756–577
software, 762–763
triangle, 736
work breakdown structure, 739, 739f
Project Management Institute (PMI), 13, 737
Project managers, 736
critical need for, 738
selecting, 735
Project processing, 247, 247t
Projects
explanation of, 732
nature of, 734
pros and cons of working on, 737–738
Project slippage, 762
Project (time) buffer, 761
Property, plant, and equipment (PPE), 113
Prototype development, 162
Public relations, 11f, 12
Publishers, GIS data and, 355
Pull systems, 624
Purchase cost (inventory), 557
Purchasing, 16, 32
centralized vs. decentralized, 665
ethics in, 665–666, 666t
negotiated, 334–335
Purchasing cycle, 664–666
Push systems, 624–625

Qualitative forecasts, 82–84
Quality, 26, 42
benefits of good quality, 383
compensation and, 304–305
of conformance, 381–382
consequences of poor quality, 383–384
continuous improvement and, 621–622
of design, 381, 382
determinants of, 381–382
dimensions of product quality, 378, 378t
dimensions of service quality, 379–380, 379t
ease of use and, 382
ethical issues and, 30
explanation of, 373
in global operations, 348
house of quality, 158, 158f–160f
image, waiting lines and, 786
Kano model, 160–161, 161f
in lean systems, 610
operations failures, 27
process design and, 617
sounds of, 380
Wegmans Food Markets and, 34
Quality assurance, 9, 15, 382, 417, 418f
Quality at the source, 392
Quality awards, 386–387
Quality-based strategies, 53
Quality certification, 387–389
Quality circles, 404–405
Quality control. See also Statistical process control
explanation of, 417
hospitals and, 447
inspection, 418–423, 420f

operations strategy, 446–447
overview, 448f
process capability, 441–446
statistical procedures for, 23
Quality function deployment (QFD), 157–160, 158f, 159f
Quality is Free (Crosby), 377
Quality management
costs of quality, 384–385, 385t
defining quality, 378–380
ethics and, 386
evolution of, 374–375
gurus of, 375–377
insights, 378–386
operations strategy and, 406
plan-do-study-act (PDSA) cycle, 394–395, 395f
problem solving/process improvement, 394–398
quality tools, 398–406, 399f
responsibility for quality, 382–383
Six Sigma, 396–398
supply chain and, 389–390
total quality management (TQM), 26, 374, 390–393, 393t
Quality of conformance, 381–382, 423
Quality of design, 381
Quality of work life, 301–306, 302f, 303f
Quality revolution, 24
Quality tools, 391, 398–406, 399f
graphical tools, 403–404, 403f
idea generation tools, 404–406
Quality transactions, 629
Quality Without Tears: The Art of Hassle-Free Management (Crosby), 377
Quantity discounts, 568–572, 569f–572f
Quantity requirements to labor/machine requirements conversion, 520
Queen Mary 2, 263
Questionnaires, for risk identification, 764
Queuing systems. See Waiting lines
Queuing theory, 783–784. See also Waiting lines
Quick response, 42
Quick response strategy, 47t, 54t

Radford, G. S., 374–375
Radio frequency identification (RFID), 251, 676–678
Random number table, 320, 321t
Random variability, 426–427
Random variation, 14, 84, 423
Range control charts, 430–431, 431t, 432, 432f
Range of feasibility, 843–844
Range of insignificance, 842
Range of optimality, 841, 842
Ratio-delay studies, 319
Reactive maintenance, 645
Real estate companies, GIS data and, 355
Receiving, 663
Recycling, 147–148
Reddy, Ram, 113–115
Redesign, 139–140
Redundancy, 175
Redundant constraints, 834–835, 835f
Regenerative system, 512
Regression, 101

Reliability, 155–156, 156t
availability, 180–181
computing, 176
explanation of, 174
improving, 156
product life probability, 178–180
quantifying, 174–180
redundancy and, 175
Remanufacturing, 147
Reorder point ordering, 573–577, 574f, 576f
Repetitive processing, 245–246, 246t, 247f, 247t
product layouts, 258–260, 259f, 261f
standardization and, 258
U-shaped layouts, 260, 260f
Research and development (R&D), 141
Reservation (scheduling) systems, 714
Resiliency, 658
Resource allocation, 25
Response time, 53, 684
Responsiveness, 44
Restaurants
aggregate planning and, 481
capacity planning, 200
layout considerations, 268
Retailers
GIS data and, 355–356
location planning and, 356, 357t
Retail layouts, 268
Return on investment (ROI), 385
Return on quality (ROQ), 385
Returns management, 680–683
Revenue management, 26
Reverse engineering, 141
Reverse logistics, 682
RFID (radio frequency identification), 251, 676–678
Right-hand-side (RHS) value of a constraint, 842–844, 844t
Right-sized equipment, 264
Rights principle, 29
Risk management, 27, 763–764, 763f, 764f
supply chains and, 657–659
uncertainty and risk reduction, 662
Risk matrix, 764f
Robots, 252–254
industrial, 255
programmable, 253
Robust design, 156–157
Rochester Institute of Technology, 28
Rolling horizon, 512
Rolling planning horizon, 466
Romig, H. G., 23, 24, 375
Roos, Daniel, 610
Rough-cut capacity planning, 485
Row reduction, 699
Run charts, 403, 403f
Run sequence, 438
Run tests, 437–441, 437f–439f
explanation of, 438
formulas summary, 448t
non-randomness testing and, 440
sampling distribution for, 440f
used with control charts, 441
Rusche, Chris, 603
Rush, 702

Safety, 303–304

Safety stock, 514–515, 554, 561, 573–574, 574f

Sales and operations planning, 463

Salesforce opinions, forecasting and, 83

Sampling, statistical procedures for, 23

Sampling distributions, 424, 426

Santa Clara University, 29

Scatter diagram, 399f, 401–402, 402f

Schedule chart, 696, 697–698, 698f

Scheduled receipts, 507

Scheduling, 15. *See also* Low-volume system
  scheduling
  backward scheduling, 697
  cyclical, 715–716
  decision making and, 691
  explanation of, 691
  forward scheduling, 697
  in high-volume systems, 692–694
  in intermediate-volume systems, 694–695
  multiple resources, 716–717
  operations strategy, 717
  services, 713–717
  small lot sizes and flexibility in, 616
  theory of constraints, 712–713
  workforce, 715

Schematic models, 18

Schiller, Zachary, 67

Schmidt, Ludwig, 686

Scientific management, 21–23

SCOR (Supply Chain Operations Reference)
  model, 680

Seasonal forecasting, 111t

Seasonal indexes, 96

Seasonality forecasts, 84, 95–100, 96t, 98f
  additive model, 96
  multiplicative model, 96, 97f

Seasonal relatives, 96, 97–98
  centered moving average, 98
  computing, 98–100, 98f
  simple average computing, 99–100

Seasonal work, 470

Self-directed teams, 300

Self-driving vehicles, 257

Sensitivity analysis, 844t
  changes in RHS value of a constraint,
    842–844
  objective function coefficient changes, 841
  using MS Excel, 841–842, 842f

Sequencing, 702–712, 702t, 703t, 705t
  explanation of, 702
  of jobs through two work centers, 709–711
  Johnson's rule and, 709
  performance measures, 703
  scheduling difficulties and, 711–712
  with sequence-dependent setup times, 711
  using various rules, 703–708

Sequential relationships, 741

Sergeev, Dimitriy, 153

Serviceability, 138

Service blueprinting, 167–168, 167f

Service delivery system, 165

Service design, 42, 165–168. *See also* Product
  and service design
  capacity and, 194
  challenges, 168

characteristics of well-designed systems, 168
  forecasting and, 77
  global product and, 145–146
  guidelines, 168
  managerial challenges and, 169
  overview, 165
  phases, 166, 167t
  and product design compared, 165–166
  service blueprinting, 167–168, 167f
  time-based strategy, 53

Service layouts, 266
  hospital rooms, 267, 268
  office, 268
  restaurant, 268
  retail, 268
  warehouse and storage, 266–267

Service level, stockout risk and, 574

Service package, 165

Service profiling, 249–250

Service quality, 42–43, 379–380, 379t
  assessing, 380
  dimensions of, 379, 379t

Services, 4. *See also* Lean services
  aggregate planning for, 481–483
  automation in, 269
  capacity planning for, 198–199
  enterprise resource planning and, 527
  explanation of, 165
  location planning and, 356, 357t
  material requirements planning (MRP), 516
  process layouts and, 261
  providing, vs. production of goods, 8–10, 10t
  variety of offerings, 14

Service scheduling, 713–717

Service sector, 17, 59–60

Service variety, 54t

SERVQUAL, 380

Setup costs, 558, 694

Setup time, 616, 633

Shadow price, 842

Shewhart, Walter, 23, 24, 375–376, 377t, 426

Shingo, Shigeo, 24, 377, 377t, 616

Shipping
  evaluating alternatives, 677, 679–680
  incoming and outgoing, 676
  quality and, 382
  supply chain management and, 33
  tracking with RFID, 676–678

Shortage costs, 558, 580

Shortest processing time (SPT), 702, 702t,
  707, 707t

Short-range capacity requirements. *See* Capacity
  requirements planning

Short-term capacity decisions, 464, 464t

Short-term capacity needs, 196

Simo chart, 311, 312f

Simple average (SA) method, 99–100

Simplex method, 838

Simulation, 210, 756–757

Single-channel system, 787, 787f

Single-minute exchange of die (SMED) system,
  264, 616

Single-period model, 580–585, 581f
  continuous stocking levels, 581–582
  decision table approach, 583–584, 584t

discrete stocking levels, 582–585, 583f
  excess costs, 581
  Poisson distribution and, 584
  shortage costs, 580

Single-phase systems, 787

Sintering, 255

Six Sigma, 26, 161, 444, 444f
  "Catch 22," 397
  consistency as key to success of, 397–398
  DMAIC process, 396–398
  guiding principles, 396
  lean systems and, 632
  practitioners of, 397–398
  project management and, 761

Skill level, of workers, 469

Skinner, W., 24

Slack, 742, 837

Slack per operation (S/O), 702, 708

Slack times, 469–470, 750, 751t

Slater, Derek, 523

Slushy phase, 485

Small businesses, supply chains and,
  660–661, 684

Small lot sizes, 610

Smith, Adam, 23, 24

Social media product manager, 12t

Social responsibility, 665

Software
  commercial analytics, 20
  ERP, 522t, 526
  forecasting, 112
  Microsoft Project, 762
  process layout design, 278
  project life cycle management, 152–153
  project management, 762–763

Space allocation, 465–466

Special variation, 424

Specifications, 441

Spence, Randy, 142

Standard deviation, 14

Standard error of estimate, 103, 116t

Standardization
  advantages and disadvantages of, 153
  explanation of, 153
  job-processing requirements, 251
  product and service design, 153
  repetitive processing and, 258

Standardized parts, 22

Standard parts, 614

Standard time, 312–313, 315–316

Starting forecast, 90

Statistical process control, 417, 423–441
  control charts, 426–437, 426f
  control process, 425–426
  explanation of, 423
  process variability, 423–424
  run tests, 437–441, 437f–439f
  sampling and sampling distributions, 424–
    425, 424f, 425f

Statistical sampling theory, 23

Steady-state conditions, 790

Step costs, 208

Stickley, Leopold and George, 546

Stoecker, Dean, 357

Stopwatch time study, 313–317, 317t, 323t

Storage layouts, 266–267
Straight piecework, 306
Strategic decisions, 16
Strategic partnerships, 662
Strategic sourcing, 680
Strategies, 41, 44
  balanced scorecard and, 54–56, 55f, 55t
  examples, 46
  formulation of, 46–50
  functional, 45
  mission, organizational, and operations
    strategies compared, 52
  operations (See Operations strategy)
  organizational, 45, 47t
  quality-based, 53
  supply chain, 50
  sustainability, 50
  tactics and, 41–51
  time-based, 53
Strategy development
  external factors, 48
  internal factors, 48–49
  questions to address, 49
Structural variation, 14
Subcontracting, 471–472
Subtractive manufacturing, 255
Supplier code of conduct, 670
Supplier forums, 670
Supplier management
  choosing suppliers, 669, 669t
  partnerships, 670
  strategic partnering, 671
  supplier audits, 669
  supplier relationship management, 670, 671t
Supplier quality, 391
Supplier relationship management, 660
Suppliers
  audits of, 669
  certification of, 670
  choosing, 669, 669t
  as partners in quality process, 392
  purchasing and, 663–664
  supplier management and JIT systems, 637
Supplier tiers, 628–629, 629f
Supply chain
  aggregate planning and, 467
  capacity and, 195
  closed-loop, 683
  complexity of, 31
  disruptions, 657
  distribution resource planning for,
    520–521, 521f
  efficiency and, 662
  ethics and, 660
  explanation of, 4, 654
  forecasting and, 78–79
  global, 659
  greening, 656
  illustrated, 5f
  JIT deliveries and, 632
  location decisions and, 345
  managing to achieve goals, 15–17
  quality management and, 389–390
  resiliency, 658
  risk management, 657–659

ROI measurement, 656
  scheduling and, 717
  simplifying (shortening), 659
  small businesses and, 660–661
  strategy, 50
  variations and uncertainty in, 684
Supply chain management, 30–31
  challenges, 683
  competitiveness and, 42
  e-business, 666–668, 667f
  economic responsibilities, 661–662
  effectiveness and, 680–684, 681t
  elements of, 32–33, 32t
  enterprise resource planning (ERP) and, 521,
    659–660
  ethical responsibilities, 662
  explanation of, 654
  inventory management, 585, 672–673
  lean principles, 657
  legal responsibilities, 661
  logistics, 674–675, 674f
  order fulfillment, 673
  overview, 654–655, 655f, 656f
  performance measures, 681t
  procurement, 662–666, 663t
  production plan, 113
  product returns, 681–683
  strategic responsibilities, 662, 663t
  strategy, 684
  supplier management, 669–671, 669t, 671t
  trends, 655–659
Supply chain manager, 12t
Supply chain visibility, 658
Supply options (aggregate planning)
  hire/lay off workers, 469
  inventories, 470–471
  overtime/slack time, 469–470
  part-time workers, 470
  subcontracting, 471–472
Supporting processes, 13
Surplus, 837–838
Sustainability, 27–28
  Kraft Foods and, 148
  packaging and, 149–150
  product and service design, 146–150
  strategy, 50
  as strategy, 54t
  sustainable production, 250
  Three Rs, 146–150
  universities and, 28
  Wegmans Food Markets and, 34
  Xerox and, 149
SWOT approach, 47
System, 20
System design, 16
System nervousness, 519
System operation, 16
System utilization, 790

Tables
  areas under normal curve, O to Z, 866
  areas under standardized normal curve,
    867–868
  cumulative Poisson probabilities, 869–870
Tactical decisions, 16

Tactics, 45
Taguchi, Genichi, 157, 377, 377t, 446
Taguchi loss function, 446
Takt time, 618–619
Tangible output, 8
Taylor, Frederick Winslow, 21, 24, 297, 301, 374
Teams and teamwork, 26, 299–301
  cross-functional teams, 610
  team approach, 306, 391
Technological innovation, 250
Technology, 25
  automation, 251–255
  explanation of, 250
  global location decisions and, 346
  management of, 25
  process selection and, 250–257
  replacement of equipment/parts and, 648
  strategy development and, 48
  Wegmans Food Markets and, 34
Telephone answering skills, 43
Terrorism, 348
Theory of constraints, 712–713
Theory X, 23
Theory Y, 23
Theory Z, 23
Therbligs, 310
Third-party logistics (3-PL), 679–680
3D printing, 255–256, 256t
3D scanning, 255
Three Rs (reduce, reuse, and recycle), 146–150
Throughput metric, in constraints theory, 713
Time-based compensation system, 304, 305t
Time-based competition, 465
Time-based strategies, 53
Time buckets, 503, 506
Time fences, 485, 485f, 519
Time framework, 696
Time horizon, in forecasts, 76, 78
Time-ordered plot, 426
Time-phased requirements, 506
Time-phasing, 695
Time-series forecasts, 82, 84–100, 85f, 86f
  averaging techniques, 86, 86f
  explanation of, 84
  naive methods, 84–85
  seasonality in, 97
Time-to-market, 42
Time wasting, 636
Tippett, L. H. C., 23, 24
Tolerances, 441
Top-down management systems, 54–56, 55f, 55t
Top management, quality and, 382
Total quality management (TQM), 26, 374, 393t
  criticisms of, 393
  culture of, 393t
  important elements of, 391–392
  key philosophies of, 390
  obstacles to implementing, 392–393
  preventive maintenance and, 647
Toyota approach, 611–613, 612f
Tracking capacity strategy, 195
Tracking signal, 108–110, 116t
Trade agreements, 346
Trade-offs, 19–20, 25
Traffic management, 676

Transaction processing, 629
Transfer batch, 713
Transfer pricing rules, 351
Transformation processes, 6, 7t, 8f
Transportation costs, 31, 478–480, 479t
    minimizing, with process layout, 279–281,
        280t, 281f
Trend-adjusted exponential smoothing, 111t
Trend-adjusted forecast (TAF), 95, 116t
Trend models, 111t
Trends, 84
    analysis of, 91–94
    linear trend equation, 92
    nonlinear types, 92, 92f
    obtaining/using a trend equation, 93–94
    trend-adjusted forecast (TAF), 95
Trial-and-error schedule development, 696
Truncated SPT rule, 707
Trust, 299
Two-bin system, 556
Type I error, 427, 427f, 428t
Type II error, 427, 428f, 428t

Uncertainty and risk reduction, 662
Uniform Commercial Code, 143–144
Union contracts, 469
Universal product code (UPC), 556–557
Universities, sustainability and, 28
University of British Columbia, 28
Up/down runs, 438
Upper control limit (UCL), 427
Upper-management processes, 13
U.S., as service-based economy, 17
U.S.-China Trade Relations Act, 346
U-shaped layouts, 260, 260f
Utilitarian Principle, 29
Utility companies, GIS data and, 356
U2 360 Tour, 735

Value-added, 6
Value analysis, 146–147
Value chain, 32
Value stream mapping, 631–632
Variable costs, 206
Variables, 428–433
Variation reduction, 585
Vegetarian vs. nonvegetarian diets, 29
Vendor analysis, 669
Vendor-managed inventory (VMI), 637,
    672–673, 675

Vendors. See also Supplier management; Suppliers
    purchasing and, 663–664
    vendor relationships, 628
Vertical skills, 306
Virtual project teams, 145–146, 761–762
Virtue Principle, 29
Visual controls, 610
Visual systems, 625
Vollmann, Thomas, 629

Wages. See Compensation
Wagner-Whitin model, 516
Wait-and-see strategy, 211
Waiting lines, 782–820. See also Finite-source
        queuing model; Infinite-source queuing model
    arrival and service patterns, 788–789, 788f, 789f
    capacity planning and, 197, 198–199
    characteristics of, 786–790
    constraint management, 811
    costs of, 785
    customer reneging, jockeying, and balking, 789
    goal of waiting-line management,
        785–786, 786f
    managerial implications of, 785
    number of servers (channels) and, 787, 787f
    operations strategy, 812–813
    population source, 786–787, 787f
    psychology of waiting, 811–812
    queue discipline, 789–790
    reasons for, 784
    waiting-line performance measures, 790, 790f
Warehoused items retrieval, 675–676
Warehouse layouts, 266–267
Waste
    enhancing production by eliminating, 613
    in kaizen philosophy, 614
    in lean philosophy, 613
    minimizing, 611, 636
    reduction, 610
The Wealth of Nations (Smith), 23
Weighted moving average, 88–89, 90f, 115t
Weightman, Clive, 527
Weinstein, Bob, 738
Wentworth, Janine, 636
Whitney, Eli, 22, 24
Wilkerson, Ella Mae, 143
Womack, James, 610
Woong, Ahn Soo, 384
Work breakdown structure, 739, 739f
Work cells, 610

Work design
    compensation, 304–306, 305t
    ergonomics, 301
    methods analysis, 306–310, 308f–310f
    motion study, 310–311, 311t
    motivation, 299
    operations strategy, 322–323
    quality of work life, 301–306
    specialization, 298, 299t
    teams, 299–301
Worker-machine chart, 309, 310f
Workers
    as assets, 469, 620
    attrition rate of, 738
    capacity and, 194
    cross-trained, 278, 621
    empowerment of, 391
    ethical issues in hiring, 30
    firing, 30
    hiring/laying off, 469
    lean production and, 27
    motivating, 15
    part-time, 470
    rights of, 30
    safety of, 30, 303–304
    skill level of, 469
    training, 15
Workforce scheduling, 715
Working conditions, 302–304, 302f, 303f
Work-in-process (WIP) inventory, 619
    constant (CONWIP), 627–628
    limited, 627–628
Work measurement
    explanation of, 311
    formulas summary, 324t
    operations strategy, 322–323
    predetermined time standards, 318
    standard elemental times, 317–318
    standard time, 312–313
    stopwatch time study, 313–317, 317t, 323t
Work sampling, 318–322, 323t, 324t
Workstations, 270, 272, 702
    parallel, 277
    process layouts, 278f
World class suppliers, 670
World Trade Organization, 346

Yield management, 77, 483, 714–715

Zero defects concept, 375, 377

Table B.2
Areas under the standardized normal curve, from $-\infty$ to $+z$

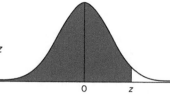

z	.00	.01	.02	.03	.04	.05	.06	.07	.08	.09
.0	.5000	.5040	.5080	.5120	.5160	.5199	.5239	.5279	.5319	.5359
.1	.5398	.5438	.5478	.5517	.5557	.5596	.5636	.5675	.5714	.5753
.2	.5793	.5832	.5871	.5910	.5948	.5987	.6026	.6064	.6103	.6141
.3	.6179	.6217	.6255	.6293	.6331	.6368	.6406	.6443	.6480	.6517
.4	.6554	.6591	.6628	.6664	.6700	.6736	.6772	.6808	.6844	.6879
.5	.6915	.6950	.6985	.7019	.7054	.7088	.7123	.7157	.7190	.7224
.6	.7257	.7291	.7324	.7357	.7389	.7422	.7454	.7486	.7517	.7549
.7	.7580	.7611	.7642	.7673	.7703	.7734	.7764	.7794	.7823	.7852
.8	.7881	.7910	.7939	.7967	.7995	.8023	.8051	.8078	.8106	.8133
.9	.8159	.8186	.8212	.8238	.8264	.8289	.8315	.8340	.8365	.8389
1.0	.8413	.8438	.8461	.8485	.8508	.8531	.8554	.8577	.8599	.8621
1.1	.8643	.8665	.8686	.8708	.8729	.8749	.8770	.8790	.8810	.8830
1.2	.8849	.8869	.8888	.8907	.8925	.8944	.8962	.8980	.8997	.9015
1.3	.9032	.9049	.9066	.9082	.9099	.9115	.9131	.9147	.9162	.9177
1.4	.9192	.9207	.9222	.9236	.9251	.9265	.9279	.9292	.9306	.9319
1.5	.9332	.9345	.9357	.9370	.9382	.9394	.9406	.9418	.9429	.9441
1.6	.9452	.9463	.9474	.9484	.9495	.9505	.9515	.9525	.9535	.9545
1.7	.9554	.9564	.9573	.9582	.9591	.9599	.9608	.9616	.9625	.9633
1.8	.9641	.9649	.9656	.9664	.9671	.9678	.9686	.9693	.9699	.9706
1.9	.9713	.9719	.9726	.9732	.9738	.9744	.9750	.9756	.9761	.9767
2.0	.9772	.9778	.9783	.9788	.9793	.9798	.9803	.9808	.9812	.9817
2.1	.9821	.9826	.9830	.9834	.9838	.9842	.9846	.9850	.9854	.9857
2.2	.9861	.9864	.9868	.9871	.9875	.9878	.9881	.9884	.9887	.9890
2.3	.9893	.9896	.9898	.9901	.9904	.9906	.9909	.9911	.9913	.9916
2.4	.9918	.9920	.9922	.9925	.9927	.9929	.9931	.9932	.9934	.9936
2.5	.9938	.9940	.9941	.9943	.9945	.9946	.9948	.9949	.9951	.9952
2.6	.9953	.9955	.9956	.9957	.9959	.9960	.9961	.9962	.9963	.9964
2.7	.9965	.9966	.9967	.9968	.9969	.9970	.9971	.9972	.9973	.9974
2.8	.9974	.9975	.9976	.9977	.9977	.9978	.9979	.9979	.9980	.9981
2.9	.9981	.9982	.9982	.9983	.9984	.9984	.9985	.9985	.9986	.9986
3.0	.9987	.9987	.9987	.9988	.9988	.9989	.9989	.9989	.9990	.9990
3.1	.9990	.9991	.9991	.9991	.9992	.9992	.9992	.9992	.9993	.9993
3.2	.9993	.9993	.9994	.9994	.9994	.9994	.9994	.9995	.9995	.9995
3.3	.9995	.9995	.9995	.9996	.9996	.9996	.9996	.9996	.9996	.9997
3.4	.9997	.9997	.9997	.9997	.9997	.9997	.9997	.9997	.9997	.9998

Credits

1. Introduction to Operations Management: *Chapter 1 from Operations Management, 13th Edition by Stevenson, 2018* 2

2. Competitiveness, Strategy, and Productivity: *Chapter 2 from Operations Management, 13th Edition by Stevenson, 2018* 40

3. Process Selection and Facility Layout: *Chapter 6 from Operations Management, 13th Edition by Stevenson, 2018* 74

4. Management of Quality: *Chapter 9 from Operations Management, 13th Edition by Stevenson, 2018* 128

5. Quality Control: *Chapter 10 from Operations Management, 13th Edition by Stevenson, 2018* 172

6. Aggregate Planning and Master Scheduling: *Chapter 11 from Operations Management, 13th Edition by Stevenson, 2018* 218

7. MRP and ERP: *Chapter 12 from Operations Management, 13th Edition by Stevenson, 2018* 256

8. Inventory Management: *Chapter 13 from Operations Management, 13th Edition by Stevenson, 2018* 306

9. JIT and Lean Operations: *Chapter 14 from Operations Management, 13th Edition by Stevenson, 2018* 364

10. Supply Chain Management: *Chapter 15 from Operations Management, 13th Edition by Stevenson, 2018* 400

11. Scheduling: *Chapter 16 from Operations Management, 13th Edition by Stevenson, 2018* 438

A. Appendix: Tables: *Chapter B from Operations Management, 13th Edition by Stevenson, 2018* 478

B. Subject Index: *Chapter from Operations Management, 13th Edition by Stevenson, 2018* 483